RAC

HOTELS IN

FRANCE

D0714248

Published by RAC Publishing, RAC House,
PO Box 100, South Croydon CR2 6XW.
© RAC Enterprises Ltd 1994

ISBN 0 86211-309 1

A CIP catalogue record for this book is available from the British Library.

Written and compiled for RAC Publishing by Millrace Books

Editorial Office
PO Box 8
Harleston
Norfolk IP20 0EZ
Tel: 01986 788 808
Fax: 01986 788 195

Managing Editor:	Lawrie Hammond
Design:	Douglas Whitworth
Editorial:	Aardvark Editorial; Zibba George; Magdalen Bear
Hotel Advertising:	Stephanie Wren
Cartography:	RAC Publishing.
Cover Design:	Chuck Goodwin
Printed and bound in Spain by:	Grafo SA, Bilbao

Bon Voyage
with the BT Chargecard

Bon Voyage, but keep in touch when travelling abroad with a BT Chargecard. A classic communication tool, the BT Chargecard can be used to make cashless calls throughout the UK, and back to the UK from millions of public, private and hotel phones across Europe. And it's absolutely FREE. You only pay when you use the card. The calls you make are charged to your home or business phone bill. When you are in the UK, you can use millions of UK phones to make BT Chargecard calls, including ALL BT public payphones. And it actually costs LESS to dial direct from a BT public payphone using a BT Chargecard than to pay cash.

When you're abroad, you can use your BT Chargecard to call home from more than 120 COUNTRIES, thanks to the BT Direct service. An English-speaking operator will help you around any language barriers. You will also be able to DIAL DIRECT from a steadily increasing number of countries back to the UK. You can already do so from France.

Good for your business

If you're travelling on business, the BT Chargecard is ideal for anyone working from home or on the move, as phone calls can be charged to an office number. This also goes for faxing and computer information transmission charges.

Good for you and your family

For you and your family, it means an end to pockets full of loose change or feeling embarrassed about asking to use someone else's phone for free. And it's easy to check how much each call costs - every BT Chargecard call is itemised on your phone bill.

And there are a host of additional benefits:

- People away on business minimise the phone call surcharges levied by many hotels.
- Discounts of up to 21% on direct dialled calls are available to Business Choices customers.
- Savings. You can claim back VAT on all BT Chargecard calls and a single statement for all your BT Chargecard holders simplifies the administration of expenses.

What your calls will cost

Direct dialled BT Chargecard calls are 5% cheaper than normal BT payphone rates.
If you call through the operator in the UK, BT will add a service charge of £1.50 per call.
If you call via the operator from abroad, there will be a service charge of 50p.
Operator calls cannot be made with a Phone Home BT Chargecard.

BT Chargecard calls are easy to make: Dial 144, tap in your account number, your PIN and then the number you want. You don't have to stick with the PIN issued by BT, you can change it yourself to any combination you find easy to remember.
When you receive your BT Chargecard(s), BT will include a pocket guidebook telling you how to use the service.

So make it even easier to stay in touch and ring
Free*fone* 0800 800 893 now, to get your FREE card.

NOTE: All Chargecard calls connected through a BT operator are more expensive than direct dialled BT Chargecard calls.
Full details of the cost of calls will be sent to you with your BT Chargecard(s).

CONTENTS

INTRODUCTION	5
GETTING THERE	9
FRINGES OF FRANCE	13
USEFUL INFORMATION	53
HOTEL DIRECTORY	63

Town features

ANGERS	72
ARRAS	81
AVIGNON	85
BESANÇON	100
BORDEAUX	105
CAEN	116
CASTRES	123
DIJON	148
GRENOBLE	169
LYON	187
NANCY	208
ORLÉANS	218
PÉRIGEUX	239
POITIERS	244
RENNES	255
ST-FLOUR	270
STRASBOURG	297
TROYES	307
VALENCE	311
VICHY	318

GLOSSARY	325
INDEX	329
MAPS	**1** – **6**

REGIONS OF FRANCE

INTRODUCTION

Welcome to the RAC's *Hotels in France*, fully revised for
1995. You will find details of more than 1300 hotels
throughout the *hexagon* of France, from the Channel to the
Med and from the Alps to the Pyrénées.

In the main editorial, Fringes of France, Simon Gooch takes
us around the coastline from Dunkerque to Monte-Carlo,
describing the beaches, places to visit and some of the history
of the varied *littoral*. In the directory, the hotels are grouped
under their town, city or resort which are in turn shown
alphabetically. This year the entries have been expanded to
include more details of the restaurants and things to do from
the hotel. You will see that in many cases the sample dishes
have been kept in French, and we have included a glossary
of French food terms to help you round these and other
tempting menus you may encounter.

For 1995 we have also asked each hotel if they would give
discounts to our readers (on accomodation only), many
have, but do note any conditions or restrictions. Please make
sure that you agree the discount when you check in or reserve
your room and be prepared to show a copy of this book.

Abbreviations are shown below. Prices are all in French
francs and so will fluctuate with exchange rates.

At the end of the book there are location maps for all of the
towns listed in the directory and a full index.

We hope that you find the information easy to use and
helpful but remember that details may change through the
year, so it is always wise to phone or fax ahead to confirm
facilities and prices. If you have any comments about these
hotels or new ones, or on the guide generally, please write
to us using the forms at the back of the book.

Map locations

*These refer to the
series of maps
near the end of the
book. The hotel
may not be in the
town itself, but
nearby. Refer to
the hotel entry in
the directory
section for the full
address and
precise location.*

Key to symbols and abbreviations

5D	map location		m	metres (1 metre is about 1 yard)
★	star rating of country or region		TARIFF	guide prices in French francs for a
☎	telephone number			typical single or double room,
BT	hotel allows use of BT Chargecard			usually with en suite facilities
♿	some facilities for disabled people		Bk	breakfast
km	kilometres (1 km is 0.62 miles)		CC	credit cards
			●	special activities arranged by hotel

PARC ASTERIX,
THE LAND OF GAULS !

Take a humorous, fun-packed romp through France's culture and history, with France's favourite comic charaters, Asterix and Obelix, and all their friends!

There's something for everyone at Parc Asterix. Everyone will love the live performances, thrilling theme areas and nail-biting rides. Everyone can live the shows and enjoy the stunning scenery at the heart of the Massif des Trois Forets, just outside Paris.

HOW TO GET TO PARC ASTERIX

If you're coming by car, you need to take the A1 to Paris (Calais-Lille-Paris). Parc Asterix is situated 40 km before Paris between the town of Senlis and Roissy-Charles de Gaulle airport. The entrance to the park is clearly signposted.

OPENNING TIMES FOR 1995

April	Every day from Sat. 8 April
May	Every day except Mon. 15, 22, 29 and Fri. 12 & 19
June	Every day
July	Every day
August	Every day
September	Every day until Mon. 4 then only Wed., Sat. & Su
October	Wed. Sat. & Sun. up to Sun. 15.

PRICES FOR 1995

Adults : 150 FF Children (up to 11 years) : 105 FF
Children up to the age of 3 are admitted free.

For all information about Parc Asterix please call the <u>Asterix Hot Line :</u>

0242 236169

So tranquil,
it's the perfect place for reflection.

J.M. BAUDET – STUDIO VISION

No wonder the French keep so hush-hush about Franche-Comté.

For this area of France, situated between Alsace and Burgundy near the Swiss border, is a haven of peace and quiet.

Its countryside is an unspoilt patchwork of green forests, like the Joux and Chaux, criss-crossed by clear flowing rivers that end in spectacular waterfalls like the Doubs, or the cascades at Herisson.

Indeed this natural wonderland can be fully explored along over 5 thousand kilometres of marked tracks and woodland paths.

As you wander, you'll be assailed by the sweet smell of spruce mixed with pine needles and mushrooms.

You'll also want to have a nose around the many small rural villages with their traditional bulb shaped bell towers.

Or sniff out the old cobbled streets and beautiful courtyards in Besançon, Franche-Comté's capital.

And you're bound to enjoy the heady bouquet of the locally produced 'Vin Jaune', best enjoyed with a plate of smoked ham and strong Comté cheese.

Thus fortified, why not visit one of the many fortified towns, such as Château-Châlon. Or indeed one of the many châteaux, at Belvoir, Joux or Montbéliard.

You will also be able to reflect upon an excellent crossing, if you take your car across to France with P&O European Ferries, Britain's No.1 Ferry Company.

Alternatively, fly Air France direct from London Heathrow to Strasbourg and Lyons any day of the week.

For more information please contact the French Government Tourist Office, 178 Piccadilly, London W1V 0AL.

Upon reflection, you'll find it's perfect.

FRANCE

FERRY PORTS AND ROUTES

GETTING THERE

When making your holiday travel arrangements think about your route through France as well as booking the most appropriate Channel crossing. You may well see the journey as an important part of your holiday or perhaps you just want to get to your destination as quickly and painlessly as possible. If so, consider using the *French Motorail* service. It may seem expensive, but weighing the cost of motorway tolls, petrol, hotels, restaurants and car wear, it can be a good deal. The car is loaded while you prepare yourself for a comfortable night's sleep, and you wake refreshed at your destination. A number of services run from Calais during the summer months to destinations all over southern France, such as Avignon, Biarritz, Brive, Bordeaux, Fréjus/St-Raphaël, Narbonne and Toulouse. The Calais – Nice service operates daily throughout the year. Or you can join the service at Lille or Paris. Alternatively, a *Fly-Drive* option may be a good idea.

Le Shuttle

'To take or not to take the Shuttle' is the question that now has to be answered by all motorists travelling to the Continent. For the Shuttle is the name given to each of the special car-carrying trains that will run through the newly opened Eurotunnel. They are advertised as providing a 'turn up anytime service running 24 hours a day in virtually all weathers' so why not forget your sea sickness pills and be one of the first to try out this 21st-century way of reaching France.

There are good motorway connections on either side with a journey time of about 65 minutes expected from the 11A exit on the M20 near Folkestone to the A16 near Calais. This time includes 35 minutes aboard the train with just 8 minutes at each side spent loading and unloading. This leaves only 15 minutes for buying your ticket and going through the appropriate frontier controls. You can buy your ticket before you leave home if this suits you, but unlike the ferry, where you have an reservation on specific boat, the Eurotunnel system guarantees you a crossing no matter when you turn up, especially comforting if you are held up by unforeseen circumstances on your way to the coast.

If you want to break your journey before boarding, the terminal complexes at both Folkestone and Calais offer a wide range of amenities with restaurants, cafes and shops as well as all the usual service station facilities. So why not make a trip through the Eurotunnel part of your holiday.

The Ferry

Just as a trip in Le Shuttle can be seen as part of your holiday, so can a ferry crossing. The longer crossings, especially, now see themselves as mini-cruises with a wide choice of on-board entertainment available. Whether it be a visit to the cinema or the casino, a fast food feast or a 5-star banquet, all tastes are catered for, so choose the ferry that suits your idea of fun as well as your pocket.

Ferry Routes

Dover – Calais, 1½ hr *Stena Sealink* – up to 22 per day
1½ hr *P & O European Ferries* – up to 25 per day
Also Hovercraft/Seacat, 35-50 min *Hoverspeed* up to 14 per day
Folkestone – Boulogne, Seacat 55 min *Hoverspeed* – up to 6 per day
Newhaven – Dieppe, 4 hr *Stena Sealink* – up to 4 per day
Plymouth – Roscoff, 6 hr *Brittany Ferries* – daily (high season) 3 per day (low season)
Poole – Cherbourg, 4¼ hr *Brittany Ferries* – 2 per day
Poole – St-Malo, 8 hr *Brittany Ferries* – (May – Sept) 4 per week

Portsmouth – Caen, 6 hr *Brittany Ferries* – up to 3 per day
Portsmouth – Cherbourg, (day) 5hr (night) 7-8¼ hr *P & O European Ferries* – up to 4 per day
Portsmouth – Le Havre, (day) 5½ hr (night) 8 hr *P & O European Ferries* – up to 4 per day
Portsmouth – St-Malo, 9 hr *Brittany Ferries* – 1 per day (high season)
Ramsgate – Dunkerque, 2½ hr *Sally Ferries* – 5 per day
Southampton – Cherbourg, (summer) 5 hr (winter) 8 hr *Stena Sealink* – 2 per day (summer) 1 per day (winter)

Ferry Companies

Brittany Ferries
Millbay Docks, Plymouth. PL1 3EW
℡ (01752) 221321
The Brittany Centre, Wharf Road, Portsmouth. PO2 8RU ℡ (01705) 827701
Caen ℡ 31 96 88 80
Cherbourg ℡ 33 43 43 68
Roscoff ℡ 98 29 28 28
St-Malo ℡ 99 40 64 41

Hoverspeed Ltd.
International Hoverport, Western Docks, Dover, Kent. CT17 9TG ℡ (01304) 240241
Boulogne ℡ 21 30 27 26
Calais ℡ 21 46 14 14

P & O European Ferries
Channel House, Channel View Road, Dover. CT17 9TJ ℡ (01304) 203388
Calais ℡ 21 46 04 40
Le Havre ℡ 35 19 78 50
Cherbourg ℡ 33 88 65 70

Sally Ferries
Sally Line Ltd., Argyle Centre, York Street, Ramsgate, Kent. CT11 9DS
℡ (01843) 595522
℡ (0181) 858 1127
Dunkerque ℡ 28 21 43 44

Stena Sealink
Charter House, Ashford, Kent. ℡ (01233) 647047
Calais ℡ 21 46 80 00
Cherbourg ℡ 33 20 43 38
Dieppe ℡ 35 06 39 00

Welcome to the Rhône-Alpes Region

*L*ying between Burgundy and Provence the region known as Rhône-Alpes has everything to make your next French holiday the best yet.

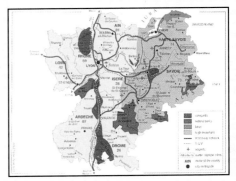
The Rhône-Alpes region

The same size as Belgium, the Rhône-Alpes is a region of infinite variety, encompassing parts of the Alps, northern Provence, the Ardèche canyon, Lyon and Grenoble, the Upper Loire and the Vercors massif. A region where Beaujolais vineyards compete for the visitor's attention with the mountain scenery of Savoy, or the countryside of the source of the Loire and the perfume of lavender fields.

Corner of old Lyon

From the drama of the Alps to the charm and tranquillity of tiny villages in the Drôme, Ardèche and Rhône *départe-ments*, a tapestry of changing landscapes. But this isn't all. Come to the Rhône-Alpes for:

– *g*astronomic *e*xcellence ... delicious regional dishes like *gratin dauphinois*, cheese fondues or *raclettes*, served with a glass of Beaujolais, or Côte du Rhône or maybe a Savoy wine ... Michelin-rated restaurants, little country inns, the *'bouchons'* of Lyon where inspired chefs serve freshly prepared dishes in true *lyonnais* style ...

continued
→

NAME: ....

ADDRESS: ....

Thank you for sending the information about the Rhône-Alps region

Welcome to the Rhône-Alpes Region

– *C*ultural *W*ealth . . .
over 110 museums and galleries, summer festivals, Medieval, Romano-Gallic, Renaissance architecture, modern art . . .

– *O*utdoor *P*ursuits . . .
summer and winter, too much to choose from.

Meribel

Produce of the Drôme département

Mountain biking, horse-riding, hiking, rafting, canoeing, golf . . . and with over 200 ski stations – village resorts and high altitude stations – you need never ski the same *piste* twice!

Last but not least come to the Rhône-Alpes to unwind, to savour the special French *art de vivre* that is surely its major attraction!

A warm welcome awaits you, whichever part of the Rhône-Alpes you choose, whether the *Ain, Ardèche, Drôme, Loire, Rhône, Isère, Savoie or Haute Savoie**.

*These departmental or county names appear after the town name throughout this guide.

For further information on accommodation, local events, route planning, etc, please return the coupon to:

Comité Régional de Tourisme, La Combe, 78 route de Paris, 69260 Lyon-Charbonnières, FRANCE.

NAME: ....
ADDRESS: ....
....
....
....

Thank you for sending the information about the Rhône-Alps region

THE FRINGES
OF FRANCE

*Travel writer Simon Gooch takes a look beyond the beach
umbrellas of the French coasts in search of the unusual and
unspoilt. His selection of high points and their history draws
on a wide experience of holiday France, taking you to the
choicest locations on a long and varied coastline – with boat
trips to the many offshore islands.*

Côte d'Opale

There is nowhere quite so loaded
with tension and expectation as the
Pas de Calais: invasion fleets,
rearguard actions, doomed expeditionary forces,
rumours of tunnelling and mass-attack by balloon
– the Opal Coast has seen many of history's great
moments and false alarms. The events of this
marine frontier have often been the cause of
much pride as well as anguish – best symbolised
by Rodin's great sculpture *The Burghers of Calais*
outside the town's Flemish-style Hôtel de Ville.

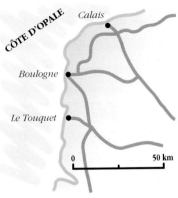

In 1909, France and Britain came several steps
closer with the first cross-Channel flight, launched
from what is now Bleriot-Plage outside Calais. Now the
long-awaited Channel Tunnel pops up nearby, behind the
dunes and the concrete blockhouses of Hitler's Atlantic Wall
at Sangatte, 450 years too late to relieve the final siege of
Calais that so grieved Mary Tudor. Now, instead of English
'sea dogs' swaggering off with their booty, the streets of
modern Calais resound to the chink and squeak of
hypermarché trolleys laden with bulk supplies of French
wine and beer.

Boulogne has kept out of the eye of most storms – though,
as the Column of the Grand Armée commemorates, this was
where Napoleon assembled his invasion fleet of barges in
1804. The local museum also contains a wooden aviary from
the Emperor's last residence – on St Helena.

The old walled town of Boulogne, the Ville Haute, sits up on
a hill quietly detached and unbothered by events. As a first
taste of the amiable pace of small town France, Boulogne

LE PAS-DE-CALAIS
REAL FRANCE ON YOUR DOORSTEP...

MAGNIFICENT BEACHES

HISTORICAL TOWNS

GOOD FOOD

GOLF

Le Pas-de-Calais may be the closest region of France to Britain but it's certainly the least well known.

For further information
contact the Pas-de-Calais tourist board:
COMITE DEPARTEMENTAL
DE TOURISM
24, rue Desille
62200 Boulogne Sur Mer
FRANCE
Tel: 010 33 21 83 32 59
Fax: 010 33 21 30 04 81

PAS
DE
CALAIS
Côte d'Opale

could hardly be better: a place for a quiet breather in an old-fashioned one-man-and-a-dog café before hitting the autoroute, or for indulging in a slap-up lunch at one of the superb seafood restaurants near the port.

From Boulogne, the coast plunges due south, almost recklessly it seems, but the drive is, in fact, a gentle glide through a green landscape of marsh and water meadows – marked out by the inevitable concrete pillboxes lurking in the dunes. At Le Touquet, the German defences part to create space for half-timbered Edwardian villas, traditionally rented for the summer by well-to-do Parisians come to confirm metropolitan ownership of Paris-Plage.

Côte d'Albâtre

With the chalky Pays de Caux, the French coast begins to shadow its southern English counterpart in a long undulating line of white cliffs, sometimes high and dramatic, elsewhere picturesquely holed or cast adrift. Behind the Alabaster Coast the landscape rolls away majestically as France gets into her stride.

Arriving by sea at Dieppe has a great sense of occasion; you get the same instant French embrace of the close-sided port, with its fish market and cluster of bars and cafés, that seduced English artists of the turn of the century, such as Walter Sickert. Before that it had been at Dieppe that the daring habit of sea-bathing, pioneered in Regency Brighton, had been introduced to France by English visitors.

Dieppe opens wide onto the Boulevard de Verdun and its formal gardens, parallel to the great shingle beach – a Second Empire perspective ending at the château, up on a rise. Below it, the Square du Canada honours both the Dieppois explorers of the New World (including Verrazano, the adopted Florentine who discovered Manhattan Island), and the 5,000 Canadian casualties of the disastrous 1942 raid.

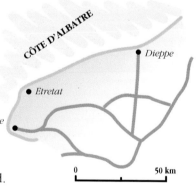

The pale red brick château at Miromesnil, near Dieppe, claims to be the writer Guy de Maupassant's birthplace. If his snobbish parents had had their way, this would be perfectly true – they'd rented out a room there in order to gain this aristocratic distinction – but the future short story specialist arrived abruptly, at home in Fécamp.

Battle of Agincourt

Not far inland from the Côte d'Opale is Azincourt (the modern French spelling). A signposted path guides you round the 'most glorious' field of battle where the flowers of French chivalry were mown down by English longbowmen. The ideal place for a luvvie row over who made the best Henry – dashing Larry or mud-spattered Ken?

The spectacular white cliffs of Etretat have inspired generations of artists, from Delacroix to Matisse

Near his true native town the coastline begins to build to its spectacular best and, at Etretat, the steepling cliffs – including a 'triumphal arch' and l'Aiguille, the 200-ft-high needle offshore – inspired a succession of awestruck canvases by painters from Delacroix and Courbet onwards.

Le Havre would not now inspire dashing brushwork, though Raoul Dufy – born here in 1877 and well represented in the Musée des Beaux Arts – revelled in the bustle of its shipping, in the heyday of the transatlantic liners *Normandie* and *La France*. Bombing in 1944 destroyed the old town, built in the 16th century to replace silted-up Harfleur – breached at great cost by Henry V on his way to Agincourt. The post war rebuilding of France's second-largest port by Auguste Perret has brute concrete strength but none of Dufy's *jeux d'esprit,* though the Pont du Tancarville, the great suspension bridge across the mouth of the Seine, might well have caught his fancy.

Côte Fleurie

Just across the Seine from Le Havre's refineries is the delightful, non-industrial port of Honfleur. The town's orderly rows of tall houses stand around the Vieux Bassin dressed for inclement weather in slate overcoats, complementing Honfleur's eccentric ship-shaped church of Ste Catherine – also sheathed in slate.

The Musée Eugène Boudin contains a number of the Honfleur painter's breezy oil sketches of the Calvados coast

Bénédictine

Herbs and wild plants from the clifftops at Fécamp make up the secret recipe for the Benedictine liqueur, produced by monks at the Abbey of the Holy Trinity since 1510. Tours of the old distillery (the main Benedictine works are now out of town) are followed by a dégustation.

whose Victorian pleasure-seekers sit on the beach on high-backed chairs and under parasols, not quite daring to unbutton.

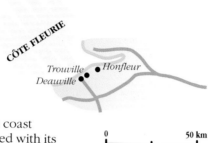

Boudin also worked at Trouville, just along the coast from Honfleur. Compared with its neighbour Deauville, across the River Touques, Trouville is the rather faded belle of the Normandy coast, a seaside spa offering *cures marines* and *thalassothérapie*. Its hotels are all in jaunty period style – pinnacles and pyramids of slate suggesting a town composed of miniature châteaux.

Deauville, built from scratch as a Belle Epoque speculation, has the smooth gloss of the haunts of the very rich: the '21st *arrondissement* of Paris'. Nothing comes cheap here, where the shops have migrated from the Rue de Rivoli. The Promenade des Planches, Deauville's catwalk, shimmers with handsome women of a certain age – preceded by skipping poodles or sulky pugs.

The Casino, its voluptuous façade decorated with plaster Gaiety Girls, forms the focus of Deauville's long, wide-open front. Little has changed at this deluxe showpiece where, with its sleek clientele, you almost expect a glimpse of Edward VII rolling along the red carpet to its Gaming Room. Polo matches and meetings at the Deauville Racecourse

Erik Satie at Honfleur

Erik Satie, the eccentric composer of the Gymnopédies, was born in Honfleur, the son of a French father (a shipping broker) and a Scottish mother, and was baptised an Anglican. After his mother's early death he was brought up by his grandparents and re-baptised a Catholic. At 12 he left for Paris and within a year had joined the Conservatoire.

Not far from Deauville, Villers-sur-Mer offers beach holidays without the stress of keeping up appearances. Walks along the beach below the crumbling Vaches Noires ('black cow') cliffs are good for finding fossils, but hunters should keep an eye out for incoming tides

(where *Le cheval est roi*) attract yet more money and high fashion on parade in the members' enclosure.

The annual Regatta and the Deauville *Festival du Cinéma Américain*, in September, add to the celebrity-spotting fun. Here, even the changing rooms on the beach are glamorously personalised with the names of Hollywood stars – Claudette Colbert, Rock Hudson, Elizabeth Taylor…

Côte du Nacre

The Pearl Coast flanks the mouth of the Orne, where ferries from Portsmouth arrive at Ouistreham; the river then leads down through Caen into the green heart of Normandy, with its cider orchards and Camembert-producing chocolate-and-cream cows. The region supports an ample gastronomy, with excellent seafood available in the resorts. Postcards and novelties make great play with the *trou Normand* – the hole between courses traditionally filled with a nip of Calvados.

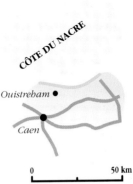

The coast road from Deauville first enters Cabourg, a sprightly survivor of the Belle Epoque. Its half-wheel of quiet streets lined with 19th-century villas has its hub in the Jardins du Casino in front of the Grand Hotel, a substantial confection with Parisian mansard roofs. It was here that Marcel Proust retreated to write *Within a Budding Grove*, part of *A la Recherche du Temps Perdu*, and based his 'Balbec' on the town. Now Cabourg is inescapably Proustian: madeleines are served for breakfast at the Grand, the seafront Boulevard des Anglais has been renamed in his

A family resort between Riva-Bella and Luc-sur-Mer, Lion-sur-Mer has a solidly historic heart: a 16th-century castle and a fine Romanesque church

honour and a *Prix Littéraire Marcel Proust* is awarded (perhaps to offset the slushier *Festival du Film Romantique*).

Not far inland, Caen is still a town of formidable landmarks: the ramparts of William the Conqueror's castle and two great abbey churches – but much else was destroyed by blanket bombing at the height of the Battle of Normandy. Thousands of Caen's terrified citizens sheltered in the Eglise St-Etienne – the church of the Abbaye aux Hommes, founded by William. They reasoned that the English wouldn't dare destroy a church containing the grave of their king. By some miracle, the church came through unscathed. But was it all down to William? During the Revolution his remains had been removed from the church and were thrown into the Orne. Only a thighbone remains.

Côte du Bessin

Omaha, Utah, Gold, Juno and Sword. The code names of the D-Day landing beaches have given permanent identities to stretches of the Normandy coast – all but one of them (Utah) on the Côte du Bessin. On 6 June 1944, wrote André Maleraux, 'the future of the world depended on this thin line of khaki on the coast of Normandy'. With or without its touching parades of old veterans, the setting for *The Longest Day* can still overwhelmingly evoke the drama of that great assault.

Nowhere is the appalling risk taken more apparent than at Arromanches – Gold Beach – where the wreck of 'Port Winston' (the Mulberry Harbour towed across in the wake of the landings) lies in the shallows gathering a camouflage of green seaweed. Ten days after its completion it was wrecked by a ferocious storm that threatened the success of the entire campaign. Seen from the front at Arromanches, the area of sea enclosed by the concrete caissons seems to stretch up to and across the whole horizon, a symbol of the massive ambition and logistical effort of Operation Overlord.

The Circuit du Débarquement is littered with relics of the time – such as Sherman tanks on plinths and German strongpoints of heavily reinforced concrete, sometimes jollied up with tubs of bright flowers. In several towns – notably Arromanches – local museums are packed with militaria and excellent D-Day displays. The details are

Tripe à la mode de Caen

Tripe à la mode de Caen, *if you can stomach it, is the much-treasured local speciality, the rubbery pride of the town. Every year a procession of the Brotherhood of the Golden Tripe-sellers moves gravely through the streets of Caen in their red gowns to the prize-giving.*

fascinating, but only on the beaches, where the veterans paraded for the 50th Anniversary and sang *We'll Meet Again*, does the salty air hold the real tang of fear and expectancy.

The ancient town of Bayeux escaped the fate that befell Caen by being liberated on D-Day plus One, before the Germans could organise an effective defence. The picturesque streets of the centre emphasise what Caen has lost: the individuality of these old Normandy townhouses can't be replicated.

The towers on the cathedral's western façade and its crypt date from William the Conqueror's reign, and were built by Bishop Odo who also commissioned Bayeux's greatest treasure. The Tapestry – in fact, embroidered wool on linen and probably Saxon handiwork – is housed in the Centre Guillaume-le-Conquérant, beside the church, and is kept in semi-darkness to preserve its colours.

You can hire a handset which will tell the whole story as you walk the tapestry's length – from Harold's own visit to Normandy to his death at Hastings. However, most of the pictures speak for themselves, especially when battle is joined. There are many vivid scenes throughout its 70 metres: shipbuilding and the provisioning of the fleet, the ominous appearance of Halley's Comet at Harold's coronation, the bodies being rudely stripped of their armour after the fight. Meanwhile crows look down greedily from the upper border at severed limbs and heads below. The tapestry stops abruptly – and perhaps thankfully – as the Normans drive away English scavengers with whips. The horrors of war are no less grim for being so long ago and rendered in such brisk style in the world's greatest strip cartoon.

D-Day Cemeteries

The Normandy campaign took a great toll on all sides, as the main cemeteries show. For the Americans, the place of pilgrimage for veterans is Colleville, for the Canadians and British Bayeux and for the Wehrmacht (many of them not, in fact, Germans but Russians, Ukrainians or Balts) La Cambe at Orglandes.

Côte du Cotentin

The modern world has created a strangely impressive industrial climax to the otherwise entirely rural Cotentin Peninsula, with a nuclear reprocessing plant sited within a mile of Cap de la Hague. Down below, at the foot of the steep cliffs of the Nez de Jobourg, dangerous currents race between the mainland and the island of Alderney (reached in summer, like the rest of the Channel Islands, by several local ferries).

But even the quietest stretches of the Côte du Cotentin have seen drama at some time. It was in 1927 at Barneville-Carteret, a sleepy west coast resort with a

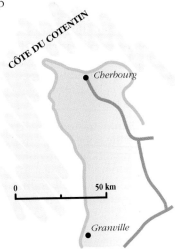

CÔTE DU COTENTIN

Cherbourg

0   50 km

Granville

As well as a picturesque old town, Granville is an elegant resort with panoramic views across the Gulf of St-Malo

wide sandy beach, that a small aeroplane, arriving out of the Atlantic blue, made its landing on what is now Lindberg-Plage.

Other Americans dropped in by parachute, targeting St-Mere-Eglise on the night before D-Day to secure the exits from Utah Beach. A dummy in Khaki uniform hanging by his harness from the church steeple perpetuates the predicament of one American – John Steele, now something of a local legend. The village's Musée des Troupes Aeroportées, shaped like a billowing parachute, gives the bigger picture.

When the breakout from the beaches finally came, the Americans raced up to Cherbourg and secured the damaged port for the Allied supply lines. PLUTO – the PipeLine Under The Ocean – brought petrol from the Isle of Wight to supply the push across France. All down the Cotentin Peninsula pink bollards emblazoned with a Torch of Freedom mark the Voie de la Liberté followed by Leclerc's Free French on their way to Paris.

South from Carteret, the coast road passes through Lessay, where the abbey is a satisfyingly complete Romanesque structure. Its harmony is not disturbed by knowing that it was flattened in 1944 and rebuilt shorn of all later additions: a Norman church literally reborn. For a Gothic contrast, a stop at Coutances is rewarded by a 13th-century gem, the spiky Cathédrale de Notre Dame, replacing a Lessay-like church built by the local Hauteville family who soon moved onto greater things – as Kings of Sicily.

The White Ship

It was near the port of Barfleur, in 1120, that the White Ship, carrying William the only son of Henry I of England, struck a rock and went down. One hundred nobles died with the prince and the only survivor was a butcher, Berold. Ships are now warned off by the Gatteville lighthouse.

Granville is unrivalled as the Cotentin's most handsome and evocative old town. It was built by the English, who dug the defensive Tranchée aux Anglais across the isthmus to cut off the citadel on its high outcrop. Nevertheless, the town soon fell to the French, becoming a base for privateers. The parapet walls command tremendous views along the coast and across the Gulf to St-Malo and Mont-St-Michel.

With the extreme rise and fall of the tides, Granville might seem cruelly exposed to the elements, but inside the old town the cottages nestle comfortably, as cosy as any fishing village. Its cliff-top situation inspires its rather forced description as 'The Monaco of the North' – a bizarre boast perhaps, although the Jardin Public Christian Dior (a native of Granville) links the little town firmly to the world of haute couture.

Côte d'Emeraude

A vision of Gothic towers rises from the sea: walls, buttresses and stone pinnacles – all culminating in a single spire topped by a golden statue of the Archangel Michael brandishing his sword. Mont-St-Michel hovers off the coast of Normandy as if shaped from sea mist. In fact, a guided tour will show how intricately the bare rock has been restructured into a place of worship.

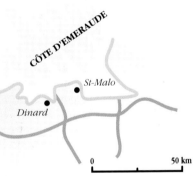

Myth clings to Mont-St-Michel like its rooftop population of gargoyles and devils: the early Celts worshipped the sun here, the Romans Jupiter and Mithras. The Archangel tricked the Devil out of his stone fortress there by building an ice palace on Mont-Dol and agreeing a swap … The only sure fact is that, in 708, Bishop Aubert of Avranches decided that this barren rock should be consecrated and a chapel built. The original Romanesque nave of the Merveille, the later abbey church – featured in a section of the Bayeux Tapestry – survives, as does the crypt and arcaded refectory.

Mont-St-Michel became one of the great pilgrimage centres of France, reached on foot at low tide – but with the risk of falling into quicksands. The tides still race in faster than a man can run, but a causeway and road now link the mount permanently and safely with the mainland. Coaches and cars arrive in huge numbers, but choose a quiet time of day or year and the contemplative calm of the cloisters will be sacrosanct.

Brittany lies just across the River Couesnon, though it is not immediately clear that you have entered a distinct region with its own Celtic culture and language. In Breton, Brittany is *Breizh* or 'Little Britain'.

Cancale, beyond the nature reserve of the Pointe du Grouin, is a famous centre of oyster production (with an Oyster Museum) and a vast acreage of mud dedicated to the production of its delicious bivalves. However, its neighbour St-Malo (where ferries from Portsmouth, Plymouth and Jersey dock) is Brittany's first major port of call.

St-Malo was originally St-Maclou, a Welsh missionary who arrived here in the 6th century, apparently paddling to Brittany on either a stone or a lettuce leaf – or should that be coracle? Under pressure from Anglo-Saxon invaders, Britons were fleeing across the sea from Wales and Cornwall, whose now almost extinct language is the closest cousin of modern Breton.

St-Malo is an autonomous sort of place, where people emphasise that they are *Malouin* first and foremost, rather than French or Breton. At night, in medieval St-Malo, a fierce pack of mastiffs – the Corps of Watchdogs – would be let out to roam beyond the walls, whose ramparts and massive Tour Solidor still protect its centre. Defensive on land, the people of St-Malo were great adventurers overseas. Like other French Channel ports, St-Malo has produced its own share of explorers, preeminently Jacques Cartier, the discoverer of the St Lawrence river – and wealth-gathering pirates.

The Falklands Connection

When the Argentines invaded Las Malvinas in 1982, they were in fact occupying not only the Falklands but also Les Malouines (from which the Spanish derives), named by de Bougainville, a corsair from St-Malo cruising the South Atlantic in 1767.

The Breton coasts aren't all rock and high seas: idyllic sandy beaches are just as common

Since the gutting of St-Malo as General Patton's forces swept into Brittany, the town centre has been rebuilt as a perfect replica in the local grey granite. For buildings of untouched character – almost eccentric in their wood-framed lurches and sags – Dinan, a few kilometres along the estuary of the River Rance from St-Malo, is all that a romantically unruly Breton town should be. The Fête des Ramparts – an annual medieval pageant – relives its great days. Dinan's close namesake, Dinard, is a total contrast: the smartest of Riviera-like resorts, warmed by the Gulf Stream and centring on the romantically-named Promenade du Clair-de-Lune. It is, flatteringly, home to a *Festival du Film Britannique* every September.

Côte de Granit Rose

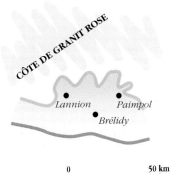

Another saintly Welshman gave his name to St-Brieuc, the capital of Côtes d'Armor, and the point from which – going westwards – the Brittany coast begins to run wild. With this growth of fiords, dramatic geological tumbles and rock stacks out to sea, comes a similar increase in tall heroic tales, semi-familiar to British visitors, involving the knights of Arthurian legend. King Arthur himself is said to be buried on the Ile Daval, near Perros-Guirec.

At St-Michel-en-Grève, he fought a dragon on the beach. Both retired exhausted after a day's huffing and puffing but, while the beast slept in its cave, Arthur prevailed upon a local hermit – St Efflam – to go and pray outside the lair. The dragon rose early next day, clambered up onto the Grand Rocher on the sands and began to spout blood, then fell into the sea and drowned.

These days, the dragons of the Pink Granite Coast exist only in their reduced, feathered form – as cormorants and gannets, who thrive on its wild shores and on the sanctuary

The Seven Saints

Inland from Lannion – a name direct from Cornwall – another early Celtic chamber tomb at Les Sept Saints has been Christianised with the addition of a chapel. The legend is that seven Christian martyrs, buried alive at Ephesus in the 4th century, were miraculously ressurected on this spot.

of the Ile de Bono, along with puffins and guillemots. The reserve is part of the Sept Iles, reached by boat from Perros-Guirec. Of equal interest for bird-watchers is the Ile Brehat, accessible from Paimpol and one of France's best-preserved habitats.

From Perros-Guirec on the Sentier des Douaniers to Ploumanach, then on to the very Cornish-sounding Trégastel and Trébeurden, the Corniche Bretonne provides a succession of dramatic rock features and giant boulders interspersed with quiet beaches. Here the first of Brittany's prehistoric megaliths appears: dolmens and menhirs enough to provide Asterix's fat friend Obelix with a lifetime's ammunition.

Jagged rocks at Le Diben, near the western end of the Pink Granite Coast. Unwelcoming for seafarers but an endless delight for landlubbers

Côte des Légendes

On balance, the Bretons' fellow-Celts, the Scots, have been more welcome along this coast than the English. In 1522, the English raided Morlaix in revenge for an attack by its pirates on Bristol. They found that most of the Breton inhabitants were off at a country fair, so looted the town, got helplessly drunk, and were surprised much later by the returning revellers. Ugly scenes ensued ...

Not long after this affair, the five-year-old Mary Queen of Scots arrived at Roscoff on her way to be betrothed to the future François II. After the failure of the 1745 Rebellion, Bonnie Prince Charlie – evading the Royal Navy on the long haul from the Hebrides after the fall of Culloden – also landed at Roscoff, returning to his final exile.

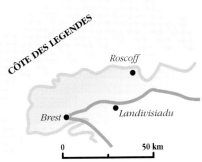

Trading connections with the rest of the Celtic fringe – suppressed after the union with France in 1532 – were revived only recently with the creation of Brittany Ferries in 1972. The company is based in the new deep-water port at Roscoff, from which regular services now run to Plymouth and Cork.

From Roscoff westward, this is Finistere – Land's End – and soon its pint-sized farms with their champion growth of cauliflowers and artichokes peter out and Brittany faces head on into the often stormy waters of the Atlantic and the Bay of Biscay.

After Molène, a small island whose inhabitants live off seaweed-gathering and crabbing, there is one last outpost of land – the Ile d'Ouessant – or, to the English, Ushant. In Breton it is *Enez Heussa*, 'the island of terror' where mermen and mermaids would carry off islanders beneath the waves. The Creac'h lighthouse on Ushant, marking the entrance to the English Channel, is the most powerful in the world – designed to keep ships off Finistere's lethal rocks and avoid

The treacherous rocks of Finistere and the Ile d'Ouessant have accounted for numerous wrecks, most famously the 1978 oil spill from the Amoco Cadiz

environmental disasters on the scale of the wrecked tanker
Amoco Cadiz.

Sited in a well-protected bay in the lee of the Pointe de St
Mathieu, Brest has been France's main naval base since
being set up by Cardinal Richelieu. Once again the last war
was the costliest for a French seaside town: Allied bombing
aimed initially at the sheltering German battleships
Scharnhorst and *Gneisenau,* then at the U-boat menace,
destroyed the centre of Brest completely. The Musée de la
Marine in a restored waterfront château retrieves Brest's long
and proud seagoing history.

Côte de la Plaisance

The long lower jaw of the gaping sea-monster
mouth of Finistere culminates in the Pointe du
Raz beyond the Baie des Trépassés – the Bay of
Departed Souls. From here, according to Breton legend,
druids were taken to their burial place in the far west, the Ile
de Sein, treeless and exposed to the full force of the Atlantic
Ocean. Boats now take day-trippers (and maybe the
occasional druid) from Audierne-Plage.

This is an area of strong Breton traditions, where you are
most likely to hear the Celtic language spoken and see older
country women wearing the tall lace head-dress – the *Coiffe
Bigoudene* – all of a foot high. Sightings of these portable,
featherweight menhirs are guaranteed at one of Brittany's
many folk festivals. At Quimper, the capital of the ancient
kingdom of Cornouaille (literally, Cornwall) the Grande Fête
in late July celebrates Breton culture noisily, with days of
music – on bagpipe and drum or Celtic harp – and dancing
in the dark at the Fest-Noz.

The oldest Breton town – Quimper – huddles
companionably beneath the twin spires of the
Gothic Cathédrale St-Corentin (where services
are sometimes conducted in the Breton
tongue), its narrow streets lined with tall
overhanging houses, half-timbered mostly. A
statue by the cathedral gives substance to
Gradlon, the mythical founder of the town and
king of the drowned city of Ys. The defences of
this Breton Atlantis – built below sea-level if not
totally submerged – were breached after his
daughter, tempted by the Devil (disguised as a
handsome young man) unlocked the city gates.
Only Gradlon survived, at the cost of sacrificing his

The Breton Closes

*Finistere has a
unique heritage
– Les Enclos
Paroissiaux – of
granite-built
churches
combined with
an ossuary, a
cemetery and
elaborately
carved Calvary.
The Closes are
often the scenes
of another
Breton speciality
– the Pardon, or
saint's day
parade.*

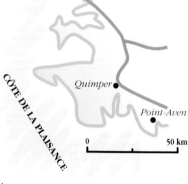

daughter to the waves. Unsceptical sailors in the Bay of Douarnenez claim to hear church bells ringing underwater on feast days.

Gradlon also, it is said, founded Concarneau. The town's Ville Close, an island fortified by Vauban for Louis XlV, overlooks a fishing port specialising in tuna and sardines. The Musée de la Pêche (housed in a former sardine cannery) and the late-August *Fête des Filets Bleus* (referring to the blue nets of the tunny fishers and initiated in 1905 to raise money for the town's poor) celebrate Brittany's toilers of the sea.

Côte des Mégalithes

In modern Lorient – like Brest, rebuilt from bombed-out ruins and with nuclear submarines now occupying the untouched former U-boat pens – history seems to have a limited span, though this was once the base for the French East India Company. The name of the port itself means 'the East'. Its link to the older Brittany comes every year with the Interceltic Festival in August, with participants from Galicia to John O'Groats.

Just down the Coast of Megaliths, at Carnac, the journey back in time is through thousands of years. The Carnac alignments of Menec, Kermario and Kerlescan together create Europe's most remarkable prehistoric landscape. Row upon row of standing stones – over 3,000 in all and set up in ten or eleven parallel lines – pre-date Stonehenge and the pyramids. They are, with the cave paintings of the

The Pont-Aven School

Paul Gauguin's years spent at Pont-Aven, from 1886–9, were crucial for his free colour revolt against Impressionism. The Vision after the Sermon, painted here, shows Jacob wrestling with an angel, watched by Breton peasant women in lace coifs. The association with Gauguin and his followers has made Pont-Aven a town overflowing with art galleries – but possessing no work by Gauguin himself.

Dordogne, France's greatest treasures from prehistory. Carnac is, however, threatened by its worldwide reputation as a wonder and, with the original heath being reduced to a dustbowl, there are already some restrictions on access.

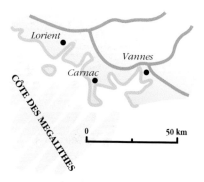

Possibly a lunar observatory, probably a temple? – the function of the Carnac alignments remains unclear. The well-presented Musée de Préhistoire at Rue du Tumulus in Carnac explores all the possibilities, studies pioneered in 1874 by a Scotsman, James Miln, who was joined in his enthusiasm by an unlikely ally – an 11-year-old local boy, Zacharie de Rouzic, who continued the work of excavation and analysis after Miln's death.

Quiberon Bay, into which the stones appear to be marching, is partially protected by the peninsula of the Presqu'île de Quiberon. The Atlantic rollers of the western Côte Sauvage, where bathing is sensibly forbidden, are calmed inside the bay. But Quiberon's geography – which makes its roads congested in summer – has often formed a fatal trap. In 1795, an army of 10,000 Royalists was landed, but the Revolutionary forces were waiting for them and soon bottled them up in the narrow peninsula. Only one in five of the king's forces survived to be taken off by the helplessly-watching Royal Navy.

In 57 BC, while all of Gaul fell to Julius Caesar's legions, the Veneti tribe (presumably the inspiration for the Asterix comics) held out at their capital – modern Vannes – set inside the Golfe du Morbihan and protected by two more peninsulas, closing like the claws of a crab. Brutus, then Caesar's trusted admiral, built a fleet of galleys in the Loire and sailed them round the coast in a surprise attack. The emperor watched, not suspecting future plots in the Senate, from the Butte de César on the Rhuys peninsula as the Veneti's helplessly becalmed small craft were overwhelmed.

Vannes was at various times the capital of the Duchy of Brittany but, in 1532, the eternal union of the Kingdom of France and the Duchy was proclaimed here, ratified by the Breton Etats and made flesh by the marriage of the Duke's daughter to François I. Since that date, the history of Brittany becomes that of France itself, though with a strong and still potent movement towards cultural if not political autonomy.

The Biggest Menhir

The peninsula of Locmariaquer half-encloses the Golfe du Morbihan, with its host of small islands whose stone circles and menhirs are partially submerged at high tide. The largest megalith of all – the Grand Menhir Brise on Locmariaquer – now lies broken in four pieces after an 18th-century earthquake. When complete, it stood 22 metres high and weighed 347 tonnes.

Côte d'Amour

You are unlikely to see Breton grannies wearing lace coifs in La Baule. The beach resort – the 'Nice of the North' – is technically outside Brittany and the *département* of Morbihan and, though Breton is still spoken even further south, La Baule is as international and luxurious as any Riviera fleshpot. The emphasis on the Côte d'Amour is beach chic and a seductive nightlife, rather than the dreamy contemplation of stone circles.

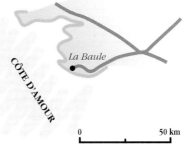

Behind the sophisticated façade of La Baule and the Côte d'Amour resorts there is a quite different reality: a wild and secret world of reedmarsh, thatched cottages and placid canals. The Norfolk Broads ... but with sun and without cabin cruisers and proud of a strong local cuisine, including frogs' legs and eels *de Roquefort*.

The Marais de Grande Briere is now an official *Parc Naturel*, 100,000 acres of wildlife reserve protected against the pressures of coastal development. In 1462 the marsh people – the Brierois – were granted autonomy in their 22 cantons by the Duke of Brittany, and carried on living by gathering reeds, cutting peat and hunting and fishing – a timeless, pastoral way of life that still in part survives. The traditional *chaland* punts (with pointed noses and tails) are still used on the canals of the *marais* and can be hired out. Thatched

The 5-mile-long sandy beach at La Baule fronts the mysterious region of the Grande Brière marshes

cottages are lived in as well, as at Kerhinet – open to the public as a folk museum with a weaver's workshop and *sabotier* clog-maker's. Their roof beams are often made from fossil trees dredged up out of the peat bog.

Some parts closest to the sea are salt-marsh – *les Marais Salants* – especially near Guérande, a delightful town whose medieval walls come complete with gates and towers. The 'white land' of the salt pans (as opposed to the Pays Noir [black land] of the Marais) provides a local industry, and fresh sea salt can be bought by the roadside. The tide washes in, then salt is deposited as the seawater evaporates on its slow progress back through the *oeillets* – a complex system of basins and dams. The salt is raked out by the *paludiers* and transported from the marshes in traditional wooden tubs. At Saille, la Maison du Paludier, a local history museum, shows how this particular form of marshland life has survived into the late 20th century.

A salty cuisine

Salt is the dominant element of the coastal cuisine at La Baule, richly flavoured and with high magnesium content. Sea bass comes baked in a crust of Guerande salt which is broken open in front of you like a sculptor's mould.

Côte de Jade

In August, the population of St-Nazaire escapes the rather bland surrounds of the rebuilt war-damaged port with its (as usual) perfectly intact U-boat pens, leaves the shut-down shipyards behind and crosses the great suspension bridge – currently Europe's longest single span – over the Loire, heading for the beaches of the Côte de Jade.

This easily overlooked corner of land between the river estuary and the sea is the Pays de Retz, an area of the larger region of the Vendée. Pornic is its prettiest resort, a fishing port and marina with a château that was one of many in the Vendée owned by the grisly Gilles de Rais, the Bluebeard of Charles Perrault's fairytale – a mythically murderous husband who was, in fact, a 15th-century Marshal of France.

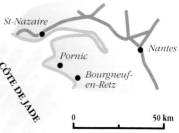

In the region's later time of troubles, Pornic was a Republican outpost in a seething tide of Monarchist revolt against Jacobin Paris which began as a protest against conscription. In the extended Vendée wars, the 'Catholic and Royal Army' was defeated several times, but savage reprisals continued to provoke unrest. In 1795, the Vendée was granted freedom from army service and liberty of worship, but the landing of the royalist exiles at Quiberon Bay sparked fresh violence, leading only to final defeat in 1796.

Pornic's château,
one of the sinister
Bluebeard's many
strongholds in the
Pays de Retz

The 'Tragic Memory' continues to resound throughout the Vendée, kept alive by reenacted battles and *son-et-lumière* spectaculars.

Bourgneuf-en-Retz is the southernmost point of this short but popular stretch of coast. The town's Musée du Pays de Retz is housed in an old convent where Bluebeard is said to have met his first victim.

Côte de la Lumière

The Ile de Noirmoutier, now connected by a toll bridge to the mainland, has a curious split personality. The west coast, pounded by ocean breakers, is one big sandy beach, an extension of the sunset-facing resort developments of the Côte de la Lumière (though without their frequent high-rises), where the light is comparable to the Midi, according to Renoir. The climate of the island is also freakishly Mediterranean – a place where mimosas bloom in winter. The east coast is, by contrast, a wild stretch of salt-marsh and polders, left to the seabirds and waders and the local salt-panners and mussel-gatherers. The similarly benign but further offshore Ile d'Yeu – 'daughter of Brittany under a Spanish sun' – can be reached via Fromentine.

Ile de Noirmoutier

La Roche-
sur-Yon

CÔTE DE LA LUMIÈRE

0   50 km

The combination of beach and marsh, divided by dunes and strips of pine forest, continues southwards. St-Jean-de-Monts boasts 24 km of sandy coast and *thalassothérapie* (sea-water therapy) using locally produced 'brown sludge'. Les Sables d'Olonne, reached across reclaimed fenland, is a busy resort built along fine, level sands. At first sight, 'the Pearl of the Coast of Light' seems an unbroken string of apartment blocks and hotels, but somewhere in there are a few retreats from the bustle of high season, such as the Musée de l'Abbaye de Ste-Croix with its fine modern art collection.

From the southernmost stretch of the Côte de la Lumière, at the junction of the départements of Vendée and Charente-Maritime, the marshes dominate, becoming a distinct region, drained and grazed since the 10th century and divided up by *conches* and *rigoles* – narrow waterways flowing into the Sèvre Niortaise. The whole area is now protected in the Parc Régional du Marais Poitevin, Val de Sèvre et Vendée – but known by the French as the *Venise Verte*.

Instead of Venetial palazzi and piazzas, there are only lines of shady poplars along the quiet canals and water meadows beyond; instead of gondolas, *les plates* – flat-bottomed punts which often provide the only access for farmers to their fields and livestock. This idyllic machine-free green world is perhaps especially vulnerable to a potential flood of visitors as the Marais Poitevin becomes more and more popular. Nevertheless, development is severely restricted and transport remains basic: horse-drawn caravans and bicycles for hire on the few roads and tracks, or *les plates*, hired by the half day.

Le Gois

The old stone causeway to the Ile de Noirmoutier is scene of the annual road (and paddling) race – Les Foulées du Gois – run against the tide. Escape platforms are sited at regular intervals along its course.

The stone causeway linking the Ile de Noirmoutier has now been replaced by a toll bridge – except for daredevil runners

Côte des Charentes

La Rochelle, France's best-preserved port and seaside town, is a lucky survivor – not least for an enlightened policy of preservation and pedestrianisation in the 1970s. Four hundred years earlier, in 1572, Catherine de Medici – in a somewhat less enlightened mood – launched the St Bartholomew's Day Massacre, a bloody purge of France's Protestants. Huguenots fled to sympathetic La Rochelle, well-defended by medieval towers – and with a chain across its harbour mouth (reaching from the still-extant Tour de la Chaîne to the Tour St-Nicolas). In the subsequent siege, La Rochelle held out and was allowed to continue its freedom of worship.

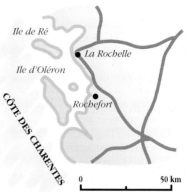

Fifty years later, Cardinal Richelieu was more determined to rid France of Calvinism. A second siege of the dissident town was waged with more ingenuity than before, the Cardinal's engineers building a mole across the bay and cutting off the town completely. By the time the siege was over, three-quarters or more of La Rochelle's inhabitants were dead.

It should have been the end of La Rochelle but, with the growth of the new trade across the Atlantic to Canada and the French West Indies, its economy recovered. The town's many substantial 17th- and 18th-century *hôtels* in the Rue du Palais flaunt this new prosperity. The Rue de l'Escale is paved with granite setts brought back as balast on voyages from Canada, while the Hôtel de la Chambre du Commerce celebrates La Rochelle's heyday with a façade decorated with trophies and ships' prows.

The boats packed into the harbour these days are more modest than those of the pioneers: mostly yachts from Britain amongst a fleet of French trawlers. To recapture the flavour of La Rochelle's enterprising years – including their most shameful aspect, the slave trade – the Musée du Nouveau Monde, in a former shipowner's house, and the Musée Maritime on board a frigate give a vivid idea of the commercial dynamo that was La Rochelle.

In contrast, the low-lying Ile de Ré – the 'White Island', with its whitewashed green-shuttered cottages, its sandy beaches and oyster beds, is tranquillity itself, unconcerned with the wider world – except, of course, in August, when the crowds

Napoleon en route *to St Helena*

The Ile d'Aix, reached by ferry from Pointe de la Fumée, near Fouras, was Napoleon's last home in France on his way to his final exile on St Helena. The Musée Africain is the proud owner of the camel (subsequently stuffed) from which he directed the Battle of the Pyramids.

invade. In St-Martin, the main town and fishing port, the Café Boucquingam commemorates the Duke of Buckingham's landing on the Ile de Ré in a failed attempt to relieve the Richelieu siege of La Rochelle.

Rochefort, at the mouth of the Charente, was in Louis XIV's reign France's main naval arsenal; the former storehouses survive, behind a triumphal arch – the Porte du Soleil. The Centre International de la Mer is situated in the Corderie Royale, the 378-metre-long former ropeworks for the navy.

French 19th-century yearning for the exotic and the oriental is lavishly indulged in Rochefort's Musée Pierre Loti. The largely forgotten novelist was a former naval officer who wrote steamy tales of the 'marvellous elsewhere', set in far-flung places he had visited such as Tahiti and Japan. Loti lived in appropriate style in his Arab drawing room and Turkish salon – not to mention a medieval banqueting hall and monastic refectory.

Like the Ile de Ré, its southern neighbour the Ile d'Oléron is a relatively quiet and local place, a winter stopover for migrant pelicans and egrets. It is also now connected to the French mainland by a toll bridge. Woods of pine and evergreen oak on Loti's 'Island of Perfume' provide shade behind sandy beaches, while mussels grow on their 'high-rise' wooden stakes and oysters lounge in their beds (*les claires*).

The Tour de la Chaîne and the Tour St-Nicolas failed to protect Huguenot La Rochelle against Richelieu's siege

Côte de Beauté

The Gironde estuary opens up like a great gash in the flank of France, out of which pour the combined waters of a dozen or more rivers, including the Garonne, the Dordogne, Lot and Tarn. Up the long reach of the Gironde, busy with ocean-going ships, lies Bordeaux and some of the greatest vineyards in the world. At the mouth of the Gironde, the Côte de Beauté fronts a less exclusive but very pleasant area of pine and

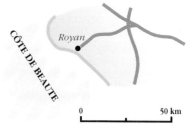

beech forest (at La Palmyre) and marshes where the *parcs à huîtres* provide oysters to accompany the white wines of the Entre deux Mers.

Beauty, at Royan – the focus of the Côte de Beauté – is a post-war planning concept. Once more Allied air-raids obliterated an elegant French seaside town, most fashionable in the Twenties, and the 1950s rebuilding was in an uncompromisingly modern manner. In France, this usually means concrete, used most daringly in Royan at the Eglise Notre Dame. A few period-piece villas survived the bombs, including No 58 Boulevard Garnier, where Emile Zola twice holidayed far from germinal country.

A more solid and substantial heritage can be found a few miles up river at Talmont, where the 12th-century Romanesque church of Ste-Radigonde stands on a cliff hard by the river's edge. Its superb carved portal contains fanciful scenes of teams hauling captive lions and acrobats forming human pyramids. The Gironde at Talmont is permanently lined with square-framed fishing nets, *les carrelets*, which are let down into the river by crane. At Saujon, not far inland from Royan, another fine Romanesque church features a stone figure of a man carrying a huge fish over his shoulder.

Modern, much rebuilt Royan still boasts the superb sands which made its reputation in the Twenties

Côte d'Argent

Running due south for 200 km from the mouth of the Gironde to the Basque Country, the Silver Coast seems as close as is possible to a physical expression of a line of longitude. A logically laid-out world would be like this, though thankfully the relentless progress from A to B of the Côte d'Argent has its hiccoughs. Infinity is briefly interrupted by the Bassin d'Arcachon and then the slight bulge that barely deserves the name of Pointe d'Arcachon. From then on it continues its unerring course.

The vast size of the Landes forests – the largest in Western Europe – can be daunting; most visitors prefer to arrive at their beach colony and stay put, like the first settlers in some strange new world. For the more adventurous, there are still deserted stretches of coast to be discovered. Until the 19th century, the Landes were even harder to penetrate, being mostly swamp. Only shepherds inhabited much of the region, and they mostly moved around on stilts. The quaggy nature of traditional *landais* life is described at the Ecomusée de Marqueze, reached by steam train from Sabres.

At Arcachon, as well as producing the irregularity of its *bassin,* the level land suddenly throws up a Saharan surprise:

To the Lighthouse

From Royan, boat trips head out to sea to the Cordouan lighthouse, sited on a lonely rock where a beacon was first set up by the Black Prince. Once again – here on the borders of Aquitaine – the English were here.

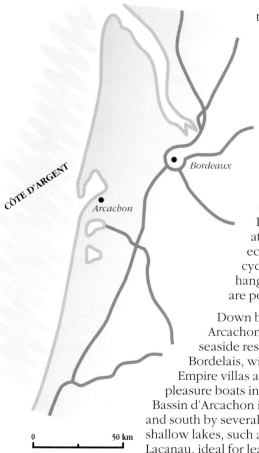

Bordeaux

Arcachon

CÔTE D'ARGENT

0   50 km

the Dune du Pilat, at 114 metres by far the highest in Europe. From the top of this great swept-up sand sculpture, the views across the forests and out across the Bay of Biscay are endless. The Dune seems to attract sporting eccentrics – cycling up it or hang-gliding off it are popular.

Down below sits Arcachon, the preferred seaside resort for the Bordelais, with its Second Empire villas and throng of pleasure boats in the marina. The Bassin d'Arcachon is flanked north and south by several quiet and shallow lakes, such as Carcans and Lacanau, ideal for learning the rudiments of sailing.

Cycling in the Landes

As an alternative to struggling up the Dune du Pilat, there are long cycle tracks laid out through the Landes forests and along the Côte d'Argent – a green alternative to reaching the Pyrénées by the Route Nationale.

The largest sand dune in Europe at Pilat is, at 114 metres high, as formidable as anything in the Sahara. Happily there are ice-cream sellers nearby!

Côte Basque

The former Kingdom of the Basques is now reduced to the département of Pyrénées-Atlantiques, French half of a divided whole yet lacking an equivalent of ETA, the Spanish Basque terrorist group. Staying in the resorts of the Côte Basque, you may not get much of a feeling of this ancient, unique culture. Only bilingual roadsigns hint at an extra dimension to this far corner of France: they are subtitled by strange clusters of consonants – the *Euskara* language, unrelated to any other European tongue.

CÔTE BASQUE

Bayonne
Biarritz
St-Jean-de-Luz

SPAIN

0   50 km

Biarritz, a name that still fizzes with glamour and style, was launched as a bathing resort by Napoleon III, who built the Villa Eugènie here for his Empress. The town was attempting to renovate some of its remnants of past glories when 'le tout Gotha' came to town. The Villa Eugènie is now the Hôtel du Palais with an enduring reputation for high society clientele, celebrated in the annual Bal Windsor. Castellated mansions abound, in all styles from Olde English to Neo-Basque. Biarritz still attracts the big spenders – with its Casino Municipal recently restored to its original Art Deco glory – but the regulars on the Miramar and Milady Plages are more likely to be international beach bums, in Biarritz for the big Atlantic breakers and the annual Quicksilver Surf Masters tournament in September.

Bayonne, effectively amalgamated with Biarritz, is easy to overlook when arriving by the Route Nationale on the Côte Basque. It has much more of a local feel, with many houses in the vernacular style, their timber frames picked out in red or green. Grand Bayonne centres on the cathedral, whose name dates from the 14th century, built during the 300-year English domination of Aquitaine and the Pays Basque. Bayonne was the regional capital until the Revolution, when it was supplanted by Pau, but retains a strong Basque flavour. The city's *Fêtes Traditionelles* at the beginning of August celebrate Basque culture and end with a *corrida*.

St-Jean-de-Luz, a well-organised resort

Nets drying at St-Jean-de-Luz, a Basque resort that also fishes for anchovy and tuna

that also preserves more of the Basque character than Biarritz, was formerly a base for whalers. It remains an active fishing port, principally for anchovy and tuna.

One of St-Jean-de-Luz's merchant houses is known as the Maison Louis XIV. The young king stayed here during his extravagantly-celebrated marriage to Maria Teresa, the Infanta of Spain, which took place in the vast Eglise St-Jean-Baptiste. The door through which the royal couple left the church has been walled up ever since. Very sensibly this did not become regular court etiquette.

The marriage contract was signed at a meeting on the tiny Ile des Faisans midway across the border river of Bidassoa, just beyond Hendaye. The French and Spanish courtiers, exotically garbed and befeathered – cock pheasants indeed – competed to make the richer show. The Spanish Court Painter, Diego Velasquez, was in charge of décor for Philip IV's suite, but it was soon apparent that the future Roi Soleil had outdressed the Imperial Court. This was a symbolic moment in European history. Velasquez, exhausted and humiliated, made the long journey back to Madrid, but developed a fever there and died.

Pelota

The Basque national game of pelota, *otherwise known as* jai alai, *is something like squash or fives, but more dangerous. Played in vast concrete two- or three-walled frontons, its fastest variation is* remonte, *a 35-point game using the* chistera *– a curved extension to the arm made out of chestnut or ash basketwork. The ball is hard and concussion or worse is common. Helmets are now worn.*

Côte Vermeille

Everywhere on Roussillon's Vermilion Coast there are flavours and hints of nearby Spain – or rather Catalonia – just a short drive away across the easternmost foothills of the Pyrénées. The vertical red and yellow stripes of the Catalan flag seem to blaze from every car window and rear bumper. Even the language here is, in fact, Catalan – a survival strengthened by the arrival in Perpignan of many refugees from Franco's Spain. Salvador Dali – the Catalan Surrealist – considered Perpignan railway station the centre of the world, though there is no sign of its clocks going soft ...

Ceremony and tradition are largely Spanish. The Good Friday Procession de la Sanch from the church of St-Jacques in Perpignan is – as in far off Seville – a line of penitents in tall hoods. The town's Casa Paival contains a Museum of Catalan Art and Popular Culture. For 500 years, Perpignan was part of the Aragonese Kingdom of Majorca, not joining France proper until Louis XIII negotiated the Treaty of the Pyrénées in 1659.

CÔTE VERMEILLE

Perpignan

Collioure

SPAIN

0   50 km

Architecture, too, in Roussillon is decidedly Catalan in style – a mixture of extreme severity and wild *churriguerresque* excess, particularly in the region's fine Romanesque and Gothic churches, such as the Cathédrale Ste-Eulalie at Elne with its richly decorated cloisters. Perpignan's Palais des Rois de Majorque, with its grand throne room, dates from the 13th century and is built of a typical local mix of river pebbles and red brick, safely contained inside a Citadelle built by Vauban, confirming French ownership.

The inhabitants of Perpignan – oven-baked on the plain of the River Têt – are easily tempted down to the pretty seaside towns of the Côte Vermeille. Collioure, with its flower-filled streets rising up from the old harbour, is the most seductive. In 1905, Matisse and Derain were inspired by the dazzling Southern sun, gaining themselves notoriety as *Les Fauves*. Since then, Collioure's charms have seduced rather than stimulated such 'wild beasts'. Works by Matisse and Derain are on show in the Musée de Peinture, while pavement artists render homage underfoot.

Catalan barques at Collioure, boats unchanged in style from the days when the Med was Le Lac Catalan

Through woods of cork oak, the road reaches Banyuls, France's most southerly resort, famous for a sweet dessert wine – then Cerbère and the Spanish frontier.

Côte des Roses

The short stretch of the Côte des Roses could almost be considered Narbonne's private beach. In fact, there is a Narbonne-Plage, built on the long curving sand bar that has slowly formed along the coast of Languedoc and is, as it says, pure beach. Gruissan has much more of it. The town runs in concentric rings around the Tour Barberousse – named after the Turkish admiral Barbarossa, said to have been its builder. Gruissan is sited on a former island, the wooded hill of the Montagne de la Clape – a rare high viewpoint on this low-

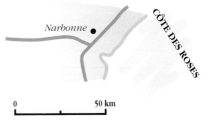

Narbonne

CÔTE DES ROSES

0   50 km

lying coast. A marina and beach houses up on stilts now link the old port to the new reality of the resorts.

Narbonne itself, stranded a few miles inland by the build-up of sand in the former gulf, is the unchallenged prize bloom on the Coast of Roses. The city is one of many in the South of France with a rich classical past as a provincial centre of the Roman Empire. Narbonne was then Colonia Narbo Martius, a major port and commercial hub, the last remains of which (apart from the universal Roman tiled roofs) is the horreum – two streets of Roman shops or storehouses, now lying beneath modern ground level.

An aerial view of the old town of Gruissan shows its concentric plan round the Tour Barberousse

The dominant building in Narbonne today is the Gothic cathedral of St-Just et St-Saveur, towering over the city and visible from many miles away. In its shadow, the fortified Palais des Archévêques, containing the Musée d'Art et d'Histoire, was inspired by the contemporary Palais des Papes in Avignon. If the cathedral's nave had been completed as planned, it would have been a vast structure, but the Narbonne town consuls of the day refused permission to demolish the nearest section of city walls. As a result, Narbonne's cathedral remains simply a sky-scraping choir, with views from its North Tower of the endless and highly productive vineyards of Corbières.

Côte d'Amethyste

A Béziers man – the engineer Paul Riquet – was responsible (despite the loss of his personal fortune) for one of the 17th century's most ambitious engineering works: the Canal des Deux Mers, now known as the Canal du Midi. The formerly strategic link between Atlantic and Mediterranean has become a leisurely holiday route, ideal for pottering across France. Here at Béziers it is close to its eastern end, finally making its exit to the sea at Sète, a major port for the landing of sardines and tunny and the export of wine.

Béziers bore the brunt of the Crusade of 1209 that suppressed the Albigensian heresy (taking its name from Albi, on the Tarn). For their notion that the world, with all its medieval miseries, was the work of the Devil, the Albigensians – and anyone else, however orthodox, who got in the way of Simon de Montfort's crusaders – paid heavily.

Langue d'oc

The ancient langue d'oc is a rival of the northern langue d'oil, both names referring to their different words for oui. Standard French derives from langue d'oil. The songs of troubadours were the greatest product of the medieval Occitan culture, though in this century Frederic Mistral, writing in the related Provençal, was awarded the Nobel Prize.

Twenty thousand were put to the sword at Béziers.

At Agde – Greek Agathe – close to the landmark Cap d'Agde, the fortified 12th-century cathedral seems to embody a distrust of fellow-Christians while ostensibly on armed watch for Saracen raiders. Made of black basalt, crenellated and machicolated, it provided shelter as the Wars of Religion raged grimly in these parts, Protestantism having for a while held sway in nonconformist Languedoc.

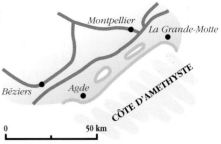

'The Oxford of France', Montpellier has always been an open-minded place, the home of one of France's oldest universities where both Rabelais and Nostradamus studied medicine. It is very much a student town: youthful, lively and diverse, its centre the egg-shaped Place de la Comédie, known locally as *l'Oeuf*. It, too, declared for Calvinism, but Louis XIII thought otherwise and ordered its city walls and all its churches pulled down. The oldest part of Montpellier is still known, in the langue d'oc, as Lou Clapas (the rubble). As a result of this trauma, rebuilt Montpellier is a trove of late-17th-century architecture: handsome *hôtels* that are best admired from within their elegant courtyards.

On the Amethyst Coast, beyond the concrete and glass pyramids of La Grande-Motte, the medieval walled city of Aigues-Mortes – meaning 'dead water' – is a last outpost of urban life before the semi-wilderness of the Camargue. Founded by St Louis as a base-camp for the Seventh Crusade, it is a last reminder of the region's associations with 'muscular Christianity'.

In a happier and perhaps holier vein, at Les Saintes-Maries-de-la-Mer on the Camargue's coastline, France's gypsies gather several times a year, but especially on 24 and 25 May.

The Camargue

The Camargue remains largely inaccessible (there is no coast road), a remote world of salt-marsh and lagoons in the broad triangle of the Rhône delta. There are farms to the north, many growing rice in paddies, but also isolated ranches rearing the famous white horses. Black bulls are bred by gardiens – the Camargue's cowboys.

Wild animals and birds are protected within the Parc Naturel Régionel de Camargue, centred on the Etang des Vaccarès, breeding ground of the pink flamingo. Elsewhere there are such diverse species as tree-frogs, badgers, turtles and wild boar – though mosquitoes are often the most numerous beneficiaries of the Camargue's non-chemical ecology.

At Sète, the Canal du Midi, one of the 17th century's greatest engineering achievements, reaches the sea

They meet to venerate and serenade their patron saint Sarah, the black servant of the two Marys (the sister of the Virgin and the mother of the apostles James and John), said to have landed here – with Mary Magdalene – after their expulsion from Judea. The festive procession carries its statues and relics from the Place des Gitans to the sea, to be blessed by the Bishop of Arles, bobbing offshore in a small fishing boat.

Côte Bleue

The black bulls of the Camargue are very likely to find themselves trotting out into the hubbub of the Arena at Arles at the latterday Roman games – the Courses à la Cocarde. The bullfighting season opens on 1 May with the *Fête des Gardiens.* Modern 'gladiators' are armed only with their wits in their attempts to grab a rosette tied to the horns – and the bull is just as likely to vault a barricade as the fleeing *razeteurs.* Bulls are never killed in a Provençal *corrida.* The Arena, built in the reign of Caligula, is an almost complete amphitheatre – with the addition of three towers from its medieval incarnation as the citadel of Arles, when it contained 200 buildings and three churches.

Arles is one of the most evocative of Provence's several well-preserved Roman towns, centred even now on its Place du Forum, and a close rival to Nîmes, Orange and St-Rémy. Next to the Arena is the much-reduced Théâtre Antique (formerly known in Arles as 'The Quarry') which still hosts open air entertainments. The Baths of Constantine, near the Rhône, are the last remnant of the former Imperial Palace – the Emperor's favourite residence when Arles was capital of a united Gaul, Britain and Spain. Here it was decided, pragmatically rather than idealistically – in 314 – to adopt Christianity as the Empire's official religion.

In 597, in the original Cathedral of St Trophime, St Augustine was consecrated England's first bishop. The later 12th-century building is one of France's greatest Romanesque relics, particularly its superb portal with teams of saints supporting a dramatic Last Judgement.

Côte des Calanques

Marseille suffers from a rather wild reputation, partly down to the film *The French Connection*, which suggested a place to be avoided like the plague. But to bypass Marseille would be to miss out on the unique bustle and verve of France's second city, where an entire section – the Quartier Belsunce – is devoted to Arab traders.

Marseille was originally a Greek (later Roman) colony – *Massilia* – founded in about 600 BC, the city from which the first traders with Britain set out, returning with cargoes of Cornish tin. Of the ancient port, a few fragments remain – in the Musée des Docks Romains – which also preserves some vast *dolia,* earthenware jars for storing wine or olives.

Much later, after the discovery of America, Marseille was eclipsed by the ports of the Atlantic coast – but trade revived with the capture of Algiers in 1830, removing the age-old threat from the Barbary pirates. The opening of the Suez Canal made Marseille the 'Gateway to Africa and the East' and the city spread rapidly, with notorious 'tin can' shanty towns (*bidonvilles*) springing up on its outskirts.

Independent-minded Marseille was a republic in the Middle Ages – and, in 1789, this spirit stirred its Jacobins, who took up the *Chant de Guerre de l'Armée du*

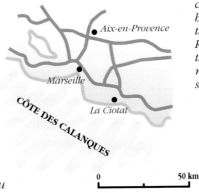

Van Gogh in Arles

Unlike Augustine, Arles' most celebrated resident had given up missionary work for his own hard-won art. Vincent Van Gogh shared a house here for a while with Paul Gauguin, producing such masterpieces as the Café de Nuit *and* Starry Night. *Just before Christmas 1888, Gauguin found himself being chased down the street by Vincent. The Dutchman was waving a razor. Returning to the house Van Gogh cut off his own earlobe, giving it to a local prostitute, saying* 'Gardez cet objet précieusement.' *Soon after, in the care of Dr Gachet, he was admitted to the asylum at St-Rémy. The café of the* Café de Nuit *is now a Monoprix supermarket.*

Rhin with such enthusiasm that it soon became known as *La Marseillaise.*

In 1943, Marseille suffered for its freewheeling ungovernability. The Germans found Le Panier, the labyrinthine quarter near the Vieux Port, impossible to control – so gave the inhabitants 24 hours to leave, then dynamited the whole area, saving only a few of the grander buildings. Forty thousand were deported.

As a result, much of Marseille is either modern or dates back to its Second Empire boom years, symbolised by the striking Basilique Notre Dame de la Garde, a landmark visible from miles out to sea – as is the notorious island prison, the Château d'If, residence of the Man in the Iron Mask and Alexandre Dumas' fictional Count of Monte Cristo.

The old character of the port is best kept in the fish market of the Quai des Belges, teeming with octopus, squid, tunny, conger eels and other creatures of the deep – many of them ingredients for the great Marseille speciality, *bouillabaisse.*

East from the city, the Corniche President J F Kennedy leads out into the rocky *calanques* that give their name to this stretch of coast, dramatic fiords often accessible only by boat or on foot, down dusty tracks through the pine woods. Cassis, famous for its fresh dry white wines – the perfect accompaniment for fish grilled over charcoal and fennel – offers boat trips to the wildest and remotest *calanques.*

Finally, at the end of the winding Corniche des Crètes, the dramatic Côte des Calanques reaches its apogee at La Ciotat with the vertiginous rock face of the Cap Canaille, France's tallest cliffs at 1,118 feet.

The Cosquer Cave

In 1991 a diver, Henri Cosquer, entered a cave on the Côte des Calanques by an underwater entrance and discovered a set of prehistoric paintings – images of animal hunts and prints of human hands – to rival Lascaux. The change in sea-level after the last Ice Age had ensured that the cave was sealed off for several millenia. Argument still rages over the authenticity of Cosquer's great find, and expert analysis awaits the digging of a new entrance from dry land, but at least it is compensation for the loss of a cave full of paintings in the Dordogne 'tidied up' a few years ago by local Boy Scouts.

Côte des Baies du Soleil

Both Bandol and its neighbour Sanary-sur-Mer live up to what one might expect of life in the 'bays of the sun': wind-surfing, good sandy beaches, promenades lined with palms and tamarisks – and, beneath the trees, games of *pétanque* clicking away the long summer afternoons.

The Mediterranean idyll peters out after Cap Sicié, but it is replaced by a fascinating peace-and-war contrast with

0   50 km

Toulon's armaments factories and military bases. Sadly, the town's long tradition of shipbuilding is on the wane.

Toulon is, however, still France's main southern naval base, created initially by the Sun King. In those first years – in fact, right up until 1748 – galley slaves and convicts were the main motive power behind the Mediterranean Fleet, chained four to an oar. They were allowed to wander the town, but only if manacled in pairs. Shore leave is now a more liberated affair, and Toulon's red light district near the port is a busy haunt of low dives and sex shops.

After the Revolution, Royalist Toulon invited the English in to secure the town. An unknown young captain of artillery from Corsica commanded the forces opposing them and, for his success at 'Little Gibraltar', Napoleon Bonaparte was rapidly promoted to Brigadier General.

Toulon's place in French history was later consolidated by a heroic act of self-destruction. In 1942, Admiral Laborde – fearing that the Fleet would fall into German hands – scuttled 60 ships in the harbour. Further damage, both by Allied air raids and German rearguard actions left Toulon battered, though happily its historic centre and the Vieux Darse (the old port), and the markets of the Place de la Poissonerie remain picturesque and increasingly fashionable, as is the Quartier Mourillon. It's somehow appropriate that the city's main thoroughfare – a wide and busy waterfront lined with cafés – should be named, with sympathy for even worse wartime destruction, the Quai Stalingrad.

Côte des Maures

The Maures are literally the 'dark woods' – a thick forest of umbrella and Aleppo pines, ilex, sweet chestnut and cork-oak covering a massif of ancient rock. The main local products of the Côte de Maures are, perhaps unsurprisingly, wine corks and *marrons glacés*.

Settled comfortably on the western fringes of the forest, Hyères is the oldest resort on the French Riviera, a place that Victorians were ordered to come to for their health. Robert Louis Stevenson, on his long tubercular quest for an equable climate, wintered at Hyères. The town has managed to remain partially independent of tourism, being surrounded by productive

St-Tropez

Hyères

CÔTE DES MAURES

0   50 km

vineyards and orchards and even exporting date palms to the Middle East.

The Iles d'Hyères – or Iles d'Or – are laid out in line parallel to the coast, like a Toulon squadron on manoeuvres. As with the mainland massif, they are thickly wooded. Wildlife is protected on the Ile de Port-Cros, a place for long walks through the shady Vallon de la Solitude. Humans are also found in a state of nature at Heliopolis, a nudist colony established in the Thirties on the Ile du Levant, though more than half the island is firmly set aside for (fully-clothed, one presumes) military use.

Back on the Côte des Maures, Le Lavandou is, as the name suggests, a major producer of lavender for use in the Provençal perfumeries of Grasse. The coast road, the Corniche des Maures, enters the deluxe zone of the Riviera, skirts forest and clifftops and dips down to the beach at pretty Cavalière – not to be confused with the busier Cavalaire-sur-Mer.

St-Tropez will need to be approached cautiously, and preferably entered on foot. Its fame has caused excessive crowding in high summer around the small harbour. Park and walk to study the luxury yachts closely – they are only there for public flaunting. The beaches – such as Tahiti-Plage, initiator of toplessness in the Thirties – are slightly separate from the town but are accessible by minibus.

For a buoyant seaside resort with scorching sun and a rich blue sea, St-Tropez has always had somewhat world-weary, Bohemian associations. It was 'discovered' by the high-living but doomed Maupassant, touring on his yacht, when the port was still inaccessible by land. In the Thirties, Colette and her cats settled in. Even in her own less hectic time, Colette was appalled by the arrival in August of the 'fancy dress ball' set, who invaded the quiet fishing port in their Bugattis and Hispano-Suizas.

In May and June, St-Tropez forgets its own poise and pretentions and lets rip in the unashamedly rowdy *Bravades*. The first celebrates the arrival of the headless body of the saint – Torpes or Tropez – which is claimed to have floated here from Pisa, where he was beheaded on Nero's orders. The second – perhaps more appropriately, given the din created – marks the defeat of a Spanish fleet by local ships in 1637. Processions of *Bravadeurs* in 18th-century uniform swagger through St-Tropez firing off ancient *tromblons* (blunderbusses) panicking the otherwise pampered St Trop cats and dogs.

Bardot in St-Tropez

St-Tropez is home to elusive Brigitte Bardot and her animal refuge. Bardot, star of And God Created Woman, *filmed here by Roger Vadim in 1956, is perhaps responsible for the glamorous myth of modern St-Tropez and the hunger for celebrity that brings the crowds.*

Côte de l'Estérel

The Estérel is another ancient *massif,* even older in geological time than the Massif des Maures, a vast block of pink porphyry worn down to a stump – the oldest landmass in Europe.

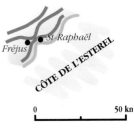

On the coastal fringe of the massif, modern resorts mix with historic towns, linked by a route pioneered as late as the turn of the century by the Touring Club de France. Before that, the few roads through the forests of Estérel – badly scarred by several major forest fires in recent years – were notorious for highway robbery.

Fréjus was originally *Forum Julii*, a Roman naval base joined to the sea by a canal, where the galleys that defeated Antony and Cleopatra at Actium were built. A more-or-less intact Arena survives from the 1st century, used now for bullfights and rock concerts. There are also remains of a theatre and aqueduct. The 'Lantern of Augustus' is, however, a medieval beacon on a Roman tower base.

Stone seats from the former amphitheatre at Fréjus are reused in the staircase leading from the cathedral cloisters to the Musée Archaéologique which contains relics of Forum Julii, including a superb Roman mosaic of a leopard. The octagonal 4th-century baptistery adjoining the cathedral is the oldest in France and contains a font dating from the beginnings of official, above-ground Christianity.

The Roman naval veterans settled at Forum Julii were granted seaside villas at St-Raphaël, the resort now merged with Fréjus. The Musée d'Archaéologie Sous-Marine continues to explore the underwater relics of St-Raphaël's classical past. The tower of the 12th-century Eglise des Templiers was used as a lookout post by the Knights Templar whose task was to defend this coast against raiding corsairs.

The pagoda and the mosque

Just outside Fréjus, the Vietnamese Pagoda and the Sudanese Mosque were both left behind by French Colonial troops stationed here in the First World War. The pagoda is still used as a Buddhist temple, but the mosque stands abandoned inside an army camp.

Côte d'Azur

The Côte d'Azur, the coast of the mountainous département of Alpes-Maritimes, is almost a country in itself: the Riviera. It contains the independent Principality of Monaco, and half of it – including Nice, where Garibaldi was born – was for centuries a part of Savoy and, until 1860, the Kingdom of Sardinia.

Cannes is effectively ceded to Hollywood for the month of May during the annual Film Festival, inaugurated in 1946.

Jury dissent, wheeling and dealing, paparazzi on heat, preening starlets … the beach at Cannes, along the Promenade de la Croisette, has probably seen more posturings than any other square mile on earth.

The sedate English gentry, led by Lord Brougham, who set the fashion for Cannes in the 1830s, would no doubt be aghast at this showbiz excess. The English milords were followed by Russian aristocrats, who nevertheless built their Orthodox Cathedral at Nice. In the Twenties, the Americans arrived, including the hard-drinking Scott and Zelda Fitzgerald. The glamorous cocktail mix of Cannes was already being shaken.

For a respite from its urbanity, a 15-minute boat trip from Cannes returns you to the simple life on the unspoiled Iles de Lérins, where no cars, bars or hotels are allowed. There are just monks on St Honorat, who since the 5th century have occupied the Abbey where St Patrick trained for seven years before setting off to convert Ireland.

At the far end of the Baie des Anges from Antibes, beyond a line of multi-storied holiday complexes, lies Nice – the grand old lady of the Côte d'Azur. The Promenade des Anglais – laid out in the 18th century by an English cleric, the Rev Lewis Way – curves along the shore, the ultimate in seaside elegance, lined with palms, tennis courts and outdoor cafés.

There is an old town at the heart of Nice, near the Rocher du Château, with winding streets, passages and stairs – formerly notorious for street crime but now much improved. But Vieux Nice is not typical of France's fifth-largest city: comfortable suburban villas and lavish hotels have made Nice into a 'Paris by the sea'. Its carefree, flag-flying days are best captured by Raoul Dufy in his sea-blue visions of the Promenade des Anglais. Nice has museums devoted to Matisse – at his studio in suburban Cimiez – and the biblical visions of Marc Chagall, the most celebrated of the Riviera's Russian emigrés.

From Nice to the Italian border, the mountains, a last flourish of the Alps, come up hard against the sea in a series of spectacular cliffs. Three roads tackle the wild landscape: the Corniche Inférieure follows the coast most faithfully, though the Moyenne Corniche has the show-stopping views of the sea and distant snow-capped peaks. At certain times of the year, it is possible to swim and ski in the same day, all in the département of the Alpes-Maritimes.

Picasso on the Côte d'Azur

At Antibes, a museum bristling with goats and satyrs is devoted to Pablo Picasso – the quintessential Riviera artist – who lived there before moving on to Vallauris where he took up ceramics, stimulating a now thriving local industry. Picasso, in striped shirt, baggy shorts and sandals lives on as the central icon of the Côte d'Azur.

Monaco is a physically precarious and tiny sovereign state, but one which has survived in the autocratic hands of the Grimaldi family since the 14th century. True Monegasques (only 16% of the population) speak *Monegasco,* a version of Genoese Italian, as well as French. Vieux Monaco contains the Prince's Palace, some parts dating from the first Grimaldi occupancy; it is open to visitors when the Prince is away.

Monte-Carlo, the newer resort, is set slightly apart from Monaco, beyond the port and its crammed-in luxury yachts. Its main institution – the Casino – was created in 1878 in order to rescue the Grimaldi finances, bringing the drama of the tables (and latterly one-armed bandits) to Monaco under the bland title of the *Société Anonyme des Bains de Mer.* Charles Garnier, architect of the Paris Opera, designed the Casino in suitably grand and spendthrift style.

At the far end of the French Riviera is Menton, its old town perhaps the most elegant on the Côte d'Azur, with hotels, promenade, botanical gardens – and another Casino – to remind you that this is not just a quiet aristocratic backwater but a rival to the big three of the Côte d'Azur.

All this and Italy too – just a few minutes away by Roman road, on the Via Aurelia.

Since its discovery by English milords, Cannes has been a byword for luxury and elegance

Corsica (La Corse)

Speaking its own variant of Italian, as well as French, Corsica has only been part of France for just over 200 years. The official purchase from the Genoese and the final defeat of Corsican nationalists occurred on 15 August 1769, the same day that Napoleon Bonaparte was born in Ajaccio.

His hometown is capital of the département of Corse-du-Sud, while its age-old rival Bastia controls Haute-Corse, the two halves of the island being divided by a chain of often inaccessible mountains.

After ruthlessly putting down Corsican rebels in 1796, Napoleon had to flee Ajaccio, moving on fatefully to the wider stage of France and Europe. His family home – now a museum – was ransacked by a mob and later during the British occupation, was the billet of a soldier who, by an extraordinary coincidence, would be amongst his guards on St Helena.

All such ironies are now lost on Ajaccio, which celebrates its local hero with numerous statues and street names. Another Musée Napoléonien fills the Mairie, but the Emperor's greatest legacy to Corsica is indirect – through his cousin Cardinal Fesch's superb legacy of Italian Old Masters at the Musée Fesch.

The western coast of Corsica is one long drama of mountains that almost topple into the sea. The seaside towns fit in where they can, most spectacularly Bonifacio, sited on top of steep limestone cliffs on a narrow peninsula.

The east coast is quite the opposite, settling into flat farmland reclaimed from long neglect by the eradication of malarial mosquitoes, and fringed with good beaches. The main city, Aleria, is the oldest on Corsica, with a fine collection of Greek ceramics and the ruins of a Roman forum, baths and governor's palace.

Beyond the Castagniccia's dense forests of sweet chestnut, and lying at the foot of the long peninsula of Cap du Corse, is Corsica's largest city – Bastia. Formerly, it was the Genoese capital, with their citadel – the Terra Nova – dominating the port from its rocky outcrop. The Terra Vecchia is, confusingly, the newer part of Bastia, built up in the 17th century. Its centre is the vast, tree-lined Place St-Nicolas, to which the city's population gravitates for a slow stroll in the cool of evening.

The western coast road returning to Ajaccio is a winding affair, through yet more rugged mountains, which passes through Cargese, a Greek town founded 300 years ago by refugees from Turkish rule. Calvi is another Genoese stronghold, their governor's palace now a barracks for the Foreign Legion. In 1794, the Royal Navy laid siege to Calvi for two months, during which one of Napoleon's greatest adversaries, Horatio Nelson, lost his eye.

USEFUL INFORMATION

This section of the book aims to give you ideas and advice, as you prepare for your trip to France, make the journey, and spend your time there. It also gives information about the way of life in France, shopping, opening hours and similar details, as well as motoring information. Please note that every effort is made to check these details, but there may be changes through the year. Wherever possible, you are advised to telephone ahead, and check the information for yourself.

Personal Insurance

Most people like to take out some insurance to cover loss of possessions, baggage and other items, as well as medical insurance. RAC Eurocover Personal Protection covers you for all of the hazards that you are likely to meet in France. Full details are obtainable from the RAC. Travel agents, ferry and rail operators, credit card companies and various other organisations also offer insurance. Shop around and ask for quotes, because the prices often differ considerably. Some organisations may give discounts or extra cover for older people, or for trips out of high season.

Medical Insurance

There are reciprocal arrangements between the UK and France to cover basic medical expenses. Ask for details and form E111 or its equivalent at your local Department of Social Security office. This enables you to claim back a certain percentage of medical expenses incurred while you are in France. However, you must obtain the form before you leave and take it with you. And you will probably have to pay the fees of the doctor, hospital or other provider while in France, and claim back the costs on your return.

People who have a private medical insurance or medical plan in the UK, may be able to extend this to cover France and other EC countries. Ask your insurance or plan operator. In addition, medical cover can also be obtained as part of the overall insurance package provided by travel agents, tour operators, and credit card companies and other financial institutions.

Motoring Insurance

Your UK motor insurance may provide only third party cover abroad, with no cover for loss or damage to your own vehicle. Though it is not legally necessary, you are strongly advised to take out extra insurance to provide comprehensive cover from your motor insurance company. This is called the "Green Card" and it usually costs only a few pounds.

French Tourist Office

The French Government Tourist Office can provide a wide range of information concerning travel, accommodation, activities and attractions in France. Write to or visit them at 178 Piccadilly, London W1V OAL.

It is advisable to enclose a minimum of £1 with written enquiries to cover postage costs on any material sent to you.

Motoring Assistance

Breakdown insurance or cover is not essential, but it does give
great peace of mind. For a modest outlay, RAC Eurocover gives you
cover for your whole holiday. As well as roadside assistance from
partner motoring organisations, and help in finding spare parts,
Eurocover also offers reimbursement of extra expenses, such as a
night in a hotel, hire of another car, or travel onwards by rail or
coach. For full details, ring the RAC in Croydon on 0800 550055 or
write to RAC Motoring and Personal Insurance at PO Box 100,
Bartlett Street, South Croydon, CR2 6XW.

RAC Reflex Europe membership gives you motoring cover
throughout the UK and Europe for a year, no matter how many
times you go abroad. It is ideally suited to those on a long touring
trip. For details ring the RAC on 0345 331133. Travel agents, tour
operators and other motoring organisations also offer schemes.

UK and French Time

French time is one hour ahead of UK time for most of the year,
including summer, when the clocks are put forward one hour for
summer time, as in the UK. However, France usually puts the clocks
back from summer time to winter time earlier than in the UK. So
there is a period of around four weeks in September to October
when French and UK times are the same.

Across the Channel

It is now possible to take your car on Le Shuttle through the
Channel Tunnel, in addition to the ferries sea routes – see page 9.
Which port you leave from, and where you go to, can depend on
several factors. These include the location of your home in the UK,
your destination in France, the time of your journey, whether the
ferry or rail companies are offering discounts or other special deals,
and whether you like the independence of driving, or prefer to sit
in comfort, resting on the train or boat.

It is a worthwhile exercise to do some rough price estimates on the
various alternatives. If you add up the costs of petrol, car wear and
French motorway tolls on the *péages*, you may be surprised at the
competitive prices offered by a long ferry route or the motorail
services. RAC Travel Services at Croydon, telephone 0345 333222,
provide advice on crossing routes and times.

French Roads

France has an excellent system of motorways which have A
numbers. For example, the A1 is the Paris–Lille motorway. Some of
the motorways are part of European routes and have E numbers.

In and around Paris and some other major cities, some stretches of
motorway are free. On most motorways, tolls are payable. A toll
route or toll point is called a *péage*. In most cases, you take a ticket
as you join the motorway, and pay when you leave at the required

exit. On a few motorways, you pay the toll in coins as you enter. On most of the major routes, credit cards such as Visa and MasterCard (Access) are accepted. *Péage* tolls can add considerably to the cost of your travel. However the motorways are well maintained, and they are rarely as crowded as UK motorways such as the M25 and M6, except during public holidays and the French holiday month of August.

The major roads in France have the letter N for *Nationale*, or sometimes RN for *Route National*. They are roughly equivalent to the UK's A roads. Many are wide and straight. The next category of French roads is D, *Départmentale*. These vary from wide and straight, to narrower and less frequented, but they are all surfaced. Minor roads are usually shown as VO, or *Voie ordinaire*. These are adequate for their purpose, but they are sometimes winding and narrow, and in rural areas they may resemble farm tracks.

Basic Driving Information

The French national motoring organisation is the Automobile Club de France, FIA, with offices at 6-8 Place de la Concorde, 75008 Paris, telephone 42 65 34 70. There is also the Automobile Club National (ACN), FIA & AIT, 9 rue Anatole de la Forge, 75017 Paris, telephone 42 27 82 00. Orange emergency telephones are situated every 2 kilometres along autoroutes and main roads.

French Road Signs

These mostly conform to the international pattern. Other road signs are:

Allumez vos phares	*Switch on headlights*
Attention au feu	*Fire hazard*
Attention travaux	*Road works ahead*
Chaussée deformée	*Uneven road surface*
Fin d'interdiction de stationner	*End of restricted parking*
Gravillons	*Loose chippings*
Haute tension	*Electrified lines*
Interdit aux piétons	*No pedestrians*
Nids de poules	*Pot-holes*
Priorité à droite	*Give way to traffic from the right (see page 80)*
Passage protégé	*Your right of way*
Rappel	*Remember (displayed on speed limit signs)*
Route barrée	*Road closed*

In France, the minimum age for drivers is 18 years. The standard UK driving licence is accepted. Children under 10 years of age occupying any seat must travel in an approved child seat adapted to their size. If a foreign-registered vehicle is not fitted with front-seat child restraints, children under 10 must occupy a rear seat. Crash helmets are compulsory for motorcyclists and passengers. The blood-alcohol legal limit in drinking-and-driving cases is 70 milligrams. It is compulsory for a car to carry a warning triangle, which should be erected at the roadside to warn other vehicles of obstruction. If seatbelts are fitted to a vehicle, they should be used in both front and rear seats. Do not use the horn except when it is absolutely necessary, that is, in an emergency.

Fuel and Vehicle Lights

For leaded petrol, or regular *essence*, (90 octane) and *super* (98 octane) are widely available. For unleaded petrol, or *essence sans plomb*, *super* (95-98 octane) is available. Diesel is sold at pumps marked *gas-oil* or *gaz-oil*. Most of the major credit cards are accepted, and up to 10 litres of spare fuel may be imported in cans. As a rough guide for conversion, 5 litres is just over 1 gallon.

The headlight beams on right-hand drive vehicles must be adjusted. Beam converter sets, which can be fitted quickly and easily, are obtainable from RAC Travel Centres. There is now no legal requirement for vehicles to emit a yellow beam. It is compulsory to use headlights at night in all areas, but these must be dipped in built-up areas. Motorcycle headlights are compulsory, day and night. To see and be seen, use headlights in poor visibility. Parking lights are obligatory, unless public lighting is sufficient for the vehicle to be seen distinctly from an adequate distance. Motorists are recommended to carry a set of spare bulbs.

Road manners vary from those in the UK. If a driver "flashes" you, he or she does not mean: "You go first", but "Wait and let me go first".

Overloading

The French authorities are concerned by the serious overloading of many UK-registered cars touring in France. Apart from the possible danger to the driver and passengers, if there is an accident, the driver could well be prosecuted or held responsible, if carrying more passengers and/or weight than the vehicle manufacturer recommends.

Priority

The *Priorité à droite* – give way to vehicles from the right – no longer holds for all roads. Traffic on major roads now has priority. Where two major roads cross, the sign *Danger priorité à droite* is used, indicating that traffic coming from the right has priority. *Passage protégé* (priority road) signs indicate those major roads where traffic has priority. In the absence of signs, give way to traffic coming from the right.

Miles or Kilometres?

The distance numbers on French road signs may look daunting, but of course, they are in kilometres and not in miles. To convert from kilometres to miles, multiply by 5 and divide by 8. To convert from miles to kilometres, multiply by 8 and divide by 5.

Alternatively, glance at your vehicle's speedometer, when it is safe to do so. The dial should have speeds in both mph and kph, and you can use these to do the conversion. For example, 50 mph is equivalent to 80 kph. The hours cancel out, so 50 miles is 80 kilometres.

Traffic already on a roundabout has priority. A triangular sign with a red border, showing a roundabout symbol with the legend *Vous n'avez pas la priorité*, indicates this. However, in a few areas, the old ruling still applies of priority given to traffic entering the roundabout. So, where the signs are not present, you should approach with care.

Speed limits

The first group of vehicles includes motorcycles over 80 cc, private cars, and vehicles towing a caravan or trailer with total weight under 3.5 tonnes. In built-up areas, the speed limit for these vehicles is 31 mph (50 kph), but this can be raised to 44 mph (70 kph) on important through-roads as indicated by the road signs. Outside built-up areas, on normal roads, the speed limit is 56 mph (90 kph). On priority roads and toll-free urban motorways it is 68 mph (110 kph). For toll motorways the limit is 81 mph (130 kph). However, all of these general limits may be modified by road signs at particular sites, such as accident black-spots.

The second group of vehicles includes cars towing a caravan or trailer, with total weight exceeding 3.5 tonnes. Outside built-up areas, the speed limit for these is 50 mph (80 kph) on normal roads. For priority roads it is 50 mph (80 kph), which is increased to 62 mph (100 kph) on dual carriageways, and to 68 mph (110 kph) on motorways. Special speed limits apply if the weight of the trailer exceeds that of the towing vehicle, and the RAC can supply further information. Other changes come into force according to the lane you occupy, or the weather conditions.

Traffic offences

Some French police are authorised to impose and collect fines of up to 2,500 F on the spot, from drivers who violate traffic regulations. An official receipt should be requested. If a minor offence is committed, a reduced fine is payable within 30 days. A court hearing must be arranged if the fine is to be contested. A serious offence can result in a heavy fine, suspension of driving licence and/or a prison sentence.

Maps and the *Bison Futé*

There are many excellent French-produced maps for motorists. For walking and similar activities, France's *Institut Géographique National*, which is equivalent to the UK's Ordnance Survey, produces the IGN Blue Series. These are at the large scale of 1:25,000 and show footpaths, tracks, contour lines and other details.

Around March each year, a variety of travel companies sponsors the production of a map showing alternative routes to the most congested roads. Called *Bison Futé*, it is available from the French Government Tourist Office in London. It is very useful if you are travelling during the main holiday season of June to September, and especially during August.

Traffic Lights

The lights sequence is the same as in the UK, except there is no red-and-amber light after the red light. Flashing red means no entry. Flashing yellow arrows mean that drivers may proceed in the direction indicated, but must give way to pedestrians and the traffic flow they are joining.

Rail, Bus and Coach

French Railways SNCF *(Société Nationale des Chemins de Fer Français)* have a 33,000-km network of lines and offer UK tourists some excellent special fares. The 300 km/hour TGV *(Train à Grande Vitesse)* serves south-east and northern France, and the south-west. Tickets for TGV trains are usually more expensive than those for normal trains.

When travelling by train, be sure to validate *(composter)* any ticket bought in France, using the orange automatic date-stamping machine on the platform or concourse. Failure to do so may involve a surcharge. SNCF have dozens of motorail services and the Euro Tunnel services also link into the network.

There are few regular public long-distance coach services in France. However the local services are generally good and relatively inexpensive. Look for information and timetables at bus and rail stations and tourist offices. Several companies offer Fly-Drive holidays where you drive to your destination in France, and hire a car there. Ring the general information desk at your local airport, or enquire at your travel agent or one of the major vehicle-hire companies.

The French week

The average week in France has a slightly different emphasis compared to Britain. In general, Saturday is more like a weekday, while Monday is often very quiet, with various offices and even banks closed. Also, many shops, offices and other establishments tend to open early, around 0700 or 0800 hrs, then close for a long lunch between about 1200 and 1400 or 1500 hrs. However, they remain open until 2000 hrs or later in the evening.

In addition, the day tends to be split more into two parts, compared to the UK. Many people are at work early, by 0700 to 0800 hrs, and then take a break for a long lunch and rest. They work again fairly late, often into the mid evening.

If you plan to visit any facility – a museum, gallery, sports or leisure centre, even a large store – you are strongly advised to check

USEFUL INFORMATION

ahead. Look in tourist leaflets, telephone the facility, or ask the staff at your hotel or place of residence to telephone.

Opening hours and public holidays

Most banks are open on weekdays from 0900 to 1200 hrs, and again from 1400 to 1600 hrs. Some provincial banks are closed on Mondays, and open from Tuesday to Saturday, from 0900 to 1200 hrs and again from 1400 to 1600 hrs. Post offices, in general, are open from 0800 to 1900 hrs, Monday to Friday, and on Saturday mornings from 0800 to 1200 hrs. Many smaller shops are closed on Mondays, either all day or only in the afternoon as half-day closing. Food shops may open on Sunday mornings.

Many museums, exhibitions and galleries are closed on Mondays, and open for the rest of the week. However in high season, many large tourist attractions are open all day, every day.

Public holidays are as follows: 1 January, New Year's Day; 17 April, Easter Monday; 1 May, Labour Day; 8 May, VE Day (Victory in Europe, World War Two); 25 May, Ascension Day; 5 June, Whit Monday; 14 July, Bastille Day; 15 August, Assumption; 1 November, All Saints Day; 11 November, Armistice Day; 25 December, Christmas Day.

Phoning and Faxing Home

To call the UK from France or elsewhere in Europe, you need a four-part number consisting of the access code for the country being dialled from, the country code for the destination country which is the UK, the UK area or STD code (leaving out the first 0), and the local number. In France the access code is 19, then you may have to wait for a second tone. The country code for the UK is 44. So, for example, to call the RAC in Croydon, dial 19 44 181 686 0088 (missing the 0 from the Outer London 0181 code).

Many hotel rooms have direct dialling to the UK, but the costs may well be higher than using a public pay-phone. Also, many hotels have a fax-sending facility. You can send written messages, maps and other documents to a fax machine in the UK. The dialling procedure for fax connection is the same as described below.

To make a call, lift the receiver and check for the dialling tone. This may be different from those in the UK. For a pay-phone, insert the money or the phonecard *télécarte*. Most French pay-phones accept 1, 5 and 10 F coins. The *télécarte* is available in 40 and 95 F denominations from post offices, railway ticket offices, tobacconists (*tabac*) and France Telecom agencies. You are advised to dial steadily, without pauses, except after the 19 access code. Connection can take up to one minute, so be patient. If you hear a persistent tone or a recorded message, try again, or enquire at your hotel reception or tourist centre. A signal tells you when to insert more money, or that the *télécarte* credit has expired.

For the local International Operator, dial 19 (pause) 33 44. For the UK Direct Operator, dial 19 (pause) 00 44. Cheap-rate calls are available on weekdays between 2130 and 0800, on Saturday after

1400, and all day Sunday. For more information about phoning home with a BT chargecard see page 4.

Electrical Voltages

In France, as in most of continental Europe, the standard mains voltage is 220 AC at 50 Hz (cycles per second), as it is in the UK. However the two-pin plug and socket, not the three-pin type, are in general use. If you are taking electrical equipment, obtain a special adaptor, or change the mains lead's UK three-pin plug for a continental two-pin one. Adaptors are available from RAC Travel Centres at Dover, Folkestone and Portsmouth.

Radio and Contacts in an Emergency

Several of the BBC's domestic services are audible in France, especially towards the north. They include Radio 1 on 275/285 metres (1089/1053 kHz) medium wave, Radio 4 on 1515 metres (198 kHz) long wave, and Radio 5 on 433/330 metres (693/909 kHz) medium wave.

RAC members touring abroad can be informed of serious illness in the family through the courtesy of the BBC World Service. In an emergency, contact RAC Travel Information at Croydon, telephone 0345 333222. If certain information is provided, arrangements will be made for a message to be transmitted in the relevant country. The information you will need includes the full name and home address of the person for whom the message is intended; their possible whereabouts; the registration number and description of the vehicle; the full name and address of the person who is ill, and the relationship; the name, address and telephone number of the doctor attending or of the hospital; the reason for the message, such as "Mother seriously ill"; and the full name, address and telephone number of the person sending the message.

If you foresee the use of this service, a member of your group should leave the necessary details, including your day-to-day itinerary, with the contact person back home. Note that the BBC will only accept very important messages, and it cannot broadcast a notification of death in the family.

Customs and Allowances

The EU has reprieved duty-free sales until 1999. For each journey from one member state of the EU to another, which includes the UK to France, or the return trip, the duty-free entitlements are shown in the table. For duty-paid goods, provided these are for your own use, there is no further tax to pay. "Personal use" includes gifts. Member states of the EU reserve the right to check that duty-paid goods are for personal use, and not for resale. For this reason, the EU has set guide levels, as shown in the table. If you bring more than this, you may be required to show that the goods are for your personal use. If you are travelling direct from France to the UK, you do not need to go through a red or green channel, and you do not

Emergency on the Road

In case of emergency, telephone the emergency services as appropriate. The Police are on 17, the Fire Brigade on 18, and the Ambulance number is usually given in the telephone box; if not, call the Police. In the case of an accident, you should inform the Bureau Central Français des Sociétés d'Assurances Contre les Accidents Automobiles, 36 Avenue du Général de Gaulle, 93171 Bagnolet Cédex, telephone 49 93 65 50.

need to make any declaration to Customs. However, selected checks will still be made by Customs, to detect prohibited goods.

When you return to the UK, you may be carrying cameras, radios or watches which were bought in the UK, or which have been brought through Customs before and charges paid. It is a good idea to carry receipts for these items where possible, so that they can be checked by a Customs Officer as necessary.

If you are entering the UK in a vehicle, it is important that everyone travelling with you knows what goods are prohibited or restricted. If goods are smuggled in a car, the car may be impounded or confiscated. The tobacco and alcohol allowances apply only to those aged 17 years and over.

Prohibited and Restricted Goods – Animals and Plants

In order to protect health and the environment, certain goods cannot be freely imported. The chief EU regulations apply between France and the UK, and the main items are as follows.

In general, the importation of most species of animals, including birds and reptiles, whether alive or dead (such as stuffed), is restricted. So is the importation of items derived from animals, such as fur skins, reptile

	Duty free *Goods obtained anywhere outside the EU or duty- and tax-free within the EU, including purchases from a UK duty-free shop*	*Duty paid* *Goods obtained duty- and tax-paid in the EU (guideline amounts, see text)*
Cigarettes, or	*200*	*800*
Cigarillos, or	*100*	*400*
Cigars, or	*50*	*200*
Tobacco	*250 grams*	*1 kilogram*
Still table wine	*2 litres*	**see below*
Spirits, strong liqueurs over 22% volume, or	*1 litre*	*10 litres*
Fortified or sparkling wines, other liqueurs, or	*2 litres*	**20 litres of fortified wine, or 90 litres of wine (of which no more than 60 litres of sparkling wine)*
An additional still table wine allowance	*2 litres*	
Perfume	*50 grams/60 cc (2 fl oz)*	*no limit*
Toilet water	*250 cc (9 fl oz)*	*no limit*
All other goods, including gifts and souvenirs	*£71 worth, but no more than 50 litres of beer, 25 mechanical lighters*	*no limit except for the beer allowance, which is increased to 110 litres*

leather and goods made from them. You need a licence or other authority. This restriction extends to pets such as cats and dogs, and all other mammals. These must not be brought into the UK unless a British import licence (rabies) has previously been issued. A period of six months' quarantine is required. All live birds also require an import licence.

There is currently an exception to the requirements for a health certificate for plants, and plant produce imported as passenger baggage from any country within the European-Mediterranean area. However, this is provided the consignment does not exceed these amounts: up to 2 kilograms of tubers, bulbs and corms free of soil; up to 5 plants or cuttings; a small bouquet of cut flowers; up to 2 kilograms of fruit and vegetables (but not potatoes); up to 5 retail packets of seeds.

However, this concessional arrangement does not apply to: plants and seeds of the genus *Beta*; forest trees; fruit tree material (including Bonsai); chrysanthemums; vine plants; cut gladioli; fodder pea seeds; and plants of the grass family, *Graminae*. There are no restrictions on flower seeds.

Should you wish to import more than these quantities, you will need a phytosanitary certificate from the Plant Protection Service in France or the country of origin. Further details can be obtained from the Plant Health Division, Ministry of Agriculture, Fisheries and Food, Room 504, Ergon House, c/o Nobel House, Smith Square, London SW1P 3JR, telephone 0171 238 6477/6479.

In addition, the Department of the Environment operates controls on the movement or importation of endangered species. Enquiries should be made to DoE, Endangered Species Branch, Tollgate House, Houlton Street, Bristol BS2 9DJ, telephone 0117 921 8202.

Counterfeit or "copy" goods are also prohibited. These bear a false indication of their origin or are in breach of UK copyright laws.

Foodstuffs, Drugs and Other Prohibited Goods

The importation of meat, poultry and their products, including ham, bacon, sausage, paté, eggs, milk and cream is restricted.

Do not import controlled drugs such as heroin, cocaine, cannabis, amphetamines or LSD. If you require drugs for medical reasons, obtain further information from the Home Office Drugs Branch, 50 Queen Anne's Gate, London SW1H 9AT.

There are severe restrictions on the import of firearms and ammunition, including gas pistols, gas canisters, electric-shock batons and similar weapons and devices; licence or permission is required. The import of explosives, including fireworks, is completely banned except with special licences.

Other prohibited goods include offensive weapons such as flick knives, butterfly knives, knuckle dusters, swordsticks and some martial arts weapons; counterfeit currency; radio transmitters and cordless telephones not approved for use in the UK, obscene or horror books, comics or magazines; and lead weights for angling.

No Potatoes

The importation of potatoes into the UK is prohibited because of the danger of bringing in Colorado beetle, which can devastate potato crops.

Drugs and Bombs

Never carry something into the UK for another person, no matter how innocent it may seem. Never leave your luggage unattended, or allow unauthorised people to tamper with it or open it. If you find an unfamiliar item in your vehicle, leave it alone and call the authorities. Report anything suspicious to the authorities as soon as you can.

HOTEL DIRECTORY

The Hotel Directory lists individual hotels under the town or city where they are situated. Hotels in villages or situated on their own are listed under the nearest town or other centre.

Towns on islands – Corse (Corsica) and Oléron – are listed under their island names, which appear alphabetically in the general town listing. Paris is in its alphabetical position, but is then divided into four *départements*: Central Paris, which is further divided into the twenty *arrondissements* (I–XX) spiralling from the centre; Paris West (Hauts-de-Seine); Paris North-East (Seine-St-Denis); Paris South-East (Val-de-Marne).

Addresses, Postcodes and Map References

Each hotel has its full postal address, which shows the village location if it is outside the town. The town name listed after the postcode is the postal town and may be different to the main town heading. The first two digits of the postcode are the same for all towns in each *département*, and these are listed on page 6 of the map section at the back of the guide. Each town in the hotel directory is marked on the maps, the map reference refers to its grid location there.

Detailed information

The main symbols and abbreviations used in the hotel entries are listed on page 5. It is always a good idea to phone or fax ahead to book even if your French is limited. Most hotels speak enough English to help you make a booking.

We have included extra information on restaurants within hotels, linked to a glossary of French food terms at the back of the book. Pay particular attention to details of when restaurants are closed, especially in low season (LS). General things-to-do are shown under 'Activities' and where the hotel has made special arrangements this is highlighted. Note that in star ratings, some private châteaux do not subscribe to the star scheme.

A range of prices is usually given, reflecting either seasonal or quality differences. If no price is given for single rooms, it usually means that a single occupant would pay the double rate. Price of breakfast (Bk) is also shown. Most hotels do not include the cost of breakfast in their room rates.

Discounts are available only for holders of this guide and do note any restrictions.

The "facilities for disabled" symbol (&) means, in the opinion of the hotel's management, it is suitable for the disabled.

Is it open?

Many smaller hotels have an annual closure, as shown in the details of opening. Remember that in ski resorts, high season is usually winter.

ABBEVILLE Somme   2B

A **Hôtel de France** ★★ 19 place du Pilori,
80100 Abbeville.
☎ 22 24 00 42, Fax 22 24 26 15. English spoken.

Open all year. 69 bedrooms (all en suite).
Golf 3 km, garage, parking. &

*Situated near a pretty park with flowers and a
stream, hotel is peaceful and relaxing whilst
being only 2 minutes from the pedestrian area
in the heart of the city. Comfortable
accommodation; a suite with jacuzzi is also
available. Abbeville is 15 km from the sea,
halfway between Calais and Paris (N1).*

■ RESTAURANT: Closed Sat lunch. Restaurant
specialises in regional and roasted dishes.
Terrace rôtisserie with a view over the square.
Children's menu available.
■ ACTIVITIES: Ideal base for sightseeing.
■ TARIFF: (1994) Single 244–289,
Double 285–338, Bk 39, Set menu 68–100
(Amex, Euro/Access, Visa).
■ DISCOUNT: 10% Excluding suites.

ABONDANCE Hte-Savoie   6A

Hôtel Bel Air ★★ Richebourg,
74360 Abondance.
☎ 50 73 01 71, Fax 50 73 08 37. English spoken.

Open 20/12 to 30/04 & 15/05 to 30/09.
24 bedrooms. Parking.

*Situated on a sunny, south facing hillside with
charming, comfortable rooms. Abondance is
south-east of Thonon-les-Bains.*

■ RESTAURANT: Panoramic restaurant with
international cuisine and regional specialities.
■ ACTIVITIES: Great area for exploring the
countryside, flora and fauna. Tennis, rafting
and rock climbing nearby.
■ TARIFF: (1994) Single 140–170,
Double 180–220, Bk 30, Set menu 70–130
(Euro/Access, Visa).
■ DISCOUNT: 10%

ABRESCHVILLER Moselle   3D

Hôtel des Cignognes ★★ 74 rue Jordy,
57560 Abreschviller.
☎ 87 03 70 09, Fax 87 03 79 06. English spoken.
Open all year. 29 bedrooms (27 en suite,
2 bath/shower only). Indoor swimming pool,
garage, parking.

*Situated in the Sarrebourg region with its
wealth of pine forests and trout-packed rivers.
Very comfortable, excellent facilities and
offering a warm welcome. Take Sarrebourg
exit off N4/A4 and hotel is 15 km.*

■ RESTAURANT: Traditional restaurant serving
regional dishes with fish and game specialities.
■ ACTIVITIES: Excellent walking and biking
country; owners organise trout fishing and
forest hiking expeditions.
■ TARIFF: (1994) Single 196–248,
Double 237–289, Bk 37 (Amex,
Euro/Access, Visa).

AGAY Var   6C

Hôtel Beau Site ★★ Camp Long, 83530 Agay.
☎ 94 82 00 45, Fax 94 82 71 02. English spoken.

Open all year. 20 bedrooms (17 en suite,
3 bath/shower only). Golf 1 km, parking.

10 km from the centre of St-Raphaël, on the N98 towards Cannes. Hotel is in a lively location overlooking a picturesque little cove and beach. (Guests wishing to leave hotel early/late should make prior arrangements with management as car park gate is locked at night.).

■ RESTAURANT: Closed Tues. Offers varied cuisine with aïoli specialities served on Thursdays, subject to reservation.
■ TARIFF: (1994) Single 240–320, Double 240–490, Bk 33, Set menu 135 (Amex, Euro/Access, Visa).

AGDE Hérault   5C

Hôtel Azur ★★ 18 av Illes d'Amérique, 34300 Agde.
☎ 67 26 98 22, Fax 67 26 48 14. English spoken.

Open all year. 34 bedrooms (all en suite). Outdoor swimming pool, golf 1 km, parking. &

Hotel is at Cap d'Agde just 400 m from plage Richelieu. Restaurant 50 m from hotel. Special group discounts. English satellite television in all rooms. Free private parking.

■ ACTIVITIES: Sauna.
■ TARIFF: (1994) Single 200–350, Double 250–410, Bk 32 (Amex, Euro/Access, Visa).
■ DISCOUNT: 10% Oct to Apr.

Hôtel Capao ★★★ Plage Richelieu, 34300 Agde.
☎ 67 26 99 44, Fax 67 26 55 41. English spoken.
Open 01/04 to 01/11. 55 bedrooms (all en suite). Outdoor swimming pool, golf 1 km, parking. &

The hotel stands on a private sandy beach and offers comfort as well as excellent facilities including a shopping area, hairdresser and Junior Club. Entering Cap d'Agde, follow signs to 'Plage Richelieu', turn left at third roundabout and hotel is at the end of the road.

■ RESTAURANT: Good food and a choice of 2 restaurants.
■ ACTIVITIES: Free use of the well-equipped fitness centre. Hotel operates a Privilege Card scheme enabling guests to use certain nearby facilities and charge it to the card. ● 20% reduction on green fees and tennis.
■ TARIFF: (1994) Single 370–655, Double 390–695, Bk 45, Set menu 90–145 (Amex, Euro/Access, Visa).

Hôtel La Tamarissière ★★★ lieu-dit La Tamarissière, 34300 Agde.
☎ 67 94 20 87, Fax 67 21 38 40. English spoken.

Open 01/04 to 31/10. 27 bedrooms (all en suite). Outdoor swimming pool, golf 8 km, parking.

Overlooking the Hérault estuary and tiny fishing port. Pretty bedrooms with balconies. Tempting Languedoc cuisine.

■ RESTAURANT: Closed Sun eve & Mon. Renowned for its excellent cuisine including tempting Languedoc dishes.
■ TARIFF: Single 400–620, Double 440–620, Bk 65, Set menu 145–330 (Amex, Euro/Access, Visa).

AGEN Lot/Garonne   4D

Château des Jacobins ★★★★ place des Jacobins, 47000 Agen.
☎ 53 47 03 31, Fax 53 47 02 80. English spoken.
Open all year. 15 bedrooms (all en suite). Golf 4 km, garage, parking. &

Elegant 18th-century hotel in centre of town. Antique furnishings, air-conditioned guest rooms. 100 m from the River Garonne and close to airport and A62.

■ ACTIVITIES: Guided tours, variety of sports including golf, water-skiing and cycling.
■ TARIFF: (1994) Single 280–400, Double 500–600, Bk 60 (Amex, Euro/Access, Visa).

A

Hôtel La Sauvagère ★★★ Galimas,
47340 La Croix Blanche.
☏ 53 68 81 21, Fax 53 68 82 19. English spoken.
Open all year. 12 bedrooms (all en suite).
Parking.

*10 km north of Agen, a quiet, relaxing hotel in
lovely parkland and offering a warm welcome.
(Owners unsure of 1995 opening dates when
this book went to print - please telephone in
advance if a LS reservation is required).*

■ RESTAURANT: Closed Sun & Mon lunch. An
inviting restaurant offering classic and gourmet
cuisine. Dishes are based on fresh, seasonal
produce, with meat and fish specialities.
■ ACTIVITIES: Tennis, lakeside swimming and
good walks nearby. (A swimming pool is
planned to be constructed at the hotel during
1995).
■ TARIFF: (1994) Single 278–328,
Double 298–368, Bk 35, Set menu 98–198
(Amex, Euro/Access, Visa).
■ DISCOUNT: 10%

AGON-COUTAINVILLE Manche   1B

Hôtel Neptune ★★★ promenoir Jersey,
50230 Agon-Coutainville.
☏ 33 47 07 66.
Open 31/03 to 31/10. 11 bedrooms
(all en suite). Golf 1 km. &

*Overlooking the sea, 12 km from Coutances.
Take D44 towards coast.*
■ TARIFF: (1994) Single 290–330,
Double 330–400, Bk 45 (Amex,
Euro/Access, Visa).

L'AIGLE Orne   2C

Hôtel du Dauphin ★★★ 4 place de la Halle,
61300 L'Aigle.
☏ 33 84 18 00, Fax 33 34 09 28.
English spoken.
Open all year. 30 bedrooms (28 en suite,
2 bath/shower only). Golf 15 km, parking.

*Dating from before 1618, this fine hotel
maintains many of the old French traditions.
On the N26 in the centre of Aigle.*
■ RESTAURANT: Closed 24 Dec & 01 Jan eve.
Renowned restaurant as well as a brasserie.
Specialities: homard; langouste; feuilleté
d'oeufs brouillés aux escargots; mille pommes
glaces et pommes confites au Calvados.
■ ACTIVITIES: Trout fishing and horse-riding can
be arranged by hotel.
■ TARIFF: (1994) Single 349–412,
Double 349–508, Bk 41, Set menu 128–420
(Amex, Euro/Access, Visa).

AIGUEBELETTE Savoie   6A

Hôtel de la Combe Chez Michelon ★★ La
Combe, 73610 Aiguebelette-le-Lac.
☏ 79 36 05 02, Fax 79 44 11 93. English spoken.
Open 01/01 to 31/10 & 01/12 to 31/12.
9 bedrooms (5 en suite, 4 bath/shower only).
Tennis, golf 3 km, parking. &

*Situated on a mountainside, overlooking the
lake. Exit the A43 for Aiguebelette-le-Lac.*
■ RESTAURANT: Closed Mon eve & Tues. Offers a
warm welcome, a good cellar and specialities
including foie gras frais maison, pigeon fermier à
l'ail, filet de veau aux pleurottes and crème brulée.
■ ACTIVITIES: A host of activities nearby
including swimming, windsurfing, boating,
horse-riding and hang-gliding.
■ TARIFF: (1994) Double 180–300, Bk 32,
Set menu 150–230 (Euro/Access, Visa).

AIGUES-MORTES Gard   5D

Hôtel des Croisades ★★ rue du Port,
30220 Aigues-Mortes.
☏ 66 53 67 85, Fax 66 53 72 95.
Open 16/02 to 14/11 & 16/12 to 14/01.
14 bedrooms (all en suite). Golf 6 km, garage,
parking. &

Situated in front of the Constance tower.
■ TARIFF: (1994) Single 240–250,
Double 240–300, Bk 30 (Euro/Access, Visa).

AIGUILLON Lot/Garonne   4D

Hôtel Le Jardin des Cygnes ★★ route de
Villeneuve, 47190 Aiguillon.
☏ 53 79 60 02, Fax 53 88 10 22. English spoken.
Open 10/01 to 20/12. 26 bedrooms
(24 en suite). Outdoor swimming pool,
golf 25 km, parking. &

*Most attractive hotel in this small, quiet town
by the River Lot. Lovely gardens and well-
heated swimming pool! From A61, exit for
Aiguillon. (Half-board from 180 FF to 272 FF).*
■ RESTAURANT: Has a good reputation for its
fine, home-made cuisine. Specialities include
foie gras, shellfish gratin and flaky apple pie.
■ ACTIVITIES: Fishing in the hotel grounds; spirit
tasting and duck preserve tasting nearby.
■ TARIFF: (1994) Single 160–245,
Double 185–270, Bk 32, Set menu 76–148
(Amex, Euro/Access, Visa).
■ DISCOUNT: 10%

AIGUINES Var   6C

Hôtel Grand Canyon ★★ Falaie des
Cavaliers, 83630 Aiguines.

📞 94 76 91 31, Fax 94 76 92 29. English spoken.
Open 01/05 to 17/10. 16 bedrooms
(all en suite). Parking. &

*Situated 300 m above the river, with helipad
and exceptional view of the Gorges-du-Verdon.
15 km from Aiguines on the D71.*

■ RESTAURANT: Closed Sun eve & Mon.
Panoramic restaurant with classic and regional
dishes. Specialities include soupe au pistou,
chèvre chaud and brouillade aux truffes.

■ ACTIVITIES: Footpaths to canyon; bungee
jumping, hang-gliding, horse-riding, canoeing,
fishing and rock climbing nearby.

■ TARIFF: (1994) Single 300–360,
Double 380–450, Bk 40 (Amex, Euro/Access,
Visa).

AINHOA Pyrénées-Atlan 4C

Hôtel Oppoca ★★ rue Principale, 64250 Aïnhoa.
📞 59 29 90 72, Fax 59 29 81 03. English spoken.
Open 15/03 to 15/11. 12 bedrooms
(11 en suite, 1 bath/shower only). Parking.

*In the heart of beautiful Basque country, this
hotel combines all modern comforts in a
charming 17th-century post house. Warm
welcome.*

■ RESTAURANT: Closed Mon in LS. Regional
cuisine in pleasant surroundings.

■ ACTIVITIES: Golf, walking, fishing within the
region.

■ TARIFF: (1994) Single 190–300,
Double 190–420, Bk 43, Set menu 125–220
(Amex, Euro/Access, Visa).

AIRE-SUR-L'ADOUR Landes 4D

Hôtel Chez l'Ahumat rue des Ecoles,
40800 Aire-sur-l'Adour.
📞 58 71 82 61.
Open all year. 13 bedrooms (11 en suite,
2 bath/shower only). Parking.

*Small, family-run hotel offering good value for
money. 50 km north of Pau.*

■ RESTAURANT: Closed Wed.

■ TARIFF: (1994) Single 108–135,
Double 115–170, Bk 20, Set menu 52–135
(Euro/Access, Visa).

AIRE-SUR-LA-LYS Pas-de-Calais 2B

Hostellerie des Trois Mousquetaires ★★★★
Château du Fort de la Redoute, 62120 Aire-sur-
la-Lys.
📞 21 39 01 11, Fax 21 39 50 10. English spoken.
Open 20/01 to 20/12. 33 bedrooms
(all en suite). Golf 20 km, parking.

*Restful and friendly 19th-century château.
Gardens, parkland and lakes, with views over
the Lys valley. N43.*

A

■ RESTAURANT: Closed Sun eve & Mon. Good
restaurant with regional specialites, dishes
cooked in beer and a wide selection of hot
desserts.

■ ACTIVITIES: Putting green, practice pitch and
pétanque in the grounds; reservations made
for golf.

■ TARIFF: (1994) Single 250–540,
Double 250–550, Bk 45 (Amex,
Euro/Access, Visa).

AIX-EN-PROVENCE Bches-du-Rhône 5D

Hôtel La Caravelle ★★★ 29-31 bd Roi René,
13100 Aix-en-Provence.
📞 42 21 53 05, Fax 42 96 55 46. English spoken.
Open all year. 32 bedrooms (28 en suite,
4 bath/shower only). Golf 7 km, parking. &

*Town centre hotel 300 m from Cours-
Mirabeau and 800 m from railway station.*

■ TARIFF: (1994) Single 190–390, Double 260–
390, Bk 34 (Amex, Euro/Access, Visa).

■ DISCOUNT: 10%

Domaine de Châteauneuf ★★★★ au Logis de
Nans, 83860 Nans-les-Pins.
📞 94 78 90 06, Fax 94 78 63 30. English spoken.

Open 01/03 to 30/11. 30 bedrooms
(all en suite). Outdoor swimming pool, tennis,
golf on site, parking.

*19th-century country house set on a golf
course with its own helipad. A8/E80 motorway
exit St-Maximin, N560, D80 south.*

■ RESTAURANT: Closed Mon LS. Charming
restaurant offering specialities of bouillabaisse
en gelée au safran, pigeonneau rôti et son jus
aux épices douces et truffes glacées avec
sauce au miel.

■ ACTIVITIES: ● Special half-board golf

A

package available on request.
- TARIFF: (1994) Single 560–650,
Double 600–1160, Bk 70, Set menu 170–410
(Amex, Euro/Access, Visa).

Hôtel Mas d'Entremont ★★★★ Montée
d'Avignon, 13090 Aix-en-Provence.
☏ 42 23 45 32, Fax 42 21 15 83. English spoken.
Open 15/03 to 01/11. 18 bedrooms
(17 en suite). Outdoor swimming pool, tennis,
golf, parking. ᪜

Set in lovely parkland, comfortable, air-
conditioned hotel with lots of antiques. 4 km
north of Aix on the N7 towards Avignon.
- RESTAURANT: Closed Sun eve & Mon lunch.
- TARIFF: (1994) Single 550–720,
Double 620–930, Bk 68, Set menu 200–230
(Euro/Access, Visa).

Hôtel Le Mas des Ecureuils ★★★ chemin de
Castel Blanc, petite route des Milles, 13090 Aix-
en-Provence.
☏ 42 24 40 48, Fax 42 39 24 57. English spoken.
Open all year. 23 bedrooms (all en suite).
Outdoor swimming pool, golf 2 km,
parking. ᪜

In a wooded setting yet close to motorway, exit
Les Milles or Aix-Pont-de-l'Arc.
- RESTAURANT: Refined, traditional French
cuisine.
- TARIFF: (1994) Single 380–660,
Double 480–760, Bk 50, Set menu 125–250
(Amex, Euro/Access, Visa).
- DISCOUNT: 10%

Hôtel Mascotte ★★★ av Cible, 13100 Aix-en-
Provence.
☏ 42 37 58 58, Fax 42 37 58 59. English spoken.
Open all year. 93 bedrooms (all en suite).
Outdoor swimming pool, golf 7 km,
parking. ᪜

A well-equipped and comfortable hotel near
the centre of town. Suitable for conferences
and meetings.
- RESTAURANT: Traditional and regional cuisine.
- TARIFF: (1994) Single 350–410,
Double 390–450, Bk 42 (Amex, Visa).

Hôtel Le Moulin ★★ 1 av R Schumann,
13090 Aix-en-Provence.
☏ 42 59 41 68, Fax 42 20 44 28. English spoken.
Open all year. 37 bedrooms (32 en suite).
Tennis, golf 5 km, garage, parking.

The hotel is near the university in a quiet area.
12 of the rooms have their own kitchenettes for
stays of 5 days or longer, and some have
terraces. Dinner can be arranged for groups of
20 or more.

- TARIFF: (1994) Single 215–290,
Double 215–370, Bk 37 (Amex,
Euro/Access, Visa).
- DISCOUNT: 10%

Hôtel Le Pigonnet ★★★★ 5 av Pigonnet,
13090 Aix-en-Provence.
☏ 42 59 02 90, Fax 42 59 47 77. English spoken.
Open 01/01 to 30/12. 52 bedrooms
(all en suite). Outdoor swimming pool,
golf 8 km, parking.

Beautiful old hotel once cherished by Cézanne.
Family-run, with sun terrace, gardens and
fountains, close to centre of Aix but in a
peaceful location. From Aix follow the road to
Marseille (1 km).
- RESTAURANT: Attractive décor, gourmet and
local dishes. Meals served on a shady terrace
in summer.
- ACTIVITIES: Jogging track, tennis and horse-
riding nearby.
- TARIFF: Single 500–800, Double 700–1250,
Bk 85, Set menu 250–320 (Amex,
Euro/Access, Visa).
- DISCOUNT: 10% By prior reservation.

AIX-LES-BAINS Savoie   6A

Hôtel Ariana ★★★★ av de Marlioz,
73101 Aix-les-Bains.
☏ 79 88 08 00, Fax 79 88 87 46. English spoken.

Open all year. 60 bedrooms (all en suite).
Indoor swimming pool, golf on site,
parking. ᪜

Very comfortable hotel offering a warm
welcome and a complimentary apéritif!
Situated in a 17 ha park at the foot of Mount
Revard, but only 2 km from the town centre.
Take the Aix-Sud exit from the A41.
- RESTAURANT: Very good Parisienne-style
brasserie with 30s decor.
- ACTIVITIES: Opposite golf course, tennis club,
race course and sports stadium; winter and

water sports within easy reach.
■ TARIFF: (1994) Single 390–580,
Double 410–590, Bk 58, Set menu 120 (Amex,
Euro/Access, Visa).
■ DISCOUNT: 8%

Hôtel Davat ★★ Le Grand Port,
73100 Aix-les-Bains.
☎ 79 63 40 40, Fax 79 54 35 68. English spoken.
Open 25/03 to 02/11. 20 bedrooms
(17 en suite, 3 bath/shower only). Golf 3 km,
garage, parking.
*Pretty hotel/restaurant, set close to the lake and
2 km from town centre.*
■ RESTAURANT: Closed Mon eve & Tues.
■ ACTIVITIES: Water-skiing.
■ TARIFF: (1994) Single 220–250,
Double 320–360, Set menu 100–250
(Euro/Access, Visa).

Park Hôtel ★★★★ av Charles de Gaulle, BP
525, 73105 Aix-les-Bains Cedex.
☎ 79 34 19 19, Fax 79 88 11 49. English spoken.

Open all year. 102 bedrooms (all en suite).
Golf 2 km, garage, parking. &
*Situated in large leisure complex on the shore
of Lake Bourget. Flats also available. At
crossroads of Lyons, Geneva and Turin
motorways.*
■ RESTAURANT: Gourmet restaurant 'La Symphonie'
and cafe-restaurant 'Brasserie du Parc'.
■ ACTIVITIES: Golf, tennis, horse-riding, sailing,
water-skiing, boating, walking, skiing, snow
shoes.
■ TARIFF: (1994) Single 520–710,
Double 620–810, Bk 68, Set menu 155 (Amex,
Euro/Access, Visa).
■ DISCOUNT: 15%

ALBERT Somme   2B

Hôtel Basilique ★★ 3 rue Gambetta,
80300 Albert.

☎ 22 75 04 71, Fax 22 75 10 47. English spoken.
Open 10/01 to 15/08 & 01/09 to 20/12.
10 bedrooms (all en suite). Golf 17 km.
*Comfortable, family-run hotel. In the centre of
Albert, close to the town park.*
■ RESTAURANT: Good choice of menus with
regional and house specialities.
■ TARIFF: Single 200–280, Double 280–300,
Bk 32, Set menu 85–210 (Euro/Access, Visa).

ALBI Tarn   5C

Hôtel Altea ★★★ 41 bis rue Porta, 81000 Albi.
☎ 63 47 66 66, Fax 63 46 18 40. English spoken.
Open all year. 56 bedrooms (all en suite).
Golf 2 km, parking. &
*Former mill on the River Tarn, facing the
cathedral.*
■ RESTAURANT: Closed Sat.
■ TARIFF: (1994) Double 320–500, Bk 55
(Amex, Euro/Access, Visa).

Hostellerie du Grand St-Antoine ★★★★
17 rue St-Antoine, 81000 Albi.
☎ 63 54 04 04, Fax 63 47 10 47. English spoken.
Open all year. 50 bedrooms (all en suite).
Garage, parking. &
*Comfortable and quiet 18th-century hotel, run
by the same family for five generations. Full of
antiques; garden. Close to tennis and
swimming pool. Near the cathedral and
Toulouse-Lautrec museum.*
■ RESTAURANT: Good food.
■ TARIFF: (1994) Single 360–550,
Double 400–850, Bk 60, Set menu 150–290
(Amex, Euro/Access, Visa).

Hôtel Le Vieil Alby ★★ 25 rue Toulouse-
Lautrec, 81000 Albi.
☎ 63 54 14 69, Fax 63 54 96 75. English spoken.
Open all year. 9 bedrooms (all en suite).
Golf 2 km, garage, restaurant.
■ TARIFF: (1994) Single 220, Double 220–260, Bk 28,
Set menu 80–250 (Amex, Euro/Access, Visa).

ALENCON Mayenne   2C

Hôtel Dauphin ★★ rte Alençon,
53370 St-Pierre-des-Nids.
☎ 43 03 52 12, Fax 43 03 55 49. English spoken.
Open all year. 9 bedrooms (7 en suite).
Golf 20 km, parking.
*Highly recommended small inn in a pretty
village. St-Pierre-des-Nids is on D121, 12 km
from Alençon.*
■ RESTAURANT: Seafood specialities.
■ TARIFF: (1994) Single 155–215,

A

Double 245–275, Bk 35, Set menu 85–255 (Euro/Access, Visa).

Hôtel du Grand Cerf ★★ 21 rue St-Blaise, 61000 Alençon.
☎ 33 26 00 51, Fax 33 26 63 07. English spoken

Open all year. 20 bedrooms (all en suite). Golf 2 km.

Historic building in the centre of town with lots of character and a warm atmosphere.

■ RESTAURANT: High quality cuisine including: foie gras de canard; homard flambé; plateau de fruits de mer; poêlée de ris de veau avec écrevisses.
■ ACTIVITIES: Horse-riding, tennis and lace making visits available.
■ TARIFF: (1994) Single 170–240, Double 200–270, Bk 35, Set menu 80–230 (Euro/Access, Visa).
■ DISCOUNT: 10%

Hôtel Grand St-Michel ★★ 7 rue Temple, 61000 Alençon.
☎ 33 26 04 77, Fax 33 26 71 82. English spoken.
Open 01/08 to 30/06. 13 bedrooms (6 en suite, 4 bath/shower only). Garage, parking.

Quietly situated in the historic town centre, near the town hall, lace museum and the birthplace of Ste-Thérèse.

■ RESTAURANT: Closed Mon. Excellent food prepared by the Chef, who is also owner of the hotel.
■ TARIFF: (1994) Single 150–260, Double 150–350, Bk 28, Set menu 85–265 (Amex, Euro/Access, Visa).

Hôtel Touring-Best Western ★★★ 72590 St-Leonard-des-Bois.
☎ 43 97 28 03, Fax 43 97 07 72. English spoken.
Open 15/02 to 15/11. 35 bedrooms (all en suite). Indoor swimming pool, garage, parking. &

Modern hotel in gardens on the Sarthe river in

the Mancelles Alps. The village lies south-west of Alençon. Drive south on N138, turn west to Fresnay, on the D130, then north-west on the D15.

■ RESTAURANT: Good, regional food is served in this pretty room which overlooks the gardens.
■ ACTIVITIES: River sports, hiking and trail-biking nearby.
■ TARIFF: Single 228–370, Double 305–460, Bk 45, Set menu 105–240 (Amex, Euro/Access, Visa).

L'ALPE-D'HUEZ Isère 6A

Hôtel au Chamois d'Or ★★★ 38750 L'Alpe-d'Huez.
☎ 76 80 31 32, Fax 76 80 34 90. English spoken.
Open 15/12 to 25/04. 45 bedrooms (all en suite). Indoor swimming pool, tennis, garage, parking.

Situated on the ski slopes at the highest point of the resort with views of mountain peaks. Superb south-facing terrace. North of N91.

■ RESTAURANT: Overlooking the ski slopes with meals served on the terrace; fresh fish specialities and traditional cuisine.
■ ACTIVITIES: At the hotel, sauna, hammam, jacuzzi and fitness centre; winter sports literally on the doorstep.
■ TARIFF: (1994) Double 800–1250, Bk 70, Set menu 130–260 (Euro/Access, Visa).

ALTKIRCH Ht-Rhin 3D

Hôtel La Terrasse ★★ 44-46 rue du 3ème Zouave, 68130 Altkirch.
☎ 89 40 98 02, Fax 89 08 82 92. English spoken.
Open 01/03 to 31/10. 19 bedrooms (4 en suite, 9 bath/shower only). Golf 15 km, garage, parking. &

Delightful overnight accommodation in quiet country area outside town, near St-Morand Hospital. Ideal for touring, 30 km from Basle.

■ TARIFF: (1994) Single 140–230, Double 140–250, Bk 25 (Amex, Euro/Access, Visa).

■ DISCOUNT: 20%

AMBERT Puy-de-Dôme   5A

Hôtel Les Copains ★★ 42 bd Henri IV, 63600 Ambert.
☎ 73 82 01 02, Fax 73 82 67 34. English spoken.
Open 01/10 to 31/08. 15 bedrooms (6 en suite, 4 bath/shower only).
The hotel can be found in the town centre, opposite the Mairie Ronde.
■ RESTAURANT: Closed Sept.
■ TARIFF: (1994) Single 130–220, Double 140–260, Bk 28, Set menu 62–150 (Euro/Access, Visa).

AMBIALET Tarn   5C

Hôtel Pont ★★ 81340 Ambialet.
☎ 63 55 32 07, Fax 63 55 37 21. English spoken.
Open 21/11 to 18/12. 20 bedrooms (all en suite). Outdoor swimming pool, parking. ᴗ
Charming, family-run hotel overlooking the village of Ambialet and the River Tarn. Well sited, comfortable accommodation.
■ RESTAURANT: Specialities: pigeon aux mousserons de Sieur Guirand; flan aux cheveux d'Ange.
■ ACTIVITIES: Tennis, rambling, mountain-biking and canoeing nearby.
■ TARIFF: (1994) Single 260, Double 290, Bk 35, Set menu 95–290 (Amex, Euro/Access, Visa).

AMBOISE Indre/Loire   2C

Hôtel La Brèche ★★ 26 rue J Ferry, 37400 Amboise.
☎ 47 57 00 79. English spoken.
Open 10/01 to 24/12. 13 bedrooms (10 en suite, 1 bath/shower only). Golf 10 km, garage, parking.
Small, comfortable hotel on the north side of the river towards the railway station.
■ ACTIVITIES: Sailing and boating nearby.
■ TARIFF: (1994) Single 175–290, Double 220–360 (Euro/Access, Visa).

Château de la Huberdière ★★★★ Vallée de Vaugadeland, 37530 Nazelles.
☎ 47 57 39 32, Fax 47 23 15 79. English spoken.
Open all year. 6 bedrooms (all en suite). Golf 11 km, parking, restaurant.
Private château, catering for just a few guests. Situated in the heart off the Loire valley, 7 km

north of Amboise. Just off N152, 25 km east of Tours.
■ TARIFF: Single 340, Double 390–570, Set menu 170–230 (No credit cards).

Hôtel du Parc ★★ 8 av L de Vinci, 37400 Amboise.
☎ 47 57 06 93, Fax 47 30 52 06. English spoken.
Open 15/01 to 15/12. 19 bedrooms (14 en suite, 4 bath/shower only). Golf 15 km, parking.
A French mansion dating from the turn of the century, and in a park. From the city centre follow signs to Hôtel du Parc.
■ RESTAURANT: Closed 01/11 to 01/03.
■ TARIFF: (1994) Double 230–425, Bk 35 (Amex, Euro/Access, Visa).

AMELIE-LES-BAINS Pyrénées-Or   5C

Hôtel Catalogne ★★ 67 rte Vieux Pont, 66110 Amélie-les-Bains.
☎ 68 39 80 31, Fax 69 39 20 23. English spoken.
Open 01/02 to 15/12. 38 bedrooms (all en suite). Garage, restaurant. ᴗ
A hotel with unusually large rooms and located by the river in charming Amélie-les-Bains. On D115 south of Céret. Beside the Office du Tourisme.
■ TARIFF: (1994) Single 250–300, Double 280–340, Bk 37 (Visa).

Hôtel Castel Emeraude ★★ route de la Corniche, Petit Provence, 66110 Amélie-les-Bains.
☎ 68 39 02 83, Fax 68 39 03 09. English spoken.
Open 01/02 to 30/11. 59 bedrooms (all en suite). Golf 1 km, parking. ᴗ
Set in a green landscape on a river bank and enjoying panoramic views. Every opportunity to discover the Vallespir area. On D115 just south of Céret.
■ RESTAURANT: Fine cuisine and vintage wines.
■ TARIFF: (1994) Double 230–360, Bk 39, Set menu 90–290 (Amex, Euro/Access, Visa).

AMIENS Somme 2B

A **Hôtel Normandie** ★★ 1 bis rue Lamartine, 80000 Amiens.
☏ 22 91 74 99, Fax 22 82 22 89. English spoken.

Open all year. 28 bedrooms (20 en suite). Golf 5 km, garage.

Elegant house with stained-glass windows situated in town centre. Take N1 south towards Paris opposite Amiens railway station, turn right into rue de Noyan and then take the first right.

■ ACTIVITIES: Bicycle hire and tennis courts nearby.
■ TARIFF: (1994) Single 170–250, Double 185–270, Bk 25 (Euro/Access, Visa).
■ DISCOUNT: 10%

ANDUZE Gard 5D

Hôtel Demeures du Ranquet ★★★★ Tornac, 30140 Anduze.
☏ 66 77 51 63, Fax 66 77 55 62. English spoken.
Open 01/03 to 30/11. 10 bedrooms (all en suite). Outdoor swimming pool, parking. ⚹

A converted stone farmhouse, with its own helipad, at the foot of the Cevennes. Tornac is just south of Anduze.

■ RESTAURANT: Closed Tues eve & Wed LS. Has a good reputation for cuisine prepared from fresh, top quality produce. Specialities according to season.

■ ACTIVITIES: Golf practice pitch and boulodrome. Cookery courses at hotel (except July/August). ● 10% reduction for horse-riding.
■ TARIFF: (1994) Single 500–640, Double 600–800, Bk 65 (Euro/Access, Visa).
■ DISCOUNT: 10%

ANGERS

Angers is in the Loire valley although it actually sits astride the very short River Maine, 5 km upstream from where it joins the Loire. Its position – close also to where the Mayenne and the Sarthe meet – has meant that Angers has always been a place of much importance.

Known as Black Angers, after the dark-coloured local stone of which many of the buildings are constructed, it is a far from gloomy place, being a town of flowers and gardens. One fine example of a public garden is the Jardin des Plantes, an area close to the centre with trees and flowers laid out around a lake. Each Saturday a wonderful flower market is held, where vegetables are also brought in from the surrounding countryside. It is pleasant to wander amongst the stalls especially in the early morning when the produce looks particularly tempting.

The Château is surrounded by gardens, both inside and outside its imposing wall. This dark stone wall linking the 17 defensive towers (now minus their original pepper-pot roofs) is a kilometre in length. Climb to the top of one of the towers for a view across the gardens, the river and the town. Within the wall, visit the contrastingly white-stoned chapel and the real wonder of Angers – the Apocalypse Tapestry.

Thought to be the oldest and largest ever woven, this tapestry was made in Paris in the 14th century. It survived well until the French Revolution when it was taken from the cathedral and torn up into useful blanket-sized pieces. In 1843, the then Bishop of Angers decided to try and resurrect it. He found about sixty per cent and had it carefully pieced back together.

The imposing wall of the Château at Angers and its surrounding garden

There are now 70 panels on display measuring in all about 100 metres.

Inspired by this huge masterpiece, Jean Lurçat designed his own series of tapestries, *Le Chant du Monde*, in 1957, now housed in the Hôpital de St-Jean which dates from 1174. As well as the tapestries and Lurçat's experimental paintings, there is a pleasant walk around the cloisters at the back of the building.

For a more informed insight into the town's architecture, join an official tour organised by the local tourist information service. With an official party you can go inside buildings that are otherwise not open to the public. You can, though, visit the Cathédrale St-Maurice on your own. Approached from the river up a long flight of steps, the building is of dark local stone pierced by 12th-century stained glass windows.

ANGERS Maine/Loire 2C

A

(See feature)

Château des Briottières ★★★★
49330 Champigné.
☎ 41 42 00 02, Fax 41 42 01 55.
English spoken.

Open all year. 9 bedrooms (all en suite). Outdoor swimming pool, golf 4 km, garage, parking. ⅋

The château is not a hotel, but a family home which welcomes guests. Beautifully furnished and stands in large grounds. From A11, take Durtal exit between Angers and Le Mans, and carry on to Champigné.

■ RESTAURANT: There is no separate restaurant as such, meals are usually taken alongside the family in their dining room. Alternative menus around 300F per head including wine and aperitif. Cuisine is traditional.
■ ACTIVITIES: Within the grounds (about 90 acres) you can walk, play billiards, taste wine etc. ● 3 golf courses within reach, with 20% discounts on green fees via the château.
■ TARIFF: (1994) Single 450, Double 450–900, Bk 45, Set menu 250 (Amex, Euro/Access, Visa).
■ DISCOUNT: 15% B&B.

Hôtel Climat de France ★★ rue du Château-d'Orgemont, 49100 Angers.
☎ 41 66 30 45, Fax 41 66 76 08.
English spoken.
Open all year. 42 bedrooms (all en suite). Golf 5 km, parking. ⅋

Enjoy the friendly atmosphere of the Climat de France. 5 minutes from the city centre.

■ RESTAURANT: Good regional cooking and wines.
■ TARIFF: (1994) Double 270–275, Bk 32, Set menu 85–125 (Amex, Euro/Access, Visa).

A

Hôtel de France ★★★ 8 place de la Gare, 49100 Angers.
✆ 41 88 49 42, Fax 41 86 76 70.

Open all year. 56 bedrooms (all en suite). Golf 5 km, garage. ♿
The Bouyer family has run the hotel since 1893, offering traditional hospitality. In the centre of Angers.
■ RESTAURANT: 'Les Plantagenets' offers a good range of gourmet menus.
■ TARIFF: (1994) Single 330–480, Double 480–600, Bk 50, Set menu 95–150 (Amex, Euro/Access, Visa).

Hôtel Univers ★★ 16 rue de la Gare, 49100 Angers.
✆ 41 88 43 58, Fax 41 86 97 28. English spoken.

Open all year. 45 bedrooms (35 en suite, 7 bath/shower only). ♿
Comfortably furnished town centre hotel, facing the station and within walking distance

of the castle and cathedral. From the A11 take the turning marked Château and follow signs to the station.
■ TARIFF: (1994) Single 150–260, Double 150–280, Bk 28 (Amex, Euro/Access, Visa).

ANGOULEME Charente   4B

Hôtel Orée des Bois ★★ Maison Neuve, 16410 Angoulême.
✆ 45 24 94 38. English spoken.
Open 21/11 to 01/11. 7 bedrooms (all en suite). Garage, parking. ♿
In a tranquil setting of forest and countryside. 15 km from Angoulême on the D25.
■ RESTAURANT: Closed Sun eve & Mon LS. Restaurant has a good reputation.
■ TARIFF: (1994) Single 200–250, Double 250–280, Bk 30, Set menu 95–250 (Amex, Euro/Access, Visa).

ANNECY Hte-Savoie   6A

Hôtel Arcalod ★★ Doussard, 74210 Bout-du-Lac.
✆ 50 44 30 22, Fax 50 44 85 03. English spoken.

Open 15/02 to 15/10. 33 bedrooms (all en suite). Outdoor swimming pool, golf 3 km, garage, parking. ♿
Family-run hotel in unspoilt countryside, 1 km from Lake Annecy. Doussard is on N508 between Annecy and Albertville.
■ RESTAURANT: Specialities: terrine de canard, filet de féra, parfait chartreux.
■ ACTIVITIES: Very good sporting activities nearby as well as helicopter trips and mountain hiking.
■ TARIFF: (1994) Single 250–350, Double 250–450, Bk 45, Set menu 85–140 (Amex, Euro/Access, Visa).
■ DISCOUNT: 10% LS.

Hôtel Faisan Doré ★★★ 34 av Albigny, 74000 Annecy.
☏ 50 23 02 46, Fax 50 23 11 10. English spoken.

Open 25/01 to 12/12. 40 bedrooms (all en suite). Golf 15 km, garage, parking.
1 km from the old town of Annecy and 100 m from the lake, the casino and the beach. From the centre of Annecy follow directions to the Imperial and Thônes.
■ RESTAURANT: Traditional restaurant. Specialities are fresh lake fish and Savoyard dishes.
■ ACTIVITIES: Water sports on the doorstep in summer, winter sports within easy reach.
■ TARIFF: (1994) Single 300–400, Double 330–470, Bk 45, Set menu 140–220 (Euro/Access, Visa).

Hôtel Ibis ★★ 12 rue de la Gare, 74000 Annecy.
☏ 50 45 43 21, Fax 50 52 81 08. English spoken. Open all year. 85 bedrooms (all en suite). Golf 15 km, parking, restaurant. &
In the old town by the River Thiou which is overlooked by some of the bedrooms' balconies. Take Annecy-Sud exit from A41, follow signs for the station then park at the Sainte-Claire municipal car park as the Ibis is in a pedestrianised area.
■ TARIFF: (1994) Single 305–310, Double 340–350, Bk 34 (Amex, Euro/Access, Visa).

Hôtel L'Imperial Palace ★★★★ 32 av Albigny, 74000 Annecy.
☏ 50 09 30 00, Fax 50 09 33 33. English spoken. Open all year. 98 bedrooms (all en suite). Indoor swimming pool, outdoor swimming pool, golf 8 km, garage, parking. &
This grand hotel has recently been completely renovated, and stands on its own wooded peninsula, right on the lake, from where the

views are stunning. The old town is just 800 m away, a pleasant walk through the park. The hotel also has its own casino.
■ RESTAURANT: Excellent French restaurant 'La Voile' has splendid views over the lake. American restaurant, the 'Jackpot Café', is in the casino.

■ ACTIVITIES: Water sports, mountain activities and tennis nearby. NB The indoor/outdoor swimming pool opens in summer 1995.
■ TARIFF: Single 800–1100, Double 1050–1200, Bk 90, Set menu 140–190 (Amex, Euro/Access, Visa).

Hôtel du Lac ★★ 74410 Duingt.
☏ 50 68 90 90, Fax 50 68 50 18. English spoken.

Open 12/02 to 31/10. 23 bedrooms (all en suite). Golf 10 km, parking.
Recently fully renovated. Has beautiful views of the surrounding lake and countryside plus its own private beach and pontoon. 12 km from Annecy towards Albertville.
■ RESTAURANT: Closed 31/10 to 30/04. Good, imaginative menus. Meals can be taken outside on the terrace in summer.
■ ACTIVITIES: On the spot water sports, hiking.
■ TARIFF: (1994) Double 280–370, Bk 39, Set menu 130–250 (Euro/Access, Visa).

A

Hôtel Mercure ★★★ rte Aix-les-Bains, 74600 Annecy.
✆ 50 52 09 66, Fax 50 69 29 32. English spoken. Open all year. 69 bedrooms (all en suite). Outdoor swimming pool, golf 15 km, parking. ♿

Comfortable hotel with good facilities. Leave A41 at Annecy-Sud exit.
■ RESTAURANT: Closed Sun & Mon lunch. Fish and meat specialities.
■ ACTIVITIES: Lake and mountain sports almost on the doorstep.
■ TARIFF: (1994) Single 325–425, Double 325–485, Bk 55, Set menu 90 (Amex, Euro/Access, Visa).
■ DISCOUNT: 10%

Hôtel La Reserve ★★★ 21 av Albigny, 74000 Annecy.
✆ 50 23 50 24, Fax 50 23 51 17. English spoken. Open all year. 12 bedrooms (all en suite). Golf 10 km, parking, restaurant.

Stunning position overlooking Lake Annecy and near beach, just a ten-minute stroll through the park to town centre. Sympathetically renovated.
■ TARIFF: (1994) Single 300–350, Double 370–430, Bk 38 (Euro/Access, Visa).

Hôtel Splendid ★★★ 4 quai E Chappuis, 74000 Annecy.
✆ 50 45 20 00, Fax 50 51 26 23. English spoken. Open 12/01 to 18/12. 52 bedrooms (50 en suite). Golf 14 km, parking. ♿

Large hotel with all modern amenities, close to the old town, overlooking the lake, on the Canal du Vassé.
■ ACTIVITIES: Canoeing and other water sports, cross-country biking and para-gliding. ● Hotel will reserve tables at any of the town's restaurants including the 'Libellule' a paddleboat restaurant that cruises the lake.
■ TARIFF: (1994) Single 520–630, Double 520–630, Bk 45 (Amex, Euro/Access, Visa).

ANNONAY Ardèche   5B

Hôtel Schaeffer ★★ 07340 Serrières.
✆ 75 34 00 07, Fax 75 34 08 79. English spoken. Open 20/01 to 31/12. 12 bedrooms (8 en suite, 4 bath/shower only). Golf 12 km, garage, parking.
Small hotel in a village on the banks of the Rhône. Take the Chanas exit from the A7 north of Valence and it is found on the N82.
■ RESTAURANT: Closed Sun eve & Mon LS.

Modern and stylish, concentrates on fresh local produce.
■ TARIFF: (1994) Single 180–260, Double 230–280, Bk 35, Set menu 140–320 (Amex, Euro/Access, Visa).

ANTIBES Alpes-Mar   6D

Manoir Castel Garoupe Axa ★★★ 959 bd de la Garoupe, 06600 Cap d'Antibes.
✆ 93 61 36 51, Fax 93 67 74 88. English spoken.

Open 15/03 to 15/11. 27 bedrooms (all en suite). Outdoor swimming pool, tennis, golf 5 km, parking.

Comfortable hotel situated in the centre of the Cap d'Antibes. Take N98 11 km from Cannes toward Antibes. The hotel is on the boulevard de la Garoupe which follows the coastline.
■ TARIFF: (1994) Single 500–640, Double 690–790 (Amex, Euro/Access, Visa).

Hôtel Don César ★★★★ 46 bd de la Garoupe, 06160 Cap d'Antibes.
☎ 93 67 15 30, Fax 93 67 18 25. English spoken.

Open 01/04 to 30/11. 19 bedrooms (all en suite). Outdoor swimming pool, golf 15 km, garage, parking. ᕦ
On the east side of Cap d'Antibes overlooking the sea. All rooms have sea views, air-conditioning and are fully equipped. Meals served beside the heated pool.
■ RESTAURANT: Closed Sun eve & Mon LS. Specialities: poissons; foie gras maison cuit au torchon; poêlée de noix de St-Jacques sauce soja; strogonoff de veau à la graine de moutarde; petit feuilleté minute de pomme.
■ ACTIVITIES: Water-skiing, tennis, and boat hire available.
■ TARIFF: (1994) Double 600–1050, Bk 65, Set menu 175 (Amex, Euro/Access, Visa).

Château Fleuri ★★ 15 bd du Cap, 06600 Cap d'Antibes.
☎ 93 61 38 66, Fax 93 67 39 22. English spoken.

Open 01/04 to 01/11. 19 bedrooms (all en suite). Golf 8 km, parking.
Small hotel with a pretty garden and enclosed parking. All the rooms have terrace or balcony. Five minutes from sandy beach and fifteen minutes from old town. In direction of Cap d'Antibes.
■ ACTIVITIES: All water sports/lessons, deep sea diving at Juan-les-Pins, horse-riding and archery nearby.
■ TARIFF: (1994) Single 200–300, Double 250–400, Bk 30 (Amex, Euro/Access, Visa).
■ DISCOUNT: 10% On second week's stay.

APT Vaucluse   5D

Auberge du Lubéron ★★★ 17 quai Léon Sagy, 84400 Apt.
☎ 90 74 12 50, Fax 90 04 79 49. English spoken.
Open 19/01 to 01/07 & 08/07 to 20/12. 15 bedrooms (all en suite). Garage, parking.
Quiet hotel near town centre, with lovely views over Apt and the River Calavon. In the Lubéron Regional Park and 50 km from Avignon.
■ RESTAURANT: Closed Mon lunch. Fine food, based on fresh, quality products. Meals can be enjoyed on the pretty terrace overlooking the town and river.
■ TARIFF: (1994) Single 235–390, Double 235–490, Bk 45, Set menu 125–220 (Amex, Euro/Access, Visa).

ARBOIS Jura   3D

Hôtel Jean-Paul Jeunet ★★ rue de l'Hôtel de Ville, 39600 Arbois.
☎ 84 66 05 67, Fax 84 66 24 20. English spoken.
Open 01/02 to 30/11. 12 bedrooms (all en suite). Golf 25 km, garage, parking. ᕦ
Formerly a Carmelite convent, hotel has been skillfully transformed into a really lovely, welcoming hotel whilst still retaining its original features.
■ RESTAURANT: Closed Tues; Wed lunch ex hols & Sep. Beautifully renovated dining room with open fire and lots of beams. Creative cuisine taking advantage of fresh, country produce.
■ ACTIVITIES: Visits to cheese and wine cellars, museums and Pasteur's house.
■ TARIFF: (1994) Single 300–380, Double 350–500, Bk 60 (Euro/Access, Visa).

ARCACHON Gironde   4A

Hôtel Deganne ★★★ 4 rue du Professor Jolyet, 33120 Arcachon.
☎ 56 83 99 91, Fax 56 83 87 92. English spoken.

A

A

Open all year. 57 bedrooms (all en suite).
Golf 1 km, garage. &

Close to the Casino and 30 m from the beach.
Downtown hotel, 1 km from railway station,
60 km from Bordeaux. N250 from Bordeaux,
then D650 into Arcachon, or E5 from
Bordeaux then A66.

■ TARIFF: (1994) Single 480–1200,
Double 580–1200, Bk 58 (Amex,
Euro/Access, Visa).

ARDRES Pas-de-Calais   2B

Hôtel La Chaumière ★★ 67 av Rouville,
62610 Ardres.
☎ 21 35 41 24. English spoken.
Open all year. 12 bedrooms (10 en suite,
2 bath/shower only). Golf 5 km, parking,
restaurant. &

17 km from Calais (N43). The hotel is located
in the middle of the town. Terrace and garden.

■ TARIFF: (1994) Single 160–270,
Double 160–310, Bk 27 (Euro/Access, Visa).

ARGENTAN Orne   2C

Hôtel Faisan Dore ★★ Fontenai-sur-Orne,
61200 Argentan.
☎ 33 67 18 11, Fax 33 35 82 15. English spoken.
Open 01/01 to 15/02 & 01/03 to 31/12.
15 bedrooms (all en suite). Golf 10 km,
parking.

The hotel is a pretty, half-timbered inn with
landscaped gardens, on the road to Flers.

■ RESTAURANT: Closed Sun eve.
■ ACTIVITIES: Tennis and horse-riding nearby.
■ TARIFF: (1994) Single 250, Double 305, Bk 40,
Set menu 90–280 (Amex, Euro/Access, Visa).
■ DISCOUNT: 5%

Hôtel France ★★ 8 bd Carnot,
61200 Argentan.
☎ 33 67 03 65, Fax 33 66 22 24. English spoken.
Open all year. 13 bedrooms (11 en suite,
2 bath/shower only). Garage, parking. &

Good value for money is keyword at this
traditional hotel/restaurant set in a pretty
garden with terrace. Lots to do and see in
town.

■ RESTAURANT: Closed Sun eve & Mon.
■ TARIFF: (1994) Single 125–240,
Double 145–270, Bk 26, Set menu 68–178 (No
credit cards).

ARGENTAT Corrèze   5A

Hôtel Lac ★★ 19430 Camps.
☎ 55 28 51 83, Fax 55 28 53 71. English spoken.

Open all year. 11 bedrooms (10 en suite).
Tennis, parking. &

Modern, good value Logis hotel. From
Argentat, south on the D120, then right on the
D41 to Camps - about 25 km from Argentat.

■ RESTAURANT: Closed Sun eve & Mon LS.
■ TARIFF: (1994) Single 200, Double 220, Bk 26
(Euro/Access, Visa).

Auberge Limousine ★★ 19320 La Roche-
Canillac.
☎ 55 29 12 06, Fax 55 29 27 03.
English spoken.

Open 01/04 to 01/10. 52 bedrooms
(26 en suite, 26 bath/shower only). Outdoor
swimming pool, parking.

Pretty hotel in this lovely 'Pays Vert' village,
north-east of Argentat. Or from Tulle south on
the N120, then D10 and D29 to La Roche-
Canillac.

■ RESTAURANT: Attractive, rustic-style restaurant.
Specialities: feuilleté de sandre au beurre de
fenouil; tournedos corrézien; soufflé glacé aux
noix crème caramel.
■ ACTIVITIES: Mountain-biking, rides by horse-
drawn carriage.
■ TARIFF: (1994) Single 145–230,
Double 145–299, Bk 32, Set menu 90–200
(Euro/Access, Visa).

ARGENTON-SUR-CREUSE Indre   4B

Manoir de Boisvillers ★★ 11 rue Moulin de
Bord, 36200 Argenton-sur-Creuse.
☎ 54 24 13 88, Fax 54 24 27 83.
Open 09/01 to 03/12. 14 bedrooms
(13 en suite, 1 bath/shower only). Outdoor
swimming pool, golf 20 km, garage, parking.

In the heart of Argenton, an 18th-century
manor situated on the river in an area noted
for its Roman history. Very quiet and
charming.

■ TARIFF: (1994) Single 180–265, Double 220–365, Bk 35 (Amex, Euro/Access, Visa).
■ DISCOUNT: 10% LS only.

Château de Bouesse 36200 Bouesse.
☎ 54 25 12 20, Fax 54 25 12 30. English spoken.

Open 01/02 to 31/12. 11 bedrooms (all en suite). Golf 25 km, parking.

Medieval château three hours south of Paris on the N20 and a few minutes east of Argenton-sur-Creuse on the D927. Formerly the fortress home of one of Joan of Arc's top generals, the castle is being painstakingly restored by an English couple.

■ RESTAURANT: Closed Mon lunch LS. Carved 17th-century panelling. Home-made foie gras and fresh salmon delicacies.
■ ACTIVITIES: Cycle and hiking trails right on the doorstep.
■ TARIFF: (1994) Double 350–480, Bk 55, Set menu 145 (Amex, Euro/Access, Visa).

Hôtel Cheval Noir ★★ 27 rue Auclert-Descottes, 36200 Argenton-sur-Creuse.
☎ 54 24 00 06, Fax 54 24 11 22.
English spoken.
Open all year. 29 bedrooms (25 en suite). Parking, restaurant. ⅙

In the centre of town with a family atmosphere. 25 km south on the N20 from Châteauroux. Turn right in town heading towards Gargilesse.

■ TARIFF: (1994) Single 205–240, Double 205–290, Bk 33, Set menu 85–200 (Euro/Access, Visa).

Château du Vivier ★★★ route de Gargilesse, 36200 Argenton-sur-Creuse.
☎ 54 24 29 99, Fax 54 01 12 87. English spoken.
Open all year. 7 bedrooms (all en suite). Outdoor swimming pool, parking. ⅙

A small neo-classic manor house. Set amongst 200-year-old cedar trees in lovely parkland, the hotel offers total tranquillity and comfort.

■ RESTAURANT: Gourmet cuisine in a cosy, romantic setting. Seafood, foie gras and rare mushrooms are some of the specialities on offer. Meals are served outdoors in fine weather.
■ TARIFF: (1994) Double 300–700, Bk 65, Set menu 135–390 (Amex, Euro/Access, Visa).

ARLES Bches-du-Rhône 5D

Hôtel Les Cabanettes ★★★ St-Gilles, 13200 Saliers-par-Arles.
☎ 66 87 31 53, Fax 66 87 35 39.
English spoken.
Open 01/03 to 25/01. 29 bedrooms (all en suite). Outdoor swimming pool, garage, parking. ⅙

Modern and quiet, an attractive hotel set around the enclosed garden and pool area. 15 km from Arles, on N572 in St-Gilles.

■ RESTAURANT: With a view over the pool and the Camargue, restaurant specialities include poêlon de moules gratinées and rouille d'encornets Camarguaise.
■ ACTIVITIES: ● 10% reduction on horse-riding/trekking.
■ TARIFF: (1994) Single 350–420, Double 405–420, Bk 45 (Amex, Euro/Access, Visa).
■ DISCOUNT: 10%

Auberge des Epis ★★ 13 av Plaisance, 13310 St-Martin-de-Crau.
☎ 90 47 31 17.
Open 01/03 to 31/01. 11 bedrooms (8 en suite, 3 bath/shower only). Golf 10 km, parking.

Pleasantly situated hotel with terrace at St-Martin-de-Crau, south-east of Arles.

■ RESTAURANT: Closed Feb.
■ TARIFF: (1994) Single 200, Double 200–265, Bk 34, Set menu 98–185 (Euro/Access, Visa).

A

Auberge La Fenière ★★★
13280 Raphèle-lès-Arles.
☎ 90 98 47 44, Fax 90 98 48 39. English spoken.
Open all year. 25 bedrooms (all en suite).
Golf 15 km, garage, parking. ₺

*Overlooking the grasslands of La Crau, ideally
located for scenic trips around the region.
Traditional refined cooking. From Arles
centre, go towards Raphèle for 5 km on the
N453.*

■ RESTAURANT: Closed 10/11 to 20/12.
■ TARIFF: (1994) Single 307–363,
Double 363–640, Bk 47, Set menu 170–250
(Euro/Access, Visa).

Hôtel d'Arlatan ★★★ 26 rue Sauvage,
13200 Arles.
☎ 90 93 56 66, Fax 90 49 68 45. English spoken.
Open all year. 40 bedrooms (all en suite).
Golf 15 km, garage.

*15th-century mansion house with Roman
relics, courtyard and garden. On the east bank
of the Rhône. Leave N113 at Nouveau-Pont.*

■ TARIFF: (1994) Single 385–560, Double 465–
695, Bk 55 (Amex, Euro/Access, Visa).

Hôtel Jules Cesar ★★★★ 9 bd des Lices
BP 116, 13631 Arles.
☎ 90 93 43 20, Fax 90 93 33 47. English spoken.
Open 23/12 to 02/11. 55 bedrooms
(all en suite). Outdoor swimming pool,
golf 18 km, garage, parking. ₺

*An old Carmelite convent and now an
excellent hotel. In the heart of Provence in a
town rich in history, archaeology and culture.*

■ RESTAURANT: Closed 02/11 to 23/12. Air-
conditioned, beamed restaurant with terrace
and garden. Well known for its classic cuisine
and Provençal specialities.
■ TARIFF: (1994) Single 550–980,
Double 650–980, Bk 65, Set menu 195–380
(Amex, Euro/Access, Visa).

Hôtel Mirador ★★ 3 rue Voltaire, 13200 Arles.
☎ 90 96 28 05, Fax 90 96 59 89. English spoken.
Open 15/02 to 15/01. 15 bedrooms
(13 en suite, 2 bath/shower only). Garage,
parking.

*A comfortable family hotel, close to the town
centre, buses and railway station.*

■ TARIFF: (1994) Single 160–210, Double 180–
240, Bk 26 (Amex, Euro/Access, Visa).

Hôtel le Rodin ★★★ 20 rue Rodin,
13200 Arles-sur-Rhone.
☎ 90 49 69 10, Fax 90 93 53 12. English spoken.
Open all year. 30 bedrooms (all en suite).

Outdoor swimming pool, golf 15 km, garage,
parking. ₺

*Provence-style hotel 800 m from town centre,
situated in a quiet residential avenue. Relaxed
family atmosphere.*

■ RESTAURANT: Light and airy restaurant serving
regional cuisine.
■ ACTIVITIES: Bikes for hire, all-day fishing.
■ TARIFF: (1994) Single 260–375, Double 260–
375, Bk 47 (Amex, Euro/Access, Visa).
■ DISCOUNT: 3%

Château de Vergières
13310 St-Martin-de-Crau.
☎ 90 47 17 16, Fax 90 47 38 30.
English spoken.

Open all year. 6 bedrooms (all en suite).
Outdoor swimming pool, golf 15 km, garage,
parking.

*From Arles, east to St-Martin-de-Crau, then
follow signs for La Dynamite, and on to
Vergières. Tradition and comfort combined in
this private château.*

■ RESTAURANT: Fixed price menu. Dinner must
be reserved in advance.
■ ACTIVITIES: Sightseeing and tours; horse-riding
and bicycle hire nearby.
■ TARIFF: Double 800–900, Set menu 300
(Amex, Euro/Access, Visa).

ARMENTIERES Nord   2B

Hôtel Albert 1er ★★ 28 rue Robert Schuman,
59280 Armentières.
☎ 20 77 31 02, Fax 20 77 05 16.
English spoken.
Open all year. 21 bedrooms (all en suite).
Garage, parking.

■ TARIFF: (1994) Single 165–250,
Double 185–270, Bk 30 (Euro/Access, Visa).
■ DISCOUNT: 10%

ARRAS

One of Arras's fine squares, La Grand-Place

Taking the motorway south from Calais brings you, after about 100 km, to Arras. Although devastated by the bombardments of World War I, the town has been meticulously rebuilt and is definitely worth a visit. At its centre lie two enormous squares, the Grand-Place and the Place des Héros, thought by many to be amongst the finest in Europe. Both squares have a northern-European feel about them and are surrounded by tall narrow houses built in a distinctly Flemish style. These houses are arcaded at street level making it possible to walk around each square under cover, protected from either the sun or the rain. You can park your car under the Place des Héros and enjoy the lively markets up above.

As well as the car park, there is a whole series of rooms and passages built under the centre of Arras. The entrance to this subterranean labyrinth, known as the *souterrains*, is in the Hôtel de Ville on the Place des Héros. Having explored below ground, take the lift up to the top of the 75-m belfry and enjoy the view over Les Places, the roof tops of Arras and the surrounding countryside. Actually, the lift doesn't quite go all the way, but 33 steps are as nothing compared to the 326 you would have to climb if you walked up all the way!

Inside the town hall, there are several interesting things to look at as well as the building itself. For example, just inside the door there are two giant figures, named Colas and Jacqueline. Each year they are paraded through the streets during the Arras festival at the end of August. The state of the town following World War I is also shown in a display of photographs which impress on the visitor the enormous task undertaken by the builders of returning the town to its original appearance. One building that disappeared rather earlier than the First World War was the 12th-century cathedral, demolished in 1799. To see what it was like, look at the fresco – depicting life in 16th-century Arras – which decorates the upstairs Salle des Fêtes.

The present cathedral, which was originally the abbey church of St-Vaast, lies behind the belfry. It is next to the unusually double-cloistered Benedictine Abbaye St-Vaast. Part of this building is now used to house the Musée Municipal. Amongst a varied collection there is only one example of a local tapestry. This is surprising because Arras was particularly well known for its production of fine tapestries in the 14th and 15th centuries.

Although the town is completely restored, memories of the First World War live on. The British war cemetery, with its memorial to 36,000 missing soldiers, is in the boulevard Général de Gaulle, and 8 km outside the town lies the much fought over Vimy ridge. Here, a huge white memorial bears the names of the 60,000 Canadians killed in France between 1914 and 1918. Nearby is an information centre and remains of the trenches in which so many died. Because these war cemeteries are so immaculately laid out and still so carefully tended, they are not as depressing to visit as might be imagined.

ARRAS Pas-de-Calais 2B

(See feature)

Hôtel Le Manoir ★★ 35 route Nationale, 62580 Gavrelle.
℡ 21 58 68 58, Fax 21 55 37 87. English spoken. Open 01/01 to 24/07 & 23/08 to 25/12. 20 bedrooms (all en suite). Golf 3 km, garage, parking. ♿
Situated between Arras and Douai. Meals

A

eaten around log fire in winter and on the terrace during summer. *Take N50 Arras/Douai, then exit to Fresnes.*

■ RESTAURANT: Closed Sat lunch & Sun eve.
■ TARIFF: (1994) Single 210–240, Double 240–260, Bk 30, Set menu 68–168 (Amex, Euro/Access, Visa).

Hôtel Les 3 Luppars ★★ 49 Grand'Place, 62000 Arras.
☎ 21 07 41 41, Fax 21 24 24 80. English spoken.

Open all year. 42 bedrooms (all en suite). Golf 2 km, parking. &

15th-century house in the centre of town. Arras is a city of history and fine arts. From Lille south on the D925 to Lens, then N17 south to Arras.

■ ACTIVITIES: Guided tours.

Hôtel Moderne ★★★ 1 bd Faidherbe, 62000 Arras.
☎ 21 23 39 57, Fax 21 71 55 42. English spoken.
Open all year. 55 bedrooms (all en suite). Golf 6 km, parking, restaurant. &

A pleasant hotel on the station square in town centre.

■ TARIFF: (1994) Single 200–320, Double 250–350, Bk 35, Set menu 90–180 (Amex, Euro/Access, Visa).

ARREAU Htes-Pyrénées   4D

Hôtel Angleterre ★★ rte Luchon, 65240 Arreau.
☎ 62 98 63 30, Fax 62 98 69 66. English spoken.
Open 01/06 to 31/10 & 26/12 to 15/04. 24 bedrooms (all en suite). Golf 25 km, parking.

In the heart of the Aure Valley and offering charm and comfort. Logis de France hotel.

■ RESTAURANT: Friendly and comfortable with good food.
■ TARIFF: (1994) Single 210–250, Double 240–300, Bk 35, Set menu 70–190 (Amex, Euro/Access, Visa).

ARUDY Pyrénées-Atlan   4D

Hôtel France ★★ pl Hôtel de Ville, 64260 Arudy.
☎ 59 05 60 16, Fax 59 05 70 06.
Open all year. 19 bedrooms (11 en suite, 3 bath/shower only). Parking, restaurant.

At the foot of the Pyrénées in the centre of Arudy, a typical Bearn village. Traditional family hotel. On the D134 between Gan and Laruns, 90 minutes from the sea.

■ TARIFF: (1994) Single 120–210, Double 160–255, Bk 30, Set menu 68–110 (Euro/Access, Visa).

AUBENAS Ardèche   5D

Hôtel Persedes ★★ Lavilledieu, 07170 Aubenas.
☎ 75 94 88 08, Fax 75 94 29 02. English spoken.

Open 01/04 to 30/10. 24 bedrooms (all en suite). Outdoor swimming pool, garage, parking. &

New and comfortable hotel 25 km from the Rhône Valley motorway. At Montélimar follow N102 for 12 km to Aubenas, then over the river to Lavilledieu.

■ RESTAURANT: Closed Mon lunch except Jul & Aug. Traditional and imaginative home cooking.
■ ACTIVITIES: At the hotel, jaccuzzi and mini-golf; go-karting, boating and horse-riding nearby.
■ TARIFF: (1994) Single 260–340, Double 280–340, Bk 38, Set menu 85–170 (Euro/Access, Visa).
■ DISCOUNT: 8%

AUCH Gers   4D

Hôtel de France ★★★★ pl de la Libération, 32000 Auch.
📞 62 61 71 71, Fax 62 61 71 81. English spoken. Open all year. 29 bedrooms (all en suite). Golf 2 km, garage, parking.
Well-appointed hotel where guests are assured of a warm welcome and excellent service.
■ RESTAURANT: Closed Sun eve & Mon. Andrée Daguin, the chef, is renowned for his Gascon cuisine. Specialities: gratin d'huître au maigret fumé; cuisse de canard au miel d'épice.
■ ACTIVITIES: ● Cookery lessons; special rates for golf and hunting.
■ TARIFF: (1994) Single 290–2500, Double 360–2500, Bk 80, Set menu 180–495 (No credit cards).

AUDIERNE Finistère   1C

Hôtel Ker-Moor Plage du Loch, 29770 Plogoff.
📞 98 70 62 06, Fax 98 70 32 69. English spoken. Open all year. 17 bedrooms (10 en suite, 7 bath/shower only). Golf 8 km, parking.
Hotel/restaurant facing the Atlantic. From Audierne take the D784 west towards Plogoff. The hotel is 2 km before Plogoff.
■ RESTAURANT: Closed Wed & Thur LS. Cuisine based on fresh seafood. Sea view in dining-room.
■ TARIFF: (1994) Single 170–265, Double 170–300, Bk 34, Set menu 70–245 (Euro/Access, Visa).

AUMALE Seine-Marit   2B

Hôtel Le Dauphin ★★ 76390 Aumale.
📞 35 93 41 92, Fax 35 93 62 34. English spoken. Open 15/01 to 15/12. 10 bedrooms (7 en suite, 3 bath/shower only). Garage, parking.
Pleasant setting, near river, for this quiet family hotel set back from the N29 Amiens/Rouen road. Dieppe ferry 60 km. From Calais via Abbeville and Blangy.
■ RESTAURANT: Closed Sun eve & Mon lunch.
■ TARIFF: (1994) Single 180–225, Double 180–265, Bk 26, Set menu 82–252 (Euro/Access, Visa).

AURILLAC Cantal   5A

Auberge de la Tomette ★★ 15220 Vitrac.
📞 71 64 70 94, Fax 71 64 77 11. English spoken. Open 01/04 to 31/12. 21 bedrooms (all en suite). Outdoor swimming pool, golf 14 km, restaurant. ⅃

A

A charming, friendly hotel in lovely countryside. 25 km south of Aurillac, Vitrac is a small village amongst the hills. From Aurillac N122 south then left on to D66 to Vitrac.
■ ACTIVITIES: Cycling, canoeing.
■ TARIFF: (1994) Single 250–270, Double 250–300, Bk 40, Set menu 70–175 (Amex, Euro/Access, Visa).

Grand Hôtel St-Pierre ★★★ 16 cours Monthyon, 15000 Aurillac.
📞 71 48 00 24, Fax 71 64 81 83. English spoken. Open all year. 29 bedrooms (all en suite). Garage, parking, restaurant.
This comfortable hotel is in the town centre, near the river, and gives impeccable service. Suitable for conferences and holidays.
■ TARIFF: (1994) Single 280–320, Double 300–380, Bk 35, Set menu 98–240 (Amex, Euro/Access, Visa).

AUTUN Saône/Loire   3C

Golf Hôtel ★★ au plan d'eau du Vallon, 71400 Autun.
📞 85 52 00 00, Fax 85 52 20 20. English spoken. Open all year. 44 bedrooms (all en suite). Golf 1 km, parking. ⅃
Modern hotel with good facilities, bar and two reception rooms.
■ RESTAURANT: Closed Sun eve Nov to Mar. Light airy restaurant offering regional cuisine. Speciality: prime cuts of grilled Charollais beef. Good selection of wines.
■ ACTIVITIES: 9-hole golf course, crazy golf, horse-riding and jogging facilities are all to be found within walking distance surrounding a small lake.
■ TARIFF: (1994) Single 252, Double 273, Bk 33 (Amex, Visa).

AUXERRE

A

A view across the Yonne

One of the oldest towns in France, Auxerre, now declared a preservation area, lies on the River Yonne about 150 km to the southeast of Paris. Surrounded by vineyards and cherry orchards, this town is best viewed from the riverside where its churches rise dramatically above the many fine Renaissance-style houses. As well as admiring the houses and visiting the churches – especially the Gothic cathedral with its exceptional 13th-century stained glass windows – look out for the Tour de l'Horloge. This ancient gateway consists of a 15th-century clock, with a different face on each side, mounted above an arch.

AUXERRE Yonne   2D

(See feature)

Hôtel Cygne 14 rue 24-Août, 89000 Auxerre.
Open all year. bedrooms.

Hôtel Normandie ★★ 41 bd Vauban, 89000 Auxerre.
☎ 86 52 57 80, Fax 86 51 54 33. English spoken.
Open all year. 47 bedrooms (all en suite). Garage, parking. &
The hotel is in the centre of town and provides a good base for sightseeing. Rooms are quiet, with views of the garden and the proprietors offer traditional French hospitality.
■ ACTIVITIES: Gym, sauna and billiards.
■ TARIFF: (1994) Single 230–260, Double 260–350, Bk 32 (Amex, Euro/Access, Visa).
■ DISCOUNT: 5%

Hôtel Seignelay ★★ 2 rue Pont, 89000 Auxerre.
☎ 86 52 03 48, Fax 86 52 32 39. English spoken.
Open 01/01 to 15/02 & 15/03 to 31/12.
21 bedrooms (19 en suite). Golf 15 km, garage. &
Traditional welcome and pretty interior terrace in this town centre hotel.
■ RESTAURANT: Closed Mon LS.
■ TARIFF: (1994) Double 140–290, Bk 32, Set menu 75–160 (Euro/Access, Visa).

Hôtel Soleil d'Or ★★ 3, N77, 89230 Montigny-la-Resle.
☎ 86 41 81 21, Fax 86 41 86 88. English spoken.

Open all year. 16 bedrooms (all en suite). Indoor swimming pool, tennis, parking, restaurant. &
The hotel/restaurant is in the middle of Montigny-la-Resle village next to the church. N77 passes in front of the hotel.
■ TARIFF: (1994) Single 245, Double 275, Bk 30, Set menu 88–320 (Amex, Euro/Access, Visa).

AVALLON Yonne   3C

Hôtel Moulin des Ruats ★★★ dans la Vallée du Cousin, 89200 Avallon.
☎ 86 34 07 14, Fax 86 31 16 47. English spoken.
Open 12/02 to 12/11. 27 bedrooms (all en suite). Parking.
An old flour mill, set in a quiet valley surrounded by forests and close to the River Cousin. About 4 km from Avallon.
■ RESTAURANT: Renowned for its very good cuisine.
■ TARIFF: (1994) Double 300–550, Bk 50 (Amex, Euro/Access, Visa).

AVENE-LES-BAINS Hérault   5C

SNC Hôtel ★★★ 34260 Avène-lès-Bains.
☎ 67 23 44 45, Fax 67 23 44 03. English spoken.

Open 01/04 to 31/10. 59 bedrooms
(all en suite). Outdoor swimming pool, tennis,
parking, restaurant. &

*In a wooded area with thermal spa nearby.
Access from Lodève on N9 via D35 and D8
going westwards.*

■ TARIFF: (1994) Double 370–430, Bk 49,
Set menu 85 (Amex, Euro/Access, Visa).

AVIGNON

To save the long drive south, it is possible
to put your car on the train at Calais.
Twelve hours later you arrive at Avignon
and may be tempted to drive straight on.
Don't, this historic town is well worth a visit
and makes a good centre for touring. A visit
at the time of Avignon's Festival d'Art
Dramatique et de Danse can be especially
exciting. This festival runs from mid July to
mid August and there are plenty of fringe
events to enjoy, as well as the more formal
'official' performances.

At the heart of Avignon lies the medieval
walled town standing high above the River
Rhône. The walls were built in the 14th
century, nearly 200 years after the
completion of what is probably the most
famous bridge in France, the Pont
d'Avignon. Also known as the Pont St-
Bénézet, only 4 of its 22 original arches
remain. However, the medieval town walls,
following extensive 19th-century
restoration, are still intact forming a
complete circuit of nearly 5 km. There are
39 turrets on this formidable fortification
and 8 gates. Enter the medieval town on
foot; this is the best method of exploration
as the roads inside the walls are mostly one-
way. The Place de l'Horloge is a good
centre to head for with its numerous cafés,
14th-century clock tower and main tourist
office.

Just off the Place de l'Horloge lies the Palais
des Papes, a Gothic masterpiece. It was
built in the years between 1309 and 1377,
when the Papal court was here having been
exiled from Rome. Two of the seven popes
who lived in Avignon during this time are
particularly connected with the building,

Benedict XII who built the austere north-
east wings and Clement VI who was
responsible for the more flamboyant west
wing. These two wings are now known
respectively as the Old Palace and the New
Palace. Another of the Avignon popes,
John XXII lies buried in the adjoining
cathedral of Notre-Dame de Doms. There
are also several museums of interest within
the town walls. The Musée Lapidaire
houses examples of Roman statues and
pottery dug up in the area, while in the
Musée Calvet, a fine 18th-century house,
there is a collection of French paintings.

For an overall picture of Avignon visit the
public garden that tops the Rocher des
Doms. This lies between the Cathedral and
the Pont d'Avignon and from it there are
extensive views across the old town, the
river and the surrounding countryside. In all
directions there are places of interest to visit
and all within a day's reach of Avignon. The
Camargue, with its wild white horses, lies to
the south; Orange with its extensive Roman
remains lies to the north; and, for an even
more impressive view, travel east to Mount

Châteauneuf-du-Pape

*The name of this small town, which lies
midway between Avignon and Orange, is
famous throughout the world. It was well
known in the 14th century when the Avignon
Popes built their new château here, but now its
fame comes from its wines.*

*The name Châteauneuf-du-Pape is usually
associated with a rich red wine but a rare and
exquisite white is also produced. Neither are
cheap but free samples are available if you
happen to visit the town during the first
weekend in August. Here, at the* Fête de la
Véraison, *the colouring of the grapes is
celebrated with a lively street fair.*

*The vines on which the Châteauneuf-du-Pape
grapes grow look as if they have been planted
in a sea of stones. They are, in fact, rooted in
earth which is then covered with large pebbles.
These absorb the heat of the midday sun and
release their warmth at night into the cooling
soil. To learn more about this and other grape-
growing and wine-making techniques, visit
the specialist Musée du Père Anselme.*

A

Ventoux. Here the road climbs to the summit at 1,912 m and, although the atmosphere tends to be hazy at noon on hot summer days, at other times the Alps and the Mediterranean can be clearly seen.

AVIGNON Gard 5D

(See feature)

Hôtel de l'Atelier ★★ 5 rue de la Foire, 30400 Villeneuve-lès-Avignon.
℡ 90 25 01 84, Fax 90 25 80 06. English spoken.
Open 15/12 to 15/11. 19 bedrooms
(all en suite). Golf 10 km, parking. &

A charming, 16th-century house in the centre of Villeneuve, just 3 km from Avignon on the opposite side of the River Rhône.

■ ACTIVITIES: Horse-riding nearby.
■ TARIFF: (1994) Double 220–400, Bk 30
(Amex, Euro/Access, Visa).

Hôtel Les Cèdres ★★ 39 bd Pasteur, 30400 Villeneuve-lès-Avignon.
℡ 90 25 43 92, Fax 90 25 14 66. English spoken.
Open 01/03 to 30/11. 24 bedrooms
(all en suite). Outdoor swimming pool, golf 10 km, parking.

Not far from the gates of the city of Avignon, an 18th-century building set in a flower-filled park and shaded by 100-year-old cedar trees.

■ RESTAURANT: Closed lunch. Offers a relaxed, family atmosphere with traditional and regional cuisine.
■ TARIFF: (1994) Double 295–380, Bk 38,
Set menu 98–145 (Euro/Access, Visa).

Hôtel La Ferme ★★ chemin des Bois, Ile de la Barthelasse, 84000 Avignon.
℡ 90 82 57 53, Fax 90 27 15 47.
Open 01/02 to 31/12. 20 bedrooms
(all en suite). Outdoor swimming pool, parking. &

La Ferme is on an island on the banks of the Rhône. Take the Pont-Daladier (towards Villeneuve), turn right on to D228 for 5 km.

■ RESTAURANT: Closed Sat lunch.
■ TARIFF: (1994) Single 320–350, Double 350–
430, Bk 46 (Amex, Euro/Access, Visa).

Hôtel Mas des Amandiers ★★ rte d'Avignon, 13690 Graveson.
℡ 90 95 81 76, Fax 90 95 85 18. English spoken.
Open 01/03 to 01/11. 25 bedrooms
(all en suite). Outdoor swimming pool, tennis, golf 1 km, garage, parking. &

12 km south of Avignon, set in the heart of the countryside, this hotel has the warmth of a

Provençal home. Quiet, with all modern comforts. South on the D570 towards Arles.

■ RESTAURANT: Closed Sun eve & Mon.
■ TARIFF: (1994) Single 260–280,
Double 280–310, Bk 35, Set menu 95–125
(Amex, Euro/Access, Visa).

Hôtel La Magnaneraie ★★★ 37 rue Camp de Bataille, 30400 Villeneuve-lès-Avignon.
℡ 90 25 11 11, Fax 90 25 46 37.
English spoken.
Open all year. 27 bedrooms (all en suite).
Outdoor swimming pool, tennis, golf 4 km, garage, parking, restaurant. &

A former cardinal's house, transformed into a luxury hotel, on a hill, in a large garden with pine trees, overlooking the historic village of Villeneuve-lès-Avignon. Opposite the Pope's Palace, across the River Rhône.

■ ACTIVITIES: Horse-riding nearby.
■ TARIFF: (1994) Double 220–400, Bk 30
(Amex, Euro/Access, Visa).

AVRANCHES Manche 1D

Hôtel Patton ★★ place Général Patton, 50300 Avranches.
℡ 33 48 52 52. English spoken.
Open 01/03 to 31/12. 26 bedrooms
(25 en suite). Parking.

Approaching from the north, proceed through the town following the Mont-St-Michel signs until you come to the square (place Général Patton).

■ TARIFF: (1994) Single 160–280,
Double 160–300, Bk 30 (Euro/Access, Visa).

AYEN Corrèze 4B

La Maison Anglaise ★ St-Robert, 19310 Ayen.
℡ 55 25 19 58, Fax 55 25 23 00. English spoken.
Open 10/12 to 08/11. 6 bedrooms (all en suite). Outdoor swimming pool, parking.

Court House, dating from the early 16th-century. Complete with stone walls, large fireplaces and lots of beams. To the west of Le-Buisson-de-Cadouin, on the south bank of the Dordogne.

Most attractive converted Bourgeoise residence, with panoramic views of the Dordogne. St-Robert is considered to be one of the most beautiful villages in France. North-west of Ayen, and a 30-minute drive from Brive to the south-east.

■ RESTAURANT: Closed Tues LS. Traditional restaurant with open fireplace and panoramic views. Local specialities include foie gras and magret de canard.

■ ACTIVITIES: Rides in horse-drawn carriage; music festival at nearby 12th-century church in July/August; excellent location for touring/sightseeing and cycling.

■ TARIFF: (1994) Double 200–350, Bk 45, Set menu 65–230 (Amex, Euro/Access, Visa).

■ DISCOUNT: 15% Not Jul & Aug.

AZAY-LE-RIDEAU Indre/Loire 2C

Le Grand Monarque ★★ 3 place de la République, 37190 Azay-le-Rideau.
✆ 47 45 40 08, Fax 47 45 46 25. English spoken. Open 01/02 to 15/12. 27 bedrooms (26 en suite, 1 bath/shower only). Golf 12 km, garage, parking.

Delightful old, very cosy hotel in the town centre, with luxurious rooms and grassy courtyard. Take the St-Avertin exit from the A10 (towards Chinon).

■ RESTAURANT: Closed 15/11 to 15/03.
■ TARIFF: (1994) Single 250–500, Double 275–650, Bk 50, Set menu 95–295 (Amex, Euro/Access, Visa).

BADEFOLS Dordogne 4B

Hôtel Lou Cantou ★★ 24150 Badefols-sur-Dordogne.
✆ 53 27 95 61, Fax 53 27 22 44. English spoken. Open 01/04 to 30/11. 12 bedrooms (10 en suite). Tennis, parking.

Charming hostellerie, formerly the castle's

■ RESTAURANT: Lots of character with fireplaces and antique furniture. Specialities: confit de poule, magret de canard, foie gras.

■ ACTIVITIES: Good base for exploring the beautiful countryside and many places of cultural/historical interest.

■ TARIFF: Double 170–340, Bk 35, Set menu 59–160 (Visa).

■ DISCOUNT: 10%

BAGNERES-DE-BIGORRE Htes-Pyr 4D

Le Chalet-Hôtel ★★ 65710 Ste-Marie-de-Campan.
✆ 62 91 85 64, Fax 62 91 86 17. English spoken. Open 20/12 to 24/04 & 05/05 to 30/10. 24 bedrooms. Indoor swimming pool, outdoor swimming pool, tennis, golf 10 km, parking.

Super location beside the Aspin and Tourmalet passes, at the foot of the Pic du Midi de Bigorre. Very comfortable with excellent facilities. (Flats and bungalows are also available.) Ste-Marie is 10 km south of Bagnères-de-Bigorre, in the Vallée de Campan.

■ RESTAURANT: Traditional cuisine in pleasant restaurant with lovely views.

■ ACTIVITIES: Cross-country, Nordic and downhill skiing nearby, also fishing, rafting and horse-riding.

■ TARIFF: (1994) Double 162–294, Bk 25 (Amex, Euro/Access, Visa).

BAGNERES-DE-LUCHON Hte-Garonne 4D

Hôtel Panoramic ★★ 6 av Carnot, 31110 Luchon.
✆ 61 79 30 90, Fax 61 79 32 84. English spoken.

...ar. 30 bedrooms (26 en suite). ...parking, restaurant.

B ...posite the church in the centre of this famous spa town. *Traditional and comfortable with super views. On the D125 near Spanish border.*

■ ACTIVITIES: All summer and winter sporting activities nearby; a host of cultural and sightseeing opportunities.
■ TARIFF: (1994) Single 160–310, Double 190–380, Bk 38, Set menu 78–180 (Visa).

BAGNOLES-DE-L'ORNE Orne　　2C

Hôtel Beaumont ★★ 26 bd Le Meunier de Raillère, 61140 Bagnoles-de-l'Orne.
℡ 33 37 91 77, Fax 33 38 90 61. English spoken.

Open 01/03 to 15/12. 38 bedrooms (37 en suite). Golf 1 km, parking.
Comfortable hotel with air-conditioning. Set behind the church in peaceful surroundings but only 5 minutes from the town centre. Verandah opening onto the garden; bar and tea room.
■ RESTAURANT: Closed Sun eve & Mon Mar & 1/11-15/12. Gourmet restaurant. Specialities: foie gras maison, blanquette de homard, aigrette de canard à l'orange.
■ ACTIVITIES: Swimming pool, tennis, horse-riding and mountain-biking nearby; walks in the forest and by the lake.
■ TARIFF: (1994) Single 190–280, Double 235–320, Bk 32, Set menu 85–200 (Amex, Euro/Access, Visa).
■ DISCOUNT: 10% LS.

Hôtel Le Cheval Blanc ★★ place de l'Eglise, 61140 La Chapelle-d'Andaine.
℡ 33 38 11 88.
Open all year. 12 bedrooms (7 en suite). Golf 5 km, parking. &
An attractive Logis de France hotel. La

Chapelle-d'Andaine lies 5 km south-west of Bagnoles on the Domfront to Alençon road (D176).
■ RESTAURANT: Closed Sun eve. Traditional cuisine with regional specialities.
■ TARIFF: (1994) Double 120–200, Bk 26, Set menu 55–198 (Amex, Euro/Access, Visa).

Hôtel Gayot ★★★ pl République, 61140 Bagnoles-de-l'Orne.
℡ 33 37 90 22. English spoken.
Open 01/04 to 31/10. 17 bedrooms (13 en suite). Golf 2 km, parking, restaurant. &
This elegant hotel is on the outskirts of Bagnols, left at the first roundabout and 50 m from the town centre.
■ TARIFF: (1994) Single 190–320, Double 220–320, Bk 35, Set menu 90–175 (Amex, Euro/Access, Visa).

Hôtel Lutetia-Reine Astrid ★★★ bd Paul Chalvet, 61140 Bagnoles-de-l'Orne.
℡ 33 37 94 77, Fax 33 30 09 87. English spoken.
Open 01/04 to 01/11. 33 bedrooms (30 en suite). Tennis, golf 2 km, parking, restaurant. &
Situated in the heart of the Andaine forest, the hotel has a large sun terrace and lovely, park-like garden full of flowers. The comfortable rooms have an individual, personal touch.
■ TARIFF: (1994) Single 190–430, Double 270–430, Bk 45, Set menu 120–340 (Amex, Euro/Access, Visa).

Nouvel Hôtel ★★ av A Christophle, Tessé-la-Madeleine, 61140 Bagnoles-de-l'Orne.
℡ 33 37 81 22, Fax 33 38 04 68. English spoken.
Open 04/04 to 22/10. 30 bedrooms (3 en suite, 27 bath/shower only). Golf 1 km, garage, parking.
Recently renovated with all modern facilities in town centre and 400 m from thermal springs.
■ RESTAURANT: Healthy menus using fresh produce: magret de canard au vinaigre de cidre, saumon fumé maison.
■ ACTIVITIES: Horse-riding, mountain bikes, walking, fishing, swimming pool and casino nearby.
■ TARIFF: (1994) Single 220–306, Double 220–306, Bk , Set menu 73–145 (Visa).

BAGNOLS-SUR-CEZE Gard　　5D

Château de Montcaud ★★★★ route d'Alès, 30200 Bagnols-sur-Cèze.
℡ 66 89 60 60, Fax 66 89 45 04. English spoken.

Open 01/04 to 31/12. 32 bedrooms
(all en suite). Outdoor swimming pool, tennis,
golf 22 km, garage, parking, restaurant. &

*Peace and tranquillity in this superb country
château. In lovely grounds and surrounded by
vineyards, an ideal base for exploring
Provence. From Bagnols go towards Alès then
right after 4 km towards Donnat and
Montcaud.*

■ TARIFF: (1994) Single 640–1950,
Double 770–2500, Bk 90, Set menu 130–400
(Amex, Euro/Access, Visa).

Hôtel Valaurie ★★★ rte de Pont-St-Esprit,
30200 Bagnols-sur-Cèze.
☎ 66 89 66 22, Fax 66 89 55 80.
Open 24/01 to 24/12. 22 bedrooms
(all en suite). Garage, parking.

*Modern country hotel with panoramic views,
5 km from Bagnols on road to Pont-St-Esprit.*

■ TARIFF: (1994) Single 260, Double 300, Bk 35
(Euro/Access, Visa).

BAILLEUL Nord   2B

Belle Hôtel ★★★ 19 rue de Lille,
59270 Bailleul.
☎ 28 49 19 00, Fax 28 49 22 11. English spoken.

Open all year. 31 bedrooms (all en suite).
Parking. &

*Situated ten minutes from Lille and twenty
minutes from Dunkerque, on the A25.*

■ RESTAURANT: Closed Sun eve. Fine cuisine
with varied specialities.

■ ACTIVITIES: Hotel will organise mountain-bike
hire and pony-trekking by prior arrangement.

■ TARIFF: (1994) Single 330, Double 360–380,
Bk 36, Set menu 70–130 (Amex,
Euro/Access, Visa).

Hôtel Pomme d'Or 27 rue d'Ypres,
59270 Bailleul.
☎ 28 49 11 01, Fax 28 49 22 11. English spoken.
Open all year. 7 bedrooms (4 en suite).

*Situated on A25, 10 minutes from Lille and 20
minutes from Dunkerque.*

■ RESTAURANT: Closed Sun eve. Good food with
lots of specialities.

■ ACTIVITIES: Mountain-biking, horse-riding,
walking and guided tours nearby.

■ TARIFF: (1994) Single 110–250,
Double 140–250, Bk 29, Set menu 69–190
(Amex, Euro/Access).

BANDOL Var   6C

Golf Hôtel ★★ Plage Renécros, 83150 Bandol.
☎ 94 29 45 83, Fax 94 32 42 47. English spoken.

Open 01/04 to 31/10. 24 bedrooms
(23 en suite). Golf 3 km, parking.

*Set on a private beach with lovely sea views, the
hotel is only 300 m from the town centre. Four
apartments also available.*

■ ACTIVITIES: Scuba-diving, water sports.

■ TARIFF: (1994) Single 320, Double 320–550,
Bk 35 (Euro/Access, Visa).

BAPAUME Pas-de-Calais   2B

Hôtel Paix ★★ av A Guidet, 62450 Bapaume.
☎ 21 07 11 03, Fax 21 07 43 66. English spoken.

B

Open all year. 13 bedrooms (all en suite).
Garage, parking.
Small, friendly hotel.

B

■ RESTAURANT: Recently opened restaurant
offering regional cuisine.
■ TARIFF: (1994) Double 220–320, Bk 25,
Set menu 68–250 (Euro/Access, Visa).
■ DISCOUNT: 5%

BAR-SUR-AUBE Aube   3C

Hôtel Moulin du Landion ★★★ Bar-sur-
Aube, 10200 Dolancourt.
☎ 25 27 92 17, Fax 25 27 94 44. English spoken.
Open 01/02 to 30/11. 16 bedrooms
(all en suite). Outdoor swimming pool,
golf 20 km, parking.
9 km from Paris, in a small and peaceful
village. Magnificent landscape surrounding
the hotel, mill and river.

■ RESTAURANT: Local dishes based on seasonally
available produce. Restaurant has view of the
turning mill wheel.
■ ACTIVITIES: Fun park in the village. Tennis,
horse-riding and water sports within easy
reach. Wine tasting; Brienne Military College
and Napoleonic museum 18 km, Charles de
Gaulle museum 42 km.
■ TARIFF: (1994) Single 300–320,
Double 330–360, Bk 42, Set menu 98–305
(Amex, Euro/Access, Visa).
■ DISCOUNT: 15% LS.

BARBENTANE Bches-du-Rhône   5D

Hôtel Castel Mouisson ★★ quartier Castel
Mouisson, 13570 Barbentane.
☎ 90 95 51 17, Fax 90 95 67 63. English spoken.
Open 15/03 to 15/10. 17 bedrooms
(all en suite). Outdoor swimming pool, tennis,
golf 10 km, parking. ♿
Provençal farmhouse in a pretty setting. Leave
the A7 motorway at Avignon-Sud, follow
directions towards Noves, Châteaurenard-
Rognonas, then Barbentane.

■ ACTIVITIES: Jet-skiing and hill walking nearby.
● Golf course in the village, hotel residents
offered reduced fees.
■ TARIFF: Single 260, Double 280–310, Bk 32
(No credit cards).

BARBOTAN-LES-THERMES Gers   4D

Hôtel Cante Grit ★★ 32150 Barbotan-les-
Thermes.
☎ 62 69 52 12, Fax 62 69 53 98.
Open 15/04 to 31/12 & 31/10 to 31/12.
22 bedrooms (2 en suite,

13 bath/shower only). Golf 15 km, parking.
Quiet location away from traffic and close
to spa.

■ RESTAURANT: Gourmet restaurant, traditional
and regional cuisine: foie gras, magret de
canard, salmis des palombes.
■ ACTIVITIES: Sailing, rowing and fishing on
lake. ● 10% reduction on hire of equipment.
■ TARIFF: (1994) Single 230–260,
Double 250–310, Bk , Set menu 85–110
(Amex, Visa).

Hôtel Paix ★★ 32150 Barbotan-les-Thermes.
☎ 62 69 52 06, Fax 62 09 55 73. English spoken.
Open 01/04 to 20/11. 32 bedrooms
(all en suite). Outdoor swimming pool,
golf 25 km, parking, restaurant.
Modern hotel with a covered terrace in a
pedestrianised area with a swimming pool.
From Condom, turn off D931 at Eauze
following D626 until Cazaubon, then take the
D656 towards Cabarret.

■ TARIFF: (1994) Double 250–350, Bk 30
(Euro/Access, Visa).

BARFLEUR Manche   1B

Hôtel Moderne 50760 Barfleur.
☎ 33 23 12 44, Fax 33 23 91 58.

Open 15/03 to 15/01. 8 bedrooms (4 en suite). Parking.

Hotel is situated just 50 m from the harbour in this small, pretty town.

■ RESTAURANT: Closed 15/01 to 15/03. Hotel has an every-day dining room plus a larger one for banquets. The emphasis is on traditional French cooking with some wonderful seafood specialities.

■ ACTIVITIES: Fishing, tennis and sailing nearby. Visit to Gatteville lighthouse (2 km), an important navigational aid.

■ TARIFF: (1994) Double 114–215, Bk 24, Set menu 75–235 (Euro/Access, Visa).

BARNEVILLE-CARTERET Manche   1B

Hôtel La Marine ★★★ 11 rue de Paris, Carteret, 50270 Barneville-Carteret.
☎ 33 53 83 31, Fax 33 53 39 60. English spoken.
Open 01/02 to 31/10. 31 bedrooms (all en suite). Golf 2 km, parking.

A pretty, comfortable hotel, in the village centre and right beside the sea. Carteret is a beautiful little fishing port with fine sand beaches and dunes and nearby a direct ferry connection with Jersey. Just west of Barneville-Carteret.

■ RESTAURANT: Closed Sun eve & Mon & Feb, Mar & Oct. Restaurant has a cosy atmosphere and terrace with bay windows overlooking the sea. Seafood specialities.

■ ACTIVITIES: Tennis, water sports, horse-riding nearby.

■ TARIFF: (1994) Single 290, Double 380–520, Bk 48, Set menu 135–380 (No credit cards).

BAUGE Maine/Loire   2C

Château de la Grifferaie 49150 Echemiré.
☎ 41 89 70 25. English spoken.
Open all year. 18 bedrooms (all en suite). Tennis, golf 4 km, parking.

One-time Napoleonic residence, a château set in beautiful, landscaped parkland and well placed for Loire visits. From Angers take N23, then D766 to Baugé.

■ RESTAURANT: Fine food served in elegant dining room which overlooks the gardens.

■ TARIFF: (1994) Double 450–900, Bk 45, Set menu 165–225 (Euro/Access, Visa).

LA BAULE Loire-Atlan   1D

Hôtel Bellevue Plage ★★★ 27 bd Océan, 44500 La Baule.
☎ 40 60 28 55, Fax 40 60 10 18. English spoken.
Open 15/02 to 15/11. 34 bedrooms (all en suite). Golf 5 km, parking.

Ideally situated facing the sea, in the centre of La Baule bay. The hotel offers a warm welcome and good facilities including private car park.

■ RESTAURANT: Closed Tues LS. Very good food with a separate terrace and bar.

■ ACTIVITIES: Fitness room with sunbed; water sports and horse-riding nearby.

■ TARIFF: (1994) Single 390–480, Double 490–790, Bk 50, Set menu 165–200 (Amex, Euro/Access, Visa).

Hôtel Le Clemenceau ★★ 42 avenue Georges Clemenceau, 44500 La Baule.
☎ 40 60 21 33, Fax 40 42 72 46. English spoken.
Open all year. 16 bedrooms (all en suite). Golf 6 km, restaurant.

Traditional hotel, near the railway station and a few minutes' walk from the beach. 70 km from Nantes.

■ TARIFF: (1994) Single 250–350, Double 250–370, Bk 25, Set menu 69–143 (Euro/Access, Visa).

Hôtel La Concorde ★★★ 1 av de la Concorde, 44500 La Baule.
☎ 40 60 23 09, Fax 40 42 72 14. English spoken.
Open 01/04 to 31/10. 47 bedrooms (all en suite). Garage, parking.

A pleasant, family-run hotel, facing the sea and the beach.

■ TARIFF: (1994) Double 400–530, Bk 42 (Amex, Euro/Access, Visa).

Hôtel Hermitage ★★★★★ 5 esplanade Lucien Barrière, 44504 La Baule.
☎ 40 11 46 46, Fax 40 11 46 45. English spoken.

Open 01/04 to 31/10. 217 bedrooms (all en suite). Outdoor swimming pool, tennis, golf 7 km, garage, parking. ♿

First-class hotel set on a 10 km stretch of sandy beach. Built in 1926 in French château style with direct access to the sea.

■ RESTAURANT: 3 restaurants: 'Eden Beach'

B

brasserie, the gastronomic 'Les Evens' and 'Les Ambassadeurs' which is open in July and August.

■ ACTIVITIES: ● One free sporting activity per day. For example, a green fee for the golf course, one hour of tennis, horse-riding or windsurfing (in season).

■ TARIFF: (1994) Single 860–2240, Double 950–2540 (Amex, Euro/Access, Visa).

Les Chalands Fleuris ★★★★ rue du Stade, 44117 St-André-des-Eaux.
℡ 40 01 21 40, Fax 40 61 84 10. English spoken.
Open all year. 14 bedrooms (all en suite). Indoor swimming pool, tennis, golf 3 km, parking. ⅙

Accommodation is in simple but comfortable self-contained chalets, set in La Brière natural park. 7 km from La Baule.

■ RESTAURANT: Restaurant serves breakfast and simple meals.

■ ACTIVITIES: Good sports facilities including sailing, fishing and mountain bikes. All the amenities of La Baule within easy reach.

■ TARIFF: (1994) Single 250–280, Double 350–380, Bk 25, Set menu 60–90 (Visa).

■ DISCOUNT: 5%

Castel Marie-Louise ★★★★ 1 av Andrieu, BP 409, 44504 La Baule.
℡ 40 11 48 38, Fax 40 11 48 35. English spoken.

Open 11/02 to 02/01. 31 bedrooms (all en suite). Tennis, golf 6 km, parking. ⅙

A charming Belle-Epoque manor set in attractive shaded grounds overlooking the bay. Following the esplanade, the hotel is just after the Grand Casino.

■ RESTAURANT: Restaurant will satisfy the most demanding palates with its gastronomic and traditional haute-cuisine.

■ ACTIVITIES: Good sports, cultural and leisure activities arranged by hotel.

■ TARIFF: Single 700–1540, Double 850–2200, Bk 80 (Amex, Euro/Access, Visa).

Hôtel Welcome ★★ 7 av des Impairs, 44504 La Baule.
℡ 40 60 30 25. English spoken.
Open 01/04 to 15/10. 18 bedrooms (all en suite). Golf 5 km.

Well-appointed hotel with pleasant atmosphere. Situated between the casino and shopping centre, and 30 m from the sea.

■ TARIFF: (1994) Single 340–390, Double 340–395, Bk 35 (Euro/Access, Visa).

■ DISCOUNT: 20% LS.

BAUMES-LES-DAMES Doubs ⁣ 3D

Auberge des Moulins ★★ rte Pontarlier, Pont-les-Moulins, 25110 Baumes-les-Dames.
℡ 81 84 09 99, Fax 81 84 04 44. English spoken.
Open all year. 12 bedrooms (all en suite). Golf 15 km, parking, restaurant.

5 km from Baume-les-Dames and 30 minutes from Besançon, Pontarlier and Montbéliard. Three golf courses within reach.

■ TARIFF: (1994) Single 210, Double 260–300, Bk 28, Set menu 85–135 (Amex, Euro/Access, Visa).

BAYEUX Calvados ⁣ 1B

Hôtel d'Argouges ★★ 21 rue St-Patrice, 14400 Bayeux.
℡ 31 92 88 86, Fax 31 92 69 16. English spoken.

Open all year. 25 bedrooms (all en suite). Golf 10 km, garage, parking.

In the heart of the historic and artistic city of Bayeux, with its world famous 11th-century tapestry, museums and cathedral. Rooms overlook courtyard with park and garden.

■ TARIFF: (1994) Double 190–390, Bk 38 (Amex, Euro/Access, Visa).

■ DISCOUNT: 20% 01/11 to 31/03.

Château du Baffy ★★ Colombiers-sur-Seulles,
14480 Creully.
☎ 31 08 04 57, Fax 31 08 08 29. English spoken.
Open all year. 35 bedrooms (all en suite).
Tennis, golf 20 km, parking. &
*The château and its villa Mathilda are set in
wooded parkland which the restaurant
overlooks. Between Creully and Douvres on
D176, the château is near the village centre.*
■ RESTAURANT: Closed Sun eve & Mon LS.
■ ACTIVITIES: Riding, fitness centre; bicycle hire
and sailing nearby.
■ TARIFF: (1994) Single 315–380,
Double 360–560, Set menu 95–198 (Amex,
Euro/Access, Visa).
■ DISCOUNT: 10% LS.

Hôtel La Chenevière ★★★★
14520 Port-en-Bessin.
☎ 31 21 47 96, Fax 31 21 47 98. English spoken.

Open 10/02 to 03/01. 18 bedrooms
(all en suite). Golf 1 km, garage, parking. &
*An elegant, 19th-century château set in five
acres of mature parkland just outside the
medieval town of Bayeux. From Bayeux take
D6 north for 8 km. Hotel is 1 km before
reaching Port-en-Bessin.*
■ RESTAURANT: Gourmet restaurant. Specialities
include fricassé de langoustines aux pommes
de terre, poulet fermier de Normandie, and
feuillantine de pommes aux caramel de cidre.
■ ACTIVITIES: Horse-riding; visits to D-Day
landing beaches and museums by jeep; visits to
Mont-St-Michel, Deauville and casino. ● 20%
reduction on green fees.
■ TARIFF: Double 700–1100, Bk 80,
Set menu 125–380 (Amex, Euro/Access, Visa).

Hôtel Churchill ★★★ 14 rue St-Jean,
14404 Bayeux.
☎ 31 21 31 80, Fax 31 21 41 66. English spoken.
Open 01/03 to 15/11. 32 bedrooms
(all en suite). Golf 7 km, parking, restaurant. &

*This highly recommended hotel is situated in
the centre of Bayeux, near the tapestry
museum and cathedral but in a quiet street.*
■ TARIFF: (1994) Single 260–350,
Double 280–490, Bk 40 (Amex,
Euro/Access, Visa).

Hôtel Lion d'Or ★★★ 71 rue St-Jean,
14400 Bayeux.
☎ 31 92 06 90, Fax 31 22 15 64. English spoken.

Open 20/01 to 20/12. 27 bedrooms
(all en suite). Golf 9 km, garage, parking.
*A former 17th-century coaching inn, full of
character. Heading for the town centre, turn
into rue de Crèmel by the railway station. Keep
on this road towards the town centre and hotel
is on the right.*
■ RESTAURANT: Very attractive dining room with
beamed ceiling. Specialities include l'andouille
chaude à la Bovary, fleurs de courgettes,
fricassé sole beurre de cidre.
■ ACTIVITIES: Good sports facilities nearby; ideal
base for sightseeing, including the famous
tapestery and cathedral, D-Day landing
beaches and the Juaye Mondaye abbey.
■ TARIFF: Single 300–450, Double 350–470,
Bk 55 (Amex, Euro/Access, Visa).
■ DISCOUNT: 8% LS.

B

Manoir du Carel 14400 Bayeux.
☎ 31 22 37 00, Fax 31 21 57 00.
English spoken.
Open all year. 4 bedrooms (all en suite).
Tennis, golf 2 km, garage, parking.
*Ideal base for D-Day beaches and Bayeux
tapestry. Elegantly furnished manor house
with good restaurants nearby. From Bayeux
take the D6 towards Port-en-Bessin. 4.5 km
after traffic lights turn left. Entry marked
after 1 km.*

■ ACTIVITIES: Horse-riding.
■ TARIFF: (1994) Single 350, Double 500–600,
Bk 45 (Euro/Access, Visa).
■ DISCOUNT: 10% LS.

Hôtel La Ranconnière ★★ route
d'Arromanches, 14480 Crépon.
☎ 31 22 21 73, Fax 31 22 98 39.
English spoken.
Open all year. 33 bedrooms (all en suite).
Golf 20 km, parking. &
*Converted 14th-century manor house with
period furniture. From Bayeux take D12
direction Ouistreham, then from Sommervieu
D112 to Crépon 7 km.*

■ RESTAURANT: A good choice of seasonal
menus.
■ TARIFF: (1994) Double 180–380, Bk 40,
Set menu 60–240 (Amex, Euro/Access, Visa).

Hôtel Victoria ★★ 24 chemin de l'Eglise,
14117 Tracy-sur-Mer.
☎ 31 22 35 37, Fax 31 21 41 66. English spoken.

Open 01/04 to 30/09. 13 bedrooms
(all en suite). Golf 7 km, parking. &
*Renovated 19th-century manor house, with
lovely gardens and set in parkland, 2 km from
Arromanches, towards Bayeux.*

■ TARIFF: (1994) Single 260–350,
Double 280–490, Bk 40 (Euro/Access, Visa).
■ DISCOUNT: 8%

BAYONNE Pyrénées-Atlan 4C

Le Grand Hôtel ★★★★ 21 rue Thiers,
64100 Bayonne.
☎ 59 59 14 61, Fax 59 25 61 70. English spoken.
Open all year. 56 bedrooms (all en suite).
Golf 5 km, garage.
*In the city centre, in the heart of the business
and shopping area, recently renovated, with
large quiet rooms.*

■ RESTAURANT: 'Les Carmes' has a solid
reputation for refined cuisine; traditional
setting.
■ ACTIVITIES: 5 km from Atlantic Ocean beaches,
surfing, fishing, 7 golf courses within 20 km,
mountain climbing.
■ TARIFF: (1994) Single 390–580,
Double 440–780, Bk 45, Set menu 120–200
(Amex, Euro/Access, Visa, **BT**🖊).
■ DISCOUNT: 10%

BEAUGENCY Loiret 2D

Hôtel L'Abbaye ★★★ 2 quai de l'Abbaye,
45190 Beaugency.
☎ 38 44 67 35, Fax 38 44 87 92. English spoken.
Open all year. 18 bedrooms (all en suite).
Golf 6 km, parking, restaurant.
*17th-century abbey in the town of Beaugency
on the River Loire.*

■ ACTIVITIES: Tennis and swimming pool
close by.
■ TARIFF: (1994) Single 420–480,
Double 500–560, Bk 42, Set menu 185 (Amex,
Euro/Access, Visa).

Hôtel La Tonnellerie ★★★★ 12 rue des Eaux-
Bleues, Tavers, 45190 Beaugency.
☎ 38 44 68 15, Fax 38 44 10 01. English spoken.

Open 15/04 to 15/10. 20 bedrooms
(all en suite). Outdoor swimming pool,
golf 9 km, parking.
In the Châteaux de la Loire region. Discreet

charm of an old manor in a quiet location. 3 km east of Beaugency (towards Blois).

■ RESTAURANT: One 'winter garden' dining room, another with antique furniture. Meals also served on the terrace in fine weather. Nouvelle and classic cuisine based on fresh, local produce.

■ ACTIVITIES: Lovely walks; tennis 5 minutes' walk; convenient for touring major Loire châteaux.

■ TARIFF: Single 495–880, Double 705–880, Bk 55, Set menu 125–310 (Amex, Euro/Access, Visa).

■ DISCOUNT: 10%

BEAUJEU Rhône   5B

Hôtel Anne de Beaujeu ★★ 28 rue de la République, 69430 Beaujeu.
☎ 74 04 87 58, Fax 74 69 22 13. English spoken.
Open 20/01 to 20/12. 7 bedrooms (all en suite). Parking.

Old house in old village with beautiful country around. 13 km from the Paris-Lyon motorway. Exit Belleville-sur-Saône, then west on the D37 to Beaujeu.

■ RESTAURANT: Closed Sun eve & Mon.

■ TARIFF: (1994) Double 250–350, Bk 35, Set menu 110–310 (Euro/Access, Visa).

Hôtel Mont-Brouilly ★★ 69430 Quincie-en-Beaujolais.
☎ 74 04 33 73, Fax 74 69 00 72. English spoken.
Open 01/03 to 01/02. 29 bedrooms (all en suite). Outdoor swimming pool, garage, parking, restaurant. ⓖ

In the heart of the Beaujolais region. West of Belleville and A6 on the D37, towards Beaujeu. Hotel is 1 km from the village of Cercié.

■ ACTIVITIES: Cycling, boules, good walks, wine tasting.

■ TARIFF: (1994) Single 220–300, Double 270–320, Bk 34, Set menu 90–250 (Amex, Euro/Access, Visa).

BEAULIEU-SUR-MER Alpes-Mar   6C

Hôtel Comte de Nice ★★★ bd Marinoni, 06310 Beaulieu-sur-Mer.
☎ 93 01 19 70, Fax 93 01 23 09.
English spoken.
Open all year. 33 bedrooms (all en suite). Garage, parking.

Refined and friendly hotel in the town centre but away from the traffic. 400 m from the tourist harbour and beaches and 200 m from the station. All rooms have modern facilities.

■ ACTIVITIES: Work-out room, sauna, boat rides, swimming and underwater sports. Museum, picturesque walks by the sea.

■ TARIFF: (1994) Single 235–450, Double 395–580, Bk 45 (Amex, Euro/Access, Visa).

■ DISCOUNT: 10%

Hôtel Frisia ★★★ bd Mar Leclerc, 06310 Beaulieu-sur-Mer.
☎ 93 01 01 04, Fax 93 01 31 92.
English spoken.
Open all year. 32 bedrooms (all en suite). Golf 10 km.

Beside the marina and with splendid views of the sea, the hotel has recently been completely renovated and had air-conditioning installed. Pretty garden overlooking the hills. From Nice follow the coast road to Beaulieu towards Monaco.

■ ACTIVITIES: All water sports including diving.

■ TARIFF: (1994) Single 350–480, Double 400–650, Bk 40 (Amex, Euro/Access, Visa).

■ DISCOUNT: 8%

Hôtel Metropole ★★★★ bd Mar Leclerc, 06310 Beaulieu-sur-Mer.
☎ 93 01 00 08, Fax 93 01 18 51.
English spoken.
Open 20/12 to 20/10. 50 bedrooms (all en suite). Outdoor swimming pool, golf 15 km, parking, restaurant.

Palatial hotel with excellent facilities and spectacular views over the bay. Beaulieu-sur-Mer is between Nice and Monaco. Prices quoted are for half-board.

■ TARIFF: (1994) Single 1105–2120, Double 1830–3850, Set menu 400–490 (Amex, Euro/Access, Visa).

Hôtel La Réserve ★★★★ bd Mar Leclerc, 06310 Beaulieu-sur-Mer.
☎ 93 01 00 01, Fax 93 01 28 99.
Open 01/04 to 01/11. 36 bedrooms (all en suite). Outdoor swimming pool, tennis, golf 20 km, garage.

A well-known hotel facing the sea in this picturesque town.

■ RESTAURANT: Gourmet restaurant, specialities: supions de la méditerranée, loup 'réserve', crêpes épicées à l'anis.

■ ACTIVITIES: Water sports can be arranged.

● Access from the sea to private harbour.

■ TARIFF: Single 1500–2000, Double 2000–3800, Bk 120 (Amex, Euro/Access, Visa).

B

BEAUMONT-SUR-SARTHE Sarthe   2C

Hôtel Le Chemin de Fer ★★
72170 Beaumont-sur-Sarthe.

B ✆ 43 97 00 05, Fax 43 33 52 17. English spoken.

Open 07/03 to 22/10 & 07/11 to 12/02.
15 bedrooms (12 en suite,
2 bath/shower only). Garage, parking.

Traditionally furnished hotel with attractive, shady garden. In front of a small railway station and close to the traffic lights on the main road of the town. Follow N138 north from Le Mans for 44 km.

■ RESTAURANT: Closed Sun eve Nov to Easter. Traditional dining room specialising in gourmet and classic cuisine, using fresh produce. Special menu for children.

■ ACTIVITIES: Good sports and recreational facilities nearby, including canoeing on the River Sarthe.

■ TARIFF: Double 157–357, Bk 27,
Set menu 78–225 (Euro/Access, Visa).

BEAUNE Côte-d'Or   3C

Hôtel Belle Epoque ★★★ 15 Fg Bretonnière, 21200 Beaune.
✆ 80 24 66 15, Fax 80 24 17 49. English spoken.
Open 01/03 to 31/01. 16 bedrooms
(all en suite). Golf 5 km, garage.

A medieval yet modernised local-style house close to the famous Hospices de Beaune. On the N74 from the town centre towards Autun.

■ TARIFF: (1994) Double 350–680, Bk 43
(Amex, Visa).

Hôtel Le Cep ★★★★ 27 rue Maufoux,
21200 Beaune.
✆ 80 22 35 48, Fax 80 22 76 80.
English spoken.
Open all year. 52 bedrooms (all en suite).
Golf 4 km, garage, parking, restaurant. ఉ

A 16th-century private residence in the centre

of Beaune. Stunning décor in traditional French style.

■ TARIFF: (1994) Single 500–700,
Double 600–1200, Bk 65 (Amex,
Euro/Access, Visa).

Hôtel Le Chalet d'Ivry ★★ 21340 Ivry-en-Montagne.
✆ 80 20 21 18, Fax 80 20 24 70. English spoken.
Open all year. 10 bedrooms (all en suite).
Tennis, parking.

Family atmosphere. On the N6 north of Nolay and west of Beaune.

■ RESTAURANT: Good regional food.
■ TARIFF: (1994) Double 165–190, Bk 28,
Set menu 65–145 (No credit cards).

Hôtel du Château de Challenges ★★★ rue des Templiers, 21200 Beaune.
✆ 80 26 32 62, Fax 80 26 32 52. English spoken.

Open 01/05 to 30/11. 14 bedrooms
(all en suite). Indoor swimming pool,
golf 2 km, garage, parking.

Situated in a large park, close to the historic town of Beaune. From Beaune exit off A6 follow signs towards Dole-Seurre then turn right into rte de Challenges.

■ ACTIVITIES: Jogging, mountain-biking, recreation in the grounds. Arrangements made for: golf, tennis, horse-riding, balloon flights and wine tasting tours.
■ TARIFF: Single 390–590, Double 430–650,
Bk 50 (No credit cards).

Hôtel Climat de France ★★ av Charles de Gaulle, Parc Hôtelier, 21200 Beaune.
✆ 80 22 74 10, Fax 80 22 40 45. English spoken.
Open all year. 50 bedrooms (all en suite).
Golf 2 km, parking. ఉ

A modern hotel with good facilities including several family rooms. Friendly, efficient service. Wine bar. 500 m from A6 exit towards Beaune, and 500 m from town centre.

■ RESTAURANT: Modern restaurant offering an hors d'oeuvre buffet, regional specialities and a special menu for children. Extensive list of Burgundy wines at reasonable prices.
■ ACTIVITIES: Hotel will arrange tours of Beaune, the Hospices de Beaune and vineyards on request. English speaking guides available. Cycle hire, sauna and playground at hotel.
■ TARIFF: Single 285–295, Double 285–315, Bk 35, Set menu 60–120 (Amex, Euro/Access, Visa).
■ DISCOUNT: 10% Advance bookings only.

Hôtel Les Paulands ★★★ Ladoix-Serrigny, 21550 Beaune.
☎ 80 26 41 05, Fax 80 26 47 56. English spoken. Open all year. 20 bedrooms (all en suite). Outdoor swimming pool, golf 6 km, parking. &

B

Burgundian house standing in its own vineyards. From A6, Nuits-St-George exit, take the N74 towards Aloxe-Corton/Ladoix-Serrigny. SEE ADVERTISEMENT.
■ TARIFF: (1994) Double 240–380, Bk 42 (Euro/Access, Visa).

Hôtel de la Cloche ★★★ 42 Fg Madeleine, 21200 Beaune.
☎ 80 24 66 33, Fax 80 24 04 24. English spoken.
Open all year. 22 bedrooms (all en suite). Golf 3 km, parking.

Situated near the centre of this historic town, hotel has a garden terrace and free parking facilities.
■ RESTAURANT: Regional specialities.
■ ACTIVITIES: Cycling, tennis and wine tasting nearby.
■ TARIFF: (1994) Single 250–360, Double 250–380, Bk 35 (Euro/Access, Visa).
■ DISCOUNT: 5%

B

Hôtel Le Home ★★ 138 rte Dijon,
21200 Beaune.
☎ 80 22 16 43, Fax 80 24 90 74. English spoken.

Open all year. 23 bedrooms (all en suite).
Golf 3 km, garage, parking. ♿
Charming hotel, originally a farmhouse, very quiet with attractive English-style flower garden. On the Dijon side of the town centre. Follow signs for route des Grands Cros.
■ TARIFF: (1994) Single 315–450, Double 315–450, Bk 32 (Amex, Euro/Access, Visa).
■ DISCOUNT: 10%

BEAUVAIS

Much of Beauvais – including the factory in which the famous Gobelin tapestries had been made since the 17th century – was destroyed during World War II but, miraculously, the Cathédrale de St-Pierre survived. It is the highest church in France, a truly magnificent Gothic building despite the fact that it has never been completed. If you are there at noon you will be able to see the famous astronomical clock chiming the hour, with its remarkable display of figures depicting the Last Judgement.

Almost next door is the Galerie Nationale de Tapisserie. Beauvais is an appropriate site for such a museum, being the original home of the state-subsidised factory which was established in 1664. The court painter, François Boucher, designed pastoral, Italian and Chinese scenes for the workshops here, which specialised in furniture and screen tapestries, and were well known throughout Europe.

BEAUVAIS Oise   2B
(See feature)
Hôtel Palais ★★ 9 rue St-Nicholas,
60000 Beauvais.
☎ 44 45 12 58, Fax 44 45 66 23. English spoken.
Open all year. 15 bedrooms (10 en suite,
5 bath/shower only). ♿
The hotel is just two minutes' walk from the cathedral in Beauvais.
■ TARIFF: (1994) Single 105–235,
Double 115–250, Bk 24 (Amex,
Euro/Access, Visa).
■ DISCOUNT: 5%

BELLEGARDE-SUR-VALSERINE Ain   6A
Hôtel Europa ★★ 19 rue J Bertola,
01200 Bellegarde-sur-Valserine.
☎ 50 56 04 74, Fax 50 48 19 11. English spoken.
Open all year. 22 bedrooms (all en suite).
Garage, parking.
Recently renovated, the Europa has fully equipped accommodation with the benefit of a lift and private garage. Between St-Julien-en-Genevois and Nantua on the N206, close to the TGV station.
■ TARIFF: (1994) Single 240, Double 250, Bk 30
(Amex, Euro/Access, Visa).

BELLEVILLE-SUR-SAONE Rhône   5B
Hôtel Ange Couronne ★★ 18 rue
République, 69220 Belleville.
☎ 74 66 42 00, Fax 74 66 49 20. English spoken.
Open 01/02 to 31/12. 16 bedrooms
(14 en suite, 2 bath/shower only). Garage,
parking.
Quiet comfortable hotel 500 m from the A6 motorway (Belleville/Saône exit).
■ RESTAURANT: Closed Sun eve & Mon.
Traditional gourmet cuisine.
■ ACTIVITIES: Swimming, walking and fishing
nearby.
■ TARIFF: (1994) Single 180–200, Double 220–
300, Bk 28, Set menu 85–170 (Visa).

BENODET Finistère   1C
Hôtel A l'Ancre de Marine ★★ 5 av de l'Odet,
29950 Bénodet.
☎ 98 57 05 29.
Open all year. 12 bedrooms (10 en suite).
Golf 4 km.
Small hotel on the port with views over the estuary. West of Fouesnant and south of Quimper on D34.

■ TARIFF: (1994) Single 200–310, Double 280–320, Bk 38 (Amex, Euro/Access, Visa).

Hôtel Armoric ★★ 3 rue Penfoul, 29950 Bénodet.
☎ 98 57 04 03, Fax 98 57 21 28.
English spoken.

■ ACTIVITIES: Horse-riding, parachuting and cycling.
■ TARIFF: (1994) Single 280–350, Double 320–460, Bk 48, Set menu 98–210 (Amex, Euro/Access, Visa).

Open 01/03 to 15/11. 30 bedrooms (all en suite). Tennis, golf 3 km, garage, parking.

A charming family hotel close to beaches and marina. Bar, terrace, tranquil, very pretty flower-filled garden. From Quimper go to Fouesnant and then Bénodet.

■ RESTAURANT: Hotel offers half board only to guests 01/07 to 31/08. 3 course menu 125F, children 65F.
■ ACTIVITIES: A variety of sports nearby including water sports, fishing and horse-riding. Museums and other places of cultural interest within easy reach.
■ TARIFF: (1994) Single 200–450, Double 250–750, Bk 40, Set menu 125 (Amex, Euro/Access, Visa).
■ DISCOUNT: 20% Except 02/07 to 15/09.

BERGERAC Dordogne   4B

Hôtel Bordeaux ★★★ 38 pl Gambetta, 24100 Bergerac.
☎ 53 57 12 83, Fax 53 57 72 14.
English spoken.
Open 01/02 to 20/12. 40 bedrooms (all en suite). Outdoor swimming pool, garage, parking. &

The Maury family has been welcoming guests to the hotel since 1855. All modern facilities are offered including colour TV and lifts. Garden around the pool.

■ RESTAURANT: Beautifully presented meals in a comfortable and friendly restaurant; meals also served on the shady terrace next to the pool.

Auberge de la Devinière ★★★ rte de Mussidan, 24130 Bergerac.
☎ 53 81 66 43, Fax 53 81 54 44. English spoken.

Open all year. 8 bedrooms (all en suite). Outdoor swimming pool, golf 15 km, parking.

Lovely old Périgord inn with individually decorated rooms, amid meadows, forest and little lake. Mushroom-picking in hotel grounds! North of Bergerac D709, D15.

■ RESTAURANT: Well regarded for its excellent regional cuisine. Specialities include: escalope de foie gras aux pommes; escalope de canette foie gras; mille feuille aux fraises de Périgord.
■ TARIFF: (1994) Single 360–750, Double 360–750, Bk 60, Set menu 99–170 (Euro/Access, Visa, **BT**).
■ DISCOUNT: 10% Except Jul & Aug.

Hôtel Le Relais du Petit Prince ★★★
Domaine de Lespinassat, rte d'Agen, 24100 Bergerac.
☎ 53 24 89 76, Fax 53 57 72 24. English spoken.

Open all year. 50 bedrooms (all en suite). Outdoor swimming pool, golf 15 km, parking. &

B *New hotel in quiet country surroundings 1 km from Bergerac's centre. Take N21 south towards Agen.*

■ RESTAURANT: Closed Mon lunch.
■ TARIFF: (1994) Single 320, Double 320–480, Bk 42, Set menu 70–140 (Amex, Euro/Access, Visa).

BERGUES Nord   2B

Hôtel Commerce ★★ rue du Mont de Piété, 59380 Bergues.
℡ 28 68 60 37, Fax 28 68 70 76.

Open all year. 15 bedrooms (9 en suite, 1 bath/shower only). Golf 4 km, garage, parking.
An attractive hotel next to the church and museum. Large banqueting hall and ample parking.

■ TARIFF: (1994) Single 110–200, Double 130–300, Bk 25 (Euro/Access, Visa).

Hôtel au Tonnelier ★★ 4 rue du Mont de Piété, 59380 Bergues.
℡ 28 68 70 05, Fax 28 68 21 87.
English spoken.
Open 01/01 to 18/08 & 06/09 to 31/12.
11 bedrooms (7 en suite). Golf 6 km, garage, parking.
A family-run hotel (Declercq) 9 km from Dunkerque. Close to the noted museums and monuments of Bergues. Exit Bergues from the Dunkerque/Lille motorway.

■ RESTAURANT: Closed Fri.
■ TARIFF: (1994) Single 150–250, Double 180–330, Bk 29, Set menu 80–200 (Euro/Access, Visa).

BESANÇON

Besançon lies within a loop of the River Doubs on the north-western edge of the Jura mountains in eastern France. A strategic site since Gallo-Roman times, the 120-m rock at the neck of the loop made the town easy to defend against attackers. Climb to the citadel on top of this rock for a fine view across the old town.

Your entrance fee to the citadel also covers entrance to the zoo and three museums that are built within its walls. The displays in these museums cover different subjects, so you will probably find one of more interest to you than the others. First, there is the Musée d'Histoire Naturelle, a natural history museum with a difference. It combines the live animals in the zoo outside with inside displays, an aquarium and an insectary. Then there is the Musée Populaire Comtois with 24 exhibition rooms concentrating on local folklore and culture, as well as displaying a fine collection of old agricultural implements. And, finally, there is the Musée de la Résistance et de la Déportation which deals with World War II issues, especially the part played by the French Resistance movement and the terrible plight of the many people who were deported.

Next to the Cathédrale St-Jean, just below the citadel, there is an 18th-century belfry which is the home of Besançon's famous astronomical clock. This has about 30,000 moving parts and was made in 1860. Even earlier, the town was well known for its watchmakers, as was Switzerland on the other side of the Jura mountains. This skill is commemorated at the Musée des Beaux-Arts et d'Archéologique, where a section of the display is devoted to an exhibition of clocks and watches. An important collection, it is eventually going to be rehoused in the Musée du Palais Granvelle, a 16th-century mansion, used at the moment as a local history museum.

Also next to the cathedral is the Porte Noire, a triumphal arch built by the Romans in the 2nd century, and down by the river stands another arch that is fourteen hundred years younger. This is the 16th-century Porte Rivotte, an impressive structure with two pepper-pot towers.

Having viewed Besançon from above and explored the town on foot, a trip on the river provides yet another aspect. There are several boat trips to choose from: a circular tour via a tunnel under the citadel; a meal on board, some with entertainments and a longer, 2 hour trip to the 27-metre-high Saut du Doubs waterfall.

BESANCON Doubs 3D

(See feature)

Hôtel 3 Iles ★★ Chalezeule, 25220 Besançon.
✆ 81 61 00 66, Fax 81 61 73 09. English spoken.
Open all year. 16 bedrooms (all en suite). Parking.
Pleasant hotel, 5 minutes from Besançon centre, in Chalezeule, on the banks of the River Doubs. From Besançon take N83 north-east towards Belfort then right for Carrefour supermarket, SNCF and Chalezeule.
■ TARIFF: (1994) Single 240–250, Double 260–280, Bk 28 (Euro/Access, Visa).

Hôtel Climat de France ★★ CD 108 Ecole Valentin, Miserey Salines, 25000 Besançon.
✆ 81 88 04 11, Fax 81 80 31 22. English spoken.
Open all year. 43 bedrooms (all en suite). Golf 1 km, parking, restaurant. ዉ
Leave Besançon centre via rue de Versoul, after about 5 km take right turn towards Gray. Hotel is about 500 m on the left.
■ TARIFF: (1994) Double 270, Bk 32 (Euro/Access, Visa).

Hôtel de Paris ★★ 33 rue des Granges, 25000 Besançon.
✆ 81 81 36 56, Fax 81 61 94 90. English spoken.
Open all year. 59 bedrooms (42 en suite, 17 bath/shower only). Outdoor swimming pool, golf 10 km, parking. ዉ
All rooms look on to a private courtyard and garden. The hotel is in the town centre with free private parking. Follow signs for the Hotel Centre Ville.
■ TARIFF: (1994) Single 175–320, Double 190–415, Bk 36 (Amex, Euro/Access, Visa).
■ DISCOUNT: 10%

BESSE-SUR-BRAYE Sarthe 2C

Hôtel La Chaumière ★★ rue Gambetta, 72310 Bessé-sur-Braye.
✆ 43 35 30 59.
Open 09/01 to 19/12. 15 bedrooms (all en suite). Parking. ዉ
From La Chartre-sur-Loir north-east on D305, then fork left to Bessé-sur-Braye.
■ RESTAURANT: Closed Sun eve.
■ TARIFF: (1994) Single 198–213, Double 218–195, Bk 23, Set menu 94–195 (Euro/Access, Visa).

Petit Auberge Pont-de-Braye, 72310 Bessé-sur-Braye.
✆ 43 44 45 08. English spoken.
Open all year. 3 bedrooms (all bath/shower only). Golf 8 km, parking.
Charming, rustic inn. Pont-de-Braye is 6 km south of Bessé-sur-Braye on the D303, 10 km from La Chartre-sur-Loir and 3 km from Poncé-sur-Loir, a famous craft village.
■ RESTAURANT: Closed Tues LS & Mon Jan to Mar. Candlelit, gourmet restaurant offering home-made dishes prepared by the owner-chef using fresh, local produce.
■ TARIFF: (1994) Single 150, Double 170, Bk 24, Set menu 68–165 (Euro/Access, Visa).

BETHUNE Pas-de-Calais 2B

Hôtel Chart'se du Val d'Esprit ★★★ Gosnay, 62199 Béthune.
✆ 21 62 80 00, Fax 21 62 42 50. English spoken.
Open all year. 56 bedrooms (all en suite). Tennis, parking. ዉ
Built in 1792 on the site of a 14th-century monastery, restored and converted into a luxurious hotel in 1986. Leave A26 at exit 6 and follow signs to 'Les Chartreuses'.
■ RESTAURANT: Good choice of food in the main restaurant; hotel also has a brasserie.
■ ACTIVITIES: Guided tours of the region on request.
■ TARIFF: (1994) Single 390–580, Double 450–850, Bk 50, Set menu 210–375 (Amex, Euro/Access, Visa).

Hôtel du Vieux Beffroi ★★ 48 Grand'Place, 62400 Béthune.
✆ 21 68 15 00, Fax 21 56 66 32. English spoken.
Open all year. 65 bedrooms (55 en suite). Parking, restaurant. ዉ
In the centre of town, facing the 600-year-old belfry.
■ TARIFF: (1994) Single 150–300,

Double 180–300, Bk 30, Set menu 75–220
(Amex, Euro/Access, Visa).
■ DISCOUNT: 5%

B BEYNAC Dordogne   4B

Hôtel Bonnet ★★ 24220 Beynac.
℡ 53 29 50 01, Fax 53 29 83 74. English spoken.
Open 14/04 to 16/10. 22 bedrooms
(20 en suite). Golf 10 km, garage, parking.
*Traditional Périgord hotel with lovely views on
to river and garden. From Sarlat (10 km), first
hotel on right as you enter Beynac.*
■ RESTAURANT: Rustic-style dining room with
open fireplace and verandah overlooking the
river. Fine Périgord cuisine: l'escalope de foie
frais de canard façon chef, les médaillons de
sole et bisque au whisky, carré d'agneau à la
crème d'ail.
■ ACTIVITIES: Discover the Dordogne valley by
canoe or boat; walking.
■ TARIFF: (1994) Single 185–285,
Double 260–340, Bk 35, Set menu 98–290
(Euro/Access, Visa).

BEZIERS Hérault   5C

Château de Cabrerolles ★★★
34290 Espondeilhan.
℡ 67 39 21 79, Fax 67 39 21 05. English spoken.

Open all year. 15 bedrooms (all en suite).
Outdoor swimming pool, golf 10 km, parking.
*Former 19th-century residence, now a
comfortable hotel set amongst vineyards.
10 km from Béziers taking D909 north
towards Roujan.*
■ RESTAURANT: Closed Mon. Meals are served in
front of a wood fire in winter and on outdoor
terraces in summer. Specialities include gigot
d'agneau à la crème d'ail and terrine de

saumon fumé à la sauce du Chardonnay.
■ ACTIVITIES: Visits to local cellars and wine
tasting.
■ TARIFF: (1994) Double 320–590, Bk 45,
Set menu 130 (Amex, Euro/Access, Visa).

Grand Hôtel du Nord ★★★ 15 place Jean
Jaurès, 34500 Béziers.
℡ 67 28 34 09, Fax 67 49 00 37. English spoken.
Open all year. 40 bedrooms (20 en suite,
20 bath/shower only). Garage.
*Stands in the centre of town on a square and
beside the 'Jean Jaurès' car park.*
■ TARIFF: (1994) Single 230–350,
Double 300–450, Bk (Amex,
Euro/Access, Visa).

Hôtel Splendid ★★ 24 av du 22-Août,
34500 Béziers.
℡ 67 28 23 82, Fax 67 49 94 32. English spoken.
Open all year. 24 bedrooms (16 en suite).
Golf 6 km, garage.
*This hotel is in the centre of the town, near the
theatre in a quiet location.*
■ TARIFF: (1994) Single 130–220,
Double 140–250, Bk 27 (Amex,
Euro/Access, Visa).
■ DISCOUNT: 10% Except Aug.

BIARRITZ Pyrénées-Atlan   4C

Hôtel Miramar ★★★★ av Impératrice,
64200 Biarritz.
℡ 59 41 30 00, Fax 59 24 77 20. English spoken.
Open all year. 126 bedrooms (all en suite).
Indoor swimming pool, outdoor swimming
pool, golf on site, garage, parking. &
*Hotel of great comfort and character. Facing
the sea, with its own private beach and just
3 km from the airport.*
■ RESTAURANT: Restaurant has an excellent
reputation for its gourmet cuisine. Local and
seafood specialities are prepared under the
supervision of chef André Gauzère.
■ ACTIVITIES: Gym, beauty centre,
thalassotherapy centre at hotel; water sports
and many other activities and excursion
possibilities nearby. ● Preferential rates for golf
on nearby course (500 m).
■ TARIFF: (1994) Single 725–1810,
Double 930–2405, Bk 100, Set menu 250–280
(No credit cards).
■ DISCOUNT: 10% B&B.

Novotel Biarritz ★★★ 64 av d'Espagne,
64600 Anglet.
℡ 59 58 50 50, Fax 59 03 33 55. English spoken.
Open all year. 121 bedrooms (all en suite).

Outdoor swimming pool, tennis, golf 5 km, parking. &

Quiet, comfortable hotel set in 3 acres. From the motorway, take Biarritz/La Négresse (exit 4, N10). The hotel is 1 km beyond the airport on the left.

■ RESTAURANT: Regional cuisine is served in a light, pretty room which opens on to the pool area.

■ ACTIVITIES: Horse-riding, fishing, water sports and boating.

■ TARIFF: Single 420–470, Double 470–520, Bk 52 (Amex, Euro/Access, Visa).

Hôtel Palais ★★★★ 1 av Impératrice, 64200 Biarritz.
℡ 59 41 64 00, Fax 59 41 67 99. English spoken.

Open all year. 155 bedrooms (all en suite). Outdoor swimming pool, golf 1 km, parking. &

In the heart of the city, and formerly an imperial palace, the hotel looks out on the fine beaches of Biarritz. It has recently been renovated and has a world-wide reputation for luxury.

■ RESTAURANT: Enjoy lunch around the pool and dinner in either 'La Rotonde' overlooking the sea or in the award winning 'Le Grand Siècle'. Specialities: rougets en filets poêlés, chipirons à l'encre.

■ ACTIVITIES: Good sports facilities and sea water cure centres nearby.

■ TARIFF: (1994) Single 1100–1950, Double 1400–2650, Bk 100, Set menu 300 (Amex, Euro/Access, Visa).

■ DISCOUNT: 10% Except Aug.

BIDARRAY Pyrénées-Atlan   4C

Hôtel Noblia ★★ 64780 Bidarray.
℡ 59 37 70 89.
Open 15/01 to 15/12. 23 bedrooms (15 en suite). Parking. &

30 km from the sea, standing alongside the river and with mountain view. The hotel is at the edge of town coming from Bayonne.

■ RESTAURANT: Specialities: anguille persillade, pipérade, omelette aux cèpes.

■ TARIFF: Double 140–220, Bk 25, Set menu 55–120 (Amex, Visa).

BISCARROSSE Landes   4C

Hôtel Atlantide ★★ pl Marsan, 40600 Biscarrosse.
℡ 58 78 08 86, Fax 58 78 75 98.
English spoken.
Open all year. 33 bedrooms (all en suite).
Golf 5 km, parking. &

Modern comfortable hotel in a quiet position in town centre and near beach.

■ ACTIVITIES: Cycling, tennis and sailing nearby; cultural guided tours available within the area.

■ TARIFF: (1994) Single 190–230, Double 245–360, Bk (Amex, Euro/Access, Visa).

BITCHE Moselle   3B

Hôtel Beau Rivage ★★ l'Etang de Hanau, 57230 Philippsbourg.
℡ 87 06 50 32, Fax 87 06 57 46.
Open all year. 25 bedrooms (all en suite).
Indoor swimming pool, outdoor swimming pool, tennis, golf 10 km, parking, restaurant. &

In the northern Vosges Regional Park close to Hanau Lake and Unesco's biosphere reserve. Philippsbourg is on the N62 just south-east of Bitche, which is just north-west of Haguenau.

■ TARIFF: (1994) Single 280, Double 440, Set menu 75–200 (Euro/Access, Visa).

LE BLANC Indre   4B

Hôtel Villa Varsovie 73 rue de la République, 36300 Le Blanc.
℡ 54 37 29 03, Fax 54 37 42 48.
English spoken.
Open all year. 8 bedrooms (all en suite).
Golf 10 km, parking.

Hotel is close to the Gendarmerie in the village of Le Blanc.

■ RESTAURANT: Closed Sun eve & Mon except Jul & Aug. Stylish gourmet restaurant with seafood specialities.

■ TARIFF: (1994) Double 250–350, Bk 40, Set menu 98–198 (Euro/Access, Visa).

Domaine de l'Etape ★★★ route de Bélâbre, 36300 Le Blanc.
✆ 54 37 18 02, Fax 54 37 75 59. English spoken.

Open all year. 35 bedrooms (all en suite). Golf 6 km, parking, restaurant. ⅋
Delightful 19th-century building in 380-acre park, with 45-acre boating and fishing lake. From Le Blanc head south-east on D10 for 6 km towards Bélâbre.

■ ACTIVITIES: Boating and fishing at hotel; horse-riding, flying, gliding and parachuting nearby.
■ TARIFF: (1994) Single 210–370, Double 210–430, Bk 42, Set menu 115–130 (Amex, Euro/Access, Visa).

BLOIS Loir/Cher   2C

Hôtel La Caillère ★★ 36 route des Montils, 41120 Candé-sur-Beuvron.
✆ 54 44 03 08, Fax 54 44 00 95. English spoken.

Open 01/03 to 30/11. 14 bedrooms (all en suite). Golf 8 km, parking. ⅋
La Caillère combines modern amenities with old architecture. On the left bank of the Loire, 10 minutes' drive from Blois towards Tours on the N751 at Candé-sur-Beuvron.

■ RESTAURANT: Closed Wed. Jacky Guindon,

chef and owner, has a highly original cuisine. He combines traditional ingredients with the best produce from local markets.
■ ACTIVITIES: In the heart of châteaux country, close to four of the most famous. Horse-riding and bike hire nearby.
■ TARIFF: (1994) Single 290, Double 320–360, Bk 50, Set menu 88–268 (Amex, Euro/Access, Visa).
■ DISCOUNT: 5%

Hôtel La Clé des Champs ★★
41120 Chitenay.
✆ 54 70 42 03. English spoken.
Open 01/02 to 30/12. 8 bedrooms (3 en suite). Parking.
Traditional restaurant with rooms, surrounded by the Loire châteaux. From Blois, south on the D936 towards Contres. Turn right after 10 km.

■ RESTAURANT: Traditional restaurant serving good food based on fresh, local produce. Large terrace for summer dining.
■ ACTIVITIES: Sailing, châteaux visits.
■ TARIFF: (1994) Single 130–150, Double 160, Bk 30, Set menu 135–175 (Euro/Access, Visa).

Hôtel Le Medicis ★★★ 2 allée François, 41000 Blois.
✆ 54 43 94 04, Fax 54 42 04 05. English spoken.
Open all year. 12 bedrooms (all en suite). Golf 12 km, garage, parking.
Air-conditioned, sound-proofed hotel. Close to railway station on Angers road.

■ RESTAURANT: Closed Jan. Gourmet cuisine.
■ TARIFF: (1994) Single 300–400, Double 400–550, Bk 42, Set menu 98–298 (Amex, Euro/Access, Visa).

Hôtel Le Monarque ★★ 61 rue Porte Chartraine, 41000 Blois.
✆ 54 78 02 35, Fax 54 74 82 76. English spoken.
Open all year. 25 bedrooms (22 en suite, 3 bath/shower only). Golf 15 km, garage. ⅋
Charming hotel in Loire châteaux capital. From Tours, motorway A10/E5/E60 north-east, then right on to D766 to Blois.

■ RESTAURANT: Closed Sun.
■ TARIFF: (1994) Single 190–300, Double 190–350, Bk 30, Set menu 70–160 (Euro/Access, Visa).

BLOTZHEIM Ht-Rhin   3D

Captain Hôtel ★★ rue du 19 novembre, 68730 Blotzheim.
✆ 89 68 82 82, Fax 89 68 86 43. English spoken.
Open all year. 63 bedrooms (all en suite). Parking, restaurant. ⅋

This pleasant Alsace-style hotel is 3 km from Basle-Mulhouse Airport and 5 minutes from the Swiss and German borders. The rooms are quiet and fully equipped. Restaurant serves regional specialities. Shuttle to airport. Special weekend and family rates. Leave the A35 at airport exit, then follow signs to Blotzheim.
- TARIFF: (1994) Double 260, Bk 35, Set menu 40–110 (Amex, Euro/Access, Visa).
- DISCOUNT: 10%

BOLBEC Seine-Marit 2A

Hôtel Promotour ★★ av du Marechal-Joffre, 76210 Bolbec.
☎ 35 31 88 89, Fax 35 31 94 26.
English spoken.

Open all year. 42 bedrooms (all en suite). Parking, restaurant. ♿
Pleasant 2-star hotel with fully equipped bedrooms. The restaurant specialises in regional food. Special rates for weekends and families. On the N15 between Le Havre and Rouen.
- TARIFF: (1994) Double 250, Bk 35, Set menu 69–120 (Amex, Euro/Access, Visa).
- DISCOUNT: 10%

BONNEVAL Eure/Loir 2D

Hostellerie de Bois Guibert ★★ Guibert, 28800 Bonneval.
☎ 37 47 22 33, Fax 37 47 50 69. English spoken.

B

Open 20/02 to 20/01. 14 bedrooms (all en suite). Parking.
On N10, just outside Bonneval. A 17th-century country manor house surrounded by wooded parkland. All modern comforts.
- RESTAURANT: Closed Sun eve & Mon LS. Fine cuisine.
- TARIFF: (1994) Single 270–480, Double 270–550, Bk 45, Set menu 130–295 (Amex, Euro/Access, Visa).

BORDEAUX

Bordeaux – a town renowned for the export of the fine wines that bear its name – stands on the River Garonne, not far upstream from where it joins the Dordogne. Together, these two rivers form the wide Gironde estuary that flows north-west for about 90 km before reaching the Atlantic Ocean.

An important sea port for over 2,000 years, the old town lies on the west bank of the river which is about 400 m wide at this point. Napoleon built the Pont de Pierre here, a bridge with 17 arches, an arch for each of his victories. This was the most northerly bridge over the Garonne until 1967 when the suspension bridge, the Pont d'Aquitaine, opened downstream to carry the motorway from Paris.

Called Burdigala by the Romans, there is hardly any evidence visible today of their 300-year occupation, just a small part of an

B

amphitheatre now known as the Palais Gallien. However, the town centre remains in the same place as in Roman times with the 18th-century Place de la Comédie lying on the site of the Forum. Here you will find the Grand Théâtre with its colonnaded facade and richly decorated interior. Try window-shopping in this area, too, as there are several streets of smart shops.

To the north of the Place de la Comédie lies the huge Esplanade des Quinconces, said to

Oysters

Sixty kilometres to the west of Bordeaux, on an inlet from the Atlantic Ocean, lies Arcachon – famous for its oysters. These are produced in the shallow Bassin d'Arcachon, which is the only break in the smooth line of sandy beaches that runs for 200 km from the Gironde in the north down to Biarritz.

Basically, there are two types of cultivated oyster, the Plate or Flat oyster and the Creuse. The plate is the native European oyster and you can easily recognise it by its smooth shell. But, following disease earlier this century, you are much more likely to be served with creuse oysters. These are less prone to disease, grow more quickly and have a much rougher shell. However, plate or creuse is not the description that appears on menus, because oysters take their name and taste from the waters in which they are finally fattened. So oysters described as huîtres Arcachonnaises *may be of either type.*

Legend has it that oysters first arrived in the area by accident, escaping from a ship which foundered in the Bassin d'Arcachon. The mixture of salt and fresh water here suited them perfectly and so the local tradition of oyster farming started, developing over the centuries into the major industry it is today.

Twice in the last 80 years, the oysters of Arcachon have been almost completely wiped out by disease. First in 1920, when the native population of plate oysters was destroyed and then again in 1970, when their portugaise creuse *replacements died. However, although the strains of oyster now farmed came originally from Canada and Japan, the traditional taste is still there thanks to the particular quality of the brackish waters in which they are fattened.*

be the largest municipal square in Europe. In 1829 two statues, one representing Commerce and the other Navigation, were placed here on the top of two tall columns. Symbolically built facing out over the quayside, they now also look over the industrial area across the river. At the other end of the Esplanade stands the splendid Monument aux Girondins, a lavish ensemble of statues and fountains which the Germans planned to melt down during World War II. It was saved by the local Resistance who, hearing of the plan, quickly dismantled it, hiding the pieces until the war was over. To find out more about the Resistance, visit the specialist museum, the Centre Jean-Moulin.

Within easy reach of the Centre Jean-Moulin lie several of the town's other museums – the Musée des Beaux-Arts with its collection of European paintings spanning the last 500 years, the Musée des Arts Décoratifs which concentrates on objects, both everyday and exotic from the 16th, 17th and 18th centuries, and the Musée d'Aquitaine which illustrates how life has been lived in this region from prehistoric times. All three are close to the Cathédrale St-André, a Gothic edifice almost as large as Paris's Notre-Dame. In the square outside, the attractive pavement cafés are overlooked by the Tour Pey-Berland, the cathedral's bell tower, which is, unusually, separate from the main building.

If you have had enough of architecture and museums, you could relax in the Jardin Public not far from the Esplanade des Quinconces, or travel further afield to visit some of the many vineyards for which this area is famous. The information that is available at the Maison du Vin de Bordeaux on the Cours du 30 Juillet will help you to plan a successful trip.

BORDEAUX Gironde 4B

(See feature)

Hôtel Clemenceau ★★ 4 cours G Clemenceau, 33000 Bordeaux.
☎ 56 52 38 98, Fax 56 81 24 91. English spoken. Open all year. 45 bedrooms (8 en suite, 37 bath/shower only). Parking.

Large, 18th-century house right in the city centre. All modern facilities.

■ ACTIVITIES: ● Wine tasting can be arranged at a restaurant associated with the hotel at a reduced price for RAC members.

■ TARIFF: Single 150–220, Double 190–220, Bk 25 (Amex, Euro/Access, Visa).

Hôtel Gambetta ★★ 66 rue Porte Dijeaux, 33000 Bordeaux.

☎ 56 51 21 83, Fax 56 81 00 40. English spoken. Open all year. 31 bedrooms (all en suite). Parking.

On a pedestrian street, right in the town centre. The hotel has a lift and has recently been modernised.

■ TARIFF: (1994) Single 245–285, Double 280–300, Bk 30 (Amex, Euro/Access, Visa).

Hôtel Le Méridienne ★★ 155 rue G Bonnac, 33000 Bordeaux.

☎ 56 24 08 88, Fax 56 98 14 28. English spoken. Open all year. 40 bedrooms (all en suite). Garage, parking. ♿

Comfortable, modern hotel in the centre of the Mériadeck district of Bordeaux.

■ TARIFF: (1994) Single 270–350, Double 270–390, Bk 33 (Amex, Visa).

Hôtel Résidence Corus ★★★ 42 rue Peyronnet, 33800 Bordeaux.

☎ 56 33 82 00, Fax 56 31 46 77. English spoken. Open all year. 50 bedrooms (all en suite). Golf 10 km, parking. ♿

In the centre of Bordeaux, studios with car park, telephone and satellite TV, for the independent traveller.

■ TARIFF: (1994) Double 160–320, Bk 40 (Amex, Euro/Access, Visa).

■ DISCOUNT: 5% Based on maximum room rate.

Hôtel Sofitel Aquitania ★★★★ Parc des Expositions, 33000 Bordeaux.

☎ 56 50 83 80, Fax 56 39 73 75. English spoken. Open 01/01 to 08/12 & 30/12 to 31/12. 205 bedrooms (all en suite). Outdoor swimming pool, golf 15 km. ♿

Modern hotel ten minutes from airport, town centre and station. At Pont d'Aquitaine take first exit then signs to Centre Hôtelier.

■ RESTAURANT: Closed weekends Nov to Mar. Modern restaurant with lake views. Specialities: hot scallop of duck liver with sweet grapes; crunchy monkfish with spring vegetables; gratin of fresh fruit flavoured with a sweet wine.

■ ACTIVITIES: Billiards; 40 minutes from beaches.

■ TARIFF: Single 600, Double 600, Bk 65, Set menu 175 (Amex, Euro/Access, Visa).

LA BOUILLE Seine-Marit   2A **B**

Hôtel Bellevue ★★ 13 quai Malot, 76530 La Bouille.

☎ 35 18 05 05, Fax 35 18 00 92. English spoken.

Open all year. 20 bedrooms (all en suite). Golf 15 km, garage, parking.

Pleasing, traditional hotel in a quiet position opposite the River Seine. From Rouen drive south-west on A13 for 15 km. Exit for Maison Buîlée, turn right after 500 m to the village and the river.

■ RESTAURANT: Closed 20/12 to 27/12. Gourmet cuisine with seafood specialities.

■ ACTIVITIES: Trips on the River Seine.

■ TARIFF: (1994) Single 160–320, Double 230–320, Bk 35, Set menu 98–215 (Euro/Access, Visa).

■ DISCOUNT: 10%

Hôtel St-Pierre ★★ 76530 La Bouille.

☎ 35 18 01 01, Fax 35 18 12 76. English spoken. Open all year. 7 bedrooms (all en suite). Parking.

Not far from Rouen, in the centre of a typical village. Some rooms with views over River Seine. From the Le Havre to Paris autoroute, take exit 24. From Rouen to Caen for 26 km, exit 24.

■ RESTAURANT: Overlooks the River Seine.

■ TARIFF: (1994) Single 280–320,
Double 320–350, Bk 40, Set menu 140–240
(Amex, Euro/Access, Visa).

B BOULOGNE-SUR-MER Pas-de-Calais 2B

Hôtel Clery ★★★ Hésdin-l'Abbé,
62360 Boulogne-sur-Mer.
✆ 21 83 19 83, Fax 21 87 52 59. English spoken.
Open 15/01 to 20/12. 19 bedrooms
(all en suite). Tennis, golf 9 km, parking.
*The hotel is in a 12-acre park very close to the
port of Boulogne. Take N1 from Boulogne for
10 km. In Hésdin-l'Abbé, turn left at traffic
lights.*
■ TARIFF: (1994) Single 325–400,
Double 350–560, Bk 50 (Amex,
Euro/Access, Visa).

Hôtel Lorraine ★★ 7 pl de Lorraine,
62200 Boulogne-sur-Mer.
✆ 21 31 34 78. English spoken.
Open 09/01 to 18/12. 20 bedrooms (8 en suite,
6 bath/shower only).
*In a quiet square in the town centre, just 10
minutes from the ferry terminal.*
■ TARIFF: (1994) Single 155–265,
Double 155–265, Bk 28 (Amex,
Euro/Access, Visa).
■ DISCOUNT: 5% LS.

Hôtel Metropole ★★★ 51 rue Thiers,
62200 Boulogne-sur-Mer.
✆ 21 31 54 30, Fax 21 30 45 72. English spoken.

Open 05/01 to 20/12. 25 bedrooms
(all en suite). Golf 6 km, garage.
*Located in the town centre, the hotel has
recently been completely redecorated. Rooms
have luxury bathrooms. There is a pleasant
lounge and pretty garden.*
■ TARIFF: (1994) Single 335–380,
Double 380–430, Bk 42 (Amex,
Euro/Access, Visa).

LE BOULOU Pyrénées-Or 5C

Hôtel Le Domitien ★★★ route d'Espagne
BP101, 66160 Le Boulou.
✆ 68 83 49 50, Fax 68 83 45 90. English spoken.
Open all year. 40 bedrooms (all en suite).
Outdoor swimming pool, tennis, parking,
restaurant. ⅋
*Modern hotel situated in a well-known spa
town, at the foot of the Pyrénées. 15 km south
of Perpignan and 8 km from the border.*
■ TARIFF: (1994) Single 360, Double 380, Bk 39,
Set menu 110–180 (Amex, Euro/Access, Visa).

Hôtel Village Catalan ★★★ Autoroute A9,
66300 Banyuls-dels-Aspres.
✆ 68 21 66 66, Fax 68 21 70 55. English spoken.
Open all year. 77 bedrooms (all en suite).
Outdoor swimming pool, tennis, garage,
parking. ⅋
*Situated on the A9 motorway, between
Perpignan and the Spanish border. The hotel
offers all modern day comforts including
sound-proofed, air-conditioned rooms, 8 of
them with garage. Private car parks
permanently controlled by camera.*
■ TARIFF: (1994) Single 290, Double 320–350,
Bk 39 (Euro/Access, Visa).

BOURG-EN-BRESSE Ain 5B

Hôtel Ibis ★★ bd Ch de Gaulle,
01000 Bourg-en-Bresse.
✆ 74 22 52 66, Fax 74 23 09 58. English spoken.
Open all year. 62 bedrooms (all en suite).
Golf 5 km, parking, restaurant. ⅋
*Hotel is near Brou church and has garden
and barbecue terrace.*
■ TARIFF: (1994) Single 265–295,
Double 290–320, Bk 34, Set menu 55–95
(Amex, Euro/Access, Visa).
■ DISCOUNT: 5%

Hôtel Le Logis de Brou ★★ 132 bd de Brou,
01000 Bourg-en-Bresse.
✆ 74 22 11 55, Fax 74 22 37 30. English spoken.
Open all year. 30 bedrooms. Golf 10 km,
garage, parking.
*Near the magnificent church of Brou and 7
minutes from A40 Bourg-Sud exit. Good
restaurants nearby.*
■ TARIFF: (1994) Single 260–380, Double 295–
380, Bk 35 (Amex, Euro/Access, Visa).
■ DISCOUNT: 10%

Hôtel Mercure-Chantecler ★★★ 10 av Bad-
Kreuznach, 01000 Bourg-en-Bresse.
✆ 74 22 44 88, Fax 74 23 43 57. English spoken.

Open all year. 60 bedrooms (all en suite).
Golf 10 km, garage, parking. &
In a quiet location at the entrance of the town,
heading towards Strasbourg.
■ RESTAURANT: Regional specialities.
■ TARIFF: (1994) Single 325, Double 350–450,
Bk 47, Set menu 115–240 (Amex,
Euro/Access, Visa).

Hôtel du Prieure ★★★ 49 bd de Brou,
01000 Bourg-en-Bresse.
℡ 74 22 44 60, Fax 74 22 71 07. English spoken.
Open all year. 14 bedrooms (all en suite).
Golf 10 km, garage, parking. &
Sited in a quiet position in a park, 200 m from
the church of Brou. The rooms are spacious
and stylish.
■ TARIFF: (1994) Single 380–460,
Double 400–550, Bk 46 (Amex,
Euro/Access, Visa).

BOURG-ST-MAURICE Savoie   6A

Hôtel L'Autantic ★★★ rte d'Hauteville,
73700 Bourg-St-Maurice.
℡ 79 07 01 70, Fax 79 05 51 55. English spoken.
Open all year. 23 bedrooms (all en suite).
Golf 18 km, garage, parking. &
A modern stone and pine chalet hotel set back
from the road at the edge of town offering very
comfortable bedrooms and excellent facilities
including sauna.
■ ACTIVITIES: Mountain sports, canoeing and
rafting nearby.
■ TARIFF: (1994) Double 260–440, Bk 40
(Amex, Euro/Access, Visa).

BOURGES Cher   2D

Hôtel d'Angleterre ★★★ 1 pl des Quatre
Piliers, 18000 Bourges.
℡ 48 24 68 51, Fax 48 65 21 41. English spoken.
Open all year. 31 bedrooms (all en suite).
Golf 2 km, garage.
Quiet and comfortable, the hotel has been fully
renovated and is not far from the cathedral in
the old town.
■ RESTAURANT: Closed 15/12 to 15/01. 'Le
Windsor' restaurant is decorated in Louis XVI
stlye and serves 'Berry' cuisine.
■ ACTIVITIES: Spring music festival.
■ TARIFF: (1994) Single 382, Double 430, Bk 38,
Set menu 88–139 (Amex, Euro/Access, Visa).

Hôtel Bourbon ★★★ bd République,
18000 Bourges.
℡ 48 70 70 00, Fax 48 70 21 22. English spoken.

Open all year. 60 bedrooms (all en suite).
Golf 3 km, parking. &
Opened in the spring of 1991, restored historic
abbey, situated in wooded grounds. Motorway
from Paris A 71.
■ RESTAURANT: Closed Sat lunch.
■ TARIFF: (1994) Single 400–525,
Double 485–610, Bk 65 (Amex,
Euro/Access, Visa).

Hôtel Grand Argentier ★★ 9 rue Parerie,
18000 Bourges.
℡ 48 70 84 31. English spoken.
Open 01/03 to 22/12. 14 bedrooms
(12 en suite, 2 bath/shower only). Golf 2 km,
parking.
This 15th-century hotel is in the town centre,
surrounded by greenery. The rooms are quiet
and individual.
■ TARIFF: (1994) Double 250–370, Bk 36
(Amex, Euro/Access, Visa).
■ DISCOUNT: 10% LS only.

LE BOURGET-DU-LAC Savoie   6A

Hôtel Beaurivage ★★ 73370 Le Bourget-du-
Lac.
℡ 79 25 00 38, Fax 79 25 06 49. English spoken.
Open all year. 7 bedrooms (6 en suite,
1 bath/shower only). Golf 8 km, parking.
Small hotel in quiet situation by the lakeside at
southern tip of Lake Bourget. 10 km from
either Chambery or Aix-les-Bains on the N504
linked from Annecy via the main N211.
■ RESTAURANT: Closed Tue eve & Wed Sep to
Jun. Well prepared meals served by staff in
traditional Savoyard costume.
■ TARIFF: (1994) Single 280–300,
Double 280–300, Bk 35, Set menu 99–220
(Euro/Access, Visa).
■ DISCOUNT: 5%

Relais-Château Ombremont N504,
73370 Le Bourget-du-Lac.
℡ 79 25 00 23, Fax 79 25 25 77.
English spoken.
Open 01/02 to 31/12. 19 bedrooms
(all en suite). Outdoor swimming pool,
golf 9 km, garage, parking.
Lovely hotel with warm, inviting rooms, each
one individually decorated in traditional style.
Tranquil setting in 7 acres of leafy parkland.
Access off N504 on west side of lake, 2.2 km
north of Le Bourget-du-Lac.
■ RESTAURANT: Closed Jan. Exceptional view of
lake and mountains. Gastronomic cuisine.
Specialities include filet de sandre doré à l'huile

B

B

de noisettes, cuisse de lapereau, poitrine de
pigeonneau rôtie.
■ ACTIVITIES: Table tennis, fitness room and
billiards at hotel. All water sports available on
lake. Tennis nearby.
■ TARIFF: Single 590–1280, Double 750–1400,
Bk (Amex, Euro/Access, Visa, **BT**🌀).

BOURGOIN-JALLIEU Isère　　　　5B

Hôtel Otelinn ★★ 13 rue du Creuzat,
38080 L'Isle d'Abeau.
☎ 74 27 13 55, Fax 74 27 22 21. English spoken.
Open all year. 45 bedrooms (all en suite).
Golf 3 km, parking. ♿
*Modern hotel, convenient for both the airport
and the autoroute. From A43, take exit to L'Isle
d'Abeau-Est and follow signs to L'Isle d'Abeau
village. 5 km west of Bourgoin.*
■ RESTAURANT: Closed Sun.
■ TARIFF: (1994) Single 268, Double 302, Bk 36,
Set menu 78–145 (Amex, Euro/Access, Visa).
■ DISCOUNT: 10%

BOURGUEIL Indre/Loire　　　　2C

Château des Reaux Chouzé-sur-Loire,
37140 Bourgueil.
☎ 47 95 14 40, Fax 47 95 18 34. English spoken.

Open 01/04 to 31/12 & 01/01 to 31/01.
18 bedrooms (all en suite). Tennis, golf 12 km,
parking, restaurant.
*One of the region's most outstanding châteaux,
built by the famous Briçounet family. From
Saumur 15 km east on N152 to Chouzé.*
■ TARIFF: (1994) Single 250–400, Double 450–
950, Bk 50 (Amex, Euro/Access, Visa).

BRANTOME Dordogne　　　　4B

Château de la Côte ★★★ Biras-Bourdeilles,
24310 Brantôme.
☎ 53 03 70 11, Fax 53 03 42 84. English spoken.

Open all year. 14 bedrooms (all en suite).
Outdoor swimming pool, golf 15 km, parking.
*Charming 15th-century château set on a
hillside, in the heart of a 400-acre property.
Magnificent 15-acre gardens. 17 km north of
Périgueux (D939, then left onto D106E).*
■ RESTAURANT: Closed Mon lunch.
■ ACTIVITIES: Mountain-biking, canoeing, horse-
riding, tennis 3 km.
■ TARIFF: (1994) Double 380–750, Bk 45,
Set menu 130–280 (Amex, Euro/Access, Visa).

BREHAL Manche　　　　1B

Hôtel de la Gare ★★ 1 place Cdt Godare,
50290 Bréhal.
☎ 33 61 61 11. English spoken.
Open 01/02 to 18/12. 9 bedrooms
(all en suite). Golf 5 km, garage, parking.
*Small privately-owned hotel near the sea.
Bréhal is north of Granville on the D971.*
■ RESTAURANT: Closed Sun eve & Mon.
Professionally-run restaurant with specialities
including coquilles Saint-Jacques flambées and
magret de canard aux framboises.
■ ACTIVITIES: Tennis, horse-riding and pleasure
flights nearby.
■ TARIFF: (1994) Single 160–280,
Double 280–300, Bk 37 (Euro/Access, Visa).

BREIL-SUR-ROYA Alpes-Mar　　　　6C

Hôtel Castel du Roy ★★ route de Tende,
06540 Breil-sur-Roya.
☎ 93 04 43 66, Fax 93 04 91 83. English spoken.
Open 01/03 to 31/10. 19 bedrooms
(all en suite). Outdoor swimming pool,
golf 20 km, parking. ♿
*Set in 5 acres of parkland, the hotel has a
lovely position beside the River Roya, near the
Vallée des Merveilles.*
■ RESTAURANT: Closed Tues LS.

ACTIVITIES: Mountain-bike hire; fishing, skiing, horse-riding nearby.

■ TARIFF: (1994) Single 240–280, Double 290–390, Bk 35, Set menu 100–210 (Amex, Euro/Access, Visa).

■ DISCOUNT: 5% LS.

BRELIDY Côtes-du-Nord   1C

Château de Brelidy ★★★ 22140 Brelidy.
℃ 96 95 69 38, Fax 96 95 18 03. English spoken.

Open 01/04 to 02/11. 10 bedrooms (all en suite). Golf 25 km, parking, restaurant. &

Beautiful 16th-century château in 25 acres of parkland, with woods and river. Rooms furnished in keeping with period.

■ ACTIVITIES: Fishing within the property. Footpath in the woods. Mountain bikes available.

■ TARIFF: (1994) Single 350–410, Double 380–680, Bk 50, Set menu 135–175 (Amex, Euro/Access, Visa).

LA BRESSE Vosges   3D

Résidence des Vallées ★★★ 31 rue P Claudel, 88250 La Bresse.
℃ 29 25 41 39, Fax 29 25 64 38. English spoken. Open all year. 54 bedrooms (all en suite). Indoor swimming pool, tennis, garage, parking. &

A modern hotel in the heart of the Hautes Vosges, 12 km from Gerardmer. All public rooms renovated between 1992 and 1994. Restful family atmosphere. From Paris: towards Nancy via Epinal, Remiremont, La Bresse Centre. From Strasbourg via the Col de la Schlucht. From Mulhouse: Bôle, Thann and the Col de Bramont.

■ RESTAURANT: High quality food in light, bright and very restful surroundings. Raclette evenings a speciality.

■ ACTIVITIES: Fitness room, sauna, squash, table tennis and mountain-biking.

■ TARIFF: Single 285–310, Double 350–370, Bk 37, Set menu 88–200 (Amex, Euro/Access, Visa).

BREST Finistère   1C

Novotel de Brest ★★★ 32 avenue du Baron Lacrosse, ZAC de Kergardec, 29850 Gouesnou.
℃ 98 02 32 83, Fax 98 41 69 27.
English spoken.
Open all year. 85 bedrooms (all en suite). Outdoor swimming pool, golf 15 km, parking, restaurant. &

Bar service from 6 am to midnight with a spacious recreation area. 5 minutes from town, close to the airport.

■ TARIFF: (1994) Single 410, Double 460–480, Bk 50, Set menu 78–98 (Amex, Euro/Access, Visa).

Hôtel Océania ★★★ 82 rue de Siam, 29200 Brest.
℃ 98 80 66 66, Fax 98 80 65 50. English spoken.
Open all year. 82 bedrooms (all en suite). Restaurant. &

Centre of town, situated on the main street. On the coast, main autoroute N12 to Brest.

■ TARIFF: (1994) Single 450–650, Double 500–700, Bk 50 (Amex, Euro/Access, Visa).

Hôtel de la Paix ★★★ 32 rue Algésiras, 29200 Brest.
℃ 98 80 12 97, Fax 98 43 30 95. English spoken.
Open all year. 25 bedrooms (all en suite). Golf 15 km, parking.

Located in the heart of Brest, a few steps away from the St-Louis covered market, near the post office, town hall, conference centre and famous rue de Siam. Take N12 towards the coast to Brest.

■ TARIFF: (1994) Single 245–275, Double 270–300, Bk 30 (Amex, Euro/Access, Visa).

■ DISCOUNT: 10%

BRETEUIL Oise   2B

Hôtel Cap Nord ★★ rue Paris, 60120 Breteuil.
℃ 44 07 10 33, Fax 44 80 92 71.
English spoken.
Open all year. 38 bedrooms (all en suite). Garage, parking.

Modern hotel offering a convenient stop-over point for tourism or business purposes. On the N1 between Amiens and Nantes.

B

■ RESTAURANT: Closed Fri eve & Sat. Regional dishes and charcoal grills.
■ ACTIVITIES: Tennis and other sports facilities nearby. Visit archaeological museum in town.
■ TARIFF: (1994) Single 190–200, Double 230–255, Bk 32, Set menu 65–120 (Amex, Euro/Access, Visa).

BRIANCON Htes-Alpes   6A

Hôtel Paris ★★ 41 av Gén de Gaulle, 05100 Briançon.
✆ 92 20 15 30, Fax 92 20 30 82. English spoken.
Open all year. 22 bedrooms (18 en suite, 4 bath/shower only). Golf 14 km, garage, parking. &
Near the centre of the town and the railway station. On the N94 close to the Italian border.
■ RESTAURANT: Specialises in classic and regional traditional cuisine.
■ ACTIVITIES: 300 m from sports centre and ski-lifts.
■ TARIFF: (1994) Single 160–265, Double 175– 280, Bk 30, Set menu 75–148 (Amex, Visa).
■ DISCOUNT: 5%

Hôtel Vauban ★★★ 13 av Gén de Gaulle, 05100 Briançon.
✆ 92 21 12 11, Fax 92 20 58 20. English spoken.
Open 18/12 to 06/11. 44 bedrooms (38 en suite). Golf 12 km, garage, parking, restaurant. &
A family-run hotel in the centre of town with a garden. Close to the railway station.
■ TARIFF: (1994) Single 240–350, Double 250–420, Bk 31, Set menu 115–175 (Euro/Access, Visa).

BRICQUEBEC Manche   1B

Hôtel Vieux Château ★★★ 4 cours du Château, 50260 Bricquebec.
✆ 33 52 24 49, Fax 33 52 62 71. English spoken.

Open all year. 25 bedrooms (24 en suite, 1 bath/shower only). Tennis, golf 15 km, garage, parking. &
This hotel is built within a 12th-century medieval castle, surrounded by its ramparts. Take the D900 from Cherbourg.
■ RESTAURANT: Situated in the Knights' Hall.
■ TARIFF: (1994) Single 160–300, Double 180–390, Bk 40, Set menu 80–170 (Amex, Euro/Access, Visa).

BRIONNE Eure   2A

Hôtel Le Logis de Brionne ★★ 1 place St-Denis, 27800 Brionne.
✆ 32 44 81 73, Fax 32 45 10 92. English spoken.
Open all year. 12 bedrooms (all en suite). Golf 12 km, garage, parking. &
A quiet, very comfortable hotel just in front of St-Denis church. N38 exit Brionne.
■ RESTAURANT: Classic contemporary style with local and regional cuisine.
■ ACTIVITIES: Tennis, horse-riding and swimming pool nearby.
■ TARIFF: (1994) Double 280–330, Bk 38, Set menu 90–270 (Euro/Access, Visa).

BRIVE-LA-GAILLARDE Corrèze   4B

Hôtel Mercure ★★★ Le Griffolet BP 505, 19106 Brive-la-Gaillarde Cedex.
✆ 55 86 36 35, Fax 55 87 04 40. English spoken.
Open all year. 57 bedrooms (all en suite). Outdoor swimming pool, tennis, golf 5 km, parking.
Comfortable hotel with all modern facilities.
■ RESTAURANT: Specialities: foie gras, confit, cèpes. Meals served on the terrace near swimming pool in summer.
■ ACTIVITIES: Vehicles for hire; visits to a foie gras canning factory and a distillery.

■ TARIFF: (1994) Single 395, Double 450, Bk 52 (Amex, Euro/Access, Visa).

Soph'Motel ★★★ Saint Pardoux l'Artigier, 19270 Brive.
℡ 55 84 51 02, Fax 55 84 50 14. English spoken.
Open 01/02 to 31/12. 25 bedrooms (all en suite). Outdoor swimming pool, tennis, parking, restaurant. ⚭
25 independent luxury flats and motel in peaceful surroundings. On the N20, north of Donzenac, between Brive (15 km) and Uzerche (18 km).
■ TARIFF: (1994) Double 270–320, Bk 35, Set menu 69–200 (Euro/Access, Visa).

BROUSSE-LE-CHATEAU Aveyron   5C

Le Relays du Chasteau ★★ 12480 Brousse-le-Château.
℡ 65 99 40 15. English spoken.
Open 15/01 to 15/12. 12 bedrooms (all en suite). Parking, restaurant.
Comfortable, friendly hotel, set at the foot of this medieval village in the Tarn valley. 55 km from Millau and 55 km from Albi on the D77.
■ TARIFF: (1994) Double 180–220, Bk 26, Set menu 68–175 (Euro/Access, Visa).

LE BUGUE Dordogne   4B

Manoir de Bellerive ★★★ route de Siorac, 24480 Le Buisson-de-Cadouin.
℡ 53 27 16 19, Fax 53 22 09 05. English spoken.

Open 15/04 to 31/10. 16 bedrooms (all en suite). Outdoor swimming pool, tennis, golf 10 km, garage, parking. ⚭
Small château in an 8-acre park on the edge of the Dordogne. Peaceful setting near Lascaux and Les Eyzies.
■ RESTAURANT: Specialities: seafood, foie gras

poêlé aux fruits and seasonal dishes using fresh produce.
■ ACTIVITIES: Good sports facilities plus sauna/hammam at hotel; canoeing, cycling and horse-riding nearby. In the centre of the Périgord Noir touring and rambling area.
■ TARIFF: (1994) Single 400–550, Double 450–750, Bk 60, Set menu 150–220 (Amex, Euro/Access, Visa).
■ DISCOUNT: 5%

B

Hôtel Terrasses de Beauregard ★★ route de Trémolat, 24510 Limeuil.
℡ 53 63 30 85, Fax 53 24 53 55. English spoken.
Open 01/05 to 30/09. 8 bedrooms (all en suite). Golf 10 km, parking.
5 km south of Le Bugue, the hotel is peacefully situated between the medieval town of Limeuil and Trémolat, and looks down on the confluence of the Dordogne and Vézère rivers. Limeuil is officially classified as 'one of the most beautiful villages in France'.
■ RESTAURANT: Closed Tue & Fri lunch. Creative family recipes and regional dishes are served in the spacious, light and airy dining room.
■ ACTIVITIES: Good area for walking and exploring the 'bartides' prehistoric sites and Bergerac vineyards.
■ TARIFF: (1994) Double 220–280, Bk 40, Set menu 90–300 (Euro/Access, Visa).

BUSSANG Vosges   3D

Hôtel des Sources ★★ 88540 Bussang.
℡ 29 61 51 94, Fax 29 61 60 61. English spoken.

Open all year. 11 bedrooms (all bath/shower only). Parking.
Situated in a quiet environment near the forest and on the bank of the Moselle. Between Epinal and Mulhouse in the direction of sourée de la Moselle.
■ RESTAURANT: Gourmet cuisine, extensive wine list, welcoming family atmosphere.

B

■ ACTIVITIES: For lovers of nature, skiing in winter, walking all year round.
■ TARIFF: (1994) Single 270–290, Double 270–325, Bk 32, Set menu 100–280 (Euro/Access, Visa).
■ DISCOUNT: 10% Minimum 3 nights.

Hôtel du Tremplin ★★ 8 rue du 3ème RTA, 88540 Bussang.
☎ 29 61 50 30, Fax 29 61 50 89. English spoken. Open 01/11 to 30/09. 19 bedrooms (13 en suite). Garage, parking.

Small, family-run hotel in the centre of Bussang which is in the heart of the Hautes-Vosges and the source of the Moselle river.

■ RESTAURANT: Closed Sun eve & Mon. Character dining room serving Lorraine and Alsace specialities. 1988 winner of Logis de France cooking award.
■ ACTIVITIES: Winter skiing centre. Good sports facilities nearby.
■ TARIFF: (1994) Single 150–260, Double 150–300, Bk 30, Set menu 70–300 (Amex, Euro/Access, Visa).
■ DISCOUNT: 10%

BUSSY-ST-GEORGES Seine/Marne 2B

Golf Hôtel ★★★ 15 av Golf, 77600 Bussy-St-Georges.
☎ 1 64 66 30 30, Fax 1 64 66 04 36. English spoken.
Open all year. 96 bedrooms (all en suite). Tennis, golf on site, parking, restaurant. &

14 miles from Paris and the airport, 4 miles from Euro Disney resort. By motorway A4 (Metz to Nancy) exit no 12. Alongside the golf course.

■ ACTIVITIES: ● Reduced green fees.
■ TARIFF: (1994) Single 460–580, Double 530–580, Bk 60, Set menu 65–150 (Amex, Euro/Access, Visa).
■ DISCOUNT: 20%

BUZANCAIS Indre 4B

Hôtel L'Hermitage ★★ rte d'Argy, 36500 Buzançais.
☎ 54 84 03 90, Fax 54 02 13 19. English spoken.
Open 01/01 to 18/09 & 25/09 to 31/12. 14 bedrooms (11 en suite, 3 bath/shower only). Golf 7 km, garage, parking.

A manor house peacefully set in its own grounds, 800 m from the town centre and close to the River Indre.

■ RESTAURANT: Closed Sun eve & Mon. Excellent choice of food in a 30s-style setting.

■ ACTIVITIES: Fishing close by.
■ TARIFF: (1994) Single 120–265, Double 150–310, Bk 27, Set menu 80–275 (Euro/Access, Visa).
■ DISCOUNT: 5%

CABRERETS Lot 5C

Hôtel Les Falaises ★★ Bouziès, 46330 Cabrerets.
☎ 65 31 26 83, Fax 65 30 23 87. English spoken.
Open 07/01 to 04/12. 39 bedrooms (all en suite). Outdoor swimming pool, tennis, parking. &

Bouziès is a small village on the banks of the River Lot, 27 km from historic Cahors.

■ RESTAURANT: Regional dishes and good wines.
■ ACTIVITIES: Mountain-bikes, motor boats and house boats available for hire nearby.
● Bicycles, canoes/kayaks and row boats free of charge.
■ TARIFF: (1994) Double 229–320, Bk 33 (Amex, Euro/Access, Visa).

Auberge de la Sagne ★★ rte des Grottes de Pech-Merle, 46330 Cabrerets.
☎ 65 31 26 62, Fax 65 30 27 43. English spoken.
Open 02/05 to 30/09. 10 bedrooms (all en suite). Outdoor swimming pool, parking, restaurant.

A welcoming family hotel in a rural setting. Near the Pech-Merle caves.

■ TARIFF: (1994) Double 190–270, Bk 25, Set menu 82–125 (Euro/Access, Visa).

CADENET Vaucluse 5D

Hôtel Guilles ★★★ 84160 Lourmarin.
☎ 90 68 50 55, Fax 90 68 37 41.
English spoken.
Open 15/02 to 01/10 & 15/12 to 02/01.
28 bedrooms (all en suite). Outdoor swimming pool, tennis, golf 20 km, parking. &

Situated in the heart of the Luberon in beautiful landscape, a peaceful hotel offering a warm welcome whether just for the night or for a longer stay. Near the protected village of Lourmarin, north of Cadenet on D943.

■ RESTAURANT: Closed Wed & Thur lunch. Charming restaurant. Specialities include selle d'agneau, foie gras de canard poêlé aux morilles and gougère glacé aux fruits d'Apt.

■ ACTIVITIES: Horse-riding, cycling and lovely walks nearby.
■ TARIFF: (1994) Double 390–590, Bk 60, Set menu 170–260 (Amex, Euro/Access, Visa).
■ DISCOUNT: 10% Oct to Mar.

Hôtel du Prieure ★★★ 84480 Bonnieux.
☎ 90 75 80 78, Fax 90 75 96 00. English spoken.

Open 15/02 to 05/11. 10 bedrooms (all en suite). Golf 20 km, garage, parking.
Charming 18th-century former abbey. Off the D943, north-west of Cadenet.

■ RESTAURANT: Closed Tues to Thur lunch. Gourmet restaurant with regional specialities including magret de canard avec figues, filet de boeuf au Roquefort and carré d'agneau aux herbes. Meals served in the garden in fine weather.
■ ACTIVITIES: Nearby towns and villages to visit,

hiking or pony-trekking in the Luberon hills.
■ TARIFF: (1994) Single 350–495, Double 495–595, Bk 40, Set menu 140–198 (Euro/Access, Visa).
■ DISCOUNT: 20%

LA CADIERE-D'AZUR Var   6C

Hostellerie Berard ★★★ rue Gabriel Peri, 83740 La Cadière-d'Azur.
☎ 94 90 11 43, Fax 94 90 11 71. English spoken. Open 20/02 to 15/01. 40 bedrooms (all en suite). Outdoor swimming pool, golf 7 km, garage, parking.
The hotel is in the heart of an old Provençal town, about 7 km west of Toulon on the A50.

■ RESTAURANT: Gourmet cuisine in a pretty dining room with lovely views.
■ ACTIVITIES: Cookery courses available.
■ TARIFF: (1994) Single 400–510, Double 510–850, Bk 60 (Amex, Euro/Access, Visa).

CADILLAC Gironde   4D

Château de la Tour ★★★ 33410 Cadillac.
☎ 56 76 92 00, Fax 56 62 11 59. English spoken.

Open all year. 32 bedrooms (all en suite). Outdoor swimming pool, tennis, golf 10 km, garage, parking. &
Standing in 10 acres between two other châteaux. Leave the A62 Bordeaux/Toulouse road at Podensac exit, head towards Cadillac, over lights and river, turn left on to D10.

■ RESTAURANT: Closed Fri eve & Sat lunch Nov to Mar. Well regarded for its fine cuisine.
■ ACTIVITIES: Within hotel: sauna, jacuzzi, solarium, fitness room, billiards, boules and table tennis. Visits to wine caves and walks beside the Garonne.
■ TARIFF: (1994) Single 340–450, Double 380–490, Bk 40, Set menu 87–198 (Amex, Euro/Access, Visa).
■ DISCOUNT: 10%

C

CAEN

Unlike many French towns which have been rebuilt to look exactly as they did before the war devastation of this century, the citizens of Caen took the decision to create a modern town. This they have done most successfully, after three-quarters of their original town was destroyed in July 1944.

Although most of the town is modern, the major historic buildings have been restored so that the links with the town's founder, William the Conqueror, have been maintained. At the centre of Caen is his castle. It stands on a hill, more visible from the streets below than it has been for centuries because the houses that clustered around it were destroyed in 1944. There are two museums set within the castle ramparts; one, the Musée de la Normandie, specialises in displays connected with Norman history; the other is the Musée des Beaux-Arts. This has a particularly fine collection of paintings with masterpieces from every century, from the 15th onwards, hung in its galleries.

To the west of the castle walls is the street called the Fosse St-Julien, which is where the town's weekly market is held each Friday. Walk down it and you will come to one of Caen's two great religious buildings, the Abbaye aux Hommes. This was founded by William the Conqueror and it is here, in the church of St-Etienne, that he was buried. His tomb remains but his body was dug up and his bones scattered during the French Revolution. William's queen, Matilda, is also buried in Caen, her tomb being in the church she founded, La Trinité, in the Abbaye aux Dames. Both buildings are well worth a visit but perhaps William's is the finer. It was here that the citizens of Caen gathered for protection when their town was bombarded in 1944.

To commemorate the events of World War II, a museum for peace has been established to the north of the town centre. The Caen Memorial uses modern audiovisual techniques to illustrate, first, the events that led from the ending of the First World War to the start of the Second; and then the major battles of World War II are charted, as well as the part played by the ordinary people of France. Finally, there is a section devoted to all the world's conflicts since 1945.

Following last year's 50th anniversary of the Normandy landings, you may want to visit the famous beaches that lie to the north of the town. The small towns that line this coast each have their own story to tell and very often this can be seen and heard in the local museum.

So if you arrive in France on the ferry from Portsmouth at Ouistreham, 15 km north of Caen, or at any of the other channel ports, do not rush past Caen. It is a town both ancient and modern whose history, since the time of William the Conqueror, has been inextricably mixed with the history of Britain.

CAEN Calvados   2A

(See feature)

Hôtel Climat de France ★★ av Montgomery, quartier du Mémorial, 14000 Caen.
☎ 31 44 36 36, Fax 31 95 62 62. English spoken.
Open all year. 72 bedrooms (all en suite).
Golf 7 km, parking. &

Recently-built hotel near the Mémorial museum in Caen. Travelling on the north ring-road in the direction of Cherbourg, take the Mémorial or Creully exit and the hotel is 400 m from Mémorial.

■ RESTAURANT: Good food with hors d'oeuvres and desserts served buffet-style.
■ TARIFF: (1994) Double 270–304, Bk 34 (Amex, Euro/Access, Visa).
■ DISCOUNT: 10%

Friendly Hôtel ★★★ 2 pl de Boston Citis, à Hérouville-St-Clair, 14200 Caen.
☎ 31 44 05 05, Fax 31 44 95 94.
English spoken.
Open all year. 90 bedrooms (all en suite).
Indoor swimming pool, golf 4 km, parking. &

Comfortable hotel with excellent service and facilities. Follow the directions for Côte de Nacre, Douvres.

■ RESTAURANT: Traditional restaurant with classic and regional cuisine.
■ ACTIVITIES: Gym, sauna, spa and children's play area at hotel; good area for sightseeing, including Bayeux and landing beaches.

■ TARIFF: (1994) Single 390–430, Double 420–460, Bk 48, Set menu 125–155 (Amex, Euro/Access, Visa).
■ DISCOUNT: 10%

CAHORS Lot 4D

Hôtel Terminus ★★★ 5 av Charles de Freycinet, 46000 Cahors.
☎ 65 35 24 50. English spoken.
Open all year. 31 bedrooms (all en suite).
Golf 20 km, garage, parking. &
Elegant, traditional hotel offering comfortable accommodation. Near town centre and station.
■ RESTAURANT: Closed Mon LS. Turn-of-the-century décor. Quality dishes using local produce. Specialities: oeuf Pierre Marre; filet d'agneau fermier; panaché de fois gras de canard.
■ ACTIVITIES: Mountain-biking; visits to wine cellars and local producers of foie gras and truffles.
■ TARIFF: (1994) Single 230–390, Double 260–415, Bk 38, Set menu 120–300 (Amex, Euro/Access, Visa).

CALAIS Pas-de-Calais 2B

Hôtel Climat de France ★★ digue Gaston Berthe, 62100 Calais.
☎ 21 34 64 64, Fax 21 34 35 39. English spoken.
Open all year. 44 bedrooms (all en suite).
Parking. &
Modern hotel on the seafront with private parking. From town centre take road to La Plage.
■ RESTAURANT: Closed Sun eve Oct to Mar. Overlooks the seafront; mussels are a house speciality.
■ TARIFF: (1994) Double 275–304, Bk 38 (Amex, Euro/Access, Visa).

Hôtel George V ★★★ 36 rue Royale, 62100 Calais.
☎ 21 97 68 00, Fax 21 97 34 73. English spoken.
Open all year. 45 bedrooms (all en suite).
Golf 15 km, parking. &
In the centre of Calais, quiet, comfortable hotel. Follow Calais-Nord signs from the car ferry terminal and the brown arrow marked George V.
■ RESTAURANT: Closed Sat lunch & Sun eve. Choice of 2 restaurants.
■ TARIFF: (1994) Single 220–300, Double 300–460, Bk 40, Set menu 80–265 (Amex, Euro/Access, Visa).

Hôtel du Golf ★★ digue Gaston Berthe, 62100 Calais.
☎ 21 96 88 99, Fax 21 34 35 39. English spoken.
Open all year. 31 bedrooms (all en suite).
Parking, restaurant. &
Hôtel du Golf has been open since 1989. From the centre of the town take the road La Plage. The hotel overlooks the sea. Self-catering facilities available.
■ TARIFF: (1994) Double 275–304, Bk 38 (Amex, Euro/Access, Visa).

C

Holiday Inn Garden Court ★★★ bd Alliés, 62100 Calais.
☎ 21 34 69 69, Fax 21 97 09 15. English spoken.

Open all year. 65 bedrooms (all en suite).
Golf 15 km, garage, parking. &
In the town centre overlooking the harbour and the sea. 5 minutes from the ferry terminal and channel tunnel. Comfortable, modern hotel offering excellent family rates. There is some underground parking at the hotel, but as it is limited it's a good idea to check the details at reception first.
■ RESTAURANT: Closed Sat lunch.
■ ACTIVITIES: Horse-riding and mountain bike tracks nearby.
■ TARIFF: (1994) Double 500–600, Bk 55 (Amex, Euro/Access, Visa).

Metropol Hôtel ★★★ 45 quai du Rhin, 62100 Calais.
☎ 21 97 54 00, Fax 21 96 69 70. English spoken.
Open 02/01 to 23/12. 40 bedrooms (all en suite). Garage, parking. &
A quiet hotel in the town centre, behind the railway station.
■ TARIFF: (1994) Single 200–280, Double 300–380, Bk 40 (Amex, Euro/Access, Visa).

Hôtel Meurice ★★★ 5 rue Edmond Roche, 62100 Calais.
☎ 21 34 57 03, Fax 21 34 14 71. English spoken.

Open all year. 39 bedrooms (all en suite).
Golf 20 km, garage, parking. &
*In the centre of Calais, but in a particularly
quiet, residential quarter, by the Richelieu
Park. The hotel has a long tradition of quality
and service. Suites are also available.*
■ RESTAURANT: Renowned for its fine cuisine.
■ TARIFF: (1994) Double 375–500, Bk 40,
Set menu 100–280 (Amex, Euro/Access, Visa).

CAMBRAI Nord   2B

Hôtel Mouton Blanc ★★★ 33 rue Alsace-
Lorraine, 59400 Cambrai.
& 27 81 30 16, Fax 27 81 83 54. English spoken.
Open all year. 32 bedrooms
(all bath/shower only). Parking.
*Family-run traditional hotel in the town
centre. Take one-way system from railway
station to the centre.*
■ RESTAURANT: Closed Sun eve & Mon. Gourmet
restaurant with traditional specialities.
■ TARIFF: (1994) Single 200–350,
Double 260–350, Bk 30, Set menu 95–225
(Amex, Euro/Access, Visa).

CAMIERS Pas-de-Calais   2B

Hôtel Logis de France Les Cèdres ★★
62176 Camiers.
& 21 84 94 54, Fax 21 09 23 29.
English spoken.
Open 15/01 to 15/12. 29 bedrooms
(all en suite). Golf 8 km, parking, restaurant. &
*At Hardelot, 8 km from Le Touquet off the
D940 Boulogne to Le Touquet road. Close to
Ste-Cécile beach.*
■ TARIFF: (1994) Double 305, Bk 35,
Set menu 80–203 (Amex, Euro/Access, Visa).

CAMORS Morbihan   1C

Hôtel Les Bruyères ★★★ 56330 Camors.
& 97 39 29 99, Fax 97 39 28 34.
English spoken.
Open all year. 15 bedrooms (all en suite).
Golf 15 km, garage, parking. &
*Small and comfortable, in the centre of the
small town of Camors. From Rennes-Lorient
expressway, exit Baud and Camors is 4 km.*
■ RESTAURANT: Private restaurant for hotel
guests only.
■ ACTIVITIES: Sightseeing, cycling, water sports,
cultural visits.
■ TARIFF: (1994) Double 270–300, Bk 30,
Set menu 80–100 (Euro/Access, Visa).
■ DISCOUNT: 10% Minimum stay 3 nights.

CANCALE Ille/Vil   1D

Hôtel l'Emeraude ★★ 7 quai Thomas,
35260 Cancale.
& 99 89 61 76, Fax 99 89 88 21. English spoken.
Open 15/12 to 15/11. 16 bedrooms
(15 en suite, 1 bath/shower only). Golf 20 km.
*Seafront hotel having a further building with
accommodation and wonderful views on top
of a nearby cliff. Hotel offers all modern
conveniences and overlooks the fishing/oyster
farming port.*
■ RESTAURANT: Closed 15/11 to 15/02 and Thur.
Overlooking the port, the restaurant has a
definite maritime feel to it and specialises in
fresh seafood dishes.
■ ACTIVITIES: Ideal base for touring, water
sports, fishing.
■ TARIFF: (1994) Double 285–480, Bk 42,
Set menu 95–300 (Amex, Euro/Access, Visa).
■ DISCOUNT: 10% Room rate and restaurant.

CANNES Alpes-Mar   6C

Hôtel America ★★★ 13 rue St-Honoré,
06400 Cannes.
& 96 68 36 36, Fax 93 68 04 58. English spoken.

Open all year. 30 bedrooms (all en suite).
Golf 6 km, parking.
*New hotel with air-conditioning, sound-
proofing and all modern conveniences.
Situated behind the Majestic Palace, 30 m
from the beach and La Croisette.*
■ TARIFF: (1994) Single 450–600, Double 550–
750, Bk 55 (Amex, Euro/Access, Visa).

Hôtel Amarante ★★★ 78 bd Carnot,
06400 Cannes.
& 93 39 22 23, Fax 93 39 40 22. English spoken.
Open all year. 71 bedrooms (all en suite).
Outdoor swimming pool, golf 6 km, garage. &

In the centre of Cannes, hotel has harmonious decor and air-conditioned rooms. 1 km from the beach.

■ RESTAURANT: Pleasing atmosphere, overlooking the pool. Specialises in Mediterranean/Provençal cuisine.
■ ACTIVITIES: Tennis and horse-riding within easy reach.
■ TARIFF: (1994) Single 390–630, Double 490–730, Bk 55, Set menu 120 (Amex, Euro/Access, Visa).

Hôtel Belle Plage ★★★★ square Mistral, 06400 Cannes.
☎ 93 39 86 25, Fax 93 99 61 06. English spoken.

Open 01/06 to 31/12. 50 bedrooms (all en suite). Garage. ♿

At the foot of the old town in a shady park, 50 m from beach and 200 m from the port. A new, air-conditioned and sound-proofed hotel with some sea views.

■ TARIFF: (1994) Single 560–960, Double 560–1460, Bk 70 (Amex, Euro/Access, Visa).
■ DISCOUNT: 10%

Hôtel L'Horset-Savoy ★★★★
5 rue F Einessy, 06400 Cannes.
☎ 92 99 72 00, Fax 93 68 25 59. English spoken.

Open all year. 106 bedrooms (all en suite). Outdoor swimming pool, golf 15 km, garage. ♿

Recently renovated hotel, at the centre of La Croisette, just 100 m from the sea and close to the shops.

■ RESTAURANT: Air-conditioned restaurant offering top quality cuisine. Meals served on a shady terrace overlooking the pool and town when weather permits.
■ ACTIVITIES: ● Reduced entry to Festival Beach for hotel guests.
■ TARIFF: Single 575–900, Double 660–1130, Bk 90, Set menu 140 (Amex, Euro/Access, Visa).

Le Grand Hôtel ★★★★ 45 bd Croisette, 06400 Cannes.
☎ 93 38 15 45, Fax 93 68 97 45. English spoken.
Open 01/01 to 01/11 & 10/12 to 31/12. 76 bedrooms (all en suite). Parking. ♿

The hotel has a unique position on La Croisette, standing in the solitude of parkland which leads to the sea and private beach. All the rooms have a terrace. Approach from La Croisette via rue de CDT André or rue Amoretti.

■ RESTAURANT: Closed Sun eve & Mon.
■ TARIFF: (1994) Single 550–1110, Double 660–1460, Bk 60, Set menu 120–180 (Amex, Euro/Access, Visa).

Hôtel de l'Olivier ★★★
5 rue Tambourinaires, 06400 Cannes.
☎ 93 39 53 28, Fax 93 39 55 85. English spoken.

Open all year. 24 bedrooms (all en suite). Outdoor swimming pool, golf 3 km, parking.

Luxuriously furnished hotel with a covered terrace by a swimming pool. Located looking down on the old town in Le Suquet. Quiet spot but only 5 minutes' walk from beaches and old port. From A8 turn right from Pont-Carnot heading along 'voie rapide', turning right off the rue Clemenceau.

■ TARIFF: (1994) Single 285–475, Double 365–665, Bk 50 (Amex, Euro/Access, Visa).

C

CAP GRIS-NEZ Pas-de-Calais   2B

Hôtel Les Mauves ★★ Audinghen, 62179 Cap Gris-Nez.
☎ 21 32 96 06. English spoken.
Open 01/04 to 15/11. 16 bedrooms (12 en suite). Golf 12 km, parking.

Small, charming hotel with comfortable rooms. In a leafy setting, 500 m from the sea. Between Calais and Boulogne-sur-Mer on D191. Exit D940 at Audinghen or take exit 7 from A16.

■ RESTAURANT: Seafood and regional home-made dishes in a pleasant setting.
■ TARIFF: (1994) Single 220–380, Double 230–420, Bk 34, Set menu 100–210 (Euro/Access, Visa).

CARCASSONNE Aude   5C

Hôtel Donjon ★★★ 2 rue Comte Roger, Cité Medievale, 11000 Carcassonne.
☎ 68 71 08 80, Fax 68 25 06 60. English spoken.
Open all year. 38 bedrooms (all en suite).
Golf 3 km, garage, parking. ᵹ

In the middle of the medieval city, the hotel dates back to the middle ages and provides modern comforts, tranquillity and a warm welcome. From the motorway A61, exit at Carcassonne-Est towards Cité.

■ RESTAURANT: Closed Sun 01/11 to 31/03. Modern brasserie. Specialities: cassoulet Languedocien, saumon fumé Danemark, foie gras, confit, fruit flambé.
■ ACTIVITIES: Guided walk around the old town; tennis nearby.
■ TARIFF: (1994) Single 290–600, Double 360–750, Bk 50, Set menu 70–120 (Amex, Euro/Access, Visa).
■ DISCOUNT: 10%

Hôtel Espace Cité ★★ 132 rue Trivalle, 11000 Carcassonne.
☎ 68 25 24 24, Fax 68 25 17 17. English spoken.
Open all year. 48 bedrooms (all en suite).
Golf 3 km, garage, parking. ᵹ

Take Carcassone-Est exit from motorway towards town centre. Turn left at 2nd set of lights and hotel is 200 m from entrance to the medieval city. Sound-proofed, air-conditioned rooms, all with full facilities.

■ TARIFF: (1994) Double 190–310, Bk 30 (Euro/Access, Visa).

Hôtel La Gentilhommière ★★
11800 Carcassonne.
☎ 68 78 74 74, Fax 68 78 65 80. English spoken.

Open all year. 31 bedrooms (all en suite). Outdoor swimming pool, golf 5 km, parking, restaurant. ᵹ

Very comfortable hotel, of typical local architecture. Countryside situation with light, airy rooms, and only 2 km from the old city of Carcassonne. Motorway A61, exit Carcassonne-Est.

■ TARIFF: (1994) Single 250, Double 270–290, Bk 35, Set menu 80–180 (Amex, Euro/Access, Visa).
■ DISCOUNT: 10%

Hôtel Mercure la Viconte ★★★ 18 rue Camille Saint-Saëns, 11000 Carcassonne.
☎ 68 71 45 45, Fax 68 71 11 45. English spoken.
Open all year. 61 bedrooms (all en suite).
Outdoor swimming pool, tennis, golf 4 km, parking. ᵹ

The hotel is situated just outside the walls of the medieval fortified town with views of the ramparts.

■ RESTAURANT: Terraced restaurant with regional cuisine; specialities include paté de foie gras and cassoulet. Summertime bar/restaurant beside the pool.
■ TARIFF: (1994) Double 370–440, Bk 50 (Amex, Euro/Access, Visa).

Hôtel Montsegur ★★★ 27 allée Léna, 11000 Carcassonne.
☎ 68 25 31 41, Fax 68 47 13 22. English spoken.
Open all year. 21 bedrooms (all en suite).
Golf 2 km, parking.

Spacious and elegant 19th-century manor in the centre of town. The restaurant is actually opposite but run by the same family.

■ RESTAURANT: Closed Sun & Mon eve LS. Very good, regional food.

■ TARIFF: (1994) Single 290–390, Double 390–490, Bk 49, Set menu 135–250 (Amex, Euro/Access, Visa).

Hôtel des Remparts ★★ 3 place du Grand Puits, Cité Medievale, 11000 Carcassonne.
☎ 68 71 27 72. English spoken.
Open all year. 18 bedrooms (all en suite). Golf 2 km, parking. ♿

The hotel is converted from an old house within the walls of the medieval city of Carcassonne. From A61 exit at Carcassonne-Est and follow signs to Cité Medievale.

■ TARIFF: Single 280, Double 280–330, Bk 35 (Amex, Euro/Access, Visa).

Hôtel Sarl Neotel ★★ 5 square Gambetta, 11000 Carcassonne.
☎ 68 72 37 37, Fax 68 25 38 39. English spoken.
Open all year. 48 bedrooms (all en suite). Golf 5 km, garage, parking. ♿

Located in the town centre, bordering a park and just across the river from the medieval quarter.

■ RESTAURANT: Contemporary style restaurant 'Le Gargantua' is 100 m away. Specialities include confit de canard, foie gras and cassoulet.
■ ACTIVITIES: Sailing and horse-riding nearby.
■ TARIFF: (1994) Single 275–285, Double 285–300, Bk 34, Set menu 60–140 (Amex, Euro/Access, Visa).
■ DISCOUNT: 10% LS.

CARENNAC Lot 5A

Hôtel Fenelon ★★ 46110 Carennac.
☎ 65 10 96 46, Fax 65 10 94 86.

Open 10/03 to 06/01. 16 bedrooms (all en suite). Outdoor swimming pool, parking.

A charming, comfortable hostellerie located in the centre of picturesque Carennac and overlooking the River Dordogne. Carennac is about 15 km east of St-Céré, on the D30.

■ RESTAURANT: Closed Fri & Sat lunch LS. Specialities of truite farcie aux écrevisses, confit de canard and minute de veau au citron can be enjoyed in the traditional dining room or outside in summer.
■ ACTIVITIES: Fishing and boating.
■ TARIFF: (1994) Single 220–230, Double 260–280, Bk 38, Set menu 83–260 (Amex, Euro/Access, Visa).

CARENTAN Manche 1B

Hôtel Aire de la Baie ★★ 50500 Carentan.
☎ 33 42 20 99, Fax 33 71 06 94. English spoken.
Open 10/01 to 23/12. 40 bedrooms (all en suite). Parking.

Not far from Second World War landing beaches and the junctions of N13 and N174. 50 km south-east of Cherbourg.

■ RESTAURANT: Closed 23/12 to 05/01.
■ TARIFF: (1994) Single 240–250, Double 250–280, Bk 35, Set menu 70–140 (Amex, Euro/Access, Visa).

CARNAC Morbihan 1C

Hôtel Armoric ★★★ 53 av de la Poste, 56340 Carnac.
☎ 97 52 13 47, Fax 97 52 98 66. English spoken.
Open 01/06 to 15/09. 25 bedrooms (all en suite). Golf 6 km, parking.

Quiet, relaxing hotel in extensive grounds, set back from the beach opposite the salt marshes. Access from D781 coastal road.

■ RESTAURANT: Traditional cuisine with an emphasis on seafood.
■ ACTIVITIES: ● Hotel has arranged price reductions for a number of activities including sightseeing tours.
■ TARIFF: (1994) Single 260, Double 360, Bk 41, Set menu 150 (Euro/Access, Visa).

Hôtel La Licorne ★★ 5 av Atlantique, 56340 Carnac.
☎ 97 52 10 59, Fax 97 52 80 30. English spoken.
Open all year. 27 bedrooms (24 en suite). Golf 5 km, parking. ♿

Modern, comfortable hotel facing a salt water lake. 700 m from the main beach and 500 m from the salt water cure centre.

■ ACTIVITIES: Yacht club and swimming pool 500 m.
■ TARIFF: (1994) Double 200–500, Bk 40 (Amex, Euro/Access, Visa).
■ DISCOUNT: 15% LS.

C

Hôtel Celtique ★★★ 17 av de Kermario, 56340 Carnac.
☎ 97 52 11 49, Fax 97 52 71 10. English spoken.

Open all year. 49 bedrooms (all en suite). Golf 7 km, parking. &

A recently renovated hotel, quietly situated amongst pine trees. Just a stone's throw from the beach and next to the tourist office in Carnac.

■ RESTAURANT: 'Winter garden' restaurant and terrace. Specialities: tartare de saumon de la crème de gingembre au citron vert; carré d'agneau aux herbes du Maquis; duo de rouget et turbot en fricassée sauce Riviéra.
■ ACTIVITIES: Balneotherapy centre at the hotel.
● Special all-inclusive rates (individuals/groups) for golf, sailing or deep sea outings.
■ TARIFF: (1994) Single 380–575, Double 390–725, Bk 48, Set menu 98–218 (Amex, Euro/Access, Visa).
■ DISCOUNT: 10% Not Jul or Aug.

Hôtel Plancton ★★★ 12 bd Plage, 56340 Carnac.
☎ 97 52 13 65, Fax 97 52 87 63. English spoken.
Open 30/03 to 15/10. 23 bedrooms (all en suite). Golf 8 km, parking, restaurant. &

Luxury holiday hotel overlooking fine sandy beach. Sailing club and sea-water hydrotherapy centre nearby. Access via D781 coastal road running south-west from L'Orient.

■ TARIFF: (1994) Single 395–510, Double 510–580, Bk 48, Set menu 90–180 (Euro/Access, Visa).

CARPENTRAS Vaucluse 5D

Hôtel Auberge de la Fontaine 84210 Venasque.
☎ 90 66 02 96, Fax 90 66 13 14. English spoken.
Open 15/12 to 15/11. 5 bedrooms (all en suite). Golf 8 km.

Warm and cosy, the Auberge has been beautifully restored and offers accommodation made up of spacious suites, each having a fully equipped kitchen/dining room, living room with fireplace and private terrace as well as all the extras that make life just that little bit more enjoyable. South-east of Carpentras, on D4 (8 km).

■ RESTAURANT: Closed Wed. Gourmet restaurant offering regional and classic cuisine as well as a bistro (which is closed on Mondays). Specialities include wild asparagus, herb-fed rabbit and fresh Mediterranean seafood.
■ ACTIVITIES: Good sports facilities nearby; festivals, theatre; cookery courses available.
■ TARIFF: (1994) Double 700, Bk 50 (Euro/Access, Visa).
■ DISCOUNT: 8%

Hôtel Les Trois Colombes ★★★ 148 av des Garrigues, 84210 St-Didier.
☎ 90 66 07 01, Fax 90 66 11 54. English spoken.
Open 01/03 to 31/12. 30 bedrooms (all en suite). Outdoor swimming pool, tennis, golf 6 km, parking. &

Charming Provençal country residence with shady grounds covering 800 sq metres. From the A7 take the Avignon-Nord exit and go through Carpentras towards St-Didier, following signposts to the hotel.

■ RESTAURANT: Offers classic French cuisine with Provençal specialities.
■ TARIFF: (1994) Single 300, Double 320–400, Bk 45, Set menu 105–190 (Amex, Euro/Access, Visa).

CASSIS Bches-du-Rhône 6C

Hôtel La Plage du Bestouan ★★★ Plage du Bestouan, 13260 Cassis.
☎ 42 01 05 70, Fax 42 01 34 82. English spoken.
Open 15/03 to 15/10. 30 bedrooms (all en suite). Golf 10 km.

Seaside hotel with a panoramic terrace and super location right beside the beach. Cassis is a lively fishing port off the D559.

■ RESTAURANT: Traditional restuarant with gastronomic cuisine.
■ ACTIVITIES: Excellent facilities for sports, boating and fishing nearby. Good base for sightseeing and excursions.
■ TARIFF: (1994) Single 300–400, Double 400–600, Bk 40 (Amex, Euro/Access, Visa).

CASTELJALOUX Lot/Garonne   4D

Château de Ruffiac ★★★ Ruffiac, 47700 Casteljaloux.
☎ 53 93 18 63, Fax 53 89 67 93. English spoken. Open 01/03 to 31/01. 20 bedrooms (all en suite). Outdoor swimming pool, golf 8 km, parking. &

Vast 14th-century vicarage, next to church, with views of both mountains and valleys. Comfortable rooms with good facilities. From Casteljaloux, north-west on D655 for 8 km.
■ RESTAURANT: Closed Feb. Good regional cuisine; excellent choice of local and regional wines.
■ ACTIVITIES: French billiards; water sports and BMX nearby.
■ TARIFF: Single 320–420, Double 380–480, Bk 40, Set menu 150–290 (Euro/Access, Visa).

LE CASTELLET Var   6C

Hôtel Castel Lumière ★★★ rue Portail, 83330 Le Castellet.
☎ 94 32 62 20, Fax 94 32 70 33. English spoken. Open all year. 6 bedrooms (all en suite). Golf 5 km, parking.
A charming hotel with a wonderful view of this historical village, once home of cinematographers the Lumière brothers. Ten minutes' walk from the Bandol beaches.
■ RESTAURANT: Closed Jan. Restaurant has a good reputation and specialities include rouget à l'emulsion d'huile d'olive, agneau à la fleur

de thym et foie gras au miel et muscat.
■ TARIFF: (1994) Double 330–380, Bk 55, Set menu 165–250 (Visa).
■ DISCOUNT: 5%

CASTERA-VERDUZAN Gers   4D

C

Hôtel Thermes ★★ 32410 Castéra-Verduzan.
☎ 62 68 13 07, Fax 62 68 10 49. English spoken. Open 01/02 to 01/01. 47 bedrooms (37 en suite). Parking, restaurant. &
In the village centre of Castéra-Verduzan and on the D930 north west of Auch.
■ TARIFF: (1994) Single 175–198, Double 228–260, Bk 30 (Amex, Euro/Access, Visa).

CASTRES

Castres lies to the north of the Pyrenees on the River Agoût – on a line that runs roughly between Toulouse in the west and the Mediterranean coast at Montpellier, making it a good centre from which to tour this attractive region.

The town initially grew around the 9th-century abbey of St-Benoît and became an important producer of woven cloth during the Middle Ages. The industry still exists today and Castres continues to be one of the major textile centres in the south of France. Some of the houses originally used by the medieval dyers and weavers have survived along the river bank and their cellars open directly onto the Agoût. These houses have been carefully restored over the last 20 years and are known locally as *Les Maisons sur l'Agoût*. To see them from the river, you can take a trip on the local boat, the *Miredames,* which also runs north to the Parc de Gourjade. This leisure park has an archeological exhibition and a nine-hole golf course among its many attractions.

Across the river from Les Maisons sur l'Agoût is the centre of the old town. All that remains of the original abbey is La Tour Romane, now incorporated into the Hôtel de Ville, and opposite stands the 17th-century Cathedral of St-Benoît. Characteristic houses, with their curious overhanging upper storeys, can be found in

C

some of the surrounding streets, and these have also been recently restored. The Hôtel de Ville, previously the Bishop's Palace, is a fine 17th-century building which still looks out over its formal garden (designed by the famous French garden designer La Nôtre). This is only one of the several public gardens which the local tourist information states 'contribute pleasingly to the aesthetic nature of the town'.

Inside the Hôtel de Ville, the Musée Goya has an impressive collection of Spanish paintings by such masters as Murillo and Vélasquez, as well, of course, as Goya himself. Another museum in Castres dedicated to one man is the Musée Jean Jaurès which commemorates the life of this famous French orator who was born in the town.

Castres lies very close to the regional Parc du Haut Languedoc with its Montagne Noire to the south and the Sidobre area to the north-east. This is a particularly impressive region of strangely shaped rocks. There is the trembling Sept-Faux rock close to St-Salvy-de-la-Balme and, further north, the Chaos de la Resse, to mention only two of the many bizarre formations. As well as being an area of great natural beauty, it is full of legends which the local people presumably devised to try and explain the fantastic landscapes in which they lived. The park has several tourist trails for walkers to follow as well as 1800 km of marked paths, which can be used individually or as part of a guided expedition.

CASTRES Tarn   5C

(See feature)

Hôtel Café du Pont Les Salvages, 81100 Castres.
☎ 63 35 08 21, Fax 63 51 09 82.
Open all year. 6 bedrooms (1 en suite, 4 bath/shower only). Golf 2 km, parking.
A small hotel 5 km from Castres on the D89.

■ RESTAURANT: Closed Feb, Sun eve & Mon. Good restaurant with a pretty flower-bedecked and shaded terrace.
■ ACTIVITIES: Tennis, horse-riding and swimming pool close by.
■ TARIFF: (1994) Single 170–190, Double 190–240, Bk 35, Set menu 90–250 (Amex, Euro/Access, Visa).

CAUDEBEC-EN-CAUX Seine-Marit   2A

Normotel La Marine ★★ 18 quai Guilbaud, 76490 Caudebec-en-Caux.
☎ 35 96 20 11, Fax 35 56 54 40. English spoken.
Open 01/02 to 01/01. 29 bedrooms (all en suite). Parking.
The hotel overlooks the River Seine, in the town centre.

■ RESTAURANT: Closed Jan.
■ TARIFF: (1994) Double 250–420, Bk 35, Set menu 78–230 (Amex, Euro/Access, Visa).

CAUTERETS Htes-Pyrénées   4D

Hôtel Etche Ona ★★ 20 rue Richelieu, 65110 Cauterets.
☎ 62 92 51 43, Fax 62 92 54 99. English spoken.
Open 01/12 to 30/04 & 01/06 to 10/10. 32 bedrooms (27 en suite). Golf 20 km, parking.
In the centre of Cauterets, opposite the spa and close to the cable car and ice rink. Friendly hotel in comfortable, modern surroundings.

■ RESTAURANT: Basque and local specialities; children's menu.
■ ACTIVITIES: Ice skating, skiing, rock climbing, fishing and boating nearby.
■ TARIFF: (1994) Single 190–260, Double 260–320, Bk 32, Set menu 65–195 (Amex, Euro/Access, Visa).
■ DISCOUNT: 5%

CAVAILLON Vaucluse   5D

Hôtel du Parc ★★ 183 place François Tourel, 84300 Cavaillon.
☎ 90 71 57 78, Fax 90 76 10 35.
Open all year. 40 bedrooms (all en suite). Garage, parking.
At the bottom of Colline St-Jaques 300 m from the town centre. Follow signs towards Arc Romain.

■ TARIFF: (1994) Single 150–250, Double 230–300, Bk 36 (Euro/Access, Visa).

CERGY-PONTOISE Val-d'Oise   2B

Hôtel Astrée ★★★ 3 rue des Chênes Emeraude, bd de l'Oise, 95000 Cergy.
☎ 1 34 24 94 94, Fax 1 34 24 95 15. English spoken.
Open all year. 55 bedrooms (all en suite). Golf 2 km, garage, restaurant. &
Comfortable, air-conditioned hotel, in the centre of this new town. 4 suites also available. From Paris, Pte Maillot, exit no 10 (Cergy Pontoise).

■ ACTIVITIES: Free swimming at local pool; fitness centre and tennis nearby.
■ TARIFF: (1994) Double 450–500, Bk 45 (Amex, Euro/Access, Visa).

CEYRAT Puy-de-Dôme   5A

Hôtel L'Artière ★★ 75 av de la Libération, 63122 Ceyrat.
☎ 73 61 43 02, Fax 73 61 41 37. English spoken.
Open all year. 24 bedrooms (all en suite).
Tennis, golf 5 km, garage, parking, restaurant. &

A new hotel in a quiet, wooded area of the countryside. Drive south through Ceyrat, and the hotel can be found first on the left.
■ TARIFF: (1994) Single 250, Double 250–300, Bk 25, Set menu 65–120 (Amex, Euro/Access, Visa).

Hôtel La Renaissance ★★ 1 av Wilson, 63122 Ceyrat.
☎ 73 61 40 46, Fax 73 61 43 77. English spoken.
Open all year. 10 bedrooms (all en suite).
Garage, parking.

Completely renovated in 1992, Logis de France hotel with a family atmosphere. Quiet position near the town hall and a campsite.
■ RESTAURANT: A good choice of well-prepared dishes in warm, friendly surroundings. (A complimentary kir is offered to holders of this book.).
■ ACTIVITIES: Golf, tennis and swimming nearby; lots of places of archaeological/cultural interest to visit as well as the 'Puy-de-Dome', standing at 1465 m, lakes and the gorges of Ceyrat.
■ TARIFF: (1994) Single 200–300, Double 250–350, Bk 30, Set menu 100–240 (Amex, Euro/Access, Visa).
■ DISCOUNT: 10%

CHABLIS Yonne   3C

Hôtel des Clos ★★★ rue Jules Rathier, 89800 Chablis.
☎ 86 42 10 63, Fax 86 42 17 11. English spoken.
Open 10/01 to 10/12. 26 bedrooms (all en suite). Golf 25 km, garage, parking. &

Elegant hotel from which to enjoy the Chablis region. Tranquil garden setting encompassing 12th-century chapel.
■ RESTAURANT: Closed Wed & Thur lunch LS. Creative cuisine, regional dishes. Exceptional wine cellar.
■ TARIFF: (1994) Single 240–495, Double 268–530, Bk 50, Set menu 160–400 (Amex, Euro/Access, Visa).

CHAGNY Saône/Loire   3C

Hôtel Bonnard ★★ rte de Chalon, 71150 Chagny.
☎ 85 87 21 49, Fax 85 87 06 54. English spoken.
Open 01/02 to 20/12. 20 bedrooms (all en suite). Garage, parking.

In the southern outskirts of Chagny on the N6.
■ RESTAURANT: Serves Bourguignonnes specialities.
■ TARIFF: (1994) Single 205, Double 215–270, Bk 30, Set menu 80–180 (Euro/Access, Visa).

Hôtel Château de Bellecroix ★★★ rte de Chalon, 71150 Chagny.
☎ 85 87 13 86, Fax 85 91 28 62. English spoken.
Open 15/02 to 20/12. 21 bedrooms. Outdoor swimming pool, golf 10 km, garage, parking.

A pleasing combination of 12th-and-18th-century architecture and once home to a Commander of the Knights of Malta. Beautifully furnished, the hotel is set in lovely parkland and is peaceful and relaxing.
■ RESTAURANT: Classic cuisine and excellent Burgundy wines are served in the elegant dining room. Specialities include terrine de foie gras fait maison, poularde de Bresse and home-smoked salmon.

CHALLANS Vendée   1D

Hôtel Antiquité ★★ 14 rue Gallieni, 85300 Challans.
☎ 51 68 02 84, Fax 51 35 55 74. English spoken.
Open all year. 16 bedrooms (all en suite). Outdoor swimming pool, golf 15 km, parking. &

Family hotel with garden, 60 km from Nantes. 15 km from the coast. From St-Jean-de-Montes on the coast eastwards on D753 to Challans.
■ TARIFF: (1994) Single 210–350, Double 250–390, Bk 30 (Amex, Euro/Access, Visa).

CHALON-SUR-SAONE Saône/Loire   5B

Hôtel Charmilles ★★ rue de la Libération, 71100 Lux.
☎ 85 48 58 08, Fax 85 93 04 49. English spoken.
Open all year. 30 bedrooms (all en suite). Golf 4 km, garage, parking.

Traditional standards of Logis de France. 4 km from the centre of Chalon-sur-Saône and 1 km from the Chalon-Sud, A6 exit. Just off the N6 towards Mâcon.
■ RESTAURANT: Closed Mon.
■ ACTIVITIES: Fishing, sightseeing tours.

C

C

■ TARIFF: (1994) Single 190–230,
Double 205–260, Bk 30, Set menu 72–235
(Euro/Access, Visa).

Hôtel Relais du Montagny ★★ 71390 Buxy.
📞 85.92 19 90, Fax 85 92 07 19. English spoken.
Open all year. 30 bedrooms (all en suite).
Outdoor swimming pool, golf 15 km, garage,
parking, restaurant. &

From the A6, take Chalon-Sud exit towards
Monceau on the E607/N80. After 200 m turn
left onto the D981 and carry on for 13 km. The
hotel is on the outskirts of the village.

■ TARIFF: (1994) Single 275–325,
Double 305–360, Bk 40, Set menu 85–170
(Amex, Euro/Access, Visa).

CHALONS-SUR-MARNE Marne   3A

Hôtel aux Armes de Champagne ★★★ 31 av
du Luxembourg, 51460 L'Epine.
📞 26 69 30 30, Fax 26 66 92 31. English spoken.
Open 16/02 to 07/01. 37 bedrooms
(all en suite). Tennis, garage, parking.

Traditional French hostelry, very tastefully
decorated and with good facilities. In the
shadow of the basilica of Notre Dame in pretty
L'Epine. 8 km from Châlons-sur-Marne on N3
to Metz, Verdun.

■ RESTAURANT: Closed Sun eve & Mon, Nov to
Mar.
■ TARIFF: (1994) Single 320–780,
Double 400–780, Bk 55, Set menu 205–480
(Euro/Access, Visa).

Hôtel Bristol ★★ 77 av P Sémard,
51510 Fagnières.
📞 26 68 24 63, Fax 26 68 22 16. English spoken.
Open 02/01 to 23/12. 24 bedrooms
(23 en suite, 1 bath/shower only). Golf 10 km,
garage, parking.

A comfortable hotel with spacious rooms that
can accommodate extra beds for children.
■ TARIFF: (1994) Single 150–215,
Double 195–235, Bk 28 (Euro/Access, Visa).

CHAMBERY Savoie   5B

Hostellerie des Comptes de Challes
73190 Challes-les-Eaux.
📞 79 72 86 71, Fax 79 72 83 83.
English spoken.
Open all year. 45 bedrooms (all en suite).
Outdoor swimming pool, tennis, golf 15 km,
parking. &

Beautiful 15th-century building set in
parkland. 6 km from Chambéry towards
Albertville.

■ RESTAURANT: Closed Sun LS. Elegant dining
room with terrace overlooking the park.
Traditional French cuisine.
■ ACTIVITIES: Marked walking trails close to
hotel.
■ TARIFF: (1994) Single 420–520,
Double 500–600, Bk 45, Set menu 135–280
(Amex, Euro/Access, Visa).
■ DISCOUNT: 10%

CHAMBORD Loir/Cher   2D

Château de Nanteuil ★★ Huisseau-sur-
Cosson, 41350 Vineuil.
📞 54 42 61 98, Fax 54 42 37 23. English spoken.
Open 15/02 to 31/12. 9 bedrooms (7 en suite,
2 bath/shower only). Golf 10 km, parking.

A wisteria-clad château standing in peaceful
surroundings; bought by the present owner's
English grandfather.

■ RESTAURANT: Closed Mon & Tues lunch.
Attractive 18th-century dining room with family
portraits. Seafood specialities and children's
menu.
■ ACTIVITIES: Hunting, rides in horse-drawn
carriages and sightseeing all within easy reach
of hotel.
■ TARIFF: (1994) Double 190–350, Bk 30,
Set menu 90–210 (Euro/Access, Visa).

CHAMONIX Hte-Savoie   6A

Hôtel Albert 1er ★★★★ 119 impasse du
Montenvers, 74400 Chamonix-Mont-Blanc.
📞 50 53 05 09, Fax 50 55 35 48.
English spoken.

Open 01/12 to 02/05 & 10/05 to 24/10.
32 bedrooms (all en suite). Outdoor swimming
pool, golf 2 km, garage, parking. &

Beautiful hotel with a backdrop of mountains
and only a stone's throw from the centre of
town. Traditional Savoie welcome. Just to the
south of the N506.

■ RESTAURANT: Closed Wed lunch. Fine food, with specialities of the region.
■ ACTIVITIES: A variety of mountain and river activities with qualified instructors; scrambling.
■ TARIFF: (1994) Single 450–900, Double 590–1150, Bk 68, Set menu 175–410 (Amex, Euro/Access, Visa).

Hôtel Le Chantel ★★ 391 route des Pecles, 74400 Chamonix.
℡ 50 53 02 54, Fax 50 53 54 52. English spoken.

Open all year. 7 bedrooms (all en suite). Golf 2 km, parking.
A family-run chalet hotel with magnificent view of Mont Blanc and Needles. Situated in south residential area, 7 minutes' walk from town. Leave motorway at Chamonix-Sud. At lights take small road diagonally left.
■ TARIFF: (1994) Double 356–506 (Visa).

Hôtel Frantour ★★ 74400 Chamonix-Mont-Blanc.
℡ 50 53 07 56, Fax 50 53 54 79. English spoken. Open 01/12 to 31/10. 133 bedrooms (all en suite). Golf 5 km, garage. &
Large and comfortable in typical Savoie style, the hotel is in the centre of Chamonix close to the station. SEE ADVERTISEMENT.
■ RESTAURANT: Carefully prepared regional cuisine in a Savoyard atmosphere; terrace with view of Mont-Blanc.
■ ACTIVITIES: Sunbeds, sauna, jacuzzi, disco, bar-club, nursery.
■ TARIFF: (1994) Single 379–429, Double 420–476, Bk 35 (Amex, Visa).
■ DISCOUNT: 8%

Hôtel Jeu de Paume ★★★★ 705 route du Chapeau, Le Lavancher, 74400 Chamonix-Mont-Blanc.
℡ 50 54 03 76, Fax 50 54 10 75. English spoken. Open 15/12 to 15/05 & 15/06 to 15/10.

24 bedrooms (all en suite). Indoor swimming pool, outdoor swimming pool, tennis, golf 3 km, garage, parking, restaurant. &
This traditional wooden chalet-style hotel offers four-star modern accommodation in warm and elegant surroundings. For holidays in quiet scenic surroundings. From Chamonix, north towards Argentière and Switzerland, look for a right turn to Le Lavancher.
■ ACTIVITIES: Off-piste downhill and cross-country skiing. Within easy reach of Chamonix and Argentière.
■ TARIFF: (1994) Double 680–1250, Bk 55, Set menu 175–230 (Amex, Euro/Access, Visa).

Hôtel Richemond ★★ 228 rue Dr Paccard, 74400 Chamonix-Mont-Blanc.
℡ 50 53 08 85, Fax 50 55 91 69. English spoken. Open 01/01 to 20/04 & 10/06 to 17/09. 53 bedrooms (all en suite). Golf 2 km, parking, restaurant.
A traditional hotel in town centre close to cable-car and bus stations. Rear entrance on allée Recteur Payot.
■ TARIFF: (1994) Single 274–305, Double 418–490 (Amex, Euro/Access, Visa).
■ DISCOUNT: 8%

C

Hôtel Vallée Blanche ★★★ 36 rue du Lyret, 74400 Chamonix-Mont-Blanc.
☎ 50 53 04 50, Fax 50 55 97 85. English spoken.

Open all year. 24 bedrooms (all en suite). Golf 3 km, restaurant. ♿

A charming hotel, with hand-painted furniture. Piano bar and riverside terrace. 5 minutes' walk from the railway station and cable cars. From the autoroute take the first Chamonix-Sud exit, then follow signs to the town centre.
■ ACTIVITIES: Skiing, fishing, climbing and mountain-biking nearby.
■ TARIFF: (1994) Single 350–485, Double 379–485, Bk 38, Set menu 83–119 (Amex, Euro/Access, Visa).

CHAMPAGNAC Cantal 5A

Château de Lavendes ★★★ route de Neuvic, 15350 Champagnac.
☎ 71 69 62 79, Fax 71 69 65 33. English spoken.
Open 01/03 to 30/11. 8 bedrooms (all en suite). Outdoor swimming pool, golf 10 km, parking.

10 km from Bort-les-Orgues. Elegant château set in parkland, on D15 to Neuvic.
■ RESTAURANT: Closed Mon LS. Good regional food.
■ TARIFF: (1994) Double 400–540, Bk 52, Set menu 165–260 (Euro/Access, Visa).

CHAMPAGNOLE Jura 6A

Hôtel Parc ★★★ 13 rue P Cretin, 39300 Champagnole.
☎ 84 52 13 20, Fax 84 52 27 62. English spoken.
Open all year. 20 bedrooms (all en suite). Garage, parking. ♿

Traditional hotel in a quiet position just 5 minutes' walk from the town centre. Close to the River Ain and public gardens. Well located for long forest and river walks.

■ RESTAURANT: Louis XIII-style. Specialities: terrine au vin jaune; champignons du pays à la crème; coq au vin jaune.
■ ACTIVITIES: Horse-riding, fishing, canoeing and tennis can be organised through local clubs; public swimming pool nearby.
■ TARIFF: (1994) Single 220, Double 260–320, Bk 30, Set menu 75–180 (Amex, Euro/Access, Visa).
■ DISCOUNT: 5%

Hôtel Ripotot ★★ 54 rue Maréchal Foch, 39300 Champagnole.
☎ 84 52 15 45, Fax 84 52 09 11. English spoken.
Open 01/04 to 30/11. 55 bedrooms (35 en suite). Tennis, golf 19 km, garage, parking. ♿

The hotel, which is owned by the fourth generation of the Ripotot family, lies within a large garden. Rooms spacious and quiet. Motorway A36 until Dole, then N5 to Poligny then Champagnole.
■ RESTAURANT: Closed Wed 01/09 to 30/06. 19th-century décor. Overlooking the garden. Local specialities.
■ ACTIVITIES: Tennis. Horse-riding, walking, swimming, golf and trout fishing nearby.
■ TARIFF: (1994) Single 140–280, Double 180–300, Bk 35, Set menu 70–220 (Amex, Euro/Access, Visa).
■ DISCOUNT: 5%

CHAMPAGNY-EN-VANOISE Savoie 6A

Hôtel L'Ancolie ★★ 73350 Champagny-en-Vanoise.
☎ 79 55 05 00, Fax 79 55 04 42. English spoken.
Open 17/12 to 23/04 & 04/06 to 10/09. 31 bedrooms (all en suite). Outdoor swimming pool, garage, parking. ♿

Hotel L'Ancolie is in an old Savoyard village in the La Plagne area, 33 km from Albertville. (Prices quoted are for half-board.)

■ RESTAURANT: Regional Savoie specialities.
■ ACTIVITIES: Skiing in winter, mountain walking in summer.
■ TARIFF: (1994) Single 260–690, Double 550–900 (Euro/Access, Visa).

CHAMPTOCEAUX Maine/Loire 1D

Hôtel Le Champalud ★★ promenade du Champalud, 49270 Champtoceaux.
℡ 40 83 50 09, Fax 40 83 53 81. English spoken.

Open all year. 16 bedrooms (4 en suite, 12 bath/shower only). Golf 4 km, parking. &
The hotel is close to the church square and Champalud public gardens in this historic town on the River Loire. East of Nantes off the A11 and N23. Exit Ancenis.

■ RESTAURANT: Closed Wed LS. Traditional restaurant with regional specialities.
■ ACTIVITIES: Mountain-biking, tennis and swimming (summer) nearby.
■ TARIFF: (1994) Single 155–220, Double 180–240, Bk 29, Set menu 59–250 (Euro/Access, Visa).
■ DISCOUNT: 10% LS.

CHAMROUSSE Isère 6A

Hôtel Hermitage ★★★ Le Recoin, 38410 Chamrousse.
℡ 76 89 93 21, Fax 76 89 95 30. English spoken.
Open 15/12 to 15/04. 50 bedrooms (all en suite). Garage, restaurant.
Chamrousse is 32 km east of Grenoble in the hills via Uriage.
■ TARIFF: (1994) Single 300–350, Double 350–440, Bk 36, Set menu 120–170 (Amex, Euro/Access, Visa).

CHANTILLY Oise 2B

Hôtel Parc ★★★ 36 av Mar Joffre, 60500 Chantilly.
℡ 44 58 20 00, Fax 44 57 31 10. English spoken.

Open all year. 58 bedrooms (all en suite). Golf, garage. &
Located in the main avenue of Chantilly, close to the forest, castle, race course and horses museum. Access via Motorway A1 Lille/Paris exit No 8.
■ ACTIVITIES: English bar and disco. Several restaurants nearby.
■ TARIFF: (1994) Single 380, Double 420–500, Bk 40 (Amex, Euro/Access, Visa).
■ DISCOUNT: 10%

Hôtel Relais d'Aumale ★★★ Montgrésin, 60560 Chantilly.
℡ 44 54 61 31, Fax 44 54 69 15. English spoken.

Open all year. 24 bedrooms (all en suite). Tennis, golf 5 km, parking. &
Charming hotel set in the heart of Chantilly forest. Comfortable and convenient rooms with all modern facilities.
■ RESTAURANT: Several dining rooms serving refined cuisine. Open-air terrace.
■ ACTIVITIES: Horse-riding nearby.
■ TARIFF: (1994) Single 460–490, Double 490–540, Bk 45 (Amex, Euro/Access, Visa).

Hôtel Mont Royal ★★★★
60520 La Chapelle-en-Ferval.
☎ 44 54 50 50, Fax 44 54 50 21. English spoken.

Open all year. 103 bedrooms (all en suite).
Indoor swimming pool, tennis, golf 10 km,
garage, parking. &

*A former hunting lodge, this elegant 18th-
century château has been splendidly
renovated and stands in the midst of the
Chantilly Forest. It is just 35 minutes from
central Paris and only 15 minutes from
Charles de Gaulle airport. Ideal for business or
pleasure. From the A1 motorway exit at
Survilliers/St-Witz, and turn towards
Senlis/Chantilly on the N17. In La Chapelle-en-
Serval head towards Pailly-Ermenonville.*

■ RESTAURANT: 'Le Stradivarius' restaurant offers
gourmet menus in a refined setting.
■ ACTIVITIES: Sauna, gym, squash, archery and
mountain bikes. Horse-riding nearby.
■ TARIFF: Single 1100–1250,
Double 1100–1350, Bk 90 (Amex,
Euro/Access, Visa).

CHAOURCE Aube   3C

Hôtel aux Maisons ★★ Maisons-lès-
Chaource, 10210 Chaource.
☎ 25 70 07 19, Fax 25 70 07 75.
English spoken.
Open all year. 16 bedrooms (9 en suite,

2 bath/shower only). Outdoor swimming pool,
golf 6 km, parking. &
*In a little village near the Chaource Forest and
30 km from Troyes. Take the main N71 south
from Troyes turning onto D444. From A6
motorway drive 25 km following signs for Nitry
and Tonnerre.*

■ RESTAURANT: Closed Sun eve LS. Specialities:
choucroute de Brienne et saumon de la Vanne;
caille à la fondue de champignons au
Chaource.
■ ACTIVITIES: Horse-riding, rafting, mountain-
biking and 4x4 nearby. ● 1 hour's free tennis.
■ TARIFF: (1994) Single 150–230,
Double 170–250, Bk 30 (Euro/Access, Visa).
■ DISCOUNT: 15% LS.

LA CHAPELLE-EN-VALGAUDEMAR   6C

Hôtel Mont-Olan ★ 05800 St-Firmin.
☎ 92 55 23 03.
Open 01/04 to 15/09. 32 bedrooms
(17 en suite, 6 bath/shower only). Garage,
parking, restaurant.
*A quiet and comfortable chalet-style hotel in
beautiful countryside. The village is 90 km
from Grenoble and 48 km from Gap.*

■ TARIFF: (1994) Single 130–200,
Double 200–260, Bk 25, Set menu 68–120
(Euro/Access, Visa).

LA CHAPELLE-EN-VECORS Drôme   5B

Hôtel Le Veymont ★★
26420 St-Agnan-en-Vercors.
☎ 75 48 20 19, Fax 75 48 10 34. English spoken.
Open 20/12 to 31/10. 20 bedrooms
(all en suite). Golf 2 km, parking.
*Le Veymont is English-owned and is situated in
a small village in the National Park of the
Vercors, with wonderful views of the
surrounding mountains. St-Agnan-en-Vercors
is 4 km south of La Chapelle-en-Vercors.*

■ RESTAURANT: Rustic-style restaurant;
specialities include confit de canard and poulet
aux écrevisses.
■ ACTIVITIES: Excellent base for cross-country
skiing, walking, sightseeing and horse-riding.
■ TARIFF: (1994) Single 180–250,
Double 220–260, Bk 35, Set menu 95–150
(Amex, Euro/Access, Visa).
■ DISCOUNT: 10%

CHAROLLES Saône/Loire   5B

Hôtel Moderne ★★★ av Gare,
71120 Charolles.
☎ 85 24 07 02, Fax 85 24 05 21. English spoken.

Open 01/01 to 28/12. 17 bedrooms
(all en suite). Outdoor swimming pool, garage,
parking. &

*Traditionally furnished hotel in the Charolais
region, famous for its Charolais cattle.
Charolles 68 km west of Mâcon on N79.*

■ RESTAURANT: Closed Sun eve, Mon LS. Belle
époque-style, wood-panelled dining room
with open fire; in summer diners overlook pool
and meadows.
■ TARIFF: (1994) Single 250–450,
Double 250–480, Bk 42, Set menu 110–290
(Amex, Euro/Access, Visa).

LA CHARTRE-SUR-LE-LOIR Sarthe   2C

Hôtel France ★★ 20 place de la République,
72340 La Chartre-sur-le-Loir.
✆ 43 44 40 16, Fax 43 79 62 20. English spoken.
Open 15/12 to 15/11. 29 bedrooms
(all en suite). Garage, restaurant.

*Very French hotel in central position, with
pavement café in front and large garden
behind. Good local fishing.*

■ TARIFF: (1994) Double 240–320, Bk 38,
Set menu 75–230 (Euro/Access, Visa).

CHARTRES Eure/Loir   2D

Hôtel Ibis ★★ 14 pl Drouaise, 28000 Chartres.
✆ 37 36 06 36, Fax 37 36 17 20. English spoken.
Open all year. 79 bedrooms (all en suite).
Golf 15 km, garage, restaurant. &

*From Paris take the A11 and exit at Chartres.
Ten minutes' walk from the cathedral and
railway station.*

■ TARIFF: (1994) Single 285–295,
Double 320–340, Bk 34, Set menu 55–95
(Amex, Euro/Access, Visa).

Manoir du Palomino ★★★ 28300 St-Prest.
✆ 37 22 27 27, Fax 37 22 24 92. English spoken.
Open all year. 18 bedrooms (all en suite).

Tennis, golf on site, parking. &
*A 15th-century manor set in a 25-acre park
with private golf course. From Chartres take
the road to Maintenon, following the signs
Vallée-de-l'Eure.*

■ RESTAURANT: Closed Sun eve LS.
■ ACTIVITIES: Walking, hot-air ballooning.
■ TARIFF: (1994) Single 300–500,
Double 350–550, Bk 45, Set menu 135–250
(Euro/Access, Visa).

C

CHATEAU-DU-LOIR Sarthe   2C

Hôtel de la Gare ★ 170 avenue Jean Jaurès,
72500 Château-du-Loir.
✆ 43 44 00 14, Fax 43 44 11 79.
Open 04/01 to 14/08 & 30/08 to 18/12.
16 bedrooms (10 en suite). Outdoor swimming
pool, tennis, golf 2 km, parking. &

*Friendly hotel/restaurant. Halfway between Le
Mans and Tours.*

■ RESTAURANT: Freshwater fish, game and
home-made desserts.
■ TARIFF: (1994) Single 115–190,
Double 120–230, Bk 24, Set menu 55–150
(Euro/Access, Visa).

Hôtel du Port Gautier ★★
72500 Vouvray-sur-Loir.
✆ 43 79 44 62. English spoken.
Open all year. 9 bedrooms (all en suite).

*Quietly situated on the bank of a small river.
From Château-du-Loir on N138, go in the
direction of Tours and turn left.*

■ ACTIVITIES: Horse-riding, windsurfing, fishing
and swimming in nearby park.
■ TARIFF: (1994) Single 180–220,
Double 180–220, Bk 23 (Euro/Access, Visa).

Auberge du Val de Loir 72500 Dissay-sous-
Courcillon.
✆ 43 44 09 06, Fax 43 44 56 40. English spoken.
Open all year. 10 bedrooms (all en suite).
Garage, parking.

*In the very centre of Loir Valley. Between Le
Mans and Tours on N138.*

■ RESTAURANT: Closed Sun eve & Mon LS. 3
dining rooms serving fresh country produce,
home-made foie gras and fish specialities.
■ TARIFF: (1994) Single 150–200,
Double 200–300, Bk 28, Set menu 85–230
(Euro/Access, Visa).

CHATEAU-THIERRY Aisne   2B

Hôtel Ile de France ★★★ rte de Soissons,
02400 Château-Thierry.
✆ 23 69 10 12, Fax 23 83 49 70. English spoken.

C

Open all year. 50 bedrooms (all en suite).
Golf 2 km, parking.
Imposing, modern hotel set in extensive
grounds overlooking the Marne Valley.
- RESTAURANT: Offers gourmet menus.
- ACTIVITIES: 30 minutes from Euro Disney.
- TARIFF: (1994) Single 200–280,
Double 250–330, Bk 38, Set menu 98–180
(Amex, Euro/Access, Visa).

CHATEAUBOURG Ille/Vil 1D

Hôtel Ar Milin ★★★ 35220 Châteaubourg.
 99 00 30 91, Fax 99 00 37 56.
English spoken.
Open 02/01 to 23/12. 31 bedrooms
(all en suite). Tennis, golf 15 km, parking.
An old mill house built of stone and huge
beams. Cleverly restored to retain its original
character and surrounded by the river and
lovely, wooded parkland. Rooms are either in
the mill house itself or in the park. The hotel is
1 km from the Châteaubourg exit off the E50
motorway between Rennes and Laval.
- RESTAURANT: Closed Sun eve Nov to end Feb.
Lovely beamed dining room with terrace
opening on to the grounds. Specialities:
feuilleté de coquillages St-Pierre aux coteaux
du Layon, volailles fermières, poissons grillés
ou en sauce.
- ACTIVITIES: Lots to do for young and old
including boating, fishing and watching the
ducks, geese, lambs and rabbits that are kept in
the grounds.
- TARIFF: (1994) Single 320–640,
Double 360–685, Bk 49 (Amex,
Euro/Access, Visa).

Hôtel Pen'Roc ★★★ La Peinière,
35220 St-Didier.
 99 00 33 02, Fax 99 62 30 89.
English spoken.
Open all year. 33 bedrooms (all en suite).
Outdoor swimming pool, golf 15 km, garage,
parking. &
An attractive, modern hotel built in local style
and situated between Rennes and Paris in a
quiet rural setting. Take the motorway Paris to
Rennes A81/N157 then exit Châteaubourg
D857 and go 7.5 km to St-Didier (D33).
- RESTAURANT: Closed Sun eve. Refined cuisine
using local ingredients - the seafood is
especially delicious.
- ACTIVITIES: Sauna and fitness room.
- TARIFF: (1994) Single 335–370,
Double 380–430, Bk 44, Set menu 145–320
(Amex, Euro/Access, Visa).

CHATEAUBRIANT Loire-Atlan 1D

Hôtel La Ferrière ★★★ route de Nantes,
44110 Châteaubriant.
 40 28 00 28, Fax 40 28 29 21. English spoken.
Open all year. 25 bedrooms (all en suite).
Golf 10 km, parking. &
Charming, ivy-clad 18th-century manor
house, set in superb landscaped gardens. On
the outskirts of Châteaubriant, on the D178
towards Nantes.
- RESTAURANT: Traditional restaurant with meat
and seafood specialities.
- ACTIVITIES: Horse-riding nearby.
- TARIFF: (1994) Single 270–330,
Double 330–600, Bk 39, Set menu 120–220
(Amex, Euro/Access, Visa).
- DISCOUNT: 15%

CHATEAUDUN Eure/Loir 2D

Hôtel Beauce ★★ 50 rue Jallans,
28200 Châteaudun.
 37 45 14 75, Fax 37 45 87 53. English spoken.
Open 10/01 to 18/12. 24 bedrooms
(18 en suite). Garage. &
Very quiet hotel, 3 minutes' walk from the town
centre. Closed Sundays from 15 Oct to 15 May.
- TARIFF: (1994) Single 145–230,
Double 160–270, Bk 30 (Euro/Access, Visa).

Hôtel St-Michel ★★ 28 place du 18 Oct/5 rue
Péan, 28200 Châteaudun.
 37 45 15 70, Fax 37 45 83 39.
English spoken.
Open all year. 19 bedrooms (15 en suite).
Golf 20 km, garage.
An old coaching inn in the main square of the
town. Near the castle, the caves and the
museum. From Paris, take motorway to
Chartres. 40 km further south on the N10 is
Châteaudun.
- ACTIVITIES: Sauna and solarium.
- TARIFF: (1994) Single 150–245,
Double 175–325, Bk 29 (Amex,
Euro/Access, Visa).
- DISCOUNT: 5% LS.

CHATEAUNEUF-SUR-LOIRE Loiret 2D

Hôtel du Parc ★★ sq de Gaulle,
45110 Châteauneuf/Loire.
 38 58 42 16, Fax 38 58 46 81.
English spoken.
Open 01/03 to 31/01. 14 bedrooms
(12 en suite). Golf 10 km, parking.
A traditional hotel, close to the tourist route of
the châteaux of the Loire valley.

■ RESTAURANT: Closed Sun eve & Mon. Gourmet specialities.
■ TARIFF: (1994) Double 210–390, Bk 35, Set menu 124–281 (Euro/Access, Visa).

CHATEAUNEUF-SUR-SARTHE   1D

Hôtel Sarthe 49330 Châteauneuf-sur-Sarthe.
✆ 41 69 85 29. English spoken.
Open all year. 7 bedrooms (5 en suite, 2 bath/shower only). Golf 8 km, parking.
Family hotel beside River Sarthe, near to centre of town. Between Le Mans and Tour; from Angers, take N23 to Seiches then onto Durtal and D859 for 20 km westward.
■ RESTAURANT: Closed Sun & Mon eve LS. Rustic setting, terrace by the river with outside grill in summer. Fresh fish specialities, sandre beurre blanc and friture d'anguille à la Provençale.
■ ACTIVITIES: Swimming pool, tennis and boating nearby.
■ TARIFF: Double 190–265, Bk 30, Set menu 85–200 (Euro/Access, Visa).

CHATEAUROUX Indre   5A

Auberge Arc en Ciel ★★ La Forge-de-l'Ile, 36330 Châteauroux.
✆ 54 34 09 83, Fax 54 34 46 74.
English spoken.
Open all year. 24 bedrooms (18 en suite, 6 bath/shower only). Parking.
Attractive setting for this hotel with comfortable rooms beside the Indre River and near an oak-wood forest. Ten minutes from the town centre on the D943 leading to Châtre.
■ TARIFF: (1994) Single 150–195, Double 180–230, Bk 22 (Euro/Access, Visa).

CHATELAILLON-PLAGE Charente-Mar 4A

Majestic Hotel ★★ bd de la Libération, 17340 Châtelaillon-Plage.
✆ 46 56 20 53, Fax 46 56 29 24.
English spoken.
Open 10/01 to 15/12. 30 bedrooms (26 en suite, 4 bath/shower only). Golf 15 km, garage.
Built in 1927 and decorated in 20s style, the hotel is only 100 m from the beach. Follow Centre-Ville and Mairie signs in Châtelaillon-Plage.
■ RESTAURANT: Closed Sat & Sun LS. Seafood specialities.
■ ACTIVITIES: 500 m from indoor/outdoor swimming pools and tennis courts. Casino nearby; a number of excursions available.

■ TARIFF: (1994) Single 200–280, Double 220–320, Bk 32, Set menu 100–150 (Amex, Euro/Access, Visa, **BT**🌐).

Hôtel de la Plage ★★ bd de la Mer, 17340 Châtelaillon-Plage.
✆ 46 56 26 02. English spoken.
Open 01/04 to 30/09. 10 bedrooms (all en suite). Parking, restaurant.
Highly recommended restaurant with rooms, overlooking the sea. The proprietor is also the chef.
■ TARIFF: (1994) Double 220–240, Bk 30, Set menu 90 (Visa).

CHATELGUYON Puy-de-Dôme   5A

Hôtel Régence ★★ 31 av Etats-Unis, 63140 Châtelguyon.
✆ 73 86 02 60, Fax 73 86 12 49.
English spoken.

Open 10/03 to 20/11. 27 bedrooms (24 en suite). Garage.
Traditional French hotel displaying 18th-century antique furniture. Châtelguyon is a thermal spa town and can be reached from the Riom-Est exit off A71 or D78 off N9.
■ RESTAURANT: Regional and traditional dishes. Roast turkey with peaches and prunes and apple crumble are served once a week in the evening.
■ ACTIVITIES: Tennis, golf practice pitch, ballooning, hang-gliding and swimming pool nearby. Good area for astronomy as the night sky is particularly black.
■ TARIFF: (1994) Single 170–215, Double 195–230, Bk 37, Set menu 80–95 (Amex, Euro/Access, Visa).

C

C

Hôtel Bains ★★ 12/14 av Baraduc,
63140 Châtelguyon.
☏ 73 86 07 97, Fax 73 86 11 56. English spoken.

Open 25/04 to 07/10. 37 bedrooms
(30 en suite). Golf 5 km, parking.

*Town centre hotel with a pretty garden.
Châtelguyon is 15 km from Clermont-Ferrand
just off the A71.*

■ RESTAURANT: Restaurant overlooks the garden.
Auvergne specialities: truite au lard, confit
canard lentilles du Puy, chiffonade de salers.
■ ACTIVITIES: Sporting activities and volcanic
park nearby.
■ TARIFF: (1994) Single 190–275,
Double 190–315, Bk 30, Set menu 95–110
(Euro/Access, Visa).
■ DISCOUNT: 5% Including restaurant.

CHATILLON-SUR-SEINE Côte-d'Or   3C

Sylvia Hôtel ★★ 9 av Gare, 21400 Châtillon-
sur-Seine.
☏ 80 91 02 44, Fax 80 91 47 77. English spoken.

Open all year. 21 bedrooms (6 en suite,
11 bath/shower only). Garage, parking. &

*Old family mansion in a large garden with lots
of greenery. Cosy rooms and attractive
reception with Burgundy décor. 5 minutes*

*from Châtillon centre along the N71 towards
Troyes.*

■ RESTAURANT: Closed LS. Set menus, fast food,
family cooking.
■ ACTIVITIES: Swimming pool, golf, angling,
mountain-biking and hiking all within the
locality. Tours of castles, churches and abbeys;
wine tasting.
■ TARIFF: (1994) Single 195–260,
Double 205–270, Bk 26 (Euro/Access, Visa).

LA CHATRE Indre   5A

Château de la Vallée Bleue ★★★ route de
Verneuil, 36400 St-Chartier.
☏ 54 31 01 91, Fax 54 31 04 48. English spoken.
Open 01/03 to 31/01. 13 bedrooms
(all en suite). Outdoor swimming pool,
golf 15 km, parking. &

*In the heart of George Sand's country. A
romantic spot. From La Châtre D943 then D69
in St-Chartier.*

■ RESTAURANT: Regional cuisine and extensive
wine list.
■ TARIFF: (1994) Single 200–395,
Double 320–550, Bk 50, Set menu 130–350
(Euro/Access, Visa).

CHAUMONT Hte-Marne   3C

Hôtel La Chaumière ★ Condes,
52000 Chaumont.
☏ 25 03 03 84.
Open all year. 11 bedrooms (3 en suite,
5 bath/shower only). Golf 20 km, parking.

*Set in the Haute-Marne area. North of the A5
on the D10 from junction 18 towards
Chaumont.*

■ RESTAURANT: Closed Thur eve & Fri.
■ TARIFF: (1994) Double 145–215, Bk 27,
Set menu 62–150 (Visa).

Hôtel Grand Terminus Reine ★★★ place du
Général de Gaulle, 52000 Chaumont.
☏ 25 03 66 66, Fax 25 03 28 95. English spoken.
Open all year. 62 bedrooms (59 en suite).
Garage, parking, restaurant. &

*Find comfort and elegance in this recently
modernised hotel. Close to railway station in
the centre of Chaumont.*

■ TARIFF: (1994) Double 180–460, Bk 40,
Set menu 90–350 (Amex, Euro/Access, Visa).

Hôtel Le Grand Val ★★ rte Langres,
52000 Chaumont.
☏ 25 03 90 35, Fax 25 32 11 80. English spoken.
Open all year. 52 bedrooms (46 en suite).
Golf 18 km, garage, parking. &

Panoramic vista over the Marne Valley. The Grand Val is located at the southern exit of Chaumont on the road to Lausanne and the French Riviera, via Langres (N19).

■ RESTAURANT: Offers well-prepared meals and a carefully selected wine list.

■ TARIFF: (1994) Single 150–310, Double 175–320, Bk 26, Set menu 60–160 (Amex, Euro/Access, Visa).

CHAUMONT-SUR-THARONNE   2D

Hôtel La Croix Blanche ★★★
41600 Chaumont-sur-Tharonne.
☎ 54 88 55 12, Fax 54 88 60 40. English spoken.
Open all year. 14 bedrooms (all en suite).
Tennis, golf 11 km, parking. ♿

One of France's oldest hotels, in a quiet village setting. Leave the A10, A71 motorways after Orléans La Source toll. 30 km from Chaumont via La Ferte, St Aubin, and Chaumont.

■ RESTAURANT: Renowned for its Sologne and Perigord specialities.

■ ACTIVITIES: Boating; Tourist Office at hotel.

■ TARIFF: (1994) Single 250–350, Double 340–500, Bk 45 (Amex, Euro/Access, Visa).

CHELLES   Seine/Marne   2B

Hôtel Climat de France ★★ 34 rte Claye
Souilly, 77500 Chelles.
☎ 60 08 75 58, Fax 60 08 90 94. English spoken.
Open all year. 43 bedrooms (all en suite).
Parking. ♿

Quiet position in a pleasant part of town, 1 km from the centre. All rooms are comfortable and fully equipped.

■ RESTAURANT: Country dishes, choice of hors d'oeuvres and desserts from the buffet.

■ ACTIVITIES: ● 15 minutes from Euro Disney, reservations and transport organised by the hotel.

■ TARIFF: (1994) Double 270–290, Bk 32, Set menu 87–115 (Amex, Euro/Access, Visa).

■ DISCOUNT: 15%

Hôtel Relais Brunehaut 3 rue de l'Eglise,
60350 Chelles.
☎ 44 42 85 05, Fax 44 42 83 30.
Open 15/04 to 15/11. 6 bedrooms
(all en suite). Golf 15 km, parking. ♿

In the centre of the Compiègne district (4 km from Chelles), a converted mill in pretty grounds beside the river.

■ RESTAURANT: Closed Mon & Tues.

■ TARIFF: (1994) Single 230–250, Double 260–300, Bk 36, Set menu 130–250 (Euro/Access, Visa).

CHENONCEAUX   Indre/Loire   2C

Hostellerie du Château de l'Isle Château de l'Isle, 37150 Civray-de-Touraine.
☎ 47 23 80 09, Fax 47 23 82 91. English spoken.
Open all year. 10 bedrooms (all en suite).
Parking.

18th-century château set in acres of greenery, quiet and secluded. From Tours take N76 east to Chenonceaux.

■ RESTAURANT: Cuisine using fresh local produce only.

■ ACTIVITIES: Horse-riding, fishing and walking beside the River Cher.

■ TARIFF: (1994) Double 330–580, Bk 45, Set menu 98–190 (Euro/Access, Visa).

■ DISCOUNT: 10%

Hôtel du Roy ★★ rue du Dr Bretonneau,
37150 Chenonceaux.
☎ 47 23 90 17, Fax 47 23 89 81. English spoken.
Open 15/02 to 15/11. 37 bedrooms
(24 en suite). Tennis, golf 20 km, parking. ♿

Situated in the village centre, near the castle and with a garden. Access: A10, exit at Amboise or Blois.

■ RESTAURANT: Gourmet restaurant with excellent meat, fish and game specialities.

■ TARIFF: (1994) Single 100–310, Double 140–310, Bk 30 (Amex, Euro/Access, Visa).

CHERBOURG   Manche   1B

Hôtel La Lorette Cap Lévi, 50840 Fermanville.
☎ 33 44 49 49, Fax 33 44 16 15.
Open all year. 6 bedrooms (all en suite).
Parking.

Small family-run hotel right on the coast at Cap Lévi. From Cherbourg drive east on the D901. Turn left (north) after 12 km to Fermanville and Cap Lévi. Or take the pretty coast road through Bretteville.

■ RESTAURANT: Specialities: fruits de mer, fish, grills.

■ TARIFF: (1994) Double 185–215, Bk 30, Set menu 90–140 (No credit cards).

Hôtel Louvre ★★ 2 rue H Dunant,
50100 Cherbourg.
☎ 33 53 02 28, Fax 33 53 43 88. English spoken.
Open 01/01 to 24/12. 42 bedrooms
(37 en suite). Golf 2 km, garage. ♿

A cheerful, friendly hotel close to town centre. Facilities include a lift and covered, secure garage. From the town centre, turn right after the bridge and then left after statue of Napoleon and traffic lights.

C

C

■ TARIFF: (1994) Single 220–320, Double 290–350, Bk 34 (Amex, Euro/Access, Visa).

CHINON Indre/Loire 2C

Chris'Hôtel ★★ 12 pl Jeanne d'Arc, 37500 Chinon.
📞 47 93 36 92, Fax 47 98 48 92. English spoken.
Open all year. 40 bedrooms (all en suite).
Golf 15 km, garage, parking.

In a quiet square, the hotel is near the ancient part of Chinon and has private parking. Very pleasant, with some excellent rooms. Finely decorated in Louis XV style; friendly atmosphere.

■ ACTIVITIES: Bicycle hire.
■ TARIFF: (1994) Single 220–300, Double 240–400, Bk 40 (Amex, Euro/Access, Visa).

Hôtel Diderot ★★ 4 rue Buffon, 37500 Chinon.
📞 47 93 18 87, Fax 47 93 37 10. English spoken.
Open 10/01 to 20/12. 28 bedrooms (all en suite). Parking. &

Highly recommended. A few yards from place Jeanne d'Arc, this interesting 18th-century building features half-timbered walls and an especially fine staircase. Walled courtyard. Family atmosphere, home-made jams for breakfast.

■ TARIFF: (1994) Single 225–300, Double 280–400, Bk 36 (Amex, Euro/Access, Visa).
■ DISCOUNT: 20% Nov to Mar.

Hôtel de France ★★ 47 place du Gén de Gaulle, 37500 Chinon.
📞 47 93 33 91, Fax 47 98 37 03.
English spoken.
Open 01/03 to 01/12. 30 bedrooms (all en suite). Golf 15 km, garage, parking.

Renovated 16th-century building in the heart of medieval Vieux-Chinon and the Loire Valley, combines comfort with a respect for tradition. An ideal centre for exploring the 'Garden of France'. View of the château and easy access.

■ TARIFF: (1994) Single 260–320, Double 260–380, Bk 42 (Amex, Euro/Access, Visa).

LA CIOTAT Bches-du-Rhône 5D

Hôtel Miramar ★★★ 3 bd Beaurivage, La Ciotat-Plage, 13600 La Ciotat.
📞 42 83 33 79, Fax 42 83 33 79. English spoken.

Open all year. 25 bedrooms (all en suite).
Golf 7 km, parking. &

The hotel is situated opposite the main beach of La Ciotat. Follow the signs to Les Plages.

■ RESTAURANT: Well-regarded restaurant.
Specialities include: ravioli de homard, mignon de porc, civet de homard, filets de rouget.
■ TARIFF: (1994) Double 465–765, Bk 50, Set menu 125–270 (Amex, Euro/Access, Visa).

CLECY Calvados 2A

Hôtel Moulin du Vey ★★★ 14570 Clécy.
📞 31 69 71 08, Fax 31 69 14 14. English spoken.
Open 28/12 to 30/11. 25 bedrooms (all en suite). Golf 3 km, parking.

Beautiful old mill with 2 annexes, in a picturesque setting near the River l'Orne. Take the D133A, over Le Pont-du-Vey bridge.

■ RESTAURANT: Closed 30/11 to 28/12. Truly a gastronomic delight! Restaurant overlooks the river and also has a shady terrace. Specialities: homard grillé à la moulin du Vey; sandre au beurre de cidre et poivre.
■ ACTIVITIES: Canoeing, rock-climbing, mountain-biking, hiking, horse-riding, bungee jumping and hang-gliding nearby.
■ TARIFF: (1994) Double 380–500, Bk 48, Set menu 135–370 (Amex, Euro/Access, Visa).

CLERMONT-FERRAND

Clermont-Ferrand is sometimes described as the *ville-noire* after the local black lava stone from which the cathedral and some of the buildings are constructed. The town lies at the very edge of an extraordinary area dominated by the craters of extinct volcanos. Make the time to drive up the steep toll road just outside the town to the summit of the Puy-de-Dôme. From here the view is magnificent. Clermont-Ferrand lies 1,000 m below and the skyline is dominated by volcano after volcano. Although extinct, when caught by the setting sun, they can appear to be dramatically alight.

CLERMONT-FERRAND Puy-de-Dôme 5A

(See feature)

Hôtel Athena ★★ av A Rouzaud, 63130 Royat.
📞 73 35 80 32, Fax 73 35 66 26. English spoken. Open all year. 24 bedrooms (all en suite). Golf 8 km, parking.
Cheerful and bright, the hotel offers every comfort. 5 minutes' drive from centre of Clermont-Ferrand on the A71 to Royat.
■ ACTIVITIES: Fishing.
■ TARIFF: (1994) Single 220–240, Double 290–330, Bk 27 (Amex, Euro/Access, Visa).
■ DISCOUNT: 10%

Hôtel Bordeaux ★★ 39 av F Roosevelt, 63000 Clermont-Ferrand.
📞 73 37 32 32, Fax 73 31 40 56. English spoken. Open all year. 32 bedrooms (27 en suite). Golf 8 km, garage.
Well-equipped hotel with a private garage. 350 m from the town centre, at place Jaude; follow signs for Puy de Dôme.
■ ACTIVITIES: ● 10% discount at nearby school of aerial pursuits (parascending, flying etc).
■ TARIFF: (1994) Double 185–270, Bk 30 (Amex, Euro/Access, Visa).
■ DISCOUNT: 10%

Hôtel Lafayette ★★★ 53 av Union Soviétique, 63000 Clermont-Ferrand.
📞 73 91 82 27, Fax 73 91 17 26. English spoken. Open all year. 50 bedrooms (all en suite). Golf 10 km, parking. ♿
Modern hotel with friendly atmosphere, in front of the railway station and close to the beautiful Auvergne region with its lakes and volcanoes.
■ TARIFF: (1994) Single 245–300, Double 300–330, Bk 35 (Amex, Euro/Access, Visa).
■ DISCOUNT: 10%

Hôtel Relais des Puys ★★ La Baraque, 63870 Orcines.
📞 73 62 10 51, Fax 73 62 22 09. English spoken. Open 01/02 to 10/12. 28 bedrooms (23 en suite, 2 bath/shower only). Golf 3 km, garage, parking.
Standing high above Clermont-Ferrand (7 km)

at the foot of the mountains, a hotel run with enthusiasm by the Esbelin family for 6 generations. From Clermont-Ferrand follow signs for Limoges/Puy de Dôme via D941A.
■ RESTAURANT: Closed Mon lunch. Takes pride in offering home-made dishes using fresh, local produce.
■ ACTIVITIES: Horse-riding, mountain-biking, good walking country.
■ TARIFF: (1994) Single 135–222, Double 145–298, Bk 29, Set menu 75–185 (Amex, Euro/Access, Visa).

LA CLUSAZ Hte-Savoie 6A

Hôtel Christiania ★★ 74220 La Clusaz.
📞 50 02 60 60, Fax 50 02 67 30. English spoken. Open 15/12 to 15/04 & 30/06 to 15/09. 30 bedrooms (all en suite). Parking, restaurant.
Large chalet-style hotel next to the church and close to ski-lifts. 32 km from Annecy on the D909.
■ TARIFF: (1994) Single 250–330, Double 270–360, Bk 38 (Euro/Access, Visa).

COGNAC Charente 4B

Domaine du Breuil ★★ 104 av R Daugas, 16100 Cognac.
📞 45 35 32 06, Fax 45 35 48 06. Open all year. 24 bedrooms (all en suite). Tennis, golf 3 km, restaurant.
19th-century house set in a park 2 km from the town centre.
■ TARIFF: (1994) Single 290–440, Double 330–470, Bk 40, Set menu 95–250 (Amex, Euro/Access, Visa).

Hôtel Urbis ★★ 24 rue Elisée Moushier, 16100 Cognac.
📞 45 82 19 53, Fax 45 82 86 71. English spoken. Open all year. 40 bedrooms (39 en suite, 1 bath/shower only). Golf 5 km, parking. ♿
Modern hotel with garden. Conveniently situated, very helpful staff.
■ ACTIVITIES: Exploring the famous Cognac area; visit to Norman city of Saintes (25 km).
■ TARIFF: Single 270, Double 295, Bk 35 (Amex, Euro/Access, Visa).

COLLIOURE Pyrénées-Or 5C

Hôtel Madeloc ★★★ rue Romain Rolland, 66190 Collioure.
📞 68 82 07 56, Fax 68 82 55 09. English spoken. Open all year. 22 bedrooms (all en suite). Golf 15 km, parking.
Situated near mountains and 500 m from the

C

beach, this modern hotel has rooms with private terraces. Turn right off the N114 to Perpignan.

- TARIFF: (1994) Double 260–400, Bk 38 (Amex, Euro/Access, Visa).

Hôtel Méditerranée ★★★ av A Maillol, 66190 Collioure.
📞 68 82 08 60, Fax 68 82 46 29.

Open 25/03 to 30/10. 23 bedrooms (all en suite). Tennis, golf 10 km, garage, parking.

Only 250 m from beach, a quiet hotel with pleasant garden and offering room service. Is the only hotel in Collioure with a garage.

- TARIFF: (1994) Double 300–380, Bk 33 (Euro/Access, Visa).
- DISCOUNT: 5%

COLMAR Ht-Rhin   3D

Hôtel Amiral ★★★ 11a bd du Champ de Mars, 68000 Colmar.
📞 89 23 26 25, Fax 89 23 83 64. English spoken.
Open all year. 44 bedrooms (all en suite). Golf 10 km, garage. &

Contemporary hotel with simple but elegant furnishings and a warm atmosphere. In a quiet position in the town centre, in front of place Rapp.

- TARIFF: (1994) Single 320–420, Double 370–490, Bk 52 (Amex, Euro/Access, Visa).

Hôtel de la Fecht ★★★ 1 rue Fecht, 68000 Colmar.
📞 89 41 34 08, Fax 89 23 80 28. English spoken.
Open all year. 80 bedrooms (all en suite). Golf 5 km, garage, parking. &

Close to the picturesque old city, the hotel has been completely renovated and offers every comfort and a warm welcome.

- RESTAURANT: Closed Sat & Sun eve LS. Most attractive restaurant, plus lovely summer garden. A good choice of Alsace specialities accompanied by folk singing or dances some evenings.
- ACTIVITIES: Swimming and tennis nearby, as well as lovely countryside for walking.
- TARIFF: (1994) Single 290, Double 290–420, Bk 40 (Amex, Euro/Access, Visa).
- DISCOUNT: 10%

Hôtel Husseren-les-Châteaux ★★★ rue Schlossberg, 68420 Husseren-les-Châteaux.
📞 89 49 22 93, Fax 89 49 24 84. English spoken.

Open all year. 38 bedrooms (all en suite). Indoor swimming pool, tennis, golf 22 km, garage, parking. &

Modern, interesting hotel with bedrooms on two levels. Views over vineyards and the Rhine Valley. 6 km south of Colmar on the N83.

- RESTAURANT: The well-appointed restaurant and bar open out onto a terrace with breathtaking views. Excellent cuisine.
- ACTIVITIES: Good sports/health facilities and children's playroom at hotel; good area for sightseeing; hunting and skiing within easy reach.
- TARIFF: Single 390–490, Double 390–610, Bk 55, Set menu 120–320 (Amex, Euro/Access, Visa).

Hostellerie Le Maréchal ★★★★ 4 pl des 6 Montaignes Noire, Petite-Venise, 68000 Colmar.
📞 89 41 60 32, Fax 89 24 59 40. English spoken.
Open all year. 30 bedrooms (all en suite). Golf 10 km, parking.

Beautiful, old, heavily-timbered building dating back to 1565, Le Maréchal is situated in the old quarter known as Little Venice. Elegantly furnished and every comfort.

- RESTAURANT: Dining rooms overlook the river. Excellent cuisine.

Near the cathedral in the centre of this lovely old town, a nicely renovated, quiet hotel. Parks and restaurants nearby.
■ ACTIVITIES: Reservations service for tours.
■ TARIFF: (1994) Single 350–450, Double 350–600, Bk 48 (Amex, Euro/Access, Visa).

C

Hôtel Rapp ★★ 1 rue Weinemer, 68000 Colmar.
℡ 89 41 62 10, Fax 89 24 13 58.
English spoken.
Open all year. 43 bedrooms (39 en suite, 4 bath/shower only). Indoor swimming pool, golf 8 km. &
A cosy hotel in the old town, close to the place Rapp car park.
■ RESTAURANT: Closed Sat lunch. A good restaurant serving original Alsace cuisine.
■ ACTIVITIES: Sauna.
■ TARIFF: (1994) Single 260–310, Double 340–400, Bk 38, Set menu 95–300 (Amex, Euro/Access, Visa, BT⌀).

■ ACTIVITIES: Walking, cycling and exploring the wonderful countryside.
■ TARIFF: Single 450–500, Double 550–1400, Bk 60 (Amex, Euro/Access, Visa).
■ DISCOUNT: 8%

Hôtel St-Martin ★★★ 38 Grand'rue, 68000 Colmar.
℡ 89 24 11 51, Fax 89 23 47 78.
English spoken.
Open 01/03 to 31/12. 24 bedrooms (all en suite). Golf 10 km.

COLOMBEY-LES-DEUX-EGLISES 3C

Hôtel Les Dhuits ★★★ 52330 Colombey-les-Deux-Eglises.
℡ 25 01 50 10, Fax 25 01 56 22.
English spoken.

Open 05/01 to 20/12. 42 bedrooms (all en suite). Tennis, golf 25 km, garage, parking. &
Quietly situated modern hotel and restaurant in this historic town on the champagne route. On N19.
■ RESTAURANT: Closed 05/01 to 20/01. Regional specialities include chausson de fromages de Langres, saumon au champagne and gibier.
■ TARIFF: (1994) Single 250–280, Double 280–350, Bk 35, Set menu 80–160 (Amex, Euro/Access, Visa).

COLY Dordogne 4B

Manoir d'Hautegente ★★★ 24120 Coly.
☎ 53 51 68 03, Fax 53 50 38 52. English spoken.

Open 01/04 to 01/11. 10 bedrooms
(all en suite). Outdoor swimming pool,
golf 18 km, parking.

*Beautiful, ivy-clad manor house in extensive
grounds with elegant bedrooms. Just 5 minutes
off the N89 Bordeaux to Genève road and 20
minutes from the N20 Paris to Toulouse road.*

■ RESTAURANT: Excellent food.
■ ACTIVITIES: Class 1 fishing beat, tennis (2 km)
and horse-riding (10 km). Close to Sarlat, Les
Eyzies and Lascaux Caves.
■ TARIFF: (1994) Double 500–900, Bk 55
(Euro/Access, Visa, **BT**🗲).

COMBEAUFONTAINE Hte-Saône 3C

Hôtel Balcon ★★ 70120 Combeaufontaine.
☎ 84 92 11 13, Fax 84 92 15 89.
Open 12/01 to 26/12. 18 bedrooms
(16 en suite, 2 bath/shower only). Garage,
parking.

*Pretty, flower-bedecked hotel in a quiet part of
France. Comfortable, with a heavy emphasis
on the kitchen. Combeaufontaine lies on the
N19 between Langres and Vesoul.*

■ RESTAURANT: Well-regarded restaurant
specialising in regional Franche-Comté meals.
■ ACTIVITIES: Fishing, lovely walks and beautiful
countryside to explore.
■ TARIFF: (1994) Single 140–300,
Double 140–360, Bk 40, Set menu 140–360
(Amex, Euro/Access, Visa).

COMBLOUX Hte-Savoie 6A

Hôtel Feug ★★★ route de Megève,
74920 Combloux.
☎ 50 93 00 50, Fax 50 21 21 44. English spoken.
Open all year. 28 bedrooms (all en suite).

Indoor swimming pool, outdoor swimming
pool, tennis, golf 2 km, garage, parking. &
*Facing Mt Blanc, chalet-style hotel offering
every comfort and wonderful views.*

■ RESTAURANT: Very pretty, panoramic
restaurant with regional specialities such as
fondue, raclette and fresh fish dishes.
■ ACTIVITIES: Skiing and mountain sports
close by.
■ TARIFF: (1994) Double 290–550, Bk 45,
Set menu 105–195 (Amex, Euro/Access, Visa).

COMBOURG Ille/Vil 1D

Hôtel Château et Voyageurs ★★ pl
Châteaubriand, 35270 Combourg.
☎ 99 73 00 38, Fax 99 73 25 79. English spoken.
Open 20/01 to 15/12. 33 bedrooms (all en
suite). Golf 10 km, garage, parking, restaurant.

*Charming hotel situated near the lake and
château on the edge of town. Located between
the roads to Dinan and Rennes.*

■ TARIFF: (1994) Double 260–450, Bk 42
(Amex, Euro/Access, Visa).

COMPIEGNE Oise 2B

Auberge à la Bonne Idée ★★★ St-Jean-aux-
Bois, 60350 Compiègne.
☎ 44 42 84 09, Fax 44 42 80 45.
English spoken.

Open all year. 24 bedrooms (all en suite).
Parking. &

*In the heart of the Forêt de Compiègne, this
charming hotel dates back to the 17th-century.
Located in the centre of St-Jean-aux-Bois on
the D85, just 10 minutes' drive from the A1.*

■ RESTAURANT: Gourmet restaurant with lots of

atmosphere; meals served on a covered terrace when weather permits.
■ ACTIVITIES: Mountain bikes, horse-riding, archery nearby.
■ TARIFF: (1994) Double 385–430, Bk 58, Set menu 120–380 (Amex, Euro/Access, Visa).

Hôtel de France ★★ 17 rue E Floquet, 60200 Compiègne.
☎ 44 40 02 74, Fax 44 40 48 37. English spoken.
Open all year. 21 bedrooms (16 en suite, 3 bath/shower only). Golf 1 km, parking.

In town centre.

■ RESTAURANT: Furnished in Louis XVI style, gourmet menu, background music.
■ ACTIVITIES: Cycling in Compiègne forest.
■ TARIFF: (1994) Single 125–290, Double 158–357, Bk 41, Set menu 90–215 (Euro/Access, Visa).

COMPS-SUR-ARTUBY Var   6C

Grand Hôtel Bain ★★ 83840 Comps-sur-Artuby.
☎ 94 76 90 06, Fax 94 76 92 24. English spoken.
Open all year. 18 bedrooms (15 en suite). Tennis, golf 17 km, garage, parking.

Located on the road between Draguignan and Castellane, the hotel has been handed from father to son since 1737. Currently being run by Jean Marie Bain, the 8th generation, with his son Arnaud being the Chef de Cuisine.

■ RESTAURANT: Authentic Var cuisine as well as secret family recipes.
■ TARIFF: (1994) Single 165–250, Double 165–320, Bk 32, Set menu 75–180 (Euro/Access, Visa).

CONCARNEAU Finistère   1C

Hôtel de France et d'Europe ★★ 9 av de la Gare, 29900 Concarneau.
☎ 98 97 00 64, Fax 98 50 76 66. English spoken.
Open all year. 26 bedrooms (all en suite). Golf 4 km, parking.

Hotel is in the centre of the town near the fishing port and the old Ville Close. From N165 go towards coast to Concarneau.

■ TARIFF: (1994) Single 250–295, Double 270–335, Bk 30 (Amex, Euro/Access, Visa).

Hôtel Modern ★★ 5 rue du Lin, 29900 Concarneau.
☎ 98 97 03 36. English spoken.
Open all year. 17 bedrooms (7 en suite, 5 bath/shower only). Garage.

In town, close to the fishing harbour,

10 minutes to the yacht harbour and old fortified town. From the centre of town follow signs to the hotel.

■ TARIFF: (1994) Double 190–330, Bk 35 (No credit cards).

Hôtel des Sables Blancs ★★ Plage des Sables Blancs, BP 130, 29900 Concarneau.
☎ 98 98 01 39, Fax 98 50 65 88.
English spoken.

Open 01/04 to 30/10. 48 bedrooms (43 en suite). Golf 4 km.

Set on the beach this family-run hotel offers a warm welcome. All rooms have sea views. 1 km from Concarneau town.

■ RESTAURANT: Restaurant and terrace have panoramic sea views. Excellent cuisine with seafood specialities.
■ ACTIVITIES: Tennis. ● 10% discount (LS) at nearby golf course.
■ TARIFF: (1994) Single 170–300, Double 180–310, Bk 33, Set menu 75–170 (Amex, Euro/Access, Visa).

CONDE-SUR-NOIREAU Calvados   2A

Hôtel Le Cerf ★★ 18 rue de Chêne, 14110 Condé-sur-Noireau.
☎ 31 69 40 55, Fax 31 69 78 29.
English spoken.
Open all year. 9 bedrooms (all en suite). Garage, parking.

Caen Condé/Noireau first left, turn on right, 500 m on right again.

■ RESTAURANT: Closed Sun eve. Classic restaurant serving regional food.
■ ACTIVITIES: Swimming pool 5 minutes from park.
■ TARIFF: (1994) Single 204–214, Double 204–214, Bk 25, Set menu 65–155 (Amex, Euro/Access, Visa).
■ DISCOUNT: 30% LS, 15% HS.

C

CONDRIEU Rhône 5B

Hôtel Beau Rivage ★★★★ 69420 Condrieu.
✆ 74 59 52 24, Fax 74 59 59 36. English spoken.

Open all year. 25 bedrooms (all en suite).
Golf 20 km, garage, parking. &

*A former fisherman's home, beautifully
renovated, between the Rhône and the hills.
Comfortable, individually-decorated rooms,
lovely gardens and a very warm welcome.*

■ RESTAURANT: Tastefully decorated in soft
colours, the air-conditioned, relaxing dining
room overlooks the river and offers creative
gourmet cuisine with regional specialities.
■ ACTIVITIES: Wonderful area for hill walking,
visiting wine cellars and archaeological sites.
■ TARIFF: Double 500–820, Bk 60,
Set menu 180–600 (Amex, Euro/Access, Visa).

LE CONQUET Finistère 1C

Hôtel Pointe Ste-Barbe ★★
29217 Le Conquet.
✆ 98 89 00 26, Fax 98 89 14 81. English spoken.
Open 18/12 to 12/11. 49 bedrooms
(37 en suite, 12 bath/shower only). Golf 8 km,
parking. &

*Exceptional situation beside the sea and
harbour with direct access to the beach. 25 km
west of Brest on the D789.*

■ RESTAURANT: Closed Mon LS. Panoramic
restaurant with a very good reputation. French
cuisine with seafood specialities.
■ ACTIVITIES: Lots to see and do nearby.
■ TARIFF: (1994) Single 185–487,
Double 185–607, Bk 34, Set menu 92–430
(Amex, Euro/Access, Visa).

CONTRES Loir/Cher 2C

Hôtel Château de la Gondelaine
41700 Contres.
✆ 54 79 09 14, Fax 54 79 64 92. English spoken.

Open 01/03 to 15/01. 15 bedrooms
(all en suite). Golf 5 km, parking.

*Elegant, authentic 17th-century residence set
in its own 80-acre park. Peaceful, comfortable
and very welcoming.*

■ RESTAURANT: Closed Wed. Gourmet cuisine.
Fish and shellfish specialities as well as game in
season.
■ ACTIVITIES: Tennis, horse-riding, fishing,
swimming, mountain-biking and good walks
all within easy reach.
■ TARIFF: (1994) Single 450, Double 490–830,
Bk 45, Set menu 155–280 (Amex,
Euro/Access, Visa).

LA COQUILLE Dordogne 4B

Hôtel des Voyageurs ★★ 12 rue de la
République, 24450 La Coquille.
✆ 53 52 80 13, Fax 53 62 18 29. English spoken.
Open 15/04 to 30/09. 10 bedrooms (6 en suite,
1 bath/shower only). Garage, parking.

*This hotel is a former stop on the pilgrimage to
St-Jacques-de-Compostelle and is situated on
the N21 between Châlus and Thiviers, in the
village of La Coquille.*

■ RESTAURANT: Closed Mon 15/04 to 30/06.
Specialises in Périgord cuisine.
■ TARIFF: (1994) Single 150–260,
Double 170–300, Bk 35, Set menu 100–300
(Euro/Access, Visa).

CORSE (CORSICA)

AJACCIO Corse du Sud 6D

Hôtel Campo dell'Oro ★★★ Plage du
Ricanto, 20000 Ajaccio, Corse.
✆ 95 22 32 41, Fax 95 20 60 21. English spoken.
Open 01/03 to 15/11. 140 bedrooms
(all en suite). Outdoor swimming pool, tennis,
golf 10 km, garage, parking. &

Hotel has modern, comfortable rooms, some of which are air-conditioned. Bar with terrace offers an exciting choice of cocktails and overlooks the pretty gardens.

■ RESTAURANT: 'Le Méditerranée' is open year-round and offers grilled meat and fish dishes as well as regional specialities.
■ ACTIVITIES: Direct access via underpass to the beach. Sailboats, motorboats and surf boards for hire; hotel has its own sports facilities and a sauna.
■ TARIFF: (1994) Single 350–600, Double 450–700, Bk 45 (Amex, Euro/Access, Visa).
■ DISCOUNT: 10%

Hôtel Les Mouettes ★★★★ 9 cours L Bonaparte, 20000 Ajaccio, Corse.
✆ 95 21 44 38, Fax 95 21 71 80. English spoken.

Open 01/05 to 30/10. 19 bedrooms (all en suite). Outdoor swimming pool, parking. ♿

1.5 km from the centre of town (8 km from the airport, by the coast road to Iles Sanguinaires) in quiet surroundings close to the sea with direct access to the beach. The hotel is a comfortable family residence. Prices shown are for half-board.

■ RESTAURANT: Closed Mon.
■ TARIFF: (1994) Double 1560–2820, Set menu 240 (Amex, Euro/Access, Visa).

C

CALACUCCIA Corse du Sud 6D

Hôtel L'Acqua Viva ★★ 20224 Calacuccia, Corse.
✆ 95 48 06 90, Fax 95 48 08 82.
English spoken.
Open all year. 12 bedrooms (all en suite). Garage, parking.

With panoramic views across Monte Cintu this hotel, set in one of the highest villages in Corsica overlooking the lake, offers comfortable accommodation for summer and winter sports holidays.

■ ACTIVITIES: Excursions, guided walks.
■ TARIFF: (1994) Single 250–350, Double 250–380, Bk 35 (Euro/Access, Visa).

EVISA Corse du Sud 6D

Hôtel Scopa Rossa ★★ 20126 Evisa, Corse.
✆ 95 26 20 22, Fax 95 26 24 17.
Open 01/04 to 30/10. 25 bedrooms (all en suite). Garage, parking. ♿

Just outside the village of Evisa in a peaceful setting, a pleasant walk away from the Spelunca Gorges and with a playground for children. On D84.

■ RESTAURANT: Offers home-cooked Corsican food; breakfasts on the terrace.
■ ACTIVITIES: Mountain walks, tennis and horse-riding nearby.
■ TARIFF: Single 180–250, Double 200–350, Bk 35, Set menu 90–150 (Amex, Euro/Access, Visa).

ILE ROUSSE Corse du Sud 6D

Hôtel Cala di l'Oru ★★ 20220 Ile Rousse, Corse.
✆ 95 60 14 75, Fax 95 60 36 40.
English spoken.
Open all year. 24 bedrooms (all en suite). Golf 10 km, parking.

The hotel is 600 m from the beach and has panoramic views of the sea and mountains.

■ TARIFF: (1994) Single 200–400, Double 250–550, Bk 30 (Euro/Access, Visa).

CORSE (CORSICA) RESORTS CONTINUED

PORTO-POLLO Corse du Sud 6D

C

Hôtel Les Eucalyptus ★★ 20140 Petreto-Bicchisano, Corse.
✆ 95 74 01 52, Fax 95 74 06 56. English spoken.
Open 12/05 to 02/10. 27 bedrooms
(all en suite). Tennis, parking.

Les Eucalyptus is set back just 50 m from sandy beaches, in a green and pleasant position overlooking the Gulf of Valinco.

■ RESTAURANT: Fish and traditional dishes based on local produce. Nice view from restaurant and terrace.
■ ACTIVITIES: Good sports facilities close by.
■ TARIFF: (1994) Double 275–325, Bk 35, Set menu 98–150 (Amex, Euro/Access, Visa).
■ DISCOUNT: 5%

PROPRIANO Corse du Sud 6D

Hôtel Roc e Mare ★★★ 20110 Propriano, Corse.
✆ 95 76 04 85, Fax 95 76 17 55.
English spoken.
Open 01/05 to 31/10. 62 bedrooms
(all en suite). Parking.

Located in the Gulf of Valinco, overlooking the sea and 1 km from Propriano. The hotel has a bar and lounge with panoramic views and a private beach with snack bar.

■ ACTIVITIES: Water sports from the private beach.
■ TARIFF: (1994) Single 350–535, Double 370–665, Bk 45 (Amex, Euro/Access, Visa).
■ DISCOUNT: 10%

QUENZA Corse du Sud 6D

Hôtel Sole e Monti ★★ Quenza, 20122 Quenza, Corse.
✆ 95 78 72 53, Fax 95 78 63 88.
English spoken.
Open 15/03 to 31/10. 20 bedrooms
(all en suite). Parking.

In a beautiful mountain village with superb views.

■ RESTAURANT: Has excellent reputation specialising in game, trout and wild boar.
■ TARIFF: (1994) Single 250–500, Double 300–600, Bk 50 (Amex, Euro/Access, Visa).

END OF CORSE (CORSICA) RESORTS

COSNE-COURS-SUR-LOIRE Nièvre 2D

Hôtel Gd Monarque ★★ près Eglise, 58220 Donzy.
✆ 86 39 35 44, Fax 86 39 37 09. English spoken.

Open all year. 11 bedrooms (all en suite).
Garage, parking.

Small hotel with old-world charm and fine cuisine. Donzy is south-east of Cosne-Cours-sur-Loire on D33.

■ RESTAURANT: Closed Sun eve and Mon.
Gourmet restaurant. Specialities: coq au Sancerre rouge; jambon saupiquet; magrets de canard; profiteroles au chocolat.
■ ACTIVITIES: Fishing, hunting, cycling, walking, horse-riding, swimming pool, tennis nearby.
■ TARIFF: (1994) Single 230–270, Double 230–270, Bk 40, Set menu 98–200 (Euro/Access, Visa).
■ DISCOUNT: 5% LS only.

COUCOURON Ardèche 5B

Hôtel Carrefour des Lacs ★★
07470 Coucouron.
✆ 66 46 12 70. English spoken.

Open 01/02 to 17/12. 21 bedrooms
(all en suite). Garage, parking.

C

Attractive, traditional hotel set beside a lake on the Ardèche plateau. Turn north off the N102 between Aubenas and Le Puy.
■ RESTAURANT: Two large dining rooms, with a log fire in winter. Regional and classic cuisine.
■ ACTIVITIES: Wide range of sporting activities, including canoeing in summer and skiing in winter, within easy reach.
■ TARIFF: (1994) Double 130–295, Bk 28, Set menu 80–170 (Amex, Euro/Access, Visa).

COURCHEVEL Savoie 6A

Hôtel Byblos des Neiges ★★★★ BP 98, 73122 Courchevel.
☎ 79 08 12 12, Fax 79 08 19 38. English spoken.

Open 18/12 to 16/04. 77 bedrooms (all en suite). Indoor swimming pool, garage, parking. &
At the foot of the largest expanse of ski slopes in the world, in the heart of the alpine garden of Courchevel, hotel is as luxurious as a palace and as warm as a chalet. 15 minutes from the centre of the town. Prices quoted are for half-board.
■ RESTAURANT: Excellent hot or cold buffets can be enjoyed at 'La Clairière' with its pleasant outdoor terrace, or try seafood specialities at 'L'Ecailler' in the evenings.
■ ACTIVITIES: Skiing on the doorstep.
■ TARIFF: Single 1580–2120, Double 2620–4500, Bk 120, Set menu 310–350 (Amex, Euro/Access, Visa).

Hôtel du Golf de Courchevel ★★★
Courchevel 1650, 73120 Courchevel.
☎ 79 00 92 92, Fax 79 08 19 93.
English spoken.
Open 15/12 to 15/04. 57 bedrooms (all en suite). Garage, parking. &
Great location at the foot of the pistes, in the heart of Courchevel. Warm and friendly, very good facilities.

■ RESTAURANT: Choose from refined, creative cuisine in the hotel restaurant or enjoy a meal in the more casual surroundings of the terrace restaurant, 'L'ours Blanc'.
■ ACTIVITIES: Wonderful spot for mountain activities; ski school catering for everyone aged from 3 up; snow playground for tiny tots.
■ TARIFF: (1994) Single 540–950, Double 830–1650 (Amex, Euro/Access, Visa).
■ DISCOUNT: 5%

Hôtel Mercure ★★★ Jardin Alpin, 73120 Courchevel.
☎ 79 08 11 23, Fax 79 08 18 62.
English spoken.
Open 30/06 to 31/08 & 01/12 to 30/04.
127 bedrooms (all en suite). Outdoor swimming pool, golf on site, parking. &
Comfortable hotel with good facilities, almost on top of the golf course and at the foot of the pistes.
■ RESTAURANT: Panoramic views and Savoyard specialities including raclette and fondue.
■ ACTIVITIES: Winter and summer mountain sports; mountain-biking, lovely walks.
■ TARIFF: Double 295–500, Bk 75 (Amex, Euro/Access, Visa, **BT**𝄐).

COURSEULLES-SUR-MER Calvados 2A

Hôtel Paris ★★ place du 6 juin, 14470 Courseulles-sur-Mer.
☎ 31 37 45 07, Fax 31 37 51 63.
English spoken.
Open 01/04 to 31/10. 29 bedrooms (27 en suite). Golf 18 km, parking.
Comfortable hotel near the beach and town centre. Rooms have good facilities and sea views. Courseulles is on the coast north-west of Caen.
■ RESTAURANT: Closed Oct to March.
■ TARIFF: (1994) Double 200–320, Bk 35, Set menu 65–230 (Amex, Euro/Access, Visa).

C

COUTANCES Manche   1B

Hôtel Cositel ★★ route de Coutainville, 50200 Coutances.
☎ 33 07 51 64, Fax 33 07 06 23. English spoken. Open all year. 55 bedrooms (all en suite). Golf 10 km, garage, parking. &

Quiet hotel set amongst greenery and with lovely views over the town. From Coutances, head towards Coutainville. You will find the hotel on your left.

■ RESTAURANT: Closed 24 Dec eve. Comfortable restaurant with regional cuisine and seafood specialities.
■ ACTIVITIES: Tennis, swimming pool, horse-riding and beach within easy reach. Good area for sightseeing.
■ TARIFF: (1994) Single 275–325, Double 320–370, Bk 39, Set menu 78–210 (Amex, Euro/Access, Visa).
■ DISCOUNT: 5%

CREST Drôme   5B

Grand Hôtel ★★ 60 rue Hôtel de Ville, 26400 Crest.
☎ 75 25 08 17, Fax 75 25 46 42. English spoken. Open 20/01 to 20/12. 22 bedrooms (6 en suite, 8 bath/shower only). Golf 15 km.

Between Loriol and Valence, in Crest, this 19th-century hotel is both quiet and comfortable.

■ RESTAURANT: Closed Mon lunch. Traditional regional cuisine.
■ TARIFF: (1994) Single 135–250, Double 130–320, Bk 32, Set menu 80–200 (Euro/Access, Visa).

CRIEL-SUR-MER Seine-Marit   2B

Hostellerie de la Vieille Ferme ★★ Mesnil-Val-Plage, 76910 Criel-sur-Mer.
☎ 35 86 72 18, Fax 35 86 12 67. English spoken. Open all year. 34 bedrooms (all en suite). Parking, restaurant.

Charming old Norman hotel 200 m from the sea. Very comfortable, good food. Take coast road from D925.

■ TARIFF: (1994) Single 290–450, Double 340–450, Bk 35, Set menu 75–215 (Amex, Euro/Access, Visa).

LA CROIX-VALMER Var   6C

Hôtel Eucalyptus ★★ 83240 Cavalaire-sur-Mer.
☎ 94 64 01 90. English spoken. Open all year. 27 bedrooms (all en suite). Golf 1 km, parking. &

New hotel conforming to modern-day standards and with a choice of studios or rooms. 50 m from the beach and 1 km from town centre. Cavalaire-sur-Mer is south of La-Croix-Valmer.

■ ACTIVITIES: Tennis, water sports and sea fishing nearby.
■ TARIFF: (1994) Double 280–345, Bk 33 (Euro/Access, Visa).
■ DISCOUNT: 10% LS.

Thalotel Les Mas de la Magnanerie ★★★★ 10 bd de la Mer, 83420 La Croix-Valmer.
☎ 94 79 56 15, Fax 94 79 73 73. English spoken.

Open all year. 32 bedrooms (all en suite). Outdoor swimming pool, parking. &

On St-Tropez peninsula, only 400 m from the beach, the hotel consists of apartments surrounding a fountain, each with their own jacuzzi. From the A8 take the D25 to St-Maxime, N98 to Port Grimaud, then the D559 to La Croix-Valmer.

■ ACTIVITIES: Water sports, sightseeing.
■ TARIFF: (1994) Single 350–1110, Double 390–1150, Bk 55 (Amex, Euro/Access, Visa).

CROZON Finistère   1C

Hôtel Moderne ★★ 61 rue Alsace Lorraine, 29160 Crozon.
☎ 98 27 00 10, Fax 98 26 19 21. English spoken. Open all year. 37 bedrooms (22 en suite). Parking, restaurant.

In Crozon, with rustic furniture and a well-known restaurant and wine cellar.

■ TARIFF: (1994) Single 150–252, Double 170–324, Bk 32, Set menu 79–198 (Euro/Access, Visa).

CUISEAUX Saône/Loire   3C

Hôtel du Commerce Vuillot ★★ 36 rue Edouard Vuillard, 71480 Cuiseaux.
☎ 85 72 71 79, Fax 85 72 54 22.

Open all year. 16 bedrooms (all en suite).
Outdoor swimming pool, golf 20 km, garage,
parking.
*A typical city centre hotel offering good
accommodation.*
■ RESTAURANT: Very good food.
■ TARIFF: (1994) Single 190–220,
Double 200–250, Bk 30, Set menu 76–250
(Euro/Access, Visa).

DEAUVILLE Calvados 2A

Hôtel de l'Amiraute ★★★ Touques,
14800 Deauville.
℡ 31 81 82 83, Fax 31 81 82 93. English spoken.

Open all year. 121 bedrooms (all en suite).
Indoor swimming pool, outdoor swimming
pool, tennis, golf 3 km, parking, restaurant. &
*A very comfortable hotel with excellent
facilities; ideal for those wishing to keep fit!*
■ ACTIVITIES: At hotel, sauna, jacuzzi, squash
courts, indoor/outdoor pools, exercise classes.
■ TARIFF: (1994) Double 690–780, Bk 55
(Amex, Euro/Access, Visa).

Hôtel Helios ★★ 10 rue Fossorier,
14800 Deauville.
℡ 31 88 28 26, Fax 31 88 53 87. English spoken.

Open all year. 44 bedrooms (all en suite).
Outdoor swimming pool, golf 3 km. &
*The hotel is right in the centre of Deauville in a
quiet area between the beach and the race
track, a few minutes walk from the casino and
the C.I.D.(International Congress Centre).*
■ TARIFF: (1994) Single 290–460,
Double 390–460, Bk 45 (Amex,
Euro/Access, Visa).

Hôtel Normandy ★★★★ 38 rue J Mermoz,
14800 Deauville.
℡ 31 98 66 22, Fax 31 98 66 23. English spoken.
Open all year. 300 bedrooms (all en suite).
Indoor swimming pool, tennis, golf 3 km,
garage, parking. &
*Stunningly picturesque hotel, inside and out.
Every possible comfort and direct access to the
casino next door!*
■ RESTAURANT: Gourmet restaurant and deluxe
brasserie, both having an excellent reputation.
■ ACTIVITIES: ● Free cycling, tennis, use of the
olympic-sized pool (with sliding roof), health
centre, 18-hole pitch and putt and children's
nursery.
■ TARIFF: (1994) Double 980–2000, Bk 90
(Amex, Euro/Access, Visa, **BT**).

Manoir de Roncheville ★★★ St-Martin-aux-
Chartrains, 14130 Deauville.
℡ 31 65 14 14, Fax 31 65 20 44. English spoken.
Open all year. 8 bedrooms (all en suite).
Golf 2 km, garage, parking.
*On the banks of a river, this hotel has high-
class cuisine. Four golf courses nearby.
Between Deauville and Pont l'Evêque on the
D58.*
■ RESTAURANT: Closed Wed LS.
■ TARIFF: (1994) Double 450–750, Bk 50,
Set menu 140–210 (Amex, Euro/Access, Visa).

DIEPPE Seine-Marit 2A

Hôtel Plage ★★ 20 bd Verdun, 76200 Dieppe.
℡ 35 84 18 28, Fax 35 82 36 82. English spoken.
Open all year. 40 bedrooms (all en suite).
Golf 3 km.
*A modern hotel overlooking the promenade
and 2 minutes from the town centre. There are
plenty of restaurants nearby as well as the ferry
terminal.*
■ TARIFF: (1994) Double 270–320, Bk 38 (Visa).

Hôtel Windsor ★★ 18 bd de Verdun,
76200 Dieppe.
℡ 35 84 15 23, Fax 35 84 74 52. English spoken.
Open all year. 48 bedrooms (42 en suite).

D

Golf 1 km, parking, restaurant. &
Comfortable hotel situated on the seafront, between the harbour and the casino.
■ TARIFF: (1994) Double 145–345, Bk 45, Set menu 80–250 (Amex, Euro/Access, Visa).

Hôtel La Présidence ★★★ 2 bd Verdun, 76200 Dieppe.
☎ 35 84 31 31, Fax 35 84 86 70. English spoken.

Open all year. 89 bedrooms (all en suite). Golf 4 km, garage, restaurant. &
Situated on the seafront and at the foot of an old château.
■ ACTIVITIES: ● Special weekend and short break deals, including green fees.
■ TARIFF: (1994) Single 350–550, Double 400–590, Bk 50 (Amex, Euro/Access, Visa).

DIGNE-LES-BAINS Alpes-Hte-Prov   6C

Tonic Hôtel ★★ route des Thermes, 04000 Digne.
☎ 92 32 20 31, Fax 92 32 44 54. English spoken.

Open all year. 60 bedrooms (all en suite). Outdoor swimming pool, tennis, golf 6 km, parking, restaurant. &
Modern, quiet hotel near thermal baths. From

A8 going towards Cannes, turn left onto N85 towards Grasse then on to Digne.
■ ACTIVITIES: Fitness room.
■ TARIFF: (1994) Single 300–380, Double 350–430, Bk 35, Set menu 90–160 (Amex, Euro/Access, Visa).
■ DISCOUNT: 10%

DIJON

Pavement cafés on Dijon's La Place François-Rude

Dijon is famous for its restaurants, many specialising in local cuisine. During the 14th and 15th centuries famous banquets were held here in the Ducal Palace, the home of the Dukes of Burgundy. Dijon was their capital and from it they ruled over an area that ran from the River Loire to the Jura mountains and north to include a large proportion of modern-day Belgium and Holland.

A visit to the Dukes' huge kitchens gives you some idea of the scale on which this important dynasty entertained. The Ducal Palace also houses the Musée des Beaux-Arts. At the back of the palace lies the Tour de Philippe le Bon which you can climb before, after or instead of looking at the paintings in the museum. Climbing the 316 steps is ideal if you feel some exercise is required, either to whet your appetite or after indulging in a delicious dinner. At the top, you will be rewarded with extensive views in all directions – they say that you can see Mont Blanc on a very clear day!

D

The Ducal Palace faces onto the Place de la Libération at the very heart of Dijon. This 17th-century semi-circular square, which was originally called the Place Royale, is surrounded by graceful colonnaded houses. There are more fine mansions in the Rue des Forges which lies behind the palace. In fact, there are so many great houses to look at in Dijon that the tourist board has printed a special leaflet giving their locations. While looking at these, you may well come across the Place François-Rude which, with its fountain and pavement cafés, is a popular place in which to relax.

If you are on a self-catering holiday, or are just interested in food, visit the Halles Centrales, the inside food market, near to the Place François-Rude. If you prefer a picnic to a more formal meal, buy your

Mustard

The story goes that in the 4th century AD, when the Gauls occupied Rome, they took with them, amongst other things, mustard seeds. Whether it was a Gaul or a Roman who first had the idea of grinding up the seeds and mixing the resulting powder with vinegar, we will probably never know but, whoever they were, they could hardly have imagined the popularity of their invention. The name we use today – mustard – came from the word 'must' meaning unfermented grape juice, which is often used in preference to vinegar.

During the Middle Ages, the use of mustard became widespread and by the 13th century Dijon had become a centre of its production. The distinctive taste of moutarde de Dijon comes from the use of unripe grape juice in the mixture. Throughout the years, mustard has been flavoured in many interesting ways. During the 17th century, vanilla and orange blossom were popular additions while, 200 years later, the fashion was for aromatic herbs such as tarragon and chives to be included.

Pots of mustard make good presents to bring home, either to give away or to enjoy yourself. In Dijon, go to the Rue de la Liberté where Maille, one of the leading moutarde de Dijon producers, has a specialist shop. For cooking, remember to choose the yellower varieties for better looking sauces.

ingredients here and then head for the Jardin de l'Arquebuse, the local botanical garden, which is near the station. On the same site is the Musée d'Histoire Naturelle with a beautiful collection of butterflies as well as a huge array of stuffed birds and mammals.

Between here and the centre of town lies the Cathédrale St-Bénigne, built in the 14th century on top of a 10th-century Romanesque church. Now the cathedral crypt, this church is circular, its ceiling supported by many pillars. Nearby, housed in part of the abbey buildings, is the Musée Archéologique.

Another interesting church is Notre-Dame, in the Rue de la Chouette. *Chouette* is the French word for an owl and it is from a small statue of one, in the wall of Notre-Dame, that the street gets its name. Touch it for luck as the local people do, and wish for the chance to return to Dijon with its many fine houses and tempting restaurants.

DIJON Côte-d'Or   3C

(See feature)

Hostellerie de de la Côte ★★ Marsannay-la-Côte, 21160 Dijon.
☎ 80 51 10 00, Fax 80 58 82 97. English spoken. Open all year. 42 bedrooms (all en suite). Outdoor swimming pool, parking. &

In the heart of Burgundy. Comfortable hotel with pretty terraces overlooking vineyards. About 5 km south-west of Dijon, off the N74.

■ RESTAURANT: Regional specialities with Burgundy wines.
■ TARIFF: (1994) Single 250–260, Double 265–280, Bk 32, Set menu 82–125 (Amex, Euro/Access, Visa).

Hôtel du Nord ★★★ pl Darcy, 21000 Dijon.
☎ 80 30 58 58, Fax 80 30 61 26. English spoken.
Open 01/01 to 15/12. 28 bedrooms (24 en suite). Golf 20 km, parking.

The hotel is situated in the centre of Dijon, 5 minutes' walk from the station. Near information point.

■ RESTAURANT: Closed 15/12 to 01/01.
■ TARIFF: (1994) Single 310–360, Double 360–400, Bk 50, Set menu 100–190 (Amex, Euro/Access, Visa).

D

Hôtel St-Georges carrefour de l'Europe, 21700 Nuits-St-Georges.
℡ 80 61 15 00, Fax 80 61 23 80. English spoken. Open all year. 47 bedrooms (all en suite). Outdoor swimming pool, tennis, golf 15 km, garage, parking. &

Just off the Nuits-St-Georges A31 motorway exit. Drive towards the town centre.

■ RESTAURANT: Specialises in regional and traditional cuisine.
■ ACTIVITIES: Biking, horse-riding, flying and wine tasting nearby.
■ TARIFF: (1994) Single 270–300, Double 285–350, Bk 40, Set menu 90–250 (Amex, Euro/Access, Visa).

Hôtel Wilson ★★★ place Wilson, 21000 Dijon.
℡ 80 66 82 50, Fax 80 36 41 54. English spoken.

Open all year. 27 bedrooms (all en suite). Golf 10 km, garage, parking. &

A former coaching inn, this 17th-century hotel, full of character, is situated south of Dijon just 5 minutes' walk from the town centre, towards the airport.

■ RESTAURANT: Closed Sun & Mon lunch. Truly gastronomic cuisine is served in this highly-acclaimed restaurant.
■ ACTIVITIES: Visits to vineyards.
■ TARIFF: (1994) Single 340–460, Double 375–460, Bk 50 (Euro/Access, Visa).

DINAN Côtes-du-Nord   1D

Hôtel des Bains ★★★ 20 rue du Poncel, 22770 Lancieux.
℡ 96 86 31 33, Fax 96 86 22 85. English spoken. Open all year. 14 bedrooms (all en suite). Golf 3 km, parking. &

Set 200 m from the main beach, this newly refurbished hotel, once a large family mansion, is an ideal starting point for excursions along the Emerald Coast.

■ TARIFF: (1994) Single 320–500, Double 350–500, Bk 35 (Euro/Access, Visa).

Château La Motte Beaumanoir ★★★ 35720 Pleugueneuc.
℡ 99 69 46 01, Fax 99 69 42 49. English spoken.

Open all year. 8 bedrooms (all en suite). Outdoor swimming pool, tennis, golf 13 km, parking.

Château de la Motte Beaumanoir is surrounded by ornamental lakes in 60 acres of grounds. In this lovely setting, all rooms have views over the lakes and are traditionally furnished. From Pleugueneuc, take the St-Malo road, and just outside the village take the Plesder exit.

■ RESTAURANT: Closed Tues. Specialities include millefeuille aux fruits rouges and feuilleté aux St-Jacques.
■ ACTIVITIES: Lovely walks; fishing nearby.
■ TARIFF: Single 700, Double 700–900, Bk 60, Set menu 135–230 (Amex, Euro/Access, Visa).
■ DISCOUNT: 10%

Hôtel Le Manoir de Rigourdaine ★★ 22490 Plouer-sur-Rance.
℡ 96 86 89 96, Fax 96 86 92 46. English spoken. Open 01/04 to 31/10. 19 bedrooms (all en suite). Golf 19 km, parking. &

Charming, stone-built old house with beams and open fireplace. Set in extensive grounds with wonderful views of the Breton estuary. (Recommended.)

■ ACTIVITIES: Golf, tennis, sailing within 10 km of hotel, canoeing along the Rance estuary as far as medieval Dinan.

■ TARIFF: (1994) Double 290–420, Bk (Euro/Access, Visa).

■ DISCOUNT: 10% Except Jul and Aug.

DINARD Ille/Vil   1D

Hôtel Altair ★★ 18 bd Féart, 35800 Dinard.
℡ 99 46 13 58, Fax 99 88 20 49. English spoken.
Open all year. 21 bedrooms (all en suite).
Golf 6 km.

The hotel is in the centre of Dinard, has gardens and a patio and is just 30 m or so from the beach.

■ RESTAURANT: Closed Sun eve & Mon LS. Renowned restaurant offering modern-day cuisine in a cosy, old-fashioned atmosphere.

■ TARIFF: (1994) Single 200–280, Double 250–380, Bk 33, Set menu 88–190 (Amex, Euro/Access, Visa).

Hôtel Amethyste pl Calvaire, 35800 Dinard.
℡ 99 46 61 81, Fax 99 46 96 91. English spoken.
Open all year. 20 bedrooms (all en suite).
Golf 2 km, parking.

Located a stone's throw from the beach and the Sea Water Therapy Centre.

■ ACTIVITIES: ● Scuba diving course.

■ TARIFF: (1994) Single 210–250, Double 270–300, Bk 30 (Amex, Euro/Access, Visa).

■ DISCOUNT: 10% LS.

Grand Hôtel ★★★★ 46 ave George V, BP 53, 35801 Dinard.
℡ 99 88 26 26, Fax 99 88 26 27.
English spoken.

Open 01/04 to 31/10. 66 bedrooms (all en suite). Outdoor swimming pool, tennis, golf 5 km, parking, restaurant.

Dating from the second Empire, this grand hotel offers fine views across the Vicomte Bay and to St-Malo. An ideal place for discovering the Emerald Coast and enjoying the wide range of local leisure and sports.

■ TARIFF: (1994) Double 480–1200, Bk 60, Set menu 180 (Amex, Euro/Access, Visa).

D

DONZENAC Corrèze   4B

Hôtel de la Maleyrie ★★ 19270 Sadroc.
℡ 55 84 50 67, Fax 55 84 20 63.
English spoken.
Open 25/03 to 01/11. 15 bedrooms (11 en suite, 2 bath/shower only). Garage, parking, restaurant.

The hotel is 15 km north of Brive and 25 km south of Uzerche, on the N20.

■ TARIFF: (1994) Single 100–210, Double 100–230, Bk 25, Set menu 65–160 (Euro/Access, Visa).

Hôtel Relais Bas Limousin ★★ 19100 Brive.
℡ 55 84 52 06, Fax 55 84 51 05.
English spoken.

Open all year. 22 bedrooms (all en suite). Outdoor swimming pool, garage, parking.

Logis de France on N20 between Uzerche and Brive-la-Gaillarde.

■ RESTAURANT: Closed Sun eve LS. Home-made dishes in attractive dining room overlooking garden. Cèpes, girolles, saumon fumé, veau, boeuf limousin, foie gras, confit are some of the specialities on offer.

■ ACTIVITIES: Horse-riding, rambling, fishing and BMX all close by.

■ TARIFF: (1994) Single 200–280, Double 200–350, Bk 30, Set menu 75–250 (Euro/Access, Visa).

DOUAI Nord 2B

Hôtel Ibis ★★ pl St-Amé, 59500 Douai.
℡ 27 87 27 27, Fax 27 98 31 64. English spoken.
Open all year. 42 bedrooms (all en suite).
Golf 9 km, garage, parking. ⅍
*Comfortable hotel in centre of this historic
town, close to the Music Conservatoire.*
■ RESTAURANT: Closed Sat lunch & Sun eve.
■ TARIFF: (1994) Double 298, Bk 34,
Set menu 89 (Amex, Euro/Access, Visa).

DOUARNENEZ Finistère 1C

Hôtel Thalasstonic ★★★ rue des Professeurs
Curie, Tréboul, 29100 Douarnenez.
℡ 98 74 45 45, Fax 98 74 36 07. English spoken.
Open all year. 50 bedrooms (all en suite).
Parking. ⅍
*Modern hotel near the beach, Les Sables-Blanc.
From Quimper, take D765 to Douarnenez then
follow signs towards Tréboul.*
■ RESTAURANT: Creative cuisine with seafood
specialities.
■ ACTIVITIES: Hiking, water sports and tennis
nearby.
■ TARIFF: (1994) Single 340–360,
Double 430–490, Bk 45 (Amex,
Euro/Access, Visa).

DOULLENS Somme 2B

Château de Remaisnil 80600 Doullens.
℡ 22 77 07 47, Fax 22 32 43 27. English spoken.
Open 01/01 to 21/02 & 09/03 to 31/12.
20 bedrooms (all en suite). Tennis, garage,
parking.
*Elegant, 18th-century national monument,
this private château was previously the home of
Laura Ashley. Antique furnishings. 10 km
north-west of Doullens in the direction of Auxi-
le-Château.*
■ RESTAURANT: Excellent cuisine with wine
included in the price.
■ TARIFF: (1994) Single 750–1000,
Double 1100–1400, Bk 75, Set menu 365–420
(Amex, Euro/Access, Visa).
■ DISCOUNT: 10%

DRAGUIGNAN Var 6C

Hôtel du Moulin de la Foux ★★ ch St-Jean,
83300 Draguignan.
℡ 94 68 55 33, Fax 94 68 70 10. English spoken.
Open all year. 29 bedrooms (all en suite).
Golf 10 km, parking, restaurant. ⅍
*The hotel is a renovated, stone-built former
mill, in quiet surroundings by a stream.*

*Garden and private fossil collection on site.
Situated at the southern edge of Draguignan
and 30 km from the sea (Ste-Maxime/St-
Tropez).*

■ TARIFF: (1994) Double 270–280, Bk 35,
Set menu 80–300 (Amex, Euro/Access, Visa).

DUCEY Manche 1D

Auberge de la Selune ★★ 2 rue St-Germain,
50220 Ducey.
℡ 33 48 53 62, Fax 33 48 90 30. English spoken.
Open all year. 19 bedrooms (all en suite).
Parking. ⅍
*In a quiet, green setting by the River Selune,
reputed for its salmon fishing. Located south of
Avranches and only 15 km from Mont-St-
Michel.*
■ RESTAURANT: Closed Mon LS.
■ ACTIVITIES: Salmon fishing, tennis nearby.
■ TARIFF: (1994) Double 255–275, Bk 38,
Set menu 75–190 (Euro/Access, Visa).

DUNKERQUE Nord 2B

Hôtel Borel ★★★ 6 rue l'Hermitage,
59140 Dunkerque.
℡ 28 66 51 80, Fax 28 59 33 82. English spoken.
Open all year. 48 bedrooms (all en suite).
Golf 3 km, garage, parking. ⅍
*Comfortable hotel with fully equipped rooms.
Close to the yacht station in town centre.*
■ TARIFF: (1994) Single 340–370,
Double 380–400, Bk 47 (Amex,
Euro/Access, Visa).

Hôtel Climat de France ★★
59279 Loon-Plage.
℡ 28 27 32 88, Fax 28 21 36 11. English spoken.
Open all year. 53 bedrooms (all en suite).
Parking, restaurant. ⅍
*Close to business centre and only 12 km south-
west of Dunkerque, on N1.*

■ TARIFF: (1994) Double 294, Bk 30,
Set menu 84–145 (Amex, Euro/Access, Visa).

Europe'Hôtel ★★★ 13 rue Leughenaer,
59140 Dunkerque.
℆ 28 66 29 07, Fax 28 63 67 87. English spoken.
Open all year. 120 bedrooms (all en suite).
Golf 1 km, garage.
*In the heart of Dunkerque. Comfortable rooms;
piano bar.*
■ RESTAURANT: Choice of 2 restaurants:
'Avmareyeur' and 'Auberge La Ferme'.
■ TARIFF: (1994) Single 330, Double 380, Bk 46,
Set menu 90–220 (Amex, Euro/Access, Visa).

Green Hôtel ★★ route de Gravelines,
59279 Loon-Plage.
℆ 28 21 42 42, Fax 28 21 45 45. English spoken.
Open all year. 62 bedrooms (all en suite).
Parking. &
*Pleasant new hotel with fully equipped rooms.
Just two minutes from the Sally Line terminal,
and ten minutes from Dunkerque.*
■ RESTAURANT: Closed Sun. Modern, light and
airy. Very good hors d'oeuvre buffet and grill
specialities.
■ TARIFF: (1994) Double 234, Bk 32,
Set menu 43–150 (Euro/Access, Visa).

Hôtel L'Hirondelle ★★ 46 av Faidherbe,
Malo-les-Bains, 59240 Dunkerque.
℆ 28 63 17 65, Fax 28 66 15 43. English spoken.
Open all year. 42 bedrooms (39 en suite).
Golf 5 km, garage. &
*A modern comfortable Logis de France hotel in
the town centre and only 2 minutes from the
beach.*
■ RESTAURANT: Closed Sun eve & Mon lunch.
■ TARIFF: (1994) Single 145–245, Double 300,
Bk 28, Set menu 65–255 (Euro/Access, Visa).

Hôtel Trianon ★★ 20 rue Colline, Malo-les-
Bains, 59240 Dunkerque.
℆ 28 63 39 15, Fax 28 63 34 57. English spoken.
Open all year. 12 bedrooms (6 en suite,
6 bath/shower only). Golf 4 km, garage.
*Traditional hotel that is only 100 metres from
the beach. Follow directions to the beach and
then to the casino.*
■ TARIFF: (1994) Single 170–240,
Double 170–240, Bk 30 (Euro/Access, Visa).
■ DISCOUNT: 10%

Welcome Hôtel ★★★ 37 rue Poincaré,
59140 Dunkerque.
℆ 28 59 20 70, Fax 28 21 03 49. English spoken.
Open all year. 40 bedrooms (all en suite).
Golf 10 km, garage, restaurant. &

*Right in the centre of town with a large
restaurant and only 20 minutes from the sea.*
■ TARIFF: (1994) Single 330, Double 380, Bk 46,
Set menu 65–200 (Amex, Euro/Access, Visa).
■ DISCOUNT: 10%

DURAS Lot/Garonne   4D

D

Auberge du Château ★ pl Jean Bausquet,
47120 Duras.
℆ 53 83 70 58.
Open all year. 10 bedrooms (all en suite).
Golf 12 km, parking, restaurant.
Small hotel, opposite the château.
■ TARIFF: (1994) Single 165–185,
Double 220–240, Bk 30, Set menu 65–200
(Amex, Euro/Access, Visa).
■ DISCOUNT: 5%

LES ECHELLES Savoie   5B

Auberge du Morge ★ Gorges de Chailles,
73360 Les Echelles.
℆ 79 36 62 76, Fax 79 36 51 65. English spoken.
Open 15/01 to 30/11. 7 bedrooms (5 en suite).
Parking, restaurant.
*3 km north of Les Echelles, access N6; an inn
in the Gorges de Chailles, near a trout stream.*
■ TARIFF: (1994) Double 160–220, Bk 28,
Set menu 90–230 (Euro/Access, Visa).

ENTRAIGUES Vaucluse   5D

Hôtel du Parc ★★ route de Carpentras,
84320 Entraigues.
℆ 90 83 62 43, Fax 90 83 29 11.
Open all year. 30 bedrooms (all en suite).
Outdoor swimming pool, parking,
restaurant. &
*The hotel is situated in parkland. Leave the
motorway at Avignon-Nord, towards
Carpentras.*
■ TARIFF: (1994) Single 200–250,
Double 250–300, Bk 36, Set menu 90–190
(Euro/Access, Visa).

ENTRAYGUES-SUR-TRUYERE Aveyron 5C

Hôtel Deux Vallées ★★ av du Pont de
Truyère, 12140 Entraygues-sur-Truyère.
℆ 65 44 52 15.
Open 01/03 to 31/12. 16 bedrooms
(all en suite). Garage, parking.
*Restful surroundings in the Rouergue region
with the wild valleys of the Lot and Truyère
rivers. From Aurillac southwards on the D920
to Entraygues (50 km).*

■ RESTAURANT: Rustic dining room with good, traditional cuisine. Specialities include tripoux, escargots and truite.
■ ACTIVITIES: Swimming pool, canoeing/kayaking, sailing and fishing nearby.
■ TARIFF: (1994) Single 180–200, Double 200–260, Bk 30, Set menu 65–150 (Euro/Access, Visa).

EPERNAY Marne   3A

E **Château d'Etoges** ★★★ 51270 Etoges.
📞 26 59 30 08, Fax 26 59 35 57. English spoken.

Open 31/01 to 15/01. 20 bedrooms (19 en suite, 1 bath/shower only). Golf 15 km, parking.
Renovated 17th-century château in the heart of champagne region. Etoges is 20 km south of Epernay on D33.
■ RESTAURANT: Closed Wed.
■ TARIFF: (1994) Single 300–400, Double 480–950, Bk 45, Set menu 160–280 (Amex, Euro/Access, Visa).

EPINAL Vosges   3D

Hôtel Ariane ★★ 12 av Général de Gaulle, 88000 Epinal.
📞 29 82 10 74, Fax 29 35 35 14.
Open 02/01 to 23/12. 46 bedrooms (all bath/shower only). Golf 3 km, garage.
Recently renovated, comfortable hotel. Opposite the SNCF station. Near lakes and forest. Parking discount for RAC members.
■ TARIFF: (1994) Double 265–320, Bk 38 (Amex, Euro/Access, Visa).

Hôtel La Fayette ★★★ parc économique, Le Saut-Le-Cerf, 88000 Epinal.
📞 29 31 15 15, Fax 29 31 07 08. English spoken.
Open all year. 48 bedrooms (all en suite). Indoor swimming pool, tennis, golf 1 km, garage, parking, restaurant. ⅄

New large hotel facing the golf course with health and fitness facilities. From Epinal follow D46 to Rambervillers.
■ TARIFF: (1994) Double 390–520, Bk 45, Set menu 100–200 (Amex, Euro/Access, Visa).

ERDEVEN Morbihan   1C

Auberge du Sous Bois ★★ route de Pont-Lorois, 56410 Erdeven.
📞 97 55 66 10, Fax 97 55 68 82. English spoken.
Open 01/04 to 30/09. 22 bedrooms (all en suite). Golf 5 km, parking.
Typical Breton hotel set amid pines, modern and comfortable.
■ RESTAURANT: Closed lunch except Sun Jul & Aug. Large, country-style room with grilled dishes prepared in the open fireplace. Other specialities are a large buffet and seafood.
■ ACTIVITIES: Horse-riding, tennis, sailing, sea and river fishing nearby.
■ TARIFF: Double 350–385, Bk 43, Set menu 84–180 (Amex, Euro/Access, Visa).

ERNEE Mayenne   1D

Hôtel Grand Cerf ★★ 19 rue A Briand, 53500 Ernée.
📞 43 05 13 09, Fax 43 05 02 90. English spoken.
Open all year. 8 bedrooms (all en suite). Golf 30 km, garage, parking.
Quiet and comfortable. Facilities for receptions. On the N12.
■ RESTAURANT: Closed 15/01 to 30/01. Excellent cuisine with an amazing selection of exquisite wines.
■ TARIFF: (1994) Single 195, Double 230, Bk 30, Set menu 108–148 (No credit cards).

ERQUY Côtes-du-Nord   1D

Hôtel Brigantin ★★ square Hôtel de Ville, 22430 Erquy.
📞 96 72 32 14, Fax 96 72 30 44. English spoken.
Open all year. 21 bedrooms (all en suite). Outdoor swimming pool, golf 3 km.
Rooms have modern facilities.
■ RESTAURANT: Pink sandstone, traditional dining room serving unusual seafood and meat dishes.
■ TARIFF: (1994) Double 270–330, Bk 30, Set menu 89–170 (Euro/Access, Visa).
■ DISCOUNT: 10%

ESTAING Aveyron   5A

Hôtel aux Armes d'Estaing ★★ 12190 Estaing.
📞 65 44 70 02, Fax 65 44 74 54. English spoken.

Open all year. 40 bedrooms (all en suite). Garage, parking, restaurant.

Comfortable hotel situated in the medieval town of Estaing beneath the 15th-century castle. On the D920 between Entraygues-St-Truyère and Espalion.

■ TARIFF: (1994) Double 150–230, Bk 26 (Euro/Access, Visa).

EVIAN-LES-BAINS Hte-Savoie 6A

Hôtel Bois Joli ★★ La Beunaz, St-Paul-en-Chablais, 74500 Evian.
☎ 50 73 60 11, Fax 50 73 65 28. English spoken.

Open 13/04 to 06/11 & 20/12 to 13/03. 24 bedrooms (all en suite). Outdoor swimming pool, tennis, golf 8 km, parking. ♿

In a valley overlooked by the mountains, this pretty "Relais du Silence" hotel offers some spectacular views and a restful stay near Lake Léman. 13 km from Thonon-les-Bains on the N5 heading east to Evian and then take the D21.

■ RESTAURANT: Closed Wed except Jul and Aug. Fine food and a good wine list. Specialities are foie gras maison and fresh fish from Lac Léman when in season.

■ ACTIVITIES: Pétanque, sauna, solarium, table tennis and mountain-biking at hotel; alpine and cross-country skiing at Bernex (1 km) in winter.

■ TARIFF: (1994) Single 270–320, Double 290–350, Bk 38, Set menu 100–230 (Amex, Euro/Access, Visa).

■ DISCOUNT: 10%

Hôtel Chez Tante Marie ★★ BP3, 74500 Bernex.
☎ 50 73 60 35, Fax 50 73 61 73. English spoken.
Open 15/12 to 15/10. 27 bedrooms (all en suite). Golf 12 km, parking.

Very cosy chalet hotel. Close to Lac Léman and

12 km from Evian, Bernex is a pretty alpine village in lovely surroundings. From Evian D21 to St-Paul and on to Bernex.

■ RESTAURANT: Charming restaurant and terrace with some wonderful views. Traditional and local specialities using fresh, local produce as well as home-cured charcuterie.

■ ACTIVITIES: Tennis, swimming, lake and mountain sports within easy reach.

■ TARIFF: (1994) Single 280–365, Double 310–365, Bk 40, Set menu 90–270 (Euro/Access, Visa).

Hôtel Panorama ★★ Grand-Rive, 74500 Evian-les-Bains.
☎ 50 75 14 50, Fax 50 75 59 12. English spoken.

Open 30/04 to 01/10. 29 bedrooms (all en suite). Golf 3 km, garage, parking.

On the Montreux side of Evian, this hotel looks across Lac Léman to Lausanne.

■ RESTAURANT: Overlooking Lac Léman, enjoy excellent fresh fish from the lake.

■ TARIFF: (1994) Double 260–330, Bk 30, Set menu 70–170 (Amex, Euro/Access, Visa).

E

Hôtel Continental 65 rue Nationale, 74500 Evian-les-Bains.
✆ 50 75 37 54, Fax 50 75 31 11. English spoken.
Open all year. 32 bedrooms (26 bath/shower only). Golf 2 km.

Located on the pedestrian street in the centre of Evian, the hotel is 200 m from the casino, 300 m from Lake Geneva, 100 m from Palais de Congrés.

■ TARIFF: (1994) Single 200–250, Double 250–300, Bk 30 (Amex, Visa).
■ DISCOUNT: 5%

E

Hôtel Ermitage ★★★★ Rive-Sud du Lac de Genève, 74500 Evian-les-Bains.
✆ 50 26 85 00, Fax 50 75 61 00. English spoken.

Open 12/02 to 30/11. 91 bedrooms (all en suite). Indoor swimming pool, tennis, golf on site, parking. ♿

Located in a 40-acre park, with views towards Switzerland. Hôtel Ermitage is a fully restored, charming, turn-of-the-century country residence, with a warm and relaxed atmosphere.

■ RESTAURANT: 3 inviting dining rooms. Cuisine based on local products and dishes: la poêle de perches du lac au vinaigre de cidre, les salades de pays aux langoustines, le veau de lait en casserole aux morilles.
■ ACTIVITIES: The excellent facilities range from own 18-hole championship golf course and horse-riding to jogging track and rifle shooting, children's club, concerts, shows, bridge, Scrabble and chess tournaments. Nearby: rafting, water sports, paragliding, rock climbing.
● Fitness and sports packages at special rates.
■ TARIFF: (1994) Single 510–1450, Double 800–2260, Bk 85, Set menu 170–340 (Amex, Euro/Access, Visa).

EVREUX Eure 2A

Hôtel de France ★★ 29 rue St-Thomas, 27000 Evreux.
✆ 32 39 09 25, Fax 32 38 38 56. English spoken.
Open all year. 16 bedrooms (all en suite). Golf 2 km, garage, parking.

The hotel is an elegant provincial building in a quiet location off the main street and offering traditional, high quality service.

■ RESTAURANT: Closed Sun eve & Mon. Superb restaurant overlooking the River Iton and gardens. Classical cuisine with a touch of contemporary style.
■ ACTIVITIES: 4 golf courses within half an hour.
■ TARIFF: (1994) Single 245–340, Double 265–340, Bk 34, Set menu 145–190 (Euro/Access, Visa).
■ DISCOUNT: 10%

EXCIDEUIL Dordogne 4B

Hôtel Fin Chapon ★★ 24160 Excideuil.
✆ 53 62 42 38, Fax 53 62 42 38. English spoken.

Open all year. 11 bedrooms (8 en suite, 3 bath/shower only). Parking.

In the heart of the Périgord, this small hotel dates from the 1750s and stands at the foot of the castle. Sunny terrace and peaceful atmosphere.

■ RESTAURANT: Closed Sun eve & Wed. Cosy dining room offering fresh, local dishes.
■ ACTIVITIES: Keep fit room; good area for cycling, fishing and walking.
■ TARIFF: (1994) Double 180–120, Bk 30, Set menu 65–140 (Euro/Access, Visa).

LES-EYZIES-DE-TAYAC

At Les-Eyzies-de-Tayac, you will find the Musée National de Préhistoire, filled with the many prehistoric artefacts found in this area, an area which has been occupied by man and his forebears for over 60,000 years. The museum, although extremely interesting and giving a good insight into life in prehistoric times, cannot really prepare you for the fascination of a visit to the actual caves where our ancestors lived. Of the many open to the public, the Grotte de Rouffignac is to be especially recommended – there a small electric train travels through 4 km of underground chambers past an amazing display of animal paintings.

E

LES EYZIES-DE-TAYAC Dordogne   4B

(See feature)

Hôtel des Bories ★★ Le Bourg, 24620 Marquay.
☎ 53 29 67 02, Fax 53 29 64 15. English spoken.
Open 01/04 to 02/11. 30 bedrooms (all en suite). Outdoor swimming pool, golf 17 km, parking. &
In lovely Périgord Noir countryside, close to prehistoric sites at Les Eyzies. From Les Eyzies, take D47 east, fork left on to D48, then right on to D6 to Marquay.
■ RESTAURANT: Closed Mon lunch. Good traditional food.
■ TARIFF: (1994) Double 220–270, Bk 31, Set menu 85–250 (Euro/Access, Visa).

Hôtel Cro-Magnon ★★★ 24620 Les Eyzies-de-Tayac.
☎ 53 06 97 06, Fax 53 06 95 45. English spoken.
Open 01/05 to 10/10. 24 bedrooms (all en suite). Outdoor swimming pool, golf 20 km, parking.
Situated in this pre-historic centre, the Cro-Magnon is a traditional hotel set in a 5-acre park with beautiful views over the Perigord countryside. There is a prehistoric tool display on the 1st floor of the hotel.
■ RESTAURANT: Closed Wed lunch.
■ TARIFF: (1994) Single 320–550, Double 350–550, Bk 50, Set menu 140–350 (Amex, Euro/Access, Visa).

EZE Alpes-Mar   6C

Château Eza 06360 Eze.
☎ 93 41 12 24, Fax 93 41 16 64. English spoken.
Open 15/03 to 31/10 & 15/12 to 15/02. 10 bedrooms (all en suite). Golf 5 km, garage, parking.
Situated at a height of over 400 m with magnificent views. On N7 between Nice and Monaco.

■ RESTAURANT: Gourmet restaurant serving traditional Provençal cuisine.
■ ACTIVITIES: Roman remains, easy access to Mediterranean resorts.
■ TARIFF: (1994) Single 1200–2500, Double 1200–3500 (Amex, Euro/Access, Visa).

Hôtel Hermitage ★★ Grande Corniche, Eze Village, 06360 Eze.
☎ 93 41 00 68.
Open 15/02 to 11/11. 14 bedrooms (all en suite). Outdoor swimming pool, golf 5 km, parking.
From Nice, N98 coast road east to Eze. A Provençal-style hotel.
■ RESTAURANT: Closed Mon & Wed lunch.
■ ACTIVITIES: Park next to the hotel with fitness circuit and children's playground.
■ TARIFF: (1994) Double 190–290, Bk 25 (Amex, Euro/Access, Visa).

FAYENCE Var   6C

Auberge La Marjolaine ★★
83440 Montauroux.
☎ 94 76 43 32, Fax 94 47 73 09.
English spoken.
Open all year. 19 bedrooms (10 en suite, 1 bath/shower only). &
From Fayence, south on D563 then left on to D562. Look for left turn to D37 and signs to Montauroux. A quiet comfortable hotel with panoramic views.
■ RESTAURANT: Closed Wed & Sun eve. Highly rated.
■ TARIFF: (1994) Double 185–300, Bk 35, Set menu 110–280 (Amex, Euro/Access, Visa).

F

Auberge du Puits Jaubert ★ route de
Fondurane, 83440 Callian.
☎ 94 76 44 48.

Open 15/12 to 15/11. 8 bedrooms
(all en suite). Parking. ♿
*A Provençale auberge dating from the 15th
century and near Lac de St-Cassien. Exit Les
Adrets from A8 Fréjus/Cannes, past the lake.
Callian lies north of the D562 about 4 km east
of Fayence.*
■ RESTAURANT: Closed Tues. Full of character
with very good food.
■ TARIFF: (1994) Double 250–300, Bk 35,
Set menu 145–250 (Euro/Access, Visa).
■ DISCOUNT: 5%

LA FECLAZ Savoie   6A

Hôtel Le Bon Gite ★★ 73230 La Feclaz.
☎ 79 25 82 11, Fax 79 25 80 91. English spoken.
Open 18/12 to 04/04 & 17/06 to 12/09.
32 bedrooms (29 en suite). Outdoor swimming
pool, tennis, golf 20 km, garage, parking. ♿
Situated in the centre of town.
■ RESTAURANT: Regional Savoie specialities
and wines.
■ ACTIVITIES: Pot-holing, mountain-biking,
horse-riding and archery in summer. Skiing in
winter.
■ TARIFF: (1994) Double 145–330, Bk 35,
Set menu 60–120 (Euro/Access, Visa).
■ DISCOUNT: 5%

FERNEY-VOLTAIRE Ain   6A

Hôtel France ★★ 1 rue Genève,
01210 Ferney-Voltaire.
☎ 50 40 63 87, Fax 50 40 47 27. English spoken.
Open all year. 14 bedrooms (all en suite).
Golf 5 km, garage, parking.
*Small and comfortable, the hotel is the closest
French hotel to Genève and is just 1 km from
the airport.*

■ RESTAURANT: Closed Sun & Mon lunch.
Traditional French cuisine, including excellent
meat and fish dishes, prepared by a former
chef of The Ritz in Paris.
■ TARIFF: (1994) Single 270, Double 330, Bk 35,
Set menu 115–215 (Amex, Euro/Access, Visa).

FERRETTE Ht-Rhin   3D

Auberge Paysanne ★★ 24 rue de
Wolschwiller, Lutter, 68480 Ferrette.
☎ 89 40 71 67, Fax 89 07 33 38.
English spoken.

Open 07/02 to 23/01. 16 bedrooms
(all en suite). Golf 20 km, parking.
*Traditional building set in beautiful
countryside. From Ferrette take D23 south, left
on D213 to Raedersdorf and Lutter is
signposted from there.*
■ RESTAURANT: Closed Mon. Dating from the
17th century, attractive, beamed restaurant
offering delicious food including local
specialities and good selection of wine.
■ ACTIVITIES: Numerous footpaths marked by
Club Vosgien. Baggage can be transported to
the following stage.
■ TARIFF: (1994) Single 220–310,
Double 290–420, Bk 35, Set menu 120–300
(Euro/Access, Visa).

FEURS Loire   5B

Motel Etesia ★★ Le Palais, 42110 Feurs.
☎ 77 27 07 77, Fax 77 27 03 33.
English spoken.
Open all year. 15 bedrooms (all en suite).
Outdoor swimming pool, tennis, parking. ♿
*A quiet, comfortable motel. From Feurs take
N82 north. Turn right at the first roundabout.
Easy access to the autoroute and the airport.*
■ TARIFF: (1994) Single 230–250,
Double 260–280, Bk 28 (Amex,
Euro/Access, Visa).

LA FLECHE Sarthe 2C

Hôtel Haras de la Potardière ★★★ route de Bazouges, 72200 Crosmières.
℄ 43 45 83 47, Fax 43 45 81 06. English spoken. Open all year. 17 bedrooms (all en suite). Outdoor swimming pool, tennis, golf 18 km, parking. ⅊

From the A11, exit at La Flèche/Sablé. Take the La Flèche road to Crosmières, in Crosmières turn right towards Bazouges.
■ TARIFF: (1994) Double 400–900, Bk 40 (Euro/Access, Visa).

Hôtel Image ★★ 50 rue Grollier, 72200 La Flèche.
℄ 43 94 00 50, Fax 43 94 47 19.
Open all year. 20 bedrooms (13 en suite, 3 bath/shower only). Parking, restaurant.
La Flèche is appox 40 km south of Le Mans on N23.
■ TARIFF: (1994) Double 140–350, Bk 30, Set menu 78–220 (Euro/Access, Visa).

Hôtel Marmotte ★ Zac de la Monnerie, 72200 La Flèche.
℄ 43 94 70 40, Fax 43 45 64 84. English spoken. Open all year. 37 bedrooms (all en suite). Parking, restaurant. ⅊
A peaceful hotel located on the outskirts of town making access easy. Follow the N23 heading for Le Mans.
■ TARIFF: (1994) Double 175–198, Bk 27, Set menu 52–88 (Euro/Access, Visa).

Auberge du Port des Roches ★★ Le Port des Roches, 72800 Luché-Pringé.
℄ 43 45 44 48, Fax 43 45 39 61.
Open all year. 13 bedrooms (10 en suite, 3 bath/shower only). Parking, restaurant.
A small hotel on the banks of the River Loir. From Luché follow the D13, towards Mansigne for about 1.8 km, then turn on to the D214. The hotel is 800 m on right.
■ TARIFF: (1994) Double 210–300, Bk 32, Set menu 135–160 (Euro/Access, Visa).

Les Quatre Vents ★ 11 rue du Marché au Blé, 72200 La Flèche.
℄ 43 94 00 61. English spoken.
Open all year. 16 bedrooms (6 en suite, 10 bath/shower only). Garage, parking.
In town centre, well signposted.
■ TARIFF: (1994) Single 140–255, Double 160–255, Bk 26 (Euro/Access, Visa).

Hôtel Relais Cicero ★★★ 18 bd Alger, 72200 La Flèche.
℄ 43 94 14 14, Fax 43 45 98 96. English spoken.

Open 04/01 to 23/12. 21 bedrooms (20 en suite, 1 bath/shower only). Golf 20 km, parking.
Charming hotel dating from 16th century. Bedrooms overlooking tranquil garden. Two restaurants recommended by the hotel nearby. 40 km from Le Mans. 50 km from Angers.
■ ACTIVITIES: Tennis, horse-riding and a swimming pool close by.
■ TARIFF: (1994) Single 365–410, Double 410–650, Bk 45 (Amex, Euro/Access, Visa).

Hôtel Le Vert Galant ★★ 70 Grande rue, 72200 La Flèche.
℄ 43 94 00 51, Fax 43 45 11 24.
Open all year. 9 bedrooms (8 en suite).
Quiet and comfortable Loir valley hotel. Le Mans motorway exit or N23.
■ RESTAURANT: Closed Thur LS.
■ ACTIVITIES: River fishing and son et lumière nearby.
■ TARIFF: (1994) Single 170–218, Double 210–278, Bk 25, Set menu 75–165 (Euro/Access, Visa).

FLERS Orne 2C

Hôtel Galion ★★★ 5 rue Victor Hugo, 61100 Flers.
℄ 33 64 47 47, Fax 33 65 10 10. English spoken. Open all year. 31 bedrooms (all en suite). Golf 2km, garage, parking. ⅊
Charming hotel in a quiet street close to the town centre.
■ TARIFF: (1994) Single 200–220, Double 240–260, Bk 25 (Amex, Euro/Access, Visa).

FLORAC Lozère 5C

Hôtel La Lozerette ★★ Cocurès, 48400 Florac.
℄ 66 45 06 04, Fax 66 45 12 93. English spoken. Open 15/04 to 12/11. 21 bedrooms (all en suite). Tennis, golf 4 km, garage, parking. ⅊
In a small village on the Stevenson Route, a family hotel ideal for a pleasant holiday. Off the D998, 5 km north-east of Florac.
■ RESTAURANT: Closed Tues lunch May/Jun, 15/9-12/11. Regional cuisine including charcuterie maison and truite lard. Good cellar offering regional and other wines.
■ ACTIVITIES: Organised horse-riding, rock-climbing, hiking, canoeing/kayaking and mountain-biking can be arranged for individuals or groups nearby.
■ TARIFF: (1994) Double 250–300, Bk 32, Set menu 78–250 (Amex, Euro/Access, Visa).

F

FONT-ROMEU Pyrénées-Or 5C

Hôtel Le Grand-Tetras ★★ av Brousse,
66120 Font-Romeu.
☏ 68 30 01 20, Fax 68 30 35 67. English spoken.
Open all year. 36 bedrooms (all en suite). Indoor
swimming pool, golf 1 km, garage, restaurant. &
*Situated in the town centre, hotel has
panoramic views of the Pyrénées.*

■ ACTIVITIES: Fitness centre, solarium; skiing,
tennis and mountain activities nearby.
■ TARIFF: (1994) Single 230–270, Double 280–325,
Bk 34, Set menu 89 (Amex, Euro/Access, Visa).

F

FONTAINEBLEAU Seine/Marne 2D

Hôtel de l'Aigle Noir ★★★★ 27 pl Napoléon
Bonaparte, 77300 Fontainebleau.
☏ 1 64 22 32 65, Fax 1 64 22 17 33. English spoken.

Open all year. 57 bedrooms (all en suite). Indoor
swimming pool, golf 1 km, garage, parking. &

*Opposite the prestigious Château de
Fontainebleau, this elegant, luxury hotel
upholds the great traditions of French
hospitality. Price for weekend: 750F and one
week 950F. (Suites also available.)*
■ RESTAURANT: Closed 24/12 & 30/12. 'Le
Beauharnais' offers gourmet cuisine in elegant
surroundings.
■ ACTIVITIES: At hotel, sauna and gymnasium.
■ TARIFF: (1994) Double 750–950, Bk 80
(Amex, Euro/Access, Visa).

Auberge Casa del Sol ★★ 63 rue des Canches,
77760 Recloses.
☏ 1 64 24 20 35, Fax 1 64 24 26 37.
Open 01/02 to 31/12. 10 bedrooms (8 en suite,
2 bath/shower only). Golf 8 km, parking.

*Quiet village location 8 km south of
Fontainebleau. Especially good for small group
bookings. Take Ury exit off A6 onto D63.*
■ RESTAURANT: Simple meals prepared with
fresh, seasonal produce. Good cheese board.

■ ACTIVITIES: Lots of sports facilities nearby; son
et lumière in the forest; visit to Fontainebleau
palace.
■ TARIFF: (1994) Double 250–375, Bk 45,
Set menu 150 (Euro/Access, Visa).

Hôtel de la Forêt ★★ 79 av Franklin
Roosevelt, 77300 Fontainebleau.
☏ 1 64 22 39 26, Fax 1 64 22 06 94. English spoken.
Open all year. 32 bedrooms (all en suite).
Outdoor swimming pool, golf on site, garage,
parking. &
■ RESTAURANT: Closed weekends 1/10 to 31/3.
Traditional French cuisine with a good choice
of specialities.
■ TARIFF: Double 190–320, Bk 28,
Set menu 58.50–92.50 (Euro/Access, Visa).
■ DISCOUNT: 10%

Hôtel Ibis ★★ 18 rue Ferrare,
77300 Fontainebleau.
☏ 1 64 23 45 25, Fax 1 64 23 42 22. English spoken.

Open all year. 81 bedrooms (all en suite).
Tennis, golf 1 km, garage. &

*Attractive, modern hotel in the centre of town.
5 minutes' walk from the famous Château and
45 minutes from Paris.*
■ RESTAURANT: Attractive restaurant plus patio
for the summer. French regional food.
■ ACTIVITIES: Climbing, horse-riding, squash,
canoeing nearby.
■ TARIFF: (1994) Double 320–350, Bk 37
(Amex, Euro/Access, Visa).

Hôtel Londres ★★★ pl Gén de Gaulle,
77300 Fontainebleau.
☏ 1 64 22 20 21, Fax 1 60 72 39 16. English spoken.
Open 05/01 to 20/12. 18 bedrooms
(10 en suite). Golf 2 km, parking.

*Family-owned since 1850, hotel has an enviable
position opposite the main entrance of the Palace.*
■ RESTAURANT: Closed 15/10 to 15/03. Brasserie-
style, lunches only.

■ ACTIVITIES: Tennis, 'jeu de paume', water-skiing and health club nearby.
■ TARIFF: (1994) Double 250–800, Bk 50 (Amex, Euro/Access, Visa).

Hostellerie du Moulin de Flagy ★★★ 2 rue du Moulin, 77940 Flagy.
☎ 1 60 96 67 89, Fax 1 60 96 69 51. English spoken.
Open 20/01 to 17/09 & 29/09 to 17/12.
10 bedrooms (all en suite). Golf 3 km, parking. &
Enchanting 13th-century mill, beautifully converted, attractive river terrace. From Fontainebleau, take the N6 towards Sens and after 18 km turn right towards Nemours. Then immediately left to Flagy.
■ RESTAURANT: Closed Sun eve & Mon.
■ ACTIVITIES: Good area for sightseeing; close to Fontainebleau and Sens.
■ TARIFF: (1994) Single 240–300, Double 300–500, Bk 45, Set menu 170–220 (Amex, Euro/Access, Visa).

Manoir de St-Herem ★★ Parc John François Millet, 77630 Fontainebleau/Barbizon.
☎ 1 60 66 42 42, Fax 1 60 69 20 98. English spoken.
Open all year. 13 bedrooms (12 bath/shower only). Golf 10 km, parking, restaurant. &
An old manor house, behind Millet's house in a large park. Refurbished in 1985. Access by the A6 motorway (Paris to Lyon, Fontainebleau exit) and N7. In the middle of Barbizon.
■ TARIFF: Single 340–390, Double 380–430, Bk 40, Set menu 150 (Amex, Euro/Access, Visa).
■ DISCOUNT: 10%

Hôtel Victoria ★★ 112 rue de France, 77300 Fontainebleau.
☎ 1 64 22 23 33, Fax 1 64 22 47 03. English spoken.
Open all year. 18 bedrooms (17 en suite).
Golf 3 km, garage, parking.
Newly renovated, the hotel is set in large gardens at the edge of the forest and is 3 minutes from the château. Light, spacious rooms. Family atmosphere. A good stop-over on the way south and within easy reach of central Paris.
■ RESTAURANT: Room service with home-made light meals. Served on terrace when weather permits.
■ ACTIVITIES: Cycling, walking, swimming and visiting well-known artists' towns.
■ TARIFF: (1994) Single 170–230, Double 170–350, Bk 30, Set menu 55 (**BT**💲).

Hôtel Le Vieux Logis ★★★ 5 rue Sadi Carnot, Thomery, 77810 Fontainebleau.
☎ 1 60 96 44 77, Fax 1 60 96 42 71. English spoken.
Open all year. 14 bedrooms (all en suite).

Outdoor pool, tennis, golf 7 km, parking.
Until recently, a private mansion situated in the heart of the small historic village of Thomery. Cosy and finely decorated bedrooms. New heated pool. From the obelisk in Fontainebleau, take N5 to Sens and bear left at the 4th exit to Thomery.
■ RESTAURANT: Elegant, gourmet restaurant with bright, warm atmosphere and flower-filled terrace.
■ TARIFF: (1994) Double 400–400, Bk 50, Set menu 145–240 (Amex, Euro/Access, Visa).

FONTEVRAUD-L'ABBAYE Maine/Loire 2C **F**

Hôtel de la Croix Blanche ★★ 7 pl du Plantagenêt, 49590 Fontevraud-l'Abbaye.
☎ 41 51 71 11, Fax 41 38 15 38. English spoken.
Open 07/02 to 12/11 & 26/11 to 07/01.
21 bedrooms (all en suite). Golf 3 km, garage, parking. &
The hotel is central in a small village, with flowered private terraces and courtyards behind. Private parking and garages. Situated between Anjou and Touraine. From Samur take D947 east, following the Loire then D147 southwards to Fontevraud-l'Abbaye.
■ RESTAURANT: Good local cuisine, which includes unusual and exciting dishes.
■ ACTIVITIES: Sporting facilities nearby: tennis, golf, horse-riding. Ideal centre for exploring the region (plus the wine and mushroom museums). Tour around the abbey next door.
■ TARIFF: (1994) Single 255.00–368.00, Double 255.00–520.00, Bk 35.00, Set menu 95.00–200.00 (Amex, Euro/Access, Visa, **BT**💲).

Hôtellerie Prieure St-Lazare 49590 Fontevraud-l'Abbaye.
☎ 41 51 73 16, Fax 41 51 75 50. English spoken.
Open 15/03 to 15/11. 52 bedrooms (all en suite). Golf 4 km, parking, restaurant.
Large, comfortable hotel in the centre of the village near the church by the woods. 16 km from Saumur on the D947.
■ TARIFF: (1994) Single 235–335, Double 295–430, Bk 48, Set menu 98–230 (Amex, Euro/Access).
■ DISCOUNT: 5%

FORCALQUIER Alpes-Hte-Prov   6C

Auberge Charembeau ★★ 04300 Forcalquier.
☎ 92 75 05 69, Fax 92 75 24 37. English spoken.
Open 01/02 to 30/11. 12 bedrooms (all en suite). Outdoor swimming pool, tennis, parking.

F

Comfort and seclusion are offered with tennis and swimming facilities. 10 km from A5 motorway at exit no 19. From Forcalquier take N100 to La Brillanne for 3.5 km.

■ TARIFF: (1994) Double 247–320, Bk 39 (Euro/Access, Visa).

LA FORET-FOUESNANT Finistère   1C

Hôtel Beauséjour ★★ pl de la Baie, 29940 La Forêt-Fouesnant.
☎ 98 56 97 18, Fax 98 51 40 77. English spoken.
Open 15/03 to 30/10. 25 bedrooms (18 en suite). Golf 1 km, parking, restaurant. ⅁

A wonderful setting near a beautiful bay, close to Concarneau in southern Brittany.

■ TARIFF: (1994) Single 150–290, Double 200–300, Bk 33, Set menu 72–250 (Euro/Access, Visa).

FORGES-LES-EAUX Seine-Marit   2B

Auberge du Beau Lieu Le Fossé, 76440 Forges-les-Eaux.
☎ 35 90 50 36, Fax 35 90 35 98. English spoken.
Open 01/01 to 24/01 & 07/02 to 31/12.
3 bedrooms (all en suite). Parking.

Comfortable auberge with rooms, terrace and parking. The highly-rated restaurant offers excellent cuisine using local produce. On D915.

■ RESTAURANT: Closed 25/01 to 06/02. Highly rated, offering excellent cuisine using locally grown produce.
■ TARIFF: (1994) Single 250, Double 345, Bk 38, Set menu 140–350 (Amex, Euro/Access, Visa).

FORT-MAHON-PLAGE Somme   2B

Hôtel de la Terrasse ★★★ av de la Plage, 80790 Fort-Mahon-Plage.
☎ 22 23 37 77, Fax 22 23 36 74. English spoken.
Open all year. 56 bedrooms (all en suite).
Golf 1 km, garage, parking.

Overlooking the sea at Fort Mahon, a sandy-beached resort between Dieppe and Le Touquet.

■ RESTAURANT: Panoramic sea view. Specialities: turbot, sole, shellfish and lobster.
■ TARIFF: (1994) Single 200–300, Double 200–400, Bk 35, Set menu 80–160 (Amex, Euro/Access, Visa).

FOUESNANT Finistère   1C

Hôtel Bellevue ★★ Plage de Cap Coz, 29170 Fouesnant.
☎ 98 56 00 33, Fax 98 51 60 85. English spoken.

Open 15/03 to 30/10. 20 bedrooms (all en suite). Golf 5 km, parking.

A family hotel situated in front of the sandy beach of Cap Coz, between Concarneau and Bénodet. Children are welcome. From motorway N165 exit Coat-Conq and take D44 to Fouesnant.

■ RESTAURANT: Closed 20/09 to 01/04. Well prepared regional dishes and a good variety of seafood.
■ ACTIVITIES: ● Tickets on sale at hotel which give a minimum of 10% discount on a variety of activities including sailing, tennis and BMX.
■ TARIFF: (1994) Single 140–300, Double 170–316, Bk 35, Set menu 80–175 (Euro/Access, Visa).

Hôtel de Bretagne ★★ 14 rue Glénan, Beg-Meil, 29170 Fouesnant.
☎ 98 94 98 04, Fax 98 94 90 58. English spoken.

Open 01/04 to 30/09. 28 bedrooms (all en suite). Outdoor swimming pool, golf 8 km, parking. ⅁

From Quimper to Fouesnant and Beg-Meil. You will see hotel as you enter resort, 200 m from sea.

■ RESTAURANT: Closed Tues LS.
■ TARIFF: (1994) Double 270–360, Bk 35, Set menu 95–200 (Visa).

Hôtel Pointe Mousterlin ★★ Pointe de Mousterlin, 29170 Fouesnant.
☎ 98 56 04 12, Fax 98 56 61 02. English spoken.
Open 15/04 to 30/09. 52 bedrooms (all en suite). Tennis, golf 6 km, parking. ⅁

6 km from the village of Fouesnant, the hotel is only 30 m from a long sandy beach. Comfortable rooms, some of them inter-connecting.

■ RESTAURANT: Closed Sep to Apr. One rustic restaurant, one modern. Traditional cuisine with seafood specialities. Special menu for children.

■ ACTIVITIES: Health and fitness centre, including sauna and jacuzzi; games room.
■ TARIFF: (1994) Single 262–290, Double 290–425, Bk 34 (Amex, Euro/Access, Visa).

FRESNAY-SUR-SARTHE Sarthe   2C

Hôtel Ronsin ★★ 5 av Ch de Gaulle, 72130 Fresnay-sur-Sarthe.
☎ 43 97 20 10, Fax 43 33 50 47.
English spoken.
Open 06/01 to 24/12. 12 bedrooms (11 en suite, 1 bath/shower only). Garage.
The hotel is on the main road through the village, river nearby. From Alençon, N138 southwards then right onto D310 to Fresnay-sur-Sarthe.
■ RESTAURANT: Closed Sun eve & Mon lunch LS. Specialities include terrine aux foie de volaille and noisette de porc.
■ TARIFF: (1994) Double 160–298, Bk 28.50, Set menu 70–230 (Amex, Euro/Access, Visa).

LA GACILLY Morbihan   1D

Hôtel de France ★★ 15 rue Montauban, 56200 La Gacilly.
☎ 99 08 11 15. English spoken.

Open 02/01 to 24/12. 38 bedrooms (28 en suite, 2 bath/shower only). Parking. ⅙
The hotel is in the centre of La Gacilly. Countryside and forest nearby. 40 minutes from the sea. La Gacilly lies on the D773 south-west of Rennes.
■ RESTAURANT: Traditional regional cooking.
■ TARIFF: (1994) Double 110–240, Bk 25, Set menu 65–170 (Euro/Access, Visa).

GANGES Hérault   5C

Château de Madières ★★★★ 34190 Madières.
☎ 67 73 84 03, Fax 67 73 55 71. English spoken.

F

Open 08/04 to 02/11. 10 bedrooms (all en suite). Outdoor swimming pool, parking.
Delightful hostelry set in 12-acre park and dating from the 14th century. Fine views overlooking the Vis Gorge. From Ganges, cross the River Hérault onto the D25 towards Lodève. The château is in Madières village at the D48 junction.
■ RESTAURANT: Beautiful, vaulted dining room with superb views and fine cuisine.
■ ACTIVITIES: Keep fit room, games area, lovely walks.
■ TARIFF: (1994) Double 560–960, Bk 75, Set menu 190–350 (Amex, Euro/Access, Visa).

GAP

Gap lies on the edge of the high Alps in eastern France. The route Napoléon passes the town and it was here, in March 1815, that Napoleon himself was given his first warm welcome on his way north from captivity on the island of Elba. Expect an equally warm welcome today as you explore the ancient town centre. This was one of the first town centres in France to be declared traffic-free, so exploring on foot is particularly pleasant.

GAP Htes-Alpes   6C

(See feature)

Hôtel Le Clos ★★ route de Grenoble, 05000 Gap.
☎ 92 51 37 04, Fax 92 52 41 06. English spoken.
Open all year. 39 bedrooms (30 en suite, 9 bath/shower only). Tennis, golf 15 km, parking, restaurant.
A traditional family hotel, close to the town centre.

■ TARIFF: (1994) Double 160–240, Bk 33 (Euro/Access, Visa).

Hôtel Le Pavillon Carina ★★ rte de Veynes, 05000 Gap.
☎ 92 52 02 73, Fax 92 53 34 72. English spoken.
Open 10/01 to 24/12. 50 bedrooms
(all en suite). Indoor swimming pool, tennis, golf 7 km, garage, parking. &

In a leafy setting, 800 m up in the southern Alps with woods nearby and Gap town centre 2 km away.

■ RESTAURANT: Regional cuisine with Alsace specialities.
■ TARIFF: (1994) Single 170–230, Double 200–320, Bk 32, Set menu 70–194 (Amex, Euro/Access, Visa).

G

GAVARNIE Htes-Pyrénées   4D

Hôtel Le Marbore ★★ 65120 Gavarnie.
☎ 62 92 40 40, Fax 62 92 40 30. English spoken.

Open all year. 25 bedrooms (all en suite). Parking. &

In the heart of the Pyrénées National Park, a quiet, modern hotel near the ski slopes. Group discounts. Gavarnie is on the D921 south of Gedre.

■ RESTAURANT: Family cooking.
■ ACTIVITIES: Sauna at hotel; horse-riding, fishing, BMX, skiing.
■ TARIFF: (1994) Single 230, Double 270, Bk 32, Set menu 80–185 (Amex, Euro/Access, Visa).

Hôtel Vignemale ★★★ 65120 Gavarnie.
☎ 62 92 40 00, Fax 62 92 40 08. English spoken.
Open 01/04 to 31/10. 24 bedrooms
(all en suite). Parking.

A stone built, impressive, newly restored hotel in the heart of the Pyrénées National Park. River and pine forest nearby. Close to the Spanish border and 50 km from Lourdes.

■ RESTAURANT: Specialities: garbure - soupe des

montagnards à base de choux et légumes; filet de truites saumonées; confit de canard.
■ ACTIVITIES: Hotel specialises in cross-country horse-riding. Discover the famous Cirque de Gavarnie with the 'chevaux de Merens'.
■ TARIFF: (1994) Single 390–500, Double 560–650, Bk 56, Set menu 130 (Amex, Euro/Access, Visa).
■ DISCOUNT: 10% Outside school holidays.

GENLIS Côte-d'Or   3C

Hôtel de la Place-Rey ★★ Echigey, 21110 Genlis.
☎ 80 29 74 00, Fax 80 29 79 55.
English spoken.
Open 01/02 to 31/07 & 09/08 to 01/01.
13 bedrooms (9 en suite). Parking.

Comfortable hotel set in pleasant grounds. From Genlis follow signs to Echigey, cross-country to the south.

■ RESTAURANT: Closed Jan and first week Aug. Gourmet restaurant. Specialises in regional wines and cheeses.
■ ACTIVITIES: Tourist area renowned for good food and wines.
■ TARIFF: (1994) Double 120–200, Bk 28, Set menu 68–205 (Amex, Euro/Access, Visa).

GENOUILLAC Creuse   5A

Hôtel Relais d'Oc ★★ 23350 Genouillac.
☎ 55 80 72 45.
Open 30/03 to 20/11. 7 bedrooms (5 en suite, 2 bath/shower only). Golf 10 km, parking.

A 300-year-old hotel with a family atmosphere. Handy for walks and exploring the countryside.

■ RESTAURANT: Closed Sun eve & Mon. Good cuisine.
■ TARIFF: (1994) Double 200–300, Bk 32, Set menu 110–250 (Euro/Access, Visa).

GERARDMER Vosges   3D

Hôtel La Réserve esplanade du Lac, 88400 Gérardmer.
☎ 29 63 21 60, Fax 29 60 81 60.
English spoken.
Open 20/12 to 02/11. 24 bedrooms (4 en suite, 20 bath/shower only). Garage, parking. &

Renovated in 1989, the hotel is very well situated close to Lake Gerardmer, the casino and town centre. Only 5 minutes from the ski resort.

■ RESTAURANT: Closed Wed lunch except school hols. Gourmet restaurant specialities: filet de boeuf Pinot Noir Alsacien.

G

■ ACTIVITIES: 200 m from sports complex with indoor swimming pool, tennis, ice skating and sauna; mountain climbing, walking, mountain-biking nearby; visits to wine cellars.
■ TARIFF: (1994) Single 295–530, Double 295–530, Bk 42, Set menu 120–190 (Amex, Euro/Access, Visa).
■ DISCOUNT: 5%

GEVREY-CHAMBERTIN Côte-d'Or   3C

Hôtel Les Terroirs ★★★ rte Dijon, 21220 Gevrey-Chambertin.
✆ 80 34 30 76, Fax 80 34 11 79.
Open all year. 20 bedrooms (all en suite). Indoor swimming pool, golf 10 km, garage, parking.
Set in the heart of a wine-producing area, the hotel is very comfortable and has lovely antique furniture as well as a wine bar. South-west of Dijon, off A31.
■ ACTIVITIES: Exploring the region by bike; wine tasting.
■ TARIFF: (1994) Double 250–480, Bk 45 (Amex, Euro/Access, Visa).
■ DISCOUNT: 10% Except weekends.

GIEN Loiret   2D

Hôtel Rivage ★★★ 1 quai Nice, 45500 Gien.
✆ 38 37 79 00, Fax 38 38 10 21. English spoken.
Open all year. 19 bedrooms (all en suite). Golf 20 km, parking.
Family hotel in a delightful position on the banks of the Loire. The pretty rooms and suites are light and spacious. Large terrace.
■ RESTAURANT: Closed Feb to 15 Mar.
■ TARIFF: (1994) Single 295–500, Double 360–500, Bk 46, Set menu 160–380 (Amex, Euro/Access, Visa).

Château de la Verrerie 18700 Oizon.
✆ 48 58 06 91, Fax 48 58 21 25. English spoken.

Open 15/01 to 15/12. 12 bedrooms (all en suite). Tennis, garage, parking.
Comfort and tranquillity in this elegant, Renaissance château which overlooks a lake in the middle of a forest. 22 km from Gien, going south on D940 to Aubigny-sur-Nère then D89. Follow signs to the château.
■ RESTAURANT: Closed Tues. The charming restaurant 'La Maison d'Hélène' is housed in a 17th-century cottage in the grounds. Specialities include fresh fish and game.
■ ACTIVITIES: Boating, fishing, bicycles and horse-riding (experienced riders only) at hotel; hot-air ballooning and horse-drawn carriage rides on request; possibility of game shooting in season.
■ TARIFF: (1994) Double 990–1410, Set menu 80–165 (Euro/Access, Visa).
■ DISCOUNT: 10%

GIVET Ardennes   3A

Hôtel Val St-Hilaire ★★ 7 quai des Fours, 08600 Givet.
✆ 24 42 38 50, Fax 24 42 07 36. English spoken.

Open all year. 20 bedrooms (all en suite). Golf 25 km, parking. ♿
Easy to find, it's the only hotel in Givet, near

the Belgian border, on the waterfront alongside the River Meuse and bordered by a promenade. The hotel opened in 1990, is bright and cheerful and well situated in the heart of the cultural and artistic area of the town.

■ TARIFF: (1994) Single 280, Double 330, Bk 40 (Euro/Access, Visa).

GODERVILLE Seine-Marit　　　　2A

Château de Diane près d'Etretat, 76110 Ecrainville-par-Goderville.
☎ 35 27 76 02, Fax 35 22 53 42.

Open 01/08 to 30/09. 18 bedrooms (5 en suite, 2 bath/shower only). Golf 11 km, parking.
Louis XIII château, rebuilt in 19th century, standing in 18-acre estate with many interesting features. Open all of August and September, plus weekends year round. Range of rooms good for families. From Goderville, east to Ecrainville on D139, turn left by the church on D68 towards Manneville for 1.5 km.

■ ACTIVITIES: Excellent sporting facilities and activities available at nearby Etretat, which is only 11 km away.
■ TARIFF: (1994) Single 180–230, Double 290–800, Bk 40 (No credit cards).

LE GOLFE-JUAN Alpes-Mar　　　　6C

Hôtel Beau Soleil ★★★ impasse Beau Soleil, 06220 Le Golfe-Juan.
☎ 93 63 63 63, Fax 93 63 02 89. English spoken.
Open 26/03 to 15/10. 30 bedrooms (all en suite). Outdoor swimming pool, tennis, golf 10 km, garage, parking, restaurant.
1 km from the centre of Golfe-Juan, towards Antibes.

■ TARIFF: (1994) Single 300–485, Double 300–525, Bk 38, Set menu 98–135 (Euro/Access, Visa).

GORDES Vaucluse　　　　5D

Hôtel des Ocres ★★ route des Gordes, 84220 Roussillon-en-Provence.
☎ 90 05 60 50. English spoken.
Open 15/02 to 14/11 & 20/12 to 09/01.
16 bedrooms (all en suite). Garage, parking.
Charming Provençal hotel overlooking Gordes.

■ TARIFF: (1994) Single 280, Double 280–355, Bk 35 (Euro/Access, Visa).

GOURDON Lot　　　　4B

Hôtel de la Bouriane ★★★ pl Foirail, 46300 Gourdon.
☎ 65 41 16 37, Fax 65 41 04 92. English spoken.
Open 08/03 to 15/01. 20 bedrooms (all en suite). Golf 20 km, parking. &
A country inn, just five minutes' walk from the centre of Gourdon, with its Gothic cathedral. The hotel has a terrace overlooking the garden, in this lush, wooded region.

■ RESTAURANT: Closed Mon.
■ TARIFF: (1994) Single 260–280, Double 280–340, Bk 40, Set menu 80–275 (Amex, Euro/Access, Visa).

GRAMAT Lot　　　　5A

Hôtel Lion d'Or 8 pl de la République, 46500 Gramat.
☎ 65 38 73 18, Fax 65 38 84 50. English spoken.
Open 15/01 to 15/12. 15 bedrooms (all en suite). Garage, parking.
Small, quiet hotel set back from the main square in Gramat. Shady terrace and lots of parking room.

■ RESTAURANT: Closed 15/12 to 15/01. Attractive Regency-style dining room with air-conditioning. Périgord specialities and good wines.
■ ACTIVITIES: Mountain-biking, horse-riding and canoeing nearby. Good walking country.
■ TARIFF: (1994) Single 260–290, Double 290–420, Bk 45, Set menu 100–300 (Amex, Euro/Access, Visa).

Hôtel Montbertrand ★★ 46500 Padirac.
☎ 65 33 64 47.
Open 01/04 to 31/10. 7 bedrooms (all en suite). Outdoor swimming pool, golf 12 km, garage, parking.
A charming little hotel on D673 at Padirac, west of St-Céré and Montal. From Gramat, north-east on D677 for 11 km, turn left to Padirac.

■ RESTAURANT: Cuisine based on local produce. Specialities: confit, cèpes, magret de canard.

G

■ ACTIVITIES: Hotel will assist with reservations for tennis and various other local activities.
■ TARIFF: (1994) Single 210–240, Double 220–270, Bk 34, Set menu 85–225 (Euro/Access, Visa).
■ DISCOUNT: 5% Half-board basis.

Hôtel Le Relais des Gourmands ★★ av Gare, 46500 Gramat.
℡ 65 38 83 92, Fax 65 38 70 99. English spoken.

Open all year. 16 bedrooms (all en suite). Outdoor swimming pool, parking.

A pleasant hotel complex, slightly off the beaten track. Light, comfortable rooms with some lovely views over the gardens and pool area. Gramat is on the A140.

■ RESTAURANT: Closed Sun eve & Mon lunch ex Jul/Aug. Refined, imaginative and regional cuisine complemented by some wonderful sauces and an excellent cellar. Meals can be taken outside on the terrace in summer.
■ TARIFF: (1994) Single 280–400, Double 280–440, Bk 40, Set menu 80–220 (Euro/Access, Visa).

LA GRAND-MOTTE Hérault 5D

Hôtel Mercure ★★★ 140 rue du Port, 34280 La Grand-Motte.
℡ 67 56 90 81, Fax 67 56 92 29. English spoken.
Open all year. 135 bedrooms (all en suite). Outdoor swimming pool, golf 2 km, garage, parking. ♿

Air-conditioned rooms with most having private balconies overlooking the sea. Access from the A9 motorway.

■ RESTAURANT: 'Les Terrasses du Port' is a seafood restaurant which also offers regional specialities.
■ ACTIVITIES: Tennis, all water sports and horse-riding close by.
■ TARIFF: Single 320–550, Double 500–650, Bk 55, Set menu 80–120 (Amex, Euro/Access, Visa).

GRANVILLE Manche 1B

Hôtel des Bains ★★★ 19 rue G Clemenceau, 50400 Granville.
℡ 33 50 17 31, Fax 33 50 89 22. English spoken.
Open all year. 49 bedrooms (all en suite). Golf 6 km, parking. ♿

Comfortable, traditional hotel with wonderful sea views. Car parking adjacent.

■ RESTAURANT: Closed Sun eve & Mon LS. Gourmet restaurant with seafood and local specialities.
■ ACTIVITIES: Superb area for sightseeing and boat trips with Mont-St-Michel, D-Day landing beaches and the Channel Islands being within easy reach; good sports facilities nearby.
■ TARIFF: (1994) Single 300–900, Double 350–1200, Bk 45, Set menu 80–140 (Amex, Euro/Access, Visa).

Hôtel La Mougine des Moulins à Ven ★★★ Bréville-sur-Mer, 50290 Granville.
℡ 33 50 22 41.
Open all year. 7 bedrooms (all en suite). Golf 1 km, parking.

Small and comfortable, hotel has a large garden and is close to all the amenities of Granville.

■ ACTIVITIES: Tennis, sailing, horse-riding plus many more things to see and do within easy reach.
■ TARIFF: (1994) Double 340–410, Bk 38 (Euro/Access, Visa).

GRASSE Alpes-Mar 6C

Château de Cipières ★★★★ 06620 Cipières.
℡ 93 59 98 00, Fax 93 59 98 02. English spoken.

Open 01/04 to 01/11. 6 bedrooms (all en suite). Outdoor swimming pool, tennis, golf 20 km, parking.

Historic château in a panoramic setting above Grasse. Accommodation is in period-furnished

G

G

suites; one, two and three bedrooms, with two bathrooms each (100 to 150 sq m). From Grasse via Gourdon towards Gréolières on the D3/D603.

■ RESTAURANT: Restaurant is for guests only.
■ ACTIVITIES: Gym, jacuzzi and sauna, mountain bikes for hire.
■ TARIFF: (1994) Single 950, Double 1950, Set menu 200 (Amex, Euro/Access, Visa).

Hôtel Panorama ★★ 2 pl Cours, 06130 Grasse.
(93 36 80 80, Fax 93 36 92 04. English spoken.
Open all year. 36 bedrooms (all en suite).
Golf 5 km, parking. &

Conveniently situated near the town centre, 2 minutes from the Palais du Congrès and with a fine view over the countryside. A perfect location for exploring the surrounding area and visiting perfume factories.

■ TARIFF: (1994) Single 265–295, Double 295–480, Bk 40 (Amex, Euro/Access, Visa).

Hôtel Relais Imperial ★★ 06460 St-Vallier-de-Thiey.
(93 42 60 07, Fax 93 42 66 21. English spoken.
Open all year. 30 bedrooms (all en suite).
Tennis, golf 8 km, parking.

Completely refurbished period hotel just 10 minutes from the centre of Grasse. Good atmosphere.

■ RESTAURANT: Rustic restaurant with a shady terrace. Regional and traditional cuisine with homemade specialities of foie gras and smoked salmon.
■ ACTIVITIES: Good walks, rafting, canoeing, horse-riding and mountain-biking nearby.
● 10% discount on green fees.
■ TARIFF: (1994) Single 210–440, Double 230–440, Bk 34, Set menu 89–198 (Amex, Euro/Access, Visa).
■ DISCOUNT: 10%

Auberge de la Vignette Haute ★★★★ rte du Village, 06810 Auribeau-sur-Siagne.
(93 42 20 01, Fax 93 42 31 16. English spoken.
Open 05/12 to 15/11. 12 bedrooms (all en suite). Outdoor swimming pool, tennis, golf 5 km, garage, parking. &

Romantic 17th-century auberge, high above the city. Offers modern-day comfort in medieval surroundings. Garden and terrace with farm beyond. From A8 exit Mandelieu-la-Napoule, towards Grasse.

■ RESTAURANT: Closed Mon & Tues lunch LS.
■ TARIFF: (1994) Single 500–1120, Double 500–1400, Bk 70, Set menu 250–490 (Amex, Euro/Access, Visa).

LE GRAU-DU-ROI Gard   5D

Hôtel du Cap ★★★ 30240 Port Camargue.
(66 73 60 60, Fax 66 73 60 50. English spoken.

Open 01/03 to 30/11. 94 bedrooms (all en suite). Indoor swimming pool, outdoor swimming pool, tennis, golf 12 km, parking.

Modern hotel directly on the beach (50 m) offering a wide range of facilities. From Montpellier take the directions for Airport to Le Havre du roi, then Port-Camargue which is just south of Le-Grau-de-roi.

■ RESTAURANT: Panoramic views from 'Letrouvé' and the 'Passerelle' offering local fish specialities and healthy menus.
■ ACTIVITIES: Fitness room, horse-riding, mountain-biking, jeep safari in Camargue, children's activities, billiards.
■ TARIFF: (1994) Single 300–430, Double 370–550, Bk 45, Set menu 75–160 (Amex, Euro/Access, Visa).
■ DISCOUNT: 10% Not in Jul & Aug.

Relais de l'Oustau Camarguen ★★★ 3 rte Marines, Port Camargue, 30240 Le Grau-du-Roi.
(66 51 51 65, Fax 66 53 01 65. English spoken.
Open 25/03 to 11/10. 39 bedrooms (all en suite). Outdoor swimming pool, golf 5 km, garage, parking. &

An old farmhouse which has been turned into a very comfortable hotel. From Port Camargue follow signs to Plage Sud.

■ RESTAURANT: Closed Tues eve & Wed. Typical Camargue-style restaurant serving Provençal dishes: ballotine de lapin aux olives; papillote de raie au pistou; petits légumes farcis à la brandade; petite bourride de lotte.
■ ACTIVITIES: Water sports, fishing, water therapy centre nearby.
■ TARIFF: (1994) Double 380–485, Bk 45, Set menu 130–170 (Amex, Euro/Access, Visa).

GRENOBLE

Grenoble's distinctive téléférique rising above the River Isère

Cathedral of Notre-Dame, with its five naves, are both worth a visit.

You may well know of the novelist Stendhal, who was born in Grenoble in 1783. Two of his books have been adapted for broadcast in Britain within recent years, 'Scarlet and Black' for television and 'The Charterhouse of Parma' for radio. In part of the 17th-century Duc de Lesdiguière's château, a former town hall, there is a museum dedicated to Stendhal and his work. The formal gardens of the château,

Often the best way to get the feel of the layout of a city is to see it from above. Usually this is not possible unless arriving by air, but at Grenoble there is the perfect opportunity. Go to the quai Stéphanie-Jay and take the téléférique, consisting of globe like cable cars in sets of five, across the river Isère and steeply upwards to the Fort de la Bastille, 280 m above.

From here there is a fantastic view across the red roofed medieval town to the snow capped mountains beyond, and with the help of orientation tables you will be able to identify the many natural and architectural features that are visible from this point. Look to the north east on a clear day and you may be lucky enough to see Mont Blanc. It is possible to drive up to the Fort de la Bastille, but if you have come up on the téléférique you are then free to wander back down to the river through the pleasant public gardens, by way of a series of stone steps.

Having got an overall view of Grenoble you may want to explore the old town. A good starting point for this is the Place Grenetta, not far from the téléférique station. From here take a stroll through the medieval streets, do some leisurely shopping or just relax at a pavement café and watch the world go by in this lively part of the city. Of the many fine buildings you will see, the Renaissance Palais de Justice and the

Chartreuse

G

If you drive north-east of Grenoble along the D512, a winding scenic route, you will come to St-Pierre-de-Chartreuse. Here in the narrow Gorges des Guiers Mort, at La Grande Chartreuse monastery, Carthusian monks still live as they have done since their order was founded in the 11th century. Each lives alone in his cell, attending services several times a day but only eating communally in the refectory once a week.

Despite this quiet lifestyle, the monastery is known throughout the world, for it is the home of the famous green liqueur, Chartreuse. Originating in the 16th century, Carthusians in Paris made the liqueur for about 130 years up to 1737, when the recipe was given to the Prior General at La Grande Chartreuse. Modified further by the monks, the recipe remarkably survived the French Revolution when the monks were evicted from their monastery and a further period of banishment this century. The recipe, a closely-guarded secret, contains 130 different herbs, some of which the monks still collect in the woods around the monastery.

To find out more about life at La Grande Chartreuse, try to visit the Carthusian museum at La Correrie. It concentrates on the religious life of the monks, who no longer actually produce their famous liqueur. They still retain the secret recipe but Chartreuse is now made under their instruction at Voiron, to the north-west of Grenoble. Here are the cellars where you can taste Chartreuse and exhibitions and films about its production. All fascinating but, of course, you are never told the one thing you really want to know, the recipe!

now known as the Jardin de la Ville, stand in front of the museum facing onto the Place Grenette.

The most important museum in Grenoble is the Musée de Peinture et de Sculpture. Its 20th-century collection is one of the best in France, and earlier periods are also well represented. Exhibitions of today's works of art are periodically held at the Centre National d'Art Contemporain in the west of the city. This centre, opened in 1986, occupies an industrial building designed by Gustave Eiffel at about the same time as his famous Parisian tower.

As well as exploring the city an expedition to the surrounding mountains is a must. There are a series of good route descriptions available if you want to walk, and many excursions possible by car. Mountain bikes are also available for hire. For a spectacular rail journey travel on the line between St-Georges-de-Commiers and La Mure, to the south of Grenoble. On this 30 km stretch, through country inaccessible by road, there are 133 bends, 18 tunnels and 12 viaducts.

GRENOBLE Isère 6A

(See feature)

Comfort Inn Primevère ★★ 2 rue de l'Europe, 38640 Claix.
✆ 76 98 84 54, Fax 76 98 66 22. English spoken.

Open all year. 45 bedrooms (all en suite). Outdoor swimming pool, golf 5 km, parking.
Small hotel with air-conditioned rooms. Exit 9 off A48/N75 Valence/Nice. 8 km south of Grenoble centre.

■ RESTAURANT: Gourmet cuisine.
■ TARIFF: (1994) Single 280, Double 280, Bk 32, Set menu 81–190 (Euro/Access, Visa).
■ DISCOUNT: 10%

Château de la Commanderie ★★★ 17 av Echirolles, 38320 Eybens.
✆ 76 25 34 58, Fax 76 24 07 31. English spoken.

Open all year. 25 bedrooms (all en suite). Outdoor swimming pool, golf 3 km, parking.
An 18th-century house, with comfortable rooms and set in a park. From Grenoble, follow Rocade-Sud signs, then take exit 6 (Eybens/Bresson) and follow the signs.

■ RESTAURANT: Closed Sat & Sun. Refined, classic cuisine is served either in the elegant dining room or on the candlelit terrace, beneath the trees.
■ ACTIVITIES: Good sports facilities including horse-riding and tennis close by and an international golf course at Brenan (5 minutes).
■ TARIFF: (1994) Single 380–600, Double 425–650, Bk 55, Set menu 145–215 (Amex, Euro/Access, Visa).

Hôtel Patinoires ★★ 12 rue Marie Chamoux, 38100 Grenoble.
✆ 76 44 43 65, Fax 76 44 44 77. English spoken.

Open all year. 35 bedrooms (all en suite).
Golf 8 km, garage, parking.
*Comfortable hotel located in a very quiet
district and with private parking and garage.
5 minutes' drive from the city centre. Follow
signs to Palais des Sports.*
■ TARIFF: (1994) Single 210–230,
Double 230–280, Bk 25 (Amex,
Euro/Access, Visa).
■ DISCOUNT: 10%

Hôtel Terminus ★★★ 10 pl de la Gare,
38000 Grenoble.
℄ 76 87 24 33, Fax 76 50 38 28. English spoken.
Open all year. 28 bedrooms (all en suite).
Garage, parking.
City centre hotel opposite the railway station.
■ TARIFF: (1994) Single 250–400, Double 280–
450, Bk 35 (Amex, Euro/Access, Visa).
■ DISCOUNT: 10%

GREOUX-LES-BAINS Alpes-Hte-Prov   6C

Hôtel Villa Borghese ★★★ av des Thermes,
04800 Gréoux-les-Bains.
℄ 92 78 00 91, Fax 92 78 09 55. English spoken.

Open 08/03 to 27/11. 70 bedrooms
(all en suite). Outdoor swimming pool, tennis,
golf 18 km, garage, parking, restaurant.
*Facing the Thermal Park, a charming hotel
with spacious accommodation and very pretty
gardens.*
■ ACTIVITIES: Health/beauty centre, bridge club;
water sports nearby.
■ TARIFF: (1994) Single 340, Double 440–620,
Bk 50, Set menu 150–250 (Amex,
Euro/Access, Visa).

GRESSY Seine/Marne   2B

Manoir de Gressy ★★★★ 77410 Gressy.
℄ 1 60 26 68 00, Fax 1 60 26 45 46.
English spoken.

Open all year. 90 bedrooms (all en suite).
Outdoor swimming pool, golf 15 km,
parking. &
*Charming 17th-century manor house,
reconstructed as a ninety-bedroom luxury
hotel. From central Paris, head towards
Charles De Gaulle Airport, follow signs to
Soisson then A104 and N2. Exit at
Airport/Mitry then follow signs to Gressy.*
■ RESTAURANT: Informal country restaurant,
overlooking a delightful courtyard. Traditional
French cuisine with a large choice of wines.
■ ACTIVITIES: Tennis, jogging, biking and horse-
riding nearby.
■ TARIFF: (1994) Single 750–950,
Double 850–1050, Set menu 150 (Amex,
Euro/Access, Visa).
■ DISCOUNT: 10% B&B.

GRIGNAN Drôme   5D

Manoir de la Roseraie ★★★ route de Valréas,
26230 Grignan.
℄ 75 46 58 15, Fax 75 46 91 55. English spoken.

Open 14/02 to 05/11 & 14/11 to 04/01.
15 bedrooms (all en suite). Outdoor swimming
pool, tennis, golf 8 km, garage, parking. &
Deluxe 19th-century manor house in a 5-acre

G

park, set at the foot of Madame de Sevigne's château.

■ RESTAURANT: Closed Mon LS. Enjoy the culinary delights of regional cooking including foie gras maison and fish specialities, together with the great wines of the Côte du Rhône.
■ ACTIVITIES: Sauna, table tennis and mountain-biking.
■ TARIFF: (1994) Single 630–1050, Double 630–1050, Bk 85, Set menu 170–220 (Amex, Euro/Access, Visa).

GROIX Morbihan   1C

Hôtel Ty Mad au port, 56590 Ile de Groix.
℡ 97 86 80 19. English spoken.
Open 01/01 to 01/02 & 01/03 to 31/12.
32 bedrooms (7 bath/shower only). Parking, restaurant. &

This little island is reached by car ferry from Lorient and the Ty Mad is close to the little port.
■ TARIFF: (1994) Double 190–380, Set menu 80–200 (Amex, Visa).

GUEBWILLER Ht-Rhin   3D

Domaine Langmatt ★★★ 68530 Murbach.
℡ 89 76 21 12, Fax 89 74 88 77. English spoken.
Open all year. 30 bedrooms (all en suite).
Indoor swimming pool, golf 20 km, garage, parking. &

Set in 72 acres and surrounded by lovely countryside in the heart of the National Park des Ballons des Vosges. 6 km west of Guebwiller off N83 via Buhl.
■ RESTAURANT: Closed Wed lunch. Attractive restaurant with central open fireplace and Alsace specialities.
■ ACTIVITIES: Sports/health complex at hotel.
Horse-riding, fishing and skiing within easy reach.
■ TARIFF: (1994) Single 400–600, Double 480–720, Bk 50, Set menu 100–320 (Euro/Access, Visa).

GUERANDE Loire-Atlan   1D

Hôtel Les Remparts ★★ bd Nord, 44350 Guérande.
℡ 40 24 90 69. English spoken.
Open all year. 8 bedrooms (all en suite). Parking.

Small, traditional hotel at the foot of the medieval ramparts. Access is via Porte-St-Michel and hotel is 100 m to the right of gateway to the old walled town.
■ RESTAURANT: Closed Sun eve. Comfortable restaurant; has earned a good reputation for its cuisine.

■ TARIFF: (1994) Double 240–270, Bk 32, Set menu 95–205 (Euro/Access, Visa).
■ DISCOUNT: 10% LS.

GUIGNES Seine/Marne   2D

Hôtel La Chaum'Yerres ★★★ 1 av Libération, 77390 Chaumes-en-Brie.
℡ 1 64 06 03 42, Fax 1 64 06 36 15. English spoken.

Open all year. 10 bedrooms (all en suite).
Golf 10 km, garage, parking. &

Small hotel offering excellent service and a warm welcome. Comfortable rooms (3 with jacuzzi) and a pretty garden. In the heart of the village with river flowing past. Just north-east of Guignes and only 40 km from Paris.
■ RESTAURANT: Closed Sun eve. Carefully prepared, candlelit dinners with the bonus of an open log fire in winter.
■ ACTIVITIES: Horse-riding/tuition for adults and children; Euro Disney 10 km. ● Special weekend packages available (1 or 2 nights) including horse-riding and tennis. Details from hotel on request. 1 hour's tennis free.
■ TARIFF: (1994) Single 280–350, Double 300–480, Bk 40, Set menu 180–250 (Amex, Euro/Access, Visa).
■ DISCOUNT: 10%

GUISE Aisne   2B

Hôtel Guise ★★ 103 pl Lesur, 02120 Guise.
℡ 23 61 17 58.
Open all year. 8 bedrooms (all en suite). Parking.
Guise lies 25 km east of St-Quentin on the N29.
■ RESTAURANT: Closed Fri & Sun eve.
■ TARIFF: (1994) Single 180, Double 220, Bk 28, Set menu 75–130 (Euro/Access, Visa).

HAGUENAU Bas-Rhin

Hôtel Lindbergh ★★ ZI rue St-Exupéry, 67500 Haguenau.

☎ 88 93 30 13, Fax 88 73 90 04. English spoken.
Open all year. 40 bedrooms (all en suite).
Parking, restaurant. &

Haguenau lies just north of Strasbourg.

■ TARIFF: (1994) Double 265, Bk 30 (No credit cards).

HARDELOT Pas-de-Calais   2B

Hôtel du Parc ★★★ av Francois 1er,
62152 Hardelot.
☎ 21 33 22 11, Fax 21 33 29 71. English spoken.
Open 01/02 to 18/12. 81 bedrooms
(all en suite). Outdoor swimming pool, tennis,
golf on site, parking. &

*The hotel lies in the heart of the Hardelot forest
close to the beach, two golf courses and an
equestrian centre. Rooms are of the highest
standard, with most having a balcony or
terrace overlooking the forest. Between
Boulogne and Le Touquet.*

■ RESTAURANT: 2 pretty dining rooms at hotel
with local and seafood specialities. 2 further
restaurants at each golf club.
■ ACTIVITIES: Excellent sports and health
facilities at hotel and nearby. ● Special rates at
the two golf courses for hotel residents.
■ TARIFF: (1994) Single 405–505, Double 510–
610, Bk 49 (Amex, Euro/Access, Visa).

LE HAVRE Seine-Marit   2A

Hôtel d'Angleterre ★★ 1 rue Louis-Philippe,
76600 Le Havre.
☎ 35 42 48 42, Fax 35 35 22 70 69.
Open all year. 27 bedrooms (19 en suite, 6
bath/shower only). Garage.

Small quiet hotel close to the beach.

■ TARIFF: (1994) Single 200–250,
Double 220–280, Bk 30, (Euro/Access, Visa).

Hôtel Astoria ★★ 13 cours de la République,
76600 Le Havre.
☎ 35 25 00 03, Fax 35 26 48 34.
English spoken.
Open all year. 37 bedrooms (all en suite).
Indoor swimming pool, golf 5 km, garage,
parking, restaurant. &

*Large fully-equipped hotel located in the town
centre, opposite the station near the harbour.*

■ TARIFF: (1994) Single 200–300,
Double 240–330, Bk 25, Set menu 56–129
(Amex, Euro/Access, Visa).

Hôtel Bordeaux ★★★ 147 rue L Brindeau,
76600 Le Havre.
☎ 35 22 69 44, Fax 35 42 09 27. English spoken.

Open all year. 31 bedrooms (all en suite).
Golf 8 km.

*Close to the town centre, beaches, yacht
harbour and car ferry port. Hotel offers
comfortable rooms with an unobstructed view
of the Volcan theatre. Warm welcome and easy
parking facilities nearby.*

■ TARIFF: (1994) Single 360–450,
Double 430–490, Bk 42 (No credit cards).
■ DISCOUNT: 30% Excluding weekends.

Hôtel Ibis ★★ rue 129e Régt Inf,
76600 Le Havre.
☎ 35 22 29 29, Fax 35 21 00 00.
English spoken.
Open all year. 91 bedrooms (all en suite).
Golf 8 km, garage. &

*Situated in the city centre of Le Havre, 300 m
from the railway station and car ferry
terminal.*

■ RESTAURANT: A la carte or fixed price menus
with seafood specialities.
■ ACTIVITIES: Visit Le Havre harbour, Etretat and
Fécamp, and with the 'Normandy Bridge'
(open in January 95), Honfleur, Deauville etc.

Hôtel Mercure chaussée d'Angoulême,
76600 Le Havre.
☎ 35 19 50 50, Fax 35 19 50 99. English spoken.

Open all year. 96 bedrooms (all en suite).
Golf 15 km, garage. &

*Situated in town centre within easy reach of
railway station, ferries, beach and shops. 6 km
to airport.*

■ RESTAURANT: Traditional cuisine, fish
specialities.
■ ACTIVITIES: ● 1 free entry to Dock Tonic Sports
Club.
■ TARIFF: (1994) Single 495–595,
Double 545–595, Bk 55, Set menu 125–150
(Amex, Euro/Access, Visa).

H

HAZEBROUCK Nord 1A

Auberge de la Forêt ★★ Motte-au-Bois,
59190 Hazebrouck.
☎ 28 48 08 78, Fax 28 40 77 76. English spoken.

Open 01/01 to 25/12. 12 bedrooms
(all en suite). Parking.

*Comfortable hotel in the heart of the Forest of
Nieppe in French Flanders. Follow N43 from
Calais to Arques. La Motte au Bois is south of
Hazebrouck, 15 km from Arques on N42.*

■ RESTAURANT: Closed Sun eve & Mon.
Renowned for its fine cuisine and wine cellar.
■ TARIFF: (1994) Single 200−300,
Double 230−300, Bk 38, Set menu 125−360
(Euro/Access, Visa).

HONFLEUR Calvados 2A

Hôtel Castel Albertine ★★★ 19 cours Albert-
Manuel, 14600 Honfleur.
☎ 31 98 85 56, Fax 31 98 83 18. English spoken.
Open all year. 26 bedrooms (all en suite).
Golf 3 km, parking. &

*Charming 18th-century hotel set amid ancient
trees yet only 500 m from the old port and
town centre.*

■ TARIFF: (1994) Double 350−600, Bk 50
(Amex, Euro/Access, Visa).

Hôtel Le Cheval Blanc ★★★ 2 quai des
Passagers, 14600 Honfleur.
☎ 31 81 65 00, Fax 31 89 52 80.
English spoken.
Open 01/02 to 31/12. 34 bedrooms
(all en suite). Golf 7 km, restaurant.

*Built in the 15th century, the hotel occupies a
wonderful situation in the picturesque town of
Honfleur. Well-renovated rooms with harbour
views, and an ideal spot for artists who are
welcomed either in groups or as individuals.*

■ TARIFF: (1994) Single 320−550,
Double 360−600 (Euro/Access, Visa).

Hôtel Romantica ★★ chemin du Petit Paris,
Pennedepie, 14600 Honfleur.
☎ 31 81 14 00, Fax 31 81 54 78. English spoken.

Open all year. 19 bedrooms (all en suite).
Outdoor swimming pool, golf 5 km, garage,
parking. &

*From Honfleur take the coast road to
Cricqueboeuf. Turn left after the church. The
hotel is quietly situated with a view over the bay.*

■ RESTAURANT: Closed 12/11 to 01/04.
■ TARIFF: (1994) Single 280−400,
Double 280−450, Bk 35, Set menu 110−250
(Amex, Euro/Access, Visa).

HOSSEGOR Landes 4C

Hôtel Beausejour ★★★ 40150 Hossegor.
☎ 58 43 51 07, Fax 58 43 70 13. English spoken.

Open 07/05 to 15/10. 45 bedrooms
(all en suite). Outdoor swimming pool,
golf 1 km, garage, parking.

*1930s building situated in the countryside
near lake and sea in an area well known for
its golf courses. From the town centre take
directions for the sea front, after the bridge on*

the canal turn right and follow the Tour du Lac road until the hotel (400 m).

■ RESTAURANT: 1930s decor. Specialities include brouillade aux truffes; magret de canard aux fruits; saumon frais à l'oseille; omelette norvégienne.
■ ACTIVITIES: Water sports; casino and tennis 400 m at Sporting Casino.
■ TARIFF: Single 350–700, Double 480–700, Bk 65 (Amex, Euro/Access, Visa).

Hôtel Amigo ★★ place des Basques, 40150 Hossegor.
☏ 58 43 54 38, Fax 58 43 40 85. English spoken. Open 01/04 to 01/11. 12 bedrooms (10 en suite). Golf 1 km, parking. &

Just 40 m from the excellent beach. From town centre follow signs for 'Front de Mer'. Hotel and terrace is in the square just before the beach.

■ RESTAURANT: Grilled fish and seafood served at the bar or on the terrace.
■ TARIFF: (1994) Single 200–310, Double 200–350, Bk 30 (Euro/Access, Visa).

HYERES Var   6C

Hôtel Pins d'Argent ★★★ Port Saint-Pierre, bd de la Marine, 83400 Hyères-Plage.
☏ 94 57 63 60, Fax 94 38 33 65. English spoken.

Open all year. 20 bedrooms (all en suite). Outdoor swimming pool, golf 15 km, parking. &

19th-century residence elegantly converted into a hotel in the middle of a pine wood and 800 metres from the beach. From Hyères follow directions to the airport.

■ RESTAURANT: Closed Sun eve & Mon LS.
■ TARIFF: (1994) Single 420–460, Double 420–590, Bk 45, Set menu 130–210 (Amex, Euro/Access, Visa).

Hôtel Rose des Mers ★★ 83400 Hyères-Plage.
☏ 94 58 02 73, Fax 94 58 06 16.

Open 01/04 to 15/10. 21 bedrooms (all en suite). Tennis, golf 12 km, garage, parking.

Small hotel situated in a quiet, residential area. Right on the sea, with a private beach, facing the Iles d'Or and 500 m from the yacht harbour. Hotel snack bar is open at lunchtime from mid-June to mid-September.

■ ACTIVITIES: ● 10% discount on water sports, boating/sailing, horse-riding, golf and mountain bike hire.
■ TARIFF: (1994) Double 340–420, Bk 40 (Euro/Access, Visa).
■ DISCOUNT: 10% LS.

INGRANDES-SUR-LOIRE Maine/Loire   2C

Hôtel Le Lion d'Or ★★ 26 rue du Pont, 49123 Ingrandes-sur-Loire.
☏ 41 39 20 08, Fax 41 39 21 03. English spoken.

Open all year. 16 bedrooms (10 en suite, 6 bath/shower only). Garage, parking, restaurant.

Standing between Angers and Nantes, Le Lion d'Or dates from 1660 and was the first hotel in Ingrandes. Enjoy peace and relaxation in renovated, modern rooms, close to the River Loire.

H

■ ACTIVITIES: Fishing, cycling and tennis nearby.
■ TARIFF: (1994) Single 170–230, Double 170–270, Bk 26 (Amex, Euro/Access, Visa).

ISIGNY-SUR-MER Calvados 2A

Hôtel de France ★★ 15 rue Emile Demagny, 14230 Isigny-sur-Mer.
℡ 31 22 00 33, Fax 31 22 79 19. English spoken.
Open 15/01 to 15/12. 19 bedrooms
(14 en suite). Outdoor swimming pool, parking. ᏻ
On the wartime landing beaches circuit, a comfortable, attractive hotel with the quiet rooms surrounding a flowered courtyard.
■ RESTAURANT: Closed Fri eve & Sat LS. The delicious seafood specialities include oysters, mussels in cream sauce, turbot and halibut dishes.
■ ACTIVITIES: The private, heated swimming pool reserved for guests is 3 km from the hotel.
■ TARIFF: (1994) Single 160–220, Double 180–280, Bk 32 (Euro/Access, Visa).

L'ISLE-JOURDAIN Vienne 4B

Hôtel Val de Vienne ★★★ Port-de-Salle, 86150 Le Vigeant.
℡ 49 48 27 27, Fax 49 48 47 47. English spoken.
Open all year. 20 bedrooms (all en suite).
Outdoor swimming pool, garage, parking.
Beautifully situated on the banks of the River Vienne, each room has a private terrace overlooking the river. Gourmet restaurant next door. From L'Isle-Jourdain take the D10 east towards Charroux, turn left after 4 km to Port-de-Salles. Hotel well sign-posted on right. SEE ADVERTISEMENT.
■ ACTIVITIES: Mountain-bike hire, motor racing school, go-karting, 4x4 track, microlite flying, bungee jumping. Also, fishing, hunting, boat hire (summer).
■ TARIFF: Double 420–520, Bk 45 (Euro/Access, Visa).

ISSOIRE Puy-de-Dôme 5A

Hôtel Le Relais 1 av Gare, 63500 Issoire.
℡ 73 89 16 61, Fax 73 89 55 62.
English spoken.
Open all year. 6 bedrooms (3 en suite, 3 bath/shower only). Garage, restaurant.
In town centre, close to church and railway station. From Issoire, north on N9 towards Clermont-Ferrand.
■ TARIFF: (1994) Single 170–200, Double 170–230, Bk 25 (Euro/Access, Visa).

ISSOUDUN Indre 2D

Hôtel La Cognette ★★★ rue des Minimes, 36100 Issoudun.
℡ 54 21 21 83, Fax 54 03 13 03. English spoken.
Open all year. 14 bedrooms (all en suite).
Golf 8 km, garage. ᏻ
A very attractive and individual hotel with a garden. Described by Balzac.
■ RESTAURANT: Closed Sun & Mon eve LS.
Exceptional cuisine.
■ TARIFF: (1994) Single 300–900, Double 350–950, Bk 50, Set menu 210–500 (Amex, Euro/Access, Visa, ʙᴛ⌇).
■ DISCOUNT: 10%

JOINVILLE Hte-Marne 3C

Hôtel Poste pl Grève, 52300 Joinville.
℡ 25 94 12 63, Fax 25 94 36 23. English spoken.
Open 10/02 to 10/01. 10 bedrooms
(all en suite). Garage, parking.
Traditional hotel, small and comfortable. On the N67, between St-Dizier and Chaumont.
■ RESTAURANT: Well known for its fine cuisine.
■ TARIFF: (1994) Single 180–250, Double 180–280, Bk 26, Set menu 80–200 (Amex, Euro/Access, Visa).

JOYEUSE Ardèche   5D

Hôtel La Guaribote ★★ Gua, 07110 Joyeuse.
☎ 75 39 44 09, Fax 75 39 55 89. English spoken.

Open 01/04 to 09/10. 16 bedrooms
(all en suite). Parking.
*On the banks of La Beaume river, one of the
most beautiful in the south Ardèche where you
may fish and enjoy tranquil surroundings.
12 km from Joyeuse on the route de Valgorge.*
■ RESTAURANT: Closed lunch LS & Mon lunch HS.
■ TARIFF: (1994) Single 210–260,
Double 230–280, Bk 39, Set menu 110–290
(Amex, Euro/Access, Visa).

JUAN-LES-PINS Alpes-Mar   6C

Beachôtel ★★★ av Alexandre III,
06160 Juan-les-Pins.
☎ 93 61 81 85, Fax 93 61 51 97.
English spoken.
Open 15/03 to 15/10 & 20/12 to 05/01.
43 bedrooms (all en suite). Garage, parking,
restaurant. &
*Modern hotel situated a few metres from the
beach. West side of Juan.*
■ TARIFF: Single 335–550, Double 410–650,
Bk 45 (Amex, Euro/Access, Visa).
■ DISCOUNT: 5%

Garden Beach Hôtel ★★★★ 15-17 bd
Baudoin, 06160 Juan-les-Pins.
☎ 93 67 25 25, Fax 93 61 16 65.
English spoken.
Open all year. 175 bedrooms (all en suite).
Golf 7 km, garage, parking. &
*Very modern hotel on private sandy beach,
close to town centre and modern art collection
of the Maeght Foundation. 25 km from Nice on
the N98 and south of Antibes, on coast road.*
■ RESTAURANT: Beach-front restaurant has a
good reputation for its fine Provençal cuisine.
Buffet dinners on the beach in summer.

■ ACTIVITIES: Water sports, fishing and a choice
of 7 18-hole golf courses nearby.
■ TARIFF: (1994) Double 600–1900, Bk 95,
Set menu 200 (Amex, Euro/Access, Visa).

Hôtel Ste-Valerie ★★★ rue de l'Oratoire,
06160 Juan-les-Pins.
☎ 93 61 07 15, Fax 93 61 47 52. English spoken.

Open 15/04 to 30/09. 30 bedrooms
(all en suite). Golf 7 km, garage, parking.
*A comfortable hotel with air-conditioned, quiet
and well-equipped rooms. Near the casino and
beaches.*
■ RESTAURANT: Provençal cuisine, dining terrace
overlooking gardens.
■ ACTIVITIES: Boating and water skiing nearby.
■ TARIFF: (1994) Single 395–520,
Double 440–840, Bk 30, Set menu 85–115
(Amex, Euro/Access, Visa).

JULIENAS Rhône   5B

Hôtel des Vignes ★★ rte St-Amour,
69840 Julienas.
☎ 74 04 43 70, Fax 74 04 41 95. English spoken.
Open all year. 20 bedrooms (all en suite).
Garage, parking. &
The hotel is set in its own grounds in the

J

middle of a vineyard, half a mile from the village. South-west of Mâcon. Motorway A6.

■ TARIFF: (1994) Single 200, Double 240–275, Bk 35 (Euro/Access, Visa).

KAYSERSBERG Ht-Rhin 3D

Hôtel Constantin ★★★ 10 rue du Père Kohlmann, 68240 Kaysersberg.
☎ 89 47 19 90, Fax 89 47 37 82. English spoken.

Open all year. 20 bedrooms (all en suite). Golf 2 km, garage.

This 18th-century renovated wine grower's house is in the heart of the old city of Kaysersberg near the Constantin fountain.

■ ACTIVITIES: Walking, cycling and good centre for visiting interesting places in Alsace.
■ TARIFF: (1994) Single 310–330, Double 384–434 (Euro/Access, Visa).

LABASTIDE-MURAT Lot 4D

Hôtel Climat de France ★★ place de la Mairie, 46240 Labastide-Murat.
☎ 65 21 18 80, Fax 65 21 10 97. English spoken.
Open 15/01 to 15/12. 20 bedrooms (all en suite). Golf 3 km, restaurant. &

An old castle built in 1261, now completely up-to-date but with a special charm. From the N20 take the D667 to Labastide-Murat.

■ TARIFF: (1994) Double 260–310, Bk 34 (Amex, Euro/Access, Visa).
■ DISCOUNT: 10%

LABOUHEYRE Landes 4C

Hôtel Unic ★★ rte Bordeaux, 40210 Labouheyre.
☎ 58 07 00 55, Fax 58 04 50 59. English spoken.
Open all year. 8 bedrooms (all en suite). Parking, restaurant.

Small hotel south of Bordeaux on N10 towards Castets.

■ TARIFF: (1994) Single 200–250, Double 250–300, Bk 30, Set menu 85–150 (Amex, Euro/Access, Visa).

LACANAU-OCEAN Gironde 4A

Hôtel Golf ★★★ au golf, 33680 Lacanau-Océan.
☎ 56 03 23 15, Fax 56 26 30 57. English spoken.
Open 01/10 to 03/01 & 05/03 to 31/12. 50 bedrooms (all en suite). Outdoor swimming pool, parking, restaurant. &

Large chalet-style hotel also offering 2 and 3-roomed cottages for rent. In woods and near to the beach with sports and social facilities. From Bordeaux, take the D6 to Lacanau.

■ TARIFF: (1994) Single 360–565, Double 520–730 (Amex, Visa).

LALINDE Dordogne 4B

Hôtel Château ★★★ 24150 Lalinde.
☎ 53 61 01 82, Fax 53 24 74 60. English spoken.
Open 15/02 to 01/01. 7 bedrooms (all en suite). Outdoor swimming pool, golf 10 km, parking.

Between the black and purple zones of the Périgord, the Château is of 13th- and 18th-century architecture and juts out over the River Dordogne. Close to the town centre, but very peaceful with a shaded terrace and pool area.

■ RESTAURANT: Closed Fri LS, Fri lunch HS. Charming, typical of the region and overlooking the river. Creative Périgord specialities, with foie gras served in a variety of ways.
■ ACTIVITIES: Tennis nearby; good base for touring and sightseeing.
■ TARIFF: (1994) Single 350–450, Double 350–850, Bk 60, Set menu 155–310 (Euro/Access, Visa).
■ DISCOUNT: 5%

Hôtel Relais St-Jacques ★★ place de l'Eglise, 24150 St-Capraise-de-Lalinde.
☎ 53 63 47 54.
Open 16/02 to 14/01. 6 bedrooms (all en suite).

Situated in the centre of the village, near the church square.

■ RESTAURANT: Closed Wed.
■ TARIFF: (1994) Single 210–240, Double 210–270, Bk 33, Set menu 85–220 (Euro/Access, Visa).

LAMASTRE Ardèche 5B

Château d'Urbilhac ★★★ route de Vernoux, 07270 Lamastre.
℡ 75 06 42 11, Fax 75 06 52 75. English spoken.
Open 01/05 to 05/10. 13 bedrooms (all en suite). Outdoor swimming pool, tennis, garage, parking. &

A château in exceptionally beautiful, forested countryside. Elegant, comfortable rooms with panoramic views across 162-acre park. Sun terrace above pool on the château ramparts. Quiet and very relaxing.

■ RESTAURANT: Closed Mon to Fri lunch. Traditional dining room as well as a dining conservatory which overlooks the grounds and the glass-sided kitchen. Good food, beautifully presented.
■ ACTIVITIES: The preserved Vivarais Railway makes frequent trips between Tournon and Lamastre - a must for railway enthusiasts!
■ TARIFF: (1994) Single 450–600, Double 500–650, Bk 65 (Amex, Euro/Access, Visa).

LAMBALLE Côtes-du-Nord 1D

Hôtel Les Alizes ★★ La Ville-es-Lan, 22400 Lamballe.
℡ 96 31 16 37, Fax 96 31 23 89.
English spoken.

Open all year. 32 bedrooms (all en suite). Golf 12 km, parking. &

Modern hotel, not far from the Rennes to Brest dual carriageway. To the right on the N12 motorway going west towards the coast.

■ RESTAURANT: Closed Sun eve, Sat LS. Gourmet restaurant with seafood specialities.
■ ACTIVITIES: ● 20% reduction on green fees for stays of 5 days or more.
■ TARIFF: (1994) Single 260, Double 295, Bk 35, Set menu 75–250 (Amex, Visa).

Hôtel Angleterre ★★★ 29 bd Jobert, 22400 Lamballe.
℡ 96 31 00 16, Fax 96 31 91 54. English spoken.
Open all year. 20 bedrooms (19 en suite, 1 bath/shower only). Golf 8 km, garage, parking.

A modern town centre hotel with good facilities.

■ RESTAURANT: Closed 01/03 to 15/03 & Sun LS. Seafood specialities.
■ TARIFF: Single 220–290, Double 240–320, Bk 38, Set menu 82–260 (Amex, Euro/Access, Visa).

LANDIVISIAU Finistère 1C

Hôtel L'Enclos ★★ Lampaul Guimiliau, 29400 Landivisiau.
℡ 98 68 77 08, Fax 98 68 61 06. English spoken.
Open all year. 36 bedrooms (all en suite).
Parking. &

Quiet hotel in country surroundings situated in the heart of Brittany.

■ RESTAURANT: Traditional cooking in a quiet and restful setting. Speciality: seafood.
■ ACTIVITIES: Rambling, trout and salmon fishing; cycling circuit with mountain bikes for hire.
■ TARIFF: Single 224, Double 260, Bk 30 (Amex, Euro/Access, Visa).

Hôtel au Relais du Vern ★★ ZA du Vern BP 26, 29400 Landivisiau.
℡ 98 24 42 42, Fax 98 24 42 00. English spoken.
Open all year. 52 bedrooms (all en suite).
Tennis, golf 14 km, garage, parking, restaurant. &

On the crossroads N12 (Rennes/Brest) and C69 (Roscoff/Quimper). A modern hotel with comfortable, sound-proofed rooms and good facilities. Set in a large garden and close to mountains and the sea.

■ TARIFF: (1994) Single 284, Double 330, Bk 34, Set menu 68–147 (Amex, Euro/Access, Visa).

LANGEAIS Indre/Loire 2C

Auberge de la Bonde ★★ St-Michel-sur-Loire, 37130 Langeais.
℡ 47 96 83 13, Fax 47 96 85 72. English spoken.
Open 23/01 to 23/12. 13 bedrooms (8 en suite,

L

4 bath/shower only). Golf 20 km, parking.
*On châteaux and vineyards circuit, close to
banks of Loire. 30 km from Tours going
towards Saumur on the N152.*
- RESTAURANT: Closed Sat LS.
- TARIFF: (1994) Double 200–280, Bk 32,
Set menu 82–190 (Euro/Access, Visa).

LANGRES

L *Part of Langres's ancient wall*

This ancient city stands on the edge of a
high plateau above the River Marne and is
surrounded by a 5-km wall. Its narrow
cobbled streets are a delight to wander
through and a tour of the wall, which has
six gateways and seven towers, is a must.
From here there are many picturesque
views out over the surrounding countryside
and, on a clear day, it is possible to see the
snow-capped Alps as well as the nearer
Vosges and Jura mountains.

LANGRES Hte-Marne 3C

(See feature)

Grand Hôtel Europe ★★ 23 rue Diderot,
52200 Langres.
☎ 25 87 10 65, Fax 25 87 60 65. English spoken.
Open 25/10 to 08/05 & 23/05 to 01/10.
28 bedrooms (26 en suite). Garage, parking.
*A 17th-century hotel in centre of town just a
stone's throw from the city walls and the
countryside beyond.*
- RESTAURANT: Closed Sun PM & Mon lunch;
Mon eve LS.
- TARIFF: (1994) Single 150–240,
Double 220–280, Bk 32, Set menu 70–190
(Amex, Euro/Access, Visa).

Auberge des III Jumeaux ★★ St-Geosmes,
52200 Langres.
☎ 25 87 03 36, Fax 25 87 58 68. English spoken.
Open all year. 10 bedrooms (all en suite).
*This is a very comfortable family hotel in an
area rich in history and art. Leave the
autoroute at Langres-Sud and take N74 in the
direction of Dijon, then 4 km to St-Geosmes.*
- RESTAURANT: Closed Mon. Good food at this
small auberge. Try the delicious seafood Salade
des III Jumeaux - smoked salmon, crab, oysters
and prawns. Game in season and one regional
menu.
- TARIFF: (1994) Single 180–200,
Double 200–380, Bk 32, Set menu 80–300
(Amex, Euro/Access, Visa).

Auberge des Voiliers ★★ Lac de la Liez,
52200 Langres.
☎ 25 87 05 74, Fax 25 87 24 22. English spoken.
Open 15/03 to 31/01. 8 bedrooms
(all en suite). Parking. ⅃
*Small inn near Lake Liez offering a warm
welcome. Take the N19 towards Vesoul. After
4 km turn right beyond the bridge and the inn
is 2 km ahead.*
- RESTAURANT: Traditional regional cuisine.
Meals are served on the terrace in fine weather
and on a verandah overlooking the lake at
other times.
- ACTIVITIES: Excellent sailing/boating facilities
nearby, including a national sailing school
800 m away. Opportunities for fishing, cycling
and lovely walks are also on the doorstep.
- TARIFF: (1994) Double 200–280, Bk 35,
Set menu 75–200 (Euro/Access, Visa).

LANNION Côtes-du-Nord 1C

Hôtel Le Graal ★★ 30 av Gén de Gaulle,
22300 Lannion.
☎ 96 37 03 67, Fax 96 46 45 83. English spoken.
Open all year. 42 bedrooms (all en suite).
Golf 10 km, parking. ⅃
*Modern, attractive hotel, 10 minutes from
beach. Between Brest and St-Brieuc. TGV from
Paris.*
- RESTAURANT: Closed Sun & Mon lunch.
Medieval-style décor; restaurant specialises in
creative, regional cuisine.
- TARIFF: (1994) Double 290–345, Bk 29
(Amex, Euro/Access, Visa).

LANSLEBOURG Savoie 6A

Hôtel Alpazur ★★★ 73480 Val-Cenis.
☎ 79 05 93 69, Fax 79 05 81 96. English spoken.
Open 20/12 to 12/04 & 01/06 to 20/09.

24 bedrooms (all en suite). Garage, parking.
Comfortable chalet-style hotel situated at the foot of the slopes. Rooms with balconies overlooking the mountain. Access from N6.
■ RESTAURANT: Specialites based on dishes served at the court of the Dukes of Savoy.
■ ACTIVITIES: ● 1 week 'full skiing' package: half-board & ski pass - (Jan) 2571F, (Feb/Mar) 3109F; 1 week 'Club pass' package: half-board, ski pass, ski school and hire of skis and boots - (Jan) 3689F, (Feb/Mar) 4127F.
■ TARIFF: (1994) Single 290–360, Double 300–450, Bk 38, Set menu 98–300 (Amex, Euro/Access, Visa).

LANTOSQUE Alpes-Mar   6C

Hôtel L'Ancienne Gendarmerie ★★★
06450 Lantosque.
℡ 93 03 00 65, Fax 90 03 06 31. English spoken.
Open 20/12 to 08/11. 8 bedrooms (all bath/shower only). Outdoor swimming pool, tennis, parking.
Exit St-Isodore motorway towards Digne/Grenoble on D202. After Plan-du-Var turn right on D2565 and stay on it for 20 km.
■ RESTAURANT: Fresh seafood; lamb; delicious desserts.
■ ACTIVITIES: Hiking, canoeing, fishing, skiing.
■ TARIFF: (1994) Single 350, Double 350–710, Bk (Amex, Euro/Access, Visa).

LAON Aisne   2B

Château de Barive ★★★★ Ste-Preuve, 02350 Liesse.
℡ 23 22 15 15, Fax 23 22 08 39. English spoken.

Open all year. 15 bedrooms (all en suite). Indoor swimming pool, tennis, parking.

Standing in a quiet and secluded 1250-acre estate. From Laon take exit 13 to Sissonne. Then take the Ste-Preuve road and look for a left turn to the château. ■ RESTAURANT: Gourmet restaurant serving local speciality cuisine.
■ TARIFF: (1994) Single 380–580, Double 380–780, Bk 55, Set menu 150–310 (Amex, Euro/Access, Visa).

Hôtel Mercure Holigolf ★★★ Golf de l'Ailette, 02860 Chamouille.
℡ 23 24 84 85, Fax 23 24 81 20. English spoken.

Open 15/03 to 15/11. 60 bedrooms (all en suite). Outdoor swimming pool, golf on site, parking. &
Comfortable hotel in a peaceful, lakeside setting. South of Laon and accessed via N44 and Corbeny.
■ RESTAURANT: Lake views. Excellent wine list at very reasonable prices.
■ ACTIVITIES: Many leisure and sporting facilities available including mountain-biking, water sports and horse-riding.
■ TARIFF: (1994) Single 390–400, Double 430–490, Bk 50, Set menu 110–160 (Amex, Euro/Access, Visa, **BT**).

LAVAL Mayenne   2C

Hôtel Climat de France ★★ bd des Trappistines, 53000 Laval.
℡ 43 02 88 88, Fax 43 02 87 00. English spoken.
Open all year. 44 bedrooms (all en suite). Golf 5 km, parking. &
Near an abbey with woodland surroundings, this recently built hotel provides a quiet and cosy atmosphere. South of Laval off the N157.
■ RESTAURANT: Very good.
■ TARIFF: (1994) Double 268, Bk 30, Set menu 60–120 (Amex, Euro/Access, Visa).

L

Château de la Motte-Henry 53170 Meslay-du-Maine.
☎ 43 98 60 81, Fax 43 98 73 78. English spoken.

Open all year. 5 bedrooms (all en suite). Golf 25 km, garage, parking.

This de-luxe, historic château is full of family treasures and period furniture. Special two night honeymoon package available. On the D21, 4 km from Meslay-du-Maine.

■ RESTAURANT: Home-grown produce is used to create the imaginative, gourmet cuisine.
■ TARIFF: Single 600, Double 800–2500, Bk 75, Set menu 250 (Amex, Euro/Access, Visa).
■ DISCOUNT: 10% By advance booking.

LE LAVANDOU Var   6C

Hôtel Grand Pavois ★★★ Plage d'Aiguebelle, 83980 Le Lavandou.
☎ 94 05 81 38, Fax 94 05 77 88. English spoken.

Open all year. 24 bedrooms (all en suite). Golf 2 km, parking. &

The hotel stands right next to the Aiguebelle beach with views over the gardens or out across to the 'golden' isles. Comfortable rooms in a quiet spot on this delightful coastline. Handy for Toulon-Hyères airport and St-Tropez.

■ RESTAURANT: Traditional Provençale cuisine including grilled fish and meat dishes. Good selection of local wines.
■ ACTIVITIES: Boat excursions to offshore islands, water-skiing.
■ TARIFF: (1994) Single 300–500, Double 300–500, Bk 35, Set menu 100–250 (Amex, Euro/Access, Visa).
■ DISCOUNT: 10%

Hôtel Tamaris ★★★ plage de St-Clair, 83980 Le Lavandou.
☎ 94 71 79 19, Fax 94 71 88 64. English spoken. Open 01/03 to 30/10. 41 bedrooms (all en suite). Golf 5 km, parking. &

The Tamaris hotel is a new hotel situated on St-Clair beach 2 km from Le Lavandou. All rooms look on to the sea and are equipped with all modern facilities.

■ TARIFF: (1994) Single 350–450, Double 380–480, Bk 35 (Amex, Euro/Access, Visa).

LAVAUR Tarn   5C

Hôtel L'Echauguette 81500 Giroussens.
☎ 63 41 63 65. English spoken.
Open all year. 5 bedrooms (3 en suite, 2 bath/shower only). Golf 10 km, parking.

Recommended hotel. Set in a charming village, 10 km north of Lavaur. Take the D87, then left onto the D631. Or from A68 motorway between Albi and Toulouse, exit 7 and turn south.

■ RESTAURANT: Closed Mon LS. Typical restaurant with fine views and a good reputation. Specialities include magret de canard garni and filet de boeuf au poivre.
■ ACTIVITIES: 1 km from lake, sightseeing train, park and gardens, 2 golf courses.
■ TARIFF: (1994) Single 150, Double 260, Bk 25 (Amex, Euro/Access, Visa).

LESCONIL Finistère   1C

Hôtel Atlantic ★★ 11 rue Jean Jaures, 29740 Lesconil.
☎ 98 87 81 06. English spoken.
Open 01/04 to 30/09. 23 bedrooms (all en suite). Golf 20 km, parking.

In a lovely garden setting in this small Breton fishing village approx 28 km south of Quimper.

■ RESTAURANT: Very pretty, light and airy dining room. Seafood specialities.
■ ACTIVITIES: Very good sports facilities including fishing and windsurfing nearby.
■ TARIFF: (1994) Double 210–300, Bk 35, Set menu 80–200 (Amex, Euro/Access, Visa).

L

LESNEVEN Finistère   1C

Hôtel Le Week-End ★★ Pont du Châtel,
29260 Lesneven.
✆ 98 25 40 57, Fax 98 25 46 92. English spoken.
Open 01/02 to 31/12. 13 bedrooms (all en
suite). Tennis, golf 15 km, garage, parking.
*Country hotel with a waterside garden and
only 5 km from the sea. 3 minutes from
Lesneven on the D110, and 20 minutes from
Roscoff on the D788.*
■ RESTAURANT: Closed Mon lunch. Specialises in
seafood dishes, including home-made fish
soup.
■ TARIFF: (1994) Double 220–300, Bk 38
(Euro/Access, Visa).

LEVENS Alpes-Mar   6C

Hôtel Cassini ★★ 06670 Plan-du-Var.
✆ 93 08 91 03, Fax 93 08 45 48. English spoken.
Open all year. 20 bedrooms (10 en suite).
Garage.
*From Nice Airport follow the N202, direction
Digue, for 25 km to Plan du Var. The hotel is in
the middle of the village on the right.*
■ RESTAURANT: Closed Sun eve & Mon LS.
■ TARIFF: (1994) Single 110–260,
Double 150–260, Bk 25, Set menu 80–180
(Amex, Euro/Access, Visa).
■ DISCOUNT: 10%

Hôtel Malaussena ★★ 9 pl de la République,
06670 Levens.
✆ 93 79 70 06, Fax 93 79 85 89. English spoken.
Open 15/12 to 31/10. 14 bedrooms
(10 en suite, 4 bath/shower only). Outdoor
swimming pool, tennis, restaurant. &
In the centre of Levens, 22 km north of Nice.
■ ACTIVITIES: Horse-riding, mountain walks.
■ TARIFF: (1994) Double 230–310, Bk 35,
Set menu 80–150 (Amex, Euro/Access, Visa).
■ DISCOUNT: 10%

LILLE Nord   2B

Hôtel Alliance ★★★★ quai du Wault BP133,
59027 Lille.
✆ 20 30 62 62, Fax 20 42 94 85. English spoken.
Open all year. 83 bedrooms (all en suite).
Golf 5 km, parking. &
*17th-century classified convent in quiet district
only 5 minutes walk from the town centre.
Taking A1 from Paris take Lille Centre,
continue straight on as far as Champs de Mars
and there is a sign to the hotel on the right.
500 m from the station. Motorway A25 from
the coast.*

■ RESTAURANT: Regional specialities.
■ TARIFF: (1994) Single 640–1500,
Double 770–1500, Bk 70, Set menu 160–195
(Amex, Euro/Access, Visa).

Hôtel Carlton ★★★★ 3 rue de Paris, 59800 Lille.
✆ 20 13 33 13, Fax 20 51 48 17. English spoken.
Open all year. 60 bedrooms (all en suite).
Golf 7 km, garage, parking. &
*Completely renovated, and with air-
conditioned rooms, the Carlton has the class of
a de-luxe hotel. Situated in the centre of Lille,
facing the Opera.*
■ RESTAURANT: Choice of restaurants: 'Bistrot
Opera' with traditional French cuisine and the
'Brasserie Jean' with Flemish specialities.
■ TARIFF: (1994) Single 730–2400,
Double 760–2400, Bk 70, Set menu 130
(Amex, Euro/Access, Visa).

Hôtel Mercure Lille Aeroport 110 rue Jean
Jaurès, 59810 Lesquin.
✆ 20 87 46 46, Fax 20 87 46 47. English spoken.
Open all year. 213 bedrooms (all en suite).
Golf 7 km, parking, restaurant. &
*Well equipped hotel, with courtesy bus link to
the airport. From Lille, exit Lille-Lesquin.*
■ TARIFF: (1994) Single 350–470,
Double 350–520, Bk 57 (Amex,
Euro/Access, Visa).

LIMOGES Hte-Vienne   4B

Hôtel La Chapelle St-Martin ★★★★ St-
Martin-du-Fault, 87510 Limoges.
✆ 55 75 80 17, Fax 55 75 89 50. English spoken.
Open 15/02 to 31/12. 12 bedrooms
(all en suite). Outdoor swimming pool, tennis,
golf 10 km, garage, parking. &
*Elegant country house in large park with
landscaped ornamental lakes. North-west of
Limoges on D35.*
■ RESTAURANT: Closed Mon. Renowned for its

L

very good cuisine.

■ ACTIVITIES: Fishing on two private lakes.
■ TARIFF: (1994) Single 590–1100,
Double 690–1500, Bk 75, Set menu 180–380
(Amex, Euro/Access, Visa, **BT**).
■ DISCOUNT: 5%

Hôtel Climat de France ★★ Le Ponteix-
Secteur Laugerie, 87220 Feytiat.
☎ 55 06 14 60, Fax 55 06 38 93. English spoken.
Open all year. 50 bedrooms (all en suite).
Golf 3 km, parking, restaurant. &

*This recently-built hotel has a cosy atmosphere
and all rooms are well furnished and
equipped. Most rooms have a colour TV and all
have direct dial telephone and radio alarm
clock.*

■ TARIFF: (1994) Double 260–270, Bk 32,
Set menu 85–110 (Amex, Euro/Access, Visa).
■ DISCOUNT: 10%

LIMOUX Aude   5C

Gd H Moderne et Pigeon 1 pl Gén Leclerc,
11300 Limoux.
English spoken.
Open 15/01 to 15/12. 19 bedrooms
(all en suite). Garage.

*Converted 19th-century residence featuring
elegant staircase with a stained glass window
and adorned by frescoes, in a region offering
varied leisure activities. A61 from Toulouse to
Castelnaudary then onto D623 to Limoux.*

■ RESTAURANT: Closed Mon.
■ TARIFF: (1994) Single 290–370,
Double 380–470, Bk 40, Set menu 135–195
(Amex, Euro/Access, Visa).

LE LION-D'ANGERS Maine/Loire   1D

Château du Plessis 49220 La Jaille-Yvon.
☎ 41 95 12 75, Fax 41 95 14 41. English spoken.
Open 01/03 to 31/10. 8 bedrooms
(all en suite). Golf 15 km, parking.

*A private, 16th- to 17th-century château. A
quiet and comfortable base for Pays du Loire
visits or stop-over en route south. La Jaille-Yvon
is on the N162 halfway between Château-
Gontier and Le Lion-d'Angers.*

■ RESTAURANT: Closed Sun. A good variety of
traditional and regional dishes, with a selection
of 3 Loire valley wines.
■ ACTIVITIES: Nearby, hot-air ballooning,
mountain-bike hire, archery, boating/canoeing
on the Mayenne river.
■ TARIFF: (1994) Single 490–590, Double 620–
770, Set menu 270 (Amex, Euro/Access, Visa).
■ DISCOUNT: 10% LS.

LISIEUX Calvados   2A

Hôtel St-Louis ★★ 4 rue St-Jacques,
14100 Lisieux.
☎ 31 62 06 50. English spoken.
Open all year. 17 bedrooms (11 en suite).
Golf 5 km, garage.

*A quiet hotel with a garden, in the centre of the
city. Near the basilica and the cathedral.*

■ TARIFF: (1994) Single 170–250,
Double 170–280, Bk 25 (Euro/Access, Visa).

LOCHES Indre/Loire   2C

Hôtel France ★★ 6 rue Picois, 37600 Loches.
☎ 47 59 00 32, Fax 47 59 28 66. English spoken.
Open 10/02 to 09/01. 20 bedrooms
(19 en suite, 1 bath/shower only). Garage,
parking.

*With a courtyard full of flowers, the hotel has
soundproofed rooms, a covered garage and is
in the town centre next to the medieval
quarter.*

■ RESTAURANT: Closed 10/01 to 10/02. A very
good choice of menus with Touraine
specialities including game in season.
■ TARIFF: (1994) Double 180–335, Bk 31,
Set menu 82–250 (Euro/Access, Visa).

Hôtel Lucotel ★★ rue Lézards, 37600 Loches.
☎ 47 91 50 50, Fax 47 94 01 18. English spoken.
Open 15/01 to 18/12. 42 bedrooms
(all en suite). Indoor swimming pool, tennis,
golf 20 km, parking. &

*A quiet and comfortable hotel set in parkland
overlooking Loches.*

■ RESTAURANT: Closed Sat lunch.
■ TARIFF: (1994) Single 250–330,
Double 330–380, Bk 35, Set menu 90–200
(Euro/Access, Visa).

LODEVE Hérault   5C

Hôtel Croix Blanche ★★ 6 av de Fumel,
34700 Lodève.
☎ 67 44 10 87. English spoken.
Open 01/04 to 30/11. 32 bedrooms (14 en
suite, 6 bath/shower only). Garage, parking.

On the N9/E1 between Montpellier and Millau.

■ RESTAURANT: Closed Wed lunch. Traditional
restaurant serving regional dishes plus pâté de
foie gras de canard, confits, pâté truffé.
■ TARIFF: (1994) Single 120–200,
Double 120–220, Bk 25 (Euro/Access, Visa).

Hôtel Paix ★★ 11 bd Montalangue,
34700 Lodève.
☎ 67 44 07 46. English spoken.

Open all year. 21 bedrooms (all en suite).
Garage, parking, restaurant.
*The hotel is 100 years old, completely
renovated and quiet. Situated by a river in the
centre of the town. Motorway N9 north from
Béziers. N109/E11 west from Montpellier.*
■ TARIFF: (1994) Single 200, Double 220, Bk 25,
Set menu 65–160 (Euro/Access, Visa).

LONS-LE-SAUNIER Jura   5B

Hôtel Genève ★★ 39 rue J Moulin,
39000 Lons-le-Saunier.
℡ 84 24 19 11, Fax 84 24 81 42. English spoken.
Open all year. 35 bedrooms (all en suite).
Golf 5 km, garage, parking, restaurant. ಓ
*Small, 19th-century hotel in town centre with
own garden. Quiet and charming.*
■ TARIFF: (1994) Single 240–380,
Double 280–420, Bk 35 (Amex,
Euro/Access, Visa).

Hôtel du Golf ★★★ Moiron,
39570 Lons-le-Saunier.
℡ 84 43 04 80, Fax 84 47 31 21.
English spoken.
Open all year. 36 bedrooms (2 en suite,
34 bath/shower only). Outdoor swimming
pool, tennis, golf on site, parking. ಓ
*All rooms with views over golf course and
modern facilities.*
■ RESTAURANT: Gourmet restaurant overlooking
golf course. Specialities: foie gras poêlé, poulet
aux morilles.
■ ACTIVITIES: Fitness room, billiards and pool at
hotel. Visits to wine producers can be
arranged.
■ TARIFF: (1994) Double 400–490, Bk 50
(Euro/Access, Visa).
■ DISCOUNT: 10%

LOUDEAC Côtes-du-Nord   1D

Hôtel des Voyageurs ★★ 10 rue de Cadélac,
22600 Loudeac.
℡ 96 28 00 47, Fax 96 28 22 30.
English spoken.
Open all year. 25 bedrooms (all en suite).
Garage.
*In the town centre, about 100 m from the
church. A very comfortable hotel.*
■ RESTAURANT: Closed Sat. Renowned for its
very good cuisine including fish specialities in
season.
■ TARIFF: (1994) Single 160–250,
Double 186–300, Bk 30, Set menu 70–245
(Amex, Euro/Access, Visa).

LOURDES Htes-Pyrénées   4D

Grand Hôtel de la Grotte ★★★★ 66 rue
Gotte, 65100 Lourdes.
℡ 62 94 58 87, Fax 62 94 20 50. English spoken.

Open 01/04 to 25/10. 86 bedrooms
(all en suite). Golf 2 km, garage, parking. ಓ
*Very comfortable hotel with modern facilities,
lovely views from the balconies and windows,
and offering a warm welcome. At the foot of
the fortified castle and 5 minutes from the
sanctuaries.*
■ RESTAURANT: Very good food with an excellent
choice of menus.
■ ACTIVITIES: ● 20% reduction on green fees at
Lourdes Golf Club.
■ TARIFF: (1994) Single 310–455,
Double 330–510, Bk 60, Set menu 90–180
(Amex, Euro/Access, Visa).
■ DISCOUNT: 10% LS.

Hôtel Le Miramont ★★ route de Lourdes,
65380 Orincles.
℡ 62 45 41 02. English spoken.
Open all year. 10 bedrooms (9 en suite).
Outdoor swimming pool, golf 8 km, parking.
*Small hotel set in attractive grounds. 8 km
from Lourdes D937 going east, then left onto
D7 to Orincles.*
■ ACTIVITIES: Fishing, cycling, tennis and lake
nearby.
■ TARIFF: (1994) Single 200–230,
Double 200–230, Bk 26 (Euro/Access, Visa).
■ DISCOUNT: 10%

LOUVIERS Eure   2A

Hôtel Pré-St-Germain ★★★ 7 rue St-Germain,
27400 Louviers.
℡ 32 40 48 48, Fax 32 50 75 60. English spoken.
Open all year. 34 bedrooms (all en suite).
Golf 10 km, garage, parking. ಓ
Although in the town centre, this hotel stands in

L

an old orchard and retains a family atmosphere.
■ RESTAURANT: Closed Sun eve.
■ TARIFF: (1994) Single 420–450,
Double 460–560, Bk 40, Set menu 115–240
(Amex, Euro/Access, Visa).

Hôtel La Haye-le-Comte ★★★ 4 route de la
Haye-le-Comte, 27400 Louviers.
℡ 32 40 00 40, Fax 32 25 03 85. English spoken.

Open 01/04 to 01/01. 16 bedrooms
(all en suite). Tennis, golf 9 km, garage,
parking, restaurant. &

*16th-century manor house set in a 12-acre
park midway between Paris and Deauville.
Take the D133 from Louviers towards
Neubourg, turn left on the outskirts of Louviers
and the hotel is 700 m on the right. Follow the
blue signs 'La Haye-le-Comte' from town centre.*
■ ACTIVITIES: Mountain bikes and golf practice
pitch at hotel.
■ TARIFF: (1994) Single 180–450,
Double 250–450, Bk 45, Set menu 110–180
(Amex, Euro/Access, Visa).

LUC-SUR-MER Calvados   2A

Hôtel Thermes et du Casino ★★★
14530 Luc-sur-Mer.
℡ 31 97 32 37, Fax 31 96 72 57. English spoken.
Open 03/04 to 31/10. 48 bedrooms
(all en suite). Outdoor swimming pool,
golf 18 km, garage, parking, restaurant. &
*Near the beach. Follow D514 out of Caen
along the coast road for 24 km.*
■ ACTIVITIES: Health and fitness room, including
sauna and jacuzzi.
■ TARIFF: (1994) Double 300–450, Bk 38,
Set menu 120–260 (Amex, Euro/Access, Visa).

LUCON Vendée   4A

Le Château 85450 Moreilles.
℡ 51 56 17 56, Fax 51 56 30 30. English spoken.

Open all year. 8 bedrooms (all en suite).
Outdoor swimming pool, golf 25 km, parking,
restaurant.
*A private château with guest rooms at the
gateway of the marshlands of the Marais
Pritevin. From Luçon east to N137, then right
towards La Rochelle to Moreilles.*
■ TARIFF: (1994) Single 350–450, Double 450–
550, Bk 45, Set menu 185 (No credit cards).

Grand Hôtel du Croissant ★ place des
Acacias, 85400 Luçon.
℡ 51 56 11 15. English spoken.
Open 01/11 to 30/09. 40 bedrooms (20 en
suite, 10 bath/shower only). Garage, parking.
*In the centre of Luçon, the Croissant Hotel
offers a warm, family-style welcome at
reasonable prices.*
■ RESTAURANT: Closed Sun LS. Comfortable,
traditional dining room. Fine regional
specialities.
■ ACTIVITIES: Within easy reach of the coast
(20 km); boating, fishing, tennis and horse-
riding nearby.
■ TARIFF: (1994) Single 110–195,
Double 128–250, Bk 30, Set menu 60–110
(Euro/Access, Visa).

LE LUDE Sarthe   2C

Hôtel Maine ★★ 17 av de Saumur,
72800 Le Lude.
℡ 43 94 60 54, Fax 43 94 19 74. English spoken.
Open all year. 24 bedrooms (19 en suite).
Parking. &
*On the D306 east of A11 motorway (Angers to
Le Mans), exit Durtal/La Flèche/Le Lude.*
■ RESTAURANT: Closed Sat lunch. Home-made
cuisine using fresh, local produce.
■ TARIFF: (1994) Single 190–290,
Double 190–290, Bk 35, Set menu 105–195
(Euro/Access, Visa).

L

Le Vedaquais ★★ place de la Liberté, 72500 Vaas.
📞 43 46 01 41. English spoken.
Open 04/01 to 10/01 & 18/01 to 31/12.
8 bedrooms (all en suite). Tennis, parking. ♿
*Hotel is in the town centre. Vaas is between Le
Lude and Château-du-Loir on the D305.*
■ RESTAURANT: Closed Wed & Sun eve.
■ TARIFF: (1994) Double 250, Bk 27,
Set menu 60–215 (Euro/Access, Visa).
■ DISCOUNT: 5%

LUMBRES Pas-de-Calais   2B

Hostellerie du Relais 62380 Bayenghem-les-
Seninghem.
📞 21 39 64 54, Fax 21 38 28 07. English spoken.
Open all year. 6 bedrooms
(all bath/shower only). Garage, parking,
restaurant.
A few km west of Lumbries off the D225.
■ ACTIVITIES: Trout fishing.
■ TARIFF: (1994) Single 180–220,
Double 200–300, Bk 35, Set menu 120–150
(Visa).

LUSIGNAN Vienne   4B

Hôtel Chapeau Rouge ★★ rue Nationale,
86600 Lusignan.
📞 49 43 31 10. English spoken.
Open all year. 8 bedrooms (all en suite).
Golf 10 km, parking.
*Pleasant, traditional hotel in the Vonne valley,
home of the Mélusine fairy tales. Closed Feb
school holidays and 2 weeks in October.*
■ RESTAURANT: Closed Mon.
■ TARIFF: (1994) Single 200–220,
Double 220–260, Bk 30, Set menu 80–190
(Euro/Access, Visa).

LUXEUIL-LES-BAINS Hte-Saône   3D

Hôtel Beau Site ★★★ 18 rue Georges
Moulimard, 70300 Luxeuil-les-Bains.
📞 84 40 14 67, Fax 84 40 50 25.
English spoken.
Open all year. 35 bedrooms (32 en suite,
3 bath/shower only). Golf 10 km, garage,
parking.
*From Lure drive through Luxeuil-les-Bains,
following signs to Les Thermes. The hotel is
situated just behind, next to the casino and set
in a large garden.*
■ RESTAURANT: Closed Fri eve/Sat lunch 15/11–
15/03. Seafood and foie gras maison
specialities served in a rustic atmosphere, or on
the terrace in summer.

■ ACTIVITIES: Cycling.
■ TARIFF: (1994) Single 200–265,
Double 250–350, Bk 40 (Euro/Access, Visa).
■ DISCOUNT: 5%

LYON

The rooftops of Lyon

Lyon, lying as it does where the River Saône
(the longest navigable river in France) joins
the Rhône, is a natural centre of
communications and has been since Roman
times. The Romans built a series of roads
radiating from the town and these routes
still exist today in the form of motorways.

Geographically, the centre of Lyon is
divided by the two rivers into three parts:
the west bank of the Saône, the long
narrow peninsula between the two rivers
and the east bank of the Rhône.
Historically, the city is divided in roughly
the same way, with the Roman and
medieval towns on the Fourvière hill to the
west, the 18th- and 19th-century buildings
on the peninsula in the middle and 20th-
century development to the east.

L

As with most cities, the best way to explore is on foot, so leave your car in the huge underground car park beneath the grand Place Bellecour at the centre of Presqu'île (the peninsula between the two rivers). If you arrive in the morning, you could visit the food market on the quai St-Antoine where cheese is a speciality. It is open every morning except Monday. Enjoy a walk alongside the Saône or cross the river and take the funicular up the Fourvière hill to the 19th-century Basilique de Notre-Dame. From here, Lyon is spread out before you with its two rivers and many bridges.

Les Mères

Usually one thinks of the great and famous chefs of this world as male. However, throughout this century, there has been in Lyon a succession of wonderful women chefs and restaurateurs known as Les Mères.

Typical of this breed of successful women was La Mère Fillioux. Born Françoise Fayolle, she seemed destined for a life in domestic service. First she worked for a general in Grenoble but moved on from there to Lyon, to the household of Gaston Eymard, a director of an insurance company, who was very interested in food. In Lyon she met and married Louis Fillioux and they soon saved enough to buy out the owner of a bistro which occupied the ground floor of Louis's father's house. Here they set about establishing a restaurant of some reputation. In this, La Mère Fillioux was extremely successful, her luncheon menus becoming famous with lovers of good food throughout the world.

One of La Mère Fillioux's assistants was La Mère Brazier who left to start up her own restaurant. Three generations later, the present La Mère Brazier is probably the most famous female chef in Lyon today. Traditionally, Les Mères have tended to stick to well-known recipes created from the best ingredients cooked in precisely the correct way.

Expect to eat well in Lyon as the Lyonnais are themselves keen on eating out. Their interest in food guarantees that, at either the humblest bistro or the grandest restaurant, food of the highest quality can be enjoyed.

Walking down the hill, you can visit two Roman theatres as well as the Musée Gallo-Roman. This modern building is sunk into the hillside and houses a collection that traces the history of the area from neolithic times to the 7th century. At the larger of the two theatres, the oldest in France, plays are performed during the summer months. For a different kind of theatrical experience, try to go to a performance at the Nouveau Théâtre de Guignol. Here you will see puppets from the puppet museum (the Musée de la Marionette) in action. This museum and the Musée Historique de Lyon are both in the same building, the impressive Hôtel Gadagne.

Two other specialist museums especially worth a visit are the Musée Historique des Tissus, with its fine exhibition of textiles from early Christian times to the present day, and the photographic museum, housed appropriately in the home of Antoine Lumière, the grandfather of the cinema. His sons, Auguste and Louis, made the first moving picture which showed a train entering a station.

Lyon is a city of contrast; try leaving the wide expanse of the Place Bellecour and heading north-west to the narrow alleyways of the old town. These are known as the *traboules* and are used to connect streets, sometimes by way of an interior courtyard. It may be helpful to get a map of these vaulted passageways as it is sometimes difficult to see where they start and finish.

Walking around a strange city is fascinating but often tiring. A visit to a pavement café might refresh you before you head underground to try and remember where you left your car!

LYON Rhône   5B

(See feature)

Hôtel La Bourbonnaise ★★ 45 avenue du Dauphin, 69360 Serezin-du-Rhône. ✆ 78 02 80 58, Fax 78 02 17 39. English spoken. Open all year. 41 bedrooms (36 en suite, 5 bath/shower only). Golf 3 km, garage, parking. &

Modern, comfortable hotel in the country, but

L

just 10 minutes south of Lyon. 2 km from the A7 Solaise exit.

■ RESTAURANT: Gourmet restaurant with terrace and garden as well as buffet and grill restaurant.

■ ACTIVITIES: Good base for exploring the region; Lyon is 15 km and there are many Côtes du Rhône vineyards to visit.

■ TARIFF: (1994) Double 175–285, Bk 36, Set menu 69–250 (Amex, Euro/Access, Visa).

■ DISCOUNT: 10%

Hôtel Climat de France ★★ 11 chemin de Gargantua, Porte de Lyon Norde, 69570 Dardilly.

℡ 78 35 98 47, Fax 78 66 08 18. English spoken. Open all year. 50 bedrooms (all en suite). Outdoor swimming pool, golf 3 km, parking. ᕁ

Comfortable hotel with modern facilities. North-west of Lyon, off A6 towards Dardilly.

■ RESTAURANT: Traditional restaurant with regional cuisine and Lyonnaise specialities. Meals are served outside on the terrace in fine weather.

■ ACTIVITIES: Good base for sightseeing with a number of excursions departing from the hotel; children's play area.

■ TARIFF: (1994) Double 280, Bk 34, Set menu 59–105 (Amex, Euro/Access, Visa).

Grand Hôtel Concorde ★★★★ 11 rue Grolée, 69002 Lyon.

℡ 72 40 45 45, Fax 78 37 52 55. English spoken. Open all year. 140 bedrooms (all en suite). Garage, restaurant.

In the centre of Lyon on the banks of the Rhône. This 19th-century hotel has been completely redecorated to combine old world elegance with traditional charm and contemporary comfort. Follow the River Rhône up to the Wilson Bridge.

■ TARIFF: Single 595–890, Double 640–890, Bk 65 (Amex, Euro/Access, Visa).

■ DISCOUNT: 15%

Hôtel Cour des Loges ★★★★ 6 rue Boeuf, Vieux-Lyon, 69005 Lyon.

℡ 78 42 75 75, Fax 72 40 93 61. English spoken. Open all year. 63 bedrooms (all en suite). Indoor swimming pool, garage, parking. ᕁ

Four renaissance houses dating from 14th, 16th and 17th century blended with contemporary artist's furnishings and art work.

■ RESTAURANT: Informal 'Tapas Bar' offers simple dishes/snacks and main courses such as coq au vin.

L

■ ACTIVITIES: Beaujolais wine tasting excursions, Côte Rotie by car or balloon, river boat trips along the Rhône and Saône or other trips arranged on request.

■ TARIFF: (1994) Single 880–1200, Double 1000–1700, Bk 105 (Amex, Euro/Access, Visa).

Hôtel de Normandie ★★ 3 rue du Bélier, 69002 Lyon.

℡ 78 37 31 36, Fax 72 40 98 56. English spoken. Open all year. 39 bedrooms (21 en suite, 12 bath/shower only). Garage, parking.

Situated near the Perrache railway station and buses. Motorway exit at Perrache.

■ TARIFF: (1994) Single 158–256, Double 183–298, Bk 26 (Amex, Euro/Access, Visa).

Nouvel Hôtel Paris ★★ 16 rue Platière, Centre-ville, 69000 Lyon.

℡ 78 28 00 95, Fax 78 39 57 64. Open all year. 30 bedrooms (all en suite).

Classic 19th-century building in the heart of the city. Access via Quai de Saône.

■ ACTIVITIES: Opera house and museum within easy walking distance.

■ TARIFF: (1994) Single 250–300, Double 270–320, Bk 30 (Amex, Euro/Access, Visa).

Eurotel Complex ★★★ Aire de la Porte de Lyon, 69570 Dardilly.
☎ 78 66 22 66, Fax 78 35 85 71. English spoken.

Open all year. 100 bedrooms (all en suite). Golf 5 km, parking. &

All rooms have modern facilities including air-conditioning.

■ RESTAURANT: 'le Palmarium' - gourmet restaurant with terrace beside the pool; fish and shellfish specialities. 'Le Veronese' brasserie/buffet serves Italian specialities.
■ ACTIVITIES: Sauna, solarium, fitness room, billiards and piano bar in hotel. Tennis 2 km. Only 5 km from the start of the Beaujolais vinyards.
■ TARIFF: Single 300–400, Double 350–450, Bk 50 (Amex, Euro/Access, Visa).
■ DISCOUNT: 10%

Hôtel Mercure ★★★ Porte de Lyon, 69570 Lyon.
☎ 78 35 28 05, Fax 78 47 47 15. English spoken.

Open all year. 172 bedrooms (all en suite). Outdoor swimming pool, tennis, golf 10 km, garage, parking, restaurant.

Comfortable, modern hotel with garden, 10 minutes from Lyon's old town. From A6 take Limonest/Dardilly, Porte-de-Lyon exit.

■ ACTIVITIES: Sporting and leisure facilities.
■ TARIFF: (1994) Single 295–380, Double 295–420, Bk 52, Set menu 85–170 (Amex, Euro/Access, Visa).

Hôtel Pullman Part-Dieu ★★★ 129 rue Servient, La Part-Dieu, 69003 Lyon.
☎ 78 63 55 00, Fax 78 63 55 35. English spoken. Open all year. 245 bedrooms (all en suite). Golf 20 km, garage.

Striking modern hotel right in centre of the business district, a few minutes' walk from the Part-Dieu station (follow Part-Dieu-Nord).

■ RESTAURANT: Closed Sat lunch & Sun eve. Gourmet restaurant with panoramic views. Refined, inventive cuisine. Specialities: foie gras, poularde de Bresse. Also grill restaurant with regional specialities.
■ ACTIVITIES: Bowling, disco, cinemas within walking distance.
■ TARIFF: (1994) Single 520–730, Double 590–800 (Amex, Euro/Access, Visa).
■ DISCOUNT: 10%

Hôtel Pullman Perrache ★★★★ 12 cours Verdun, Perrache, 69000 Lyon.
☎ 78 37 58 11, Fax 78 37 06 56. English spoken. Open all year. 121 bedrooms (all en suite, all bath/shower only). Golf 10 km, garage, parking, restaurant. &

Traditional style hotel built in 1906 and tastefully redecorated. Centrally located in Lyon.

■ TARIFF: (1994) Single 490–820, Double 490–820, Bk 65, Set menu 135–250 (Amex, Euro/Access, Visa).

MACON Ain   5B

Auberge La Sarrasine ★★★ Le Logis-Neuf, Confrançon, 01310 Polliat.
☎ 74 30 25 65, Fax 74 25 24 23. English spoken.

L

Open 01/03 to 01/11. 11 bedrooms
(all en suite). Outdoor swimming pool,
golf 10 km, parking, restaurant. ᵹ

*From Mâcon cross the River Saône towards
Bourg-en-Bresse. Continue for 18 km on the
N79 to the village of Logis-Neuf and the hotel is
beautifully situated just 1 km beyond.*

■ TARIFF: (1994) Single 350–490,
Double 390–890, Bk 50, Set menu 100–290
(Amex, Euro/Access, Visa).

■ DISCOUNT: 5%

Hostellerie Sarrasine ★★★ 01750 Replonges.
☎ 85 31 02 41, Fax 85 31 11 74. English spoken.

Open 01/02 to 04/01. 7 bedrooms
(all en suite). Golf 2 km, parking, restaurant. ᵹ

*From Mâcon cross the River Saône towards
Bourg-en-Bresse. Continue straight ahead on
the N79 for 3 km to La Madeleine and this
small, luxuriously decorated hotel is situated
500 m after the second set of traffic lights.*

■ TARIFF: (1994) Single 350–490,
Double 390–790, Bk 50, Set menu 100–290
(Amex, Euro/Access, Visa).

MAGNANT Aube   3C

Hôtel Le Val Moret ★★ 10110 Magnant.
☎ 25 29 85 12, Fax 25 29 70 81. English spoken.
Open all year. 30 bedrooms (all en suite).
Garage, parking, restaurant. ᵹ

*Motel-style accommodation in champagne
countryside. From the A5 Chaumont/Troyes,
exit Magnant, 30 km from Troyes.*

■ TARIFF: (1994) Single 170–260,
Double 220–290, Bk 30, Set menu 50–190
(Amex, Euro/Access, Visa).

MANCIET Gers   4D

Hôtel Le Moulin du Comte ★★ D109
Bourrouillan, 32370 Manciet.
☎ 62 09 06 72, Fax 62 09 10 49.

Open all year. 10 bedrooms (all en suite).
Outdoor swimming pool, golf 18 km,
parking. ᵹ

*Tucked away in the heart of the Gers
countryside, in a wooded and flower-filled
park, is Le Moulin du Comte, a former 18th-
century mill now restored. 5 km north-west of
Manciet on the D153 to Bourrouillan.*

■ RESTAURANT: Good food with specialities of
foie gras, confit, magret and poissons.
Vegetarian dishes are also available.

■ ACTIVITIES: Visits to local producers of
Armagnac and foie gras.

■ TARIFF: (1994) Single 200–250,
Double 250–300, Bk 30, Set menu 75–230
(Amex, Euro/Access, Visa).

■ DISCOUNT: 5%

MANDELIEU LA NAPOULE Alpes-Mar   6C

Hôtel Ermitage du Riou ★★★★ avenue Henri
Clews, La Napoule, 06210 Mandelieu.
☎ 93 49 95 56, Fax 92 97 69 05.
English spoken.
Open all year. 41 bedrooms (39 en suite,
2 bath/shower only). Outdoor swimming pool,
golf on site, garage, parking. ᵹ

*Provincial house, recently renovated and
located near the harbour and golf course.
5 minutes from Cannes.*

■ RESTAURANT: Closed Nov. Friendly
atmosphere with terrace overlooking the sea.
Seafood specialities.

■ ACTIVITIES: Water-skiing, snorkelling, tennis,
horse-riding and sailing nearby.

■ TARIFF: (1994) Single 650–1300,
Double 650–1300, Bk 70, Set menu 150–290
(Amex, Euro/Access, Visa).

LE MANS Sarthe   2C

Hôtel Maine Atlantique ★★ 24 rue Emile
Chesne, 72100 Le Mans.
☎ 43 84 35 11, Fax 43 85 75 41. English spoken.
Open all year. 29 bedrooms (14 en suite,
12 bath/shower only). Golf 5 km, parking.

*Newly renovated. Tranquil family atmosphere.
Take the A11 from Paris to Le Mans, and then
follow the signs to Le Mans-Pontlieue.*

■ ACTIVITIES: Flying school nearby.

■ TARIFF: (1994) Single 155–250,
Double 160–320, Bk 30 (Amex, Euro/Access,
Visa).

■ DISCOUNT: 10%

Hôtel Relais de la Charnie ★★ 72240 St-
Symphorien.
☎ 40 20 72 06, Fax 43 20 70 59. English spoken.

M

Open all year. 13 bedrooms (all en suite).
Indoor swimming pool, parking. &

*Former coaching house with lots of character.
From Le Mans take road towards Laval. After
Longnes, take first right to Epineu-le-Charnie
and the pretty little village of St-Symphorien.*

■ RESTAURANT: Closed Sun eve & Mon.
Traditional, rustic restaurant with specialities
including poissons de rivière and volaille.
■ ACTIVITIES: ● New 8-day activity holiday
package available which includes cooking
lessons, horse-riding, lake fishing, hiking,
cycling and swimming.
■ TARIFF: (1994) Single 200–280,
Double 200–320, Bk 30, Set menu 78–180
(Amex, Visa).

MANTES Yvelines 2B

Hôtel Akena ★ rue J P Timbaud, quartier du
Lycée, 78520 Limay.
℡ 1 34 78 51 00, Fax 1 30 98 48 72.
Open all year. 59 bedrooms (all en suite).
Golf 5 km, parking. &

*Good simple accommodation for travellers on a
budget. Prices are for double rooms with a third
bed. From A13 exit Mantes-Est to roundabout,
take the fifth exit (ave Rocade) to second
roundabout. Take fourth exit, hotel on left.*

■ TARIFF: (1994) Double 145, Bk 24
(Euro/Access, Visa).

MARMANDE Lot/Garonne 4D

Hôtel Capricorne ★★ 47200 Marmande.
℡ 53 64 16 14, Fax 53 20 80 18. English spoken.
Open 09/01 to 21/12. 34 bedrooms
(all en suite). Outdoor swimming pool,
golf 3 km, parking, restaurant. &

*Modern, quiet hotel in landscaped grounds, on
the outskirts of Marmande coming from Agen.*

■ TARIFF: (1994) Single 250, Double 270, Bk 32,
Set menu 75–260 (Amex, Euro/Access, Visa).

MARNE-LA-VALLEE Seine/Marne 2B

Hôtel Akena ★ ZI Souilly, 77410 Claye-Souilly.
℡ 1 60 26 89 89, Fax 1 60 26 86 64.
English spoken.
Open all year. 76 bedrooms (all en suite).
Golf 15 km, parking. &

*The hotel is in Claye-Souilly at the interchange
of the N3 and D212, linking Charles de Gaulle
airport to Marne-la-Vallée and Euro Disney
(20 km). Airport 10 km.*

■ TARIFF: (1994) Double 145 (Amex,
Euro/Access, Visa).

Saphir Hotel ★★★ 77340 Pontault-Combault.
℡ 1 64 43 45 47, Fax 1 64 40 52 43.
English spoken.

Open all year. 180 bedrooms (all en suite).
Indoor swimming pool, tennis, golf 2 km,
garage, parking. &

*The hotel has all normal comforts, plus more,
and there are also 20 suites available. It lies
between Paris and Euro Disney in the
'Francilienne'. Leave the A4 at Pontault-
Combault exit and go towards town centre.*

■ RESTAURANT: Choose either the gourmet
restaurant which specialises in fish, or enjoy
good food in the grill restaurant.
■ ACTIVITIES: ● Fitness centre, bowling and golf
practice ground at hotel.
■ TARIFF: (1994) Single 400–485,
Double 400–530, Bk 52, Set menu 75–145
(Amex, Euro/Access, Visa).

MARSEILLE Bches-du-Rhône 5D

Hôtel Arcade ★★ sq Narvik, 13001 Marseille.
℡ 91 95 62 09, Fax 91 50 68 42. English spoken.
Open all year. 172 bedrooms (all en suite).
Parking. &

*Although located right in the centre of the city,
the hotel offers a haven of peace and greenery.
Near the Gare St-Charles.*

■ RESTAURANT: Closed Sat & Sun.
■ TARIFF: (1994) Single 295–395, Double 320–
400, Bk 34, Set menu 65–88 (Amex, Visa).

Hôtel Mascotte ★★★ 5 La Canebière,
13001 Marseille.
℡ 91 90 15 60, Fax 42 37 58 59. English spoken.
Open all year. 45 bedrooms (all en suite). &

*On the Canebière, with the old port under its
windows. Parking nearby. Motorway A50 or
from A7 southwards.*

■ TARIFF: (1994) Single 300–410, Double 300–
450, Bk 42 (Amex, Euro/Access, Visa).

M

Hôtel Sofitel Vieux Port ★★★★ 36 bd Ch
Livon, 13007 Marseille.
☎ 91 52 90 19, Fax 91 31 46 52. English spoken.
Open all year. 130 bedrooms (all en suite).
Outdoor swimming pool, golf 10 km, garage,
parking. &
*Hotel is situated by the old port. Very
comfortable with some wonderful views.*

■ RESTAURANT: Panoramic restaurant with
gourmet cuisine. Mediterranean specialities
based on seafood.
■ ACTIVITIES: All sports available in and around
Marseille.
■ TARIFF: (1994) Double 630–960, Bk 70
(Amex, Euro/Access, Visa).
■ DISCOUNT: 15%

MARTIGUES Bches-du-Rhône   5D

Hôtel Clair ★ 13500 Martigues.
☎ 42 07 02 43. English spoken.
Open all year. 38 bedrooms (14 en suite).
Parking.
*Sunny hotel in the town centre. 30 minutes
from Marseille centre, 15 minutes to the
airport.*

■ ACTIVITIES: Beach, swimming pool, tennis,
theatre etc.
■ TARIFF: (1994) Double 90–160, Bk 20 (Amex,
Euro/Access, Visa).
■ DISCOUNT: 15%

MASSIAC Cantal   5A

Grand Hôtel Poste ★★ 26 av Ch de Gaulle,
15500 Massiac.
☎ 71 23 02 01, Fax 71 23 09 23. English spoken.
Open all year. 32 bedrooms (all en suite).
Indoor swimming pool, outdoor swimming
pool, parking. &
*Comfortable hotel with good facilities. From
Clermont-Ferrand take the new motorway
south and exit at Massiac. From Clermont on
A75, exit 23, from Montpellier, exit 24.*

■ RESTAURANT: Specialities: jambon d'Auvergne,
tarte au cantal, tripoux.
■ ACTIVITIES: Turkish bath, billiards, squash and
fitness room in the hotel.
■ TARIFF: (1994) Single 320, Double 320–330,
Bk 35, Set menu 70–200 (Amex, Euro/Access,
Visa).

MAURS Cantal   5A

Hôtel La Châtelleraie ★★ 15600 St-Etienne-
de-Maurs.
☎ 71 49 09 09, Fax 71 49 07 07. English spoken.

Open 03/04 to 15/11. 23 bedrooms
(all en suite). Outdoor swimming pool,
parking, restaurant. &
*N122 north-east from Figeac to Maurs. St-
Etienne is just north of Maurs on the same
road. Converted château set in 24 acres of
parkland.*

■ ACTIVITIES: Golf driving range.
■ TARIFF: (1994) Double 300–390, Bk 40
(Euro/Access, Visa).

MAUSSANE-LES-ALPILLES   5D

Hôtel Val Baussenc ★★★ 122 av Vallée des
Baux, 13520 Maussane-les-Alpilles.
☎ 90 54 38 90, Fax 90 54 33 36.
English spoken.
Open 01/03 to 04/01. 21 bedrooms
(all en suite). Outdoor swimming pool,
golf 4 km, parking. &
*Attractive, spacious hotel offering a warm and
personal welcome.*

■ RESTAURANT: Closed Tues & Nov.
■ ACTIVITIES: ● Reduced green fees.
■ TARIFF: (1994) Single 490, Double 540–650,
Bk 60, Set menu 150–260 (Amex,
Euro/Access, Visa).

MAYENNE Mayenne   2C

Grand Hôtel ★★ 2 rue A de Loré,
53100 Mayenne.
☎ 43 00 96 00, Fax 43 32 08 49.
English spoken.
Open all year. 30 bedrooms (28 en suite).
Golf 20 km, garage, parking, restaurant.
*150-year-old hotel with modern-day comforts.
Ideally situated for exploring the Loire Valley.*

■ TARIFF: Single 199–306, Double 219–389,
Bk 42, Set menu 95–199 (Euro/Access, Visa).
■ DISCOUNT: 5%

M

MEGEVE Hte-Savoie 6A

Hôtel L'Igloo au sommet du Mont d'Arbois, 74170 Megève.
☎ 50 93 05 84, Fax 50 21 02 74. English spoken.
Open 15/06 to 15/09 & 15/12 to 20/04.
11 bedrooms (all en suite). Outdoor swimming pool, golf 1 km.
Only accessible by cable-car (altitude 1850 m), accommodation is in mountain-style chalets with fantastic views towards Mt Blanc.
■ RESTAURANT: Gourmet restaurant, excellent food.
■ ACTIVITIES: Walking, winter skiing, sauna, jaccuzzi. Tennis courts 5 minutes.
■ TARIFF: Single 500 HB–800 HB, Double 1000 HB–1600 HB (Euro/Access, Visa).

Hôtel La Prairie ★★★ av Ch Feige, 74120 Megève.
☎ 50 21 48 55, Fax 50 21 42 13. English spoken.
Open 16/12 to 01/05 & 20/06 to 30/09.
32 bedrooms (all en suite). Golf 4 km, garage, parking.
A lovely chalet hotel in the ski and hiking resort of Megève, not far from sports centre and skating rink.
■ ACTIVITIES: Mountain sports, skating.
■ TARIFF: (1994) Single 330–692, Double 372–734 (Amex, Euro/Access, Visa).

Hôtel au Vieux Moulin 4 rue A Martin, 74120 Megève.
☎ 50 21 22 23, Fax 50 93 07 91. English spoken.
Open 03/12 to 06/05 & 10/06 to 31/10.
36 bedrooms (all en suite). Outdoor swimming pool, golf 3 km, parking. &
Quiet, leafy situation in the town centre. Pretty garden and good facilities. Close to the Post Office and Tourist Office. Megève is off the N212.
■ RESTAURANT: Gourmet and traditional cuisine in comfortable, pleasant surroundings. Savoyard specialities; meals on the terrace in summer.
■ ACTIVITIES: Sauna/fitness centre; winter sports on the doorstop.
■ TARIFF: (1994) Single 403–690, Double 310–530, Set menu 95–150 (Amex, Euro/Access, Visa).
■ DISCOUNT: 10%

MENAT Puy-de-Dôme 5A

Auberge Maître Henri 63560 Pont-de-Menat.
☎ 73 85 50 20. English spoken.
Open all year. 10 bedrooms
(5 bath/shower only). Garage, parking, restaurant.

50 km from Clermont-Ferrand, the hotel is situated on the N144, by the River Sioule.
■ TARIFF: (1994) Double 120–200, Set menu 75–200 (Euro/Access, Visa).

MENDE Lozère 5C

Hôtel Pont Roupt ★★★ av 11 Novembre,. 48000 Mende.
☎ 66 65 01 43, Fax 66 65 22 96. English spoken.
Open 30/03 to 15/02. 27 bedrooms
(all en suite). Indoor swimming pool, golf 25 km, garage, parking.
In quiet quarter by the River Lot, 5 minutes from town centre going towards the Tarn Gorges.
■ RESTAURANT: Closed Sun eve and Mon.
■ TARIFF: (1994) Single 250–300, Double 250–400, Bk 45 (Euro/Access, Visa).

MENTON Alpes-Mar 6C

Hôtel Méditerranée ★★★ 5 rue République, 06500 Menton.
☎ 93 28 25 25, Fax 93 57 88 38. English spoken.

Open all year. 90 bedrooms (all en suite). Golf 18 km, garage. &
A quiet, comfortable hotel right in the heart of Menton. Just a stone's throw from old town and local market. Close to the sea. 30 minutes from Nice airport. Full and half-board terms also available.

M

■ RESTAURANT: Recently completely refurbished and air-conditioned. Traditional cuisine.
■ ACTIVITIES: Sailing, bridge, tennis. Excursions can be arranged by booking at hotel reception.
■ TARIFF: Single 350–460, Double 380–500, Bk 35, Set menu 110–120 (Amex, Euro/Access, Visa).

Hôtel Beau Rivage ★★★ 1 av Ibanez, 06500 Menton.
☎ 93 28 08 08, Fax 93 57 41 47. English spoken. Open all year. 40 bedrooms (all en suite). Garage, parking. &

Located opposite the marina, the hotel offers comfortable accommodation including air-conditioning and welcomes groups on full or half-board basis. Menton is 18 km from Monaco on the N98.
■ TARIFF: (1994) Single 310–460, Double 360–500, Bk 35 (Amex, Euro/Access, Visa).

Hôtel Prince de Galles ★★★ 4 av Gén de Gaulle, BP 21, 06500 Menton.
☎ 93 28 21 21, Fax 93 35 92 91. English spoken. Open all year. 68 bedrooms (all en suite). Golf 13 km, parking, restaurant. &

Carefully restored, overlooking beach. Tropical garden with terrace. From Menton Casino follow promenade road towards Monaco for 2 km.
■ ACTIVITIES: Within 300 m of the hotel: parc with children's play area, heated pool, tennis courts.
■ TARIFF: (1994) Single 235–305, Double 300–530, Bk 42, Set menu 90–180 (Amex, Euro/Access, Visa).

LES MENUIRES Savoie   6A

Hôtel L'Ours Blanc ★★★ Reberty 2000, 73440 Les Menuires.
☎ 79 00 61 66, Fax 79 00 63 67. English spoken.

Open 15/12 to 01/05 & 23/05 to 31/12. 49 bedrooms (all en suite). Parking. &

Situated at an altitude of 6100 ft this chalet-style hotel is in the skiing area of the 'Trois Vallées'. Take the D915 from Moutiers to the resort of Les Menuires, following the road to the left. The hotel is 1.5 km further along in Reberty 2000.
■ RESTAURANT: Breathtaking views of the mountains whilst enjoying gourmet cuisine prepared by Chef de Cuisine M. Pascal Casali.
■ ACTIVITIES: On the doorstep skiing!
■ TARIFF: (1994) Single 430–690, Double 560–720, Set menu 145–250 (Euro/Access, Visa).

MERIBEL Savoie   6A

Hôtel Antares ★★★★ Le Belvédère, 73550 Méribel-les-Allues.
☎ 79 23 28 23, Fax 79 23 28 18. English spoken.

Open 17/12 to 02/04. 76 bedrooms (all en suite). Indoor swimming pool, outdoor swimming pool, golf 1 km, garage, parking. &

Exceptionally stylish hotel offering every comfort. From Moûtiers go towards Méribel, then follow signs to Le Belvédère, which is on the right after the tunnel.
■ RESTAURANT: Choice of restaurants.
■ ACTIVITIES: Winter sports, aeroclub.
■ TARIFF: (1994) Single 1600–2500, Double 1740–2620 (Amex, Euro/Access, Visa).
■ DISCOUNT: 10% Except school holidays.

Hôtel Mont Vallon ★★★★ Le Mottaret, 73550 Méribel-les-Allues.
☎ 79 00 44 00, Fax 79 00 46 93. English spoken. Open 15/12 to 15/04. 90 bedrooms (all en suite). Indoor swimming pool, garage. &

Excellent chalet hotel/skiing centre in the heart of the Trois Vallées.

M

■ RESTAURANT: 'Le Chalet' is warm and inviting, specialising in traditional French cuisine; the brasserie 'Le Schuss' has a rustic, Sayoyard atmosphere, beautiful south facing terrace and offers lunches of grills, pizzas and pâtés.
■ ACTIVITIES: Very well-equipped health/fitness centre and squash courts; winter/mountain sports.
■ TARIFF: (1994) Single 600–1300, Double 1200–2200, Set menu 250–300 (Amex, Euro/Access, Visa).

Hôtel Les Arolles ★★★ Méribel-Mottaret, 73550 Méribel-les-Allues.
☎ 79 00 40 40, Fax 79 00 45 50. English spoken.

Open 15/12 to 03/05. 60 bedrooms (all en suite). Indoor swimming pool, garage, restaurant. ♿

Situated on main ski run with a large south-facing terrace and excellent facilities. 4 km above Méribel; turn right over river on entering Méribel-Mottaret and go to top of resort.

■ ACTIVITIES: Gym, sauna and ski shop at hotel.
■ TARIFF: Single 400–600, Double 600–1250 (Euro/Access, Visa).

Hôtel Le Chalet ★★★★ Le Belvédère, 73550 Méribel-les-Allues.
☎ 79 23 28 23, Fax 79 00 56 22. English spoken.

Open 17/12 to 23/04 & 15/07 to 15/09.
35 bedrooms (all en suite). Indoor swimming pool, outdoor swimming pool, golf 1 km, garage, parking, restaurant. ♿

A lovely alpine hotel with all the facilities expected of a luxury hotel. From Moûtiers, drive to Méribel and then follow signs for Le Belvédère. The hotel is on the left, after the tunnel.

■ ACTIVITIES: ● Winter sports, aeroclub.
■ TARIFF: (1994) Single 1470–2050, Double 1620–2240 (Amex, Euro/Access, Visa).
■ DISCOUNT: 10% Except school holidays.

METZ Moselle 3B

Hôtel Cecil ★★ 14 rue Pasteur, 57000 Metz.
☎ 87 66 66 13, Fax 87 56 96 02. English spoken.
Open all year. 39 bedrooms (36 en suite, 3 bath/shower only). Golf 8 km, garage.

Recently completely renovated, hotel is quiet and comfortable and offers personal attention. Near the station and A31 in the town centre.

■ TARIFF: (1994) Double 220–280, Bk 26 (Amex, Euro/Access, Visa).
■ DISCOUNT: 10%

Hôtel Foch ★★ 8 pl R Mondon, 57000 Metz.
☎ 87 74 40 75, Fax 87 74 49 90. English spoken.
Open all year. 38 bedrooms (32 en suite, 3 bath/shower only).

Situated in the centre of town close to the station, the hotel is near to the A31 turn off in Metz.

■ TARIFF: (1994) Single 168–288, Double 168–298, Bk 25 (Euro/Access, Visa).

Hôtel du Théâtre ★★★ Port St-Marcel, 57000 Metz.
☎ 87 31 10 10, Fax 87 30 04 66. English spoken.

Open all year. 36 bedrooms (all en suite). Outdoor swimming pool, golf 3 km, garage, parking. ♿

M

In one of the oldest parts of Metz, this hotel, right on the river, is part of a redevelopment plan for the old port of St-Marcel. Rooms with views of river or docks and waterside terraces. Next to the cathedral. Follow directions to 'Parking Port St- Marcel' (direct access to the reception).

■ RESTAURANT: Restaurant dates back to 1649 and food is served by staff in regional costume. Specialities: cochon de lait de Metz en gelée; cuisses de grenouilles au gratin à la mode de Boulay; matelote de brochet au vin de Contz. Good selection of local wines.

■ ACTIVITIES: Health and fitness room (sauna, solarium, spa) at hotel; water-skiing and boat excursions (with lunch included), within walking distance of hotel.

■ TARIFF: (1994) Single 395–550, Double 490–590, Bk 50, Set menu 98–165 (Amex, Euro/Access, Visa).

MEURSAULT Côte-d'Or 3C

Hôtel Les Magnolias ★★★ 8 rue P Joigneaux, 21190 Meursault.
☎ 80 21 23 23, Fax 80 21 29 10. English spoken.

Open 01/03 to 01/12. 12 bedrooms (all en suite). Golf 6 km, parking.

Situated in a small, quiet village surrounded by vineyards. The bedrooms are individually decorated with luxurious bathrooms. Courtyard and garden. Exit from A6 at Beaune and then N74, or A6 exit at Chalon-sur-Saône then the N6 and N74. 6 km from Beaune and 14 km from Chalon.

■ TARIFF: (1994) Single 350–480, Double 350–580, Bk 45 (Amex, Euro/Access, Visa).

Motel au Soleil Levant ★★ rte de Beaune, 21190 Meursault.
☎ 80 21 23 47, Fax 80 21 65 67.
Open all year. 35 bedrooms (all en suite). Parking, restaurant.

On leaving Beaune, take the right fork towards Meursault and the N73. A nice drive through the vineyards of Pommard and Volnay leads you to Meursault; on approaching the town you will find a left turn, and the motel is about 400 m ahead.

■ TARIFF: (1994) Single 192–224, Double 192–348, Bk 25, Set menu 64–124 (Euro/Access, Visa).

MEYRUEIS Lozère 5C

Hôtel Château d'Ayres ★★★ 48150 Meyrueis.
☎ 66 45 60 10, Fax 66 45 62 26. English spoken.
Open 01/04 to 15/11. 26 bedrooms (all en suite). Outdoor swimming pool, tennis, parking.

An old monastery dating from the 12th-century, now transformed into a lovely hotel where you are assured of a very warm welcome. Meyrueis is in the heart of the Cevennes National Park, with its wild horses and bison roaming freely.

■ RESTAURANT: Lovely old dining room offering inspired, creative cuisine.

■ ACTIVITIES: Wonderful sightseeing area with the Tarn gorges being almost on the doorstep.

■ TARIFF: (1994) Single 340–630, Double 340–800, Bk 60 (Amex, Euro/Access, Visa).

Hôtel d'Europe ★★ quai d'Orléans, 48150 Meyrueis.
☎ 66 45 60 05, Fax 66 45 65 31. English spoken.
Open 01/04 to 01/11. 30 bedrooms (all bath/shower only). Outdoor swimming pool, parking, restaurant.

In the centre of Meyrueis which is 40 km north-east of Millau via Aguessac then D907 to Le Rozier, D996 Gorges de la Jonte.

■ TARIFF: (1994) Single 205, Double 205–235, Bk 30, Set menu 70–130 (Euro/Access, Visa).

Hôtel Family ★★ 48150 Meyrueis.
☎ 66 45 60 02, Fax 66 45 66 54. English spoken.
Open 01/04 to 31/10. 48 bedrooms (all en suite). Outdoor swimming pool, garage, parking, restaurant. &

Comfortable hotel in rocky countryside. Meyrueis is 40 km north-east of Millau via Aguessac then D907 to Le Rozier, D996 to Meyrueis.

■ TARIFF: (1994) Double 200–220, Bk 32, Set menu 72–120 (Euro/Access, Visa).

Hôtel Le Mont Aigoual ★★ rue de la Barrière, 48150 Meyrueis.
☎ 66 45 65 61, Fax 66 45 64 25. English spoken.

M

Open 01/04 to 01/11. 30 bedrooms (all en suite). Outdoor swimming pool, parking.

In the heart of a typical village, comfortable hotel with gardens and lift.

■ RESTAURANT: Specialises in regional cuisine.
■ TARIFF: (1994) Single 230–250, Double 240–260, Bk 40, Set menu 80–150 (Amex, Euro/Access, Visa).

Hôtel La Renaissance et St-Sauveur ★★★
48150 Meyrueis.
☎ 66 45 60 19, Fax 66 45 65 94. English spoken.
Open 01/04 to 12/11. 34 bedrooms (all en suite).

Two old houses transformed into a country inn. La Renaissance is a 16th-century residence with garden, St-Sauveur an 18th-century town house with terrace. From Florac take D996 west to Meyrueis.

■ RESTAURANT: Elegant dining rooms and table settings. Creative local dishes.
■ ACTIVITIES: Tennis and swimming nearby; cross-country hiking and biking.
■ TARIFF: (1994) Single 200–300, Double 300–500, Bk 40, Set menu 100–200 (Amex, Euro/Access, Visa).

M

MIGENNES Yonne   2D

Hôtel Paris ★★ av J Jaurès, 89400 Migennes.
☎ 86 80 23 22, Fax 86 80 31 04. English spoken.
Open 15/01 to 30/07 & 30/08 to 31/12. 9 bedrooms (all en suite). Golf 20 km, garage, parking. ⅻ

Comfortable refurbished rooms. 150 km south of Paris on A6. Head north at Auxerre on the N6 for 20 km to Migennes.

■ RESTAURANT: Closed Fri & Sun eve. Gourmet cuisine and Burgundy wines.
■ TARIFF: (1994) Single 180–250, Double 240–350, Bk 30, Set menu 80–150 (Euro/Access, Visa).

MILLAU Aveyron   5C

Hôtel Cevenol ★★ 115 rue du Rajol, 12100 Millau.
☎ 65 60 74 44, Fax 65 60 85 99.
Open 01/01 to 30/11. 42 bedrooms (all en suite). Outdoor swimming pool, parking. ⅻ

500 m from the town centre going towards Montpellier-le-Vieux. A modern hotel with lovely views from the terrace.

■ RESTAURANT: Closed Sat & Sun lunch. Modern restaurant. Specialities: feuillete au Roquefort,

magret de canard aux baies de cassis, sabayon à la menthe chocolat chaud.
■ ACTIVITIES: Hotel will organise canoe hire for Gorges du Tarn descent.
■ TARIFF: (1994) Single 275–299, Double 299–320, Bk 35, Set menu 93–195 (Euro/Access, Visa).

MIRAMBEAU Charente-Mar   4B

Château de Mirambeau ★★★★ route de Montendre, 17150 Mirambeau.
☎ 46 70 71 77, Fax 46 70 71 10. English spoken.

Open 07/04 to 24/10. 48 bedrooms (all en suite). Indoor swimming pool, tennis, parking. ⅻ

Large château entirely renovated in its original style, dating from the 12th to the 18th century and with many fine features. Located in a 20-acre park with a 19th-century neo-Gothic chapel.

■ RESTAURANT: Award-winning, luxury, period restaurant offering beautifully presented gastronomic delights.
■ ACTIVITIES: Excellent sports/health facilities; wonderful countryside for cycling, horse-riding and exploring.
■ TARIFF: Double 680–1500, Bk 100, Set menu 240–350 (Euro/Access, Visa).

MIREBEAU Côte-d'Or   3C

Auberge des Marronniers ★★ place Général Viard, 21310 Mirebeau-sur-Bèze.
☎ 80 36 71 05, Fax 80 36 75 92.
English spoken.
Open all year. 17 bedrooms (16 en suite, 1 bath/shower only). Garage, parking. ⅻ

A peaceful hotel on the river bank with terraced flower gardens.

■ RESTAURANT: Closed Sun eve. Overlooks the gardens and river; meals served on the terrace in summer.

■ ACTIVITIES: Tennis, swimming pool, canoeing and kayaking nearby.
■ TARIFF: (1994) Single 160–220, Double 180–250, Bk 22, Set menu 58–170 (Visa).

MODANE Savoie   6A

Hôtel Bellevue ★ 15 rue de Replat, Fourneaux, 73500 Modane.
☎ 79 05 20 64, Fax 79 05 37 42. English spoken.
Open all year. 14 bedrooms (2 en suite, 10 bath/shower only). Parking.
A small, quiet and comfortable hotel. South of the N6 in the Vallée de la Maurienne. 3 km from the tunnel du Fréjus leading to Italy.
■ RESTAURANT: Relaxed, family atmosphere with good food prepared by the owner. Specialities: fondue and raclette, coq au vin de Savoie.
■ ACTIVITIES: Winter and summer mountain sports within easy reach.
■ TARIFF: (1994) Single 160–210, Double 200–260, Bk 30, Set menu 70–140 (Euro/Access, Visa).
■ DISCOUNT: 10%

MOLLKIRCH Bas-Rhin   3D

Hôtel Fischutte ★★ rte Grendelbruch, 67190 Mollkirch.
☎ 88 97 42 03, Fax 88 97 51 85. English spoken.

Open 15/03 to 15/02. 18 bedrooms (5 en suite, 10 bath/shower only). Parking.
Chalet in the centre of a forest and next to a stream. Between Mollkirch and Grendelbruch and 30 minutes from Strasbourg (on the D204 south-west of Mollkirch.
■ RESTAURANT: Closed Mon eve and Tues. Regional cuisine as well as fish and game.
■ ACTIVITIES: Mountain bikes, trout fishing, fruit picking and cookery lessons.
■ TARIFF: (1994) Single 200–300, Double 200–330, Bk 35, Set menu 70–250 (Amex, Euro/Access, Visa).

MONACO

MONTE-CARLO Alpes-Mar   6C

Hôtel La Cigogne rte de la Plage, Mala, 06320 Cap d'Ail.
☎ 93 78 29 60, Fax 93 41 86 62. English spoken.
Open 20/03 to 20/11. 15 bedrooms (all en suite). Parking.
Comfortable, modern hotel in this beautiful little town. An ideal choice for a quiet, enjoyable holiday yet only minutes from famous Monaco. From Monte-Carlo go west along the coast road to Cap d'Ail.
■ RESTAURANT: Modern terrace restaurant/dining room specialising in Provençale cuisine.
■ ACTIVITIES: Walking distance to lovely, safe beach; spectacular cliff-top walks; lots of sporting activities nearby.
■ TARIFF: (1994) Single 330–350, Double 430–450 (Euro/Access, Visa).
■ DISCOUNT: 10%

Hôtel Mirabeau 1 av Princesse Grace, 98000 Monte-Carlo, Monaco.
☎ 92 16 65 65, Fax 93 50 84 85. English spoken.

M

Open all year. 103 bedrooms. Outdoor swimming pool, garage, parking.
Located in the heart of Monte-Carlo, easily accessible from both the Place du Casino and the sea front. Spacious rooms, most overlooking the swimming pool and sea with large terraces.
■ RESTAURANT: 'La Coupole' award-winning restaurant; 'Café Mirabeau' and 'La Terrasse de La Coupole' restaurants offer a full range of dishes from gourmet to fixed price menus.
■ ACTIVITIES: Excursions and tickets to shows arranged on request. ● Free access to all SBM establishments and 50% reduction on tennis and golf (Monte-Carlo Country Club and Golf Club.)
■ TARIFF: (1994) Single 900–1,500, Double 1,000–2,000, Bk 135, Set menu 280–410 (Amex, Euro/Access, Visa).
■ DISCOUNT: 10%

Hôtel Loews Monte Carlo ★★★★ 12 avenue des Spélugues, BP 179 MC, 98000 Monte-Carlo, Monaco.
✆ 93 50 65 00, Fax 93 30 01 57. English spoken. Open all year. 640 bedrooms (all en suite). Outdoor swimming pool, golf 10 km, garage, parking. &

Loews Monte-Carlo rises imposingly on the sunbathed shores of Monaco, the heart of the fabled Riviera.

■ RESTAURANT: A choice of 6 restaurants between them offering truly international cuisine.
■ ACTIVITIES: International cabaret.
■ TARIFF: (1994) Single 1000–1850, Double 1100–1950, Bk 100 (Amex, Euro/Access, Visa).

Hôtel Olympia ★★ 17 bis bd Gén Leclerc, 06240 Beausoleil, Monaco.
✆ 93 78 12 70, Fax 93 41 85 04. English spoken.

Open all year. 32 bedrooms (all en suite). Golf 5 km. &

5 minutes' walk from the beach of Monte-Carlo, the Olympia offers en-suite facilities in all its rooms and many have balconies. From the motorway, take the Monaco exit via the tunnel, follow signs for Beausoleil, then Hotel Olympia.
■ TARIFF: (1994) Single 255–285, Double 285–305, Bk 30 (Euro/Access, Visa).

END OF MONACO HOTELS

LE MONT-DORE Puy-de-Dôme   5A

Hôtel Panorama ★★★ 27 av de la Libération, 63240 Le Mont-Dore.
✆ 73 65 11 12, Fax 73 65 20 80. English spoken.

Open 01/01 to 15/03 & 10/05 to 10/10. 40 bedrooms (all en suite). Indoor swimming pool, golf 2 km, parking, restaurant.

The hotel stands high above the town in the wooded hills. Panoramic views of the whole valley. Swimming pool, sauna. 5 minutes' walk to town centre.
■ ACTIVITIES: Excursions on request; various sporting activities nearby.
■ TARIFF: (1994) Double 340–430, Bk 38 (Euro/Access, Visa).

MONT-LOUIS Pyrénées-Or   5C

Hôtel Corrieu ★★ La Lagonne, 66210 Mont-Louis.
✆ 68 04 22 04, Fax 68 04 16 63. English spoken.

Open 17/12 to 28/03 & 02/06 to 28/09. 28 bedrooms (21 en suite). Tennis, golf 20 km, parking.

Situated in a pretty village at an altitude of 1700 m. Relaxing, family atmosphere; all the rooms have panoramic views of the Pyrénées.

M

Lounge with fireplace. On the D118, 2 km north of Mont-Louis.

■ RESTAURANT: Carefully prepared dishes in a panoramic setting. Local specialities include tourte jambon aux Banyuls, Capcir trout with almonds and Pyrénean lamb chops with herbs.
■ ACTIVITIES: ● Arrangements made for instruction and equipment hire for cross-country skiing.
■ TARIFF: (1994) Double 138–360, Bk 38, Set menu 86–170 (Amex, Euro/Access, Visa).
■ DISCOUNT: 10%

LE MONT-ST-MICHEL Manche 1D

Hôtel Altea rte du Mont-St-Michel, 50116 Le Mont-St-Michel.
℡ 33 60 14 18, Fax 33 60 39 28. English spoken.
Open 18/02 to 30/11. 100 bedrooms (all en suite). Parking. &

A modern, countryside hotel set in spacious grounds by the river. D976 Pontorson 7 km. D275 Avranches 20 km.

■ RESTAURANT: Warm and welcoming atmosphere; local specialities: filet d'agneau de pré-salé, canard mi-sauvage au poireau.
■ TARIFF: (1994) Single 350–480, Double 390–560, Bk 55 (Amex, Euro/Access, Visa).

Hôtel de la Digue ★★★
50116 Le Mont-St-Michel.
℡ 33 60 14 02, Fax 33 60 37 59.
English spoken.
Open 01/04 to 15/11. 35 bedrooms (all en suite). Golf 20 km, parking.

Located 2 km from Mont-St-Michel, which is illuminated at night, at the start of the famous dyke on the D976.

■ RESTAURANT: Restaurant with panoramic view of Mont-St-Michel and specialising in seafood.
■ TARIFF: (1994) Single 320–380, Double 350–450, Bk 48, Set menu 85–220 (Amex, Euro/Access, Visa).

MONTAIGU Vendée 1D

Hôtel des Voyageurs ★★★ 9 av Villelois-Mareuil, 85600 Montaigu.
℡ 51 94 00 71, Fax 51 94 07 78. English spoken.
Open all year. 40 bedrooms (35 en suite, 3 bath/shower only). Outdoor swimming pool, garage, parking. &

A luxury, traditional old inn with swimming pool, sauna, Italian garden and antique furniture. Conference rooms. English, German and Italian spoken.

■ RESTAURANT: French cuisine with regional specialities.
■ TARIFF: (1994) Single 190–450, Double 250–550, Bk 45, Set menu 89–175 (Amex, Euro/Access, Visa).

MONTARGIS Loiret 2D

Hôtel Ibis ★★ 2 place Victor Hugo, 45203 Montargis.
℡ 38 98 00 68, Fax 38 89 14 37. English spoken.
Open all year. 49 bedrooms (all en suite).
Golf 5 km, garage, parking. &

In the town centre known as the Little Venice of France, this hotel offers all modern conveniences.

■ RESTAURANT: Closed 25 Dec.
■ TARIFF: (1994) Single 275, Double 295, Bk 32 (Amex, Euro/Access, Visa).

MONTAUBAN Tarn/Garonne 4D

Hôtel du Commerce ★ 9 pl Franklin Roosevelt, 82000 Montauban.
℡ 63 66 31 32, Fax 63 03 18 46.
English spoken.

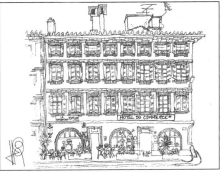

M

Open all year. 28 bedrooms (16 en suite).
Golf 10 km, garage, parking.

Quiet and comfortable, a period hotel offering good value for money. Opposite the cathedral. (Numerous restaurants in the vicinity with a wide range of menus.)

■ TARIFF: (1994) Single 90–180, Double 130–260, Bk 22 (Euro/Access, Visa).

MONTAUBAN-DE-BRETAGNE Ille/Vil 1D

Hôtel de France ★★ 34 rue de Gén de Gaulle, 35360 Montauban-de-Bretagne.
℡ 99 06 40 19. English spoken.
Open 01/02 to 20/12. 12 bedrooms (9 en suite, 3 bath/shower only). Parking, restaurant.

Hotel/restaurant set in the centre of the village.

*One hour from St-Malo, 2 hrs from Roscoff.
N12, 30 km from Rennes.*
■ TARIFF: (1994) Single 110–220, Double 220,
Bk 28, Set menu 62–150 (Euro/Access, Visa).

MONTBARD Côte-d'Or   3C

Château de Malaisy ★★★ 21500 Montbard.
℡ 80 89 46 54, Fax 80 92 30 16. English spoken.

Open all year. 22 bedrooms (3 en suite,
19 bath/shower only). Outdoor swimming
pool, golf 20 km, parking. &

M

*Quiet 19th-century château in park. Access by
A6 exit Berc-les-Semur. 70 km from Dijon via
D905.*
■ RESTAURANT: Overlooking park and woods.
Carefully prepared dishes with a variety of
specialities.
■ ACTIVITIES: Sauna, fitness, mountain-bike hire.
Tennis nearby, ballooning, canal trips and wine
cellars to visit.
■ TARIFF: (1994) Single 270–580, Double 270–
580, Bk 38, Set menu 125–245 (Visa).
■ DISCOUNT: 8%

MONTBAZON Indre/Loire

Château d'Artigny 37250 Montbazon.
℡ 47 26 24 24, Fax 47 65 92 79. English spoken.

Open 07/01 to 03/12. 53 bedrooms
(all en suite). Outdoor swimming pool, tennis,
golf 17 km, garage, parking. &
*Imposing château set in beautiful parkland.
Excellent facilities and offering every comfort.*
■ RESTAURANT: Gourmet cuisine with seafood
and meat specialities.
■ ACTIVITIES: Excellent sports facilities as well as
a fitness centre with jacuzzi and sauna. Balloon
and helicopter pleasure flights depart from the
hotel. ● Special golf packages available.
■ TARIFF: (1994) Single 500–1500,
Double 600–1575, Bk 85, Set menu 280–440
(Amex, Euro/Access, Visa).
■ DISCOUNT: 20% Nov to Mar.

Hôtel Moulin Fleuri ★★ route du Ripault,
37250 Montbazon.
℡ 47 26 01 12. English spoken.
Open 09/03 to 30/01. 12 bedrooms
(8 en suite). Golf 12 km, parking.
*Delightfully situated converted mill on the
Loire châteaux route. Take D87 off N10,
towards Azay-le-Rideau.*
■ RESTAURANT: Closed Mon. Magnificent wine
list and a cheese board with over 30 varieties
on offer.
■ ACTIVITIES: Good base for visiting Loire
châteaux and vineyards.
■ TARIFF: (1994) Single 180–270,
Double 180–320, Bk 45, Set menu 160–235
(Amex, Euro/Access, Visa).

MONTBELIARD Doubs   3D

Hôtel Bristol ★★ 2 rue Velotte,
25200 Montbéliard.
℡ 81 94 43 17, Fax 81 94 15 29. English spoken.
Open 01/01 to 31/07 & 01/09 to 24/12.
43 bedrooms (40 en suite,
1 bath/shower only). Golf 14 km, garage,
parking.
*Quiet, traditional hotel near the station and
pedestrian area in the city centre.*
■ TARIFF: (1994) Single 150–375, Double 180–
400, Bk 30 (Amex, Euro/Access, Visa).
■ DISCOUNT: 15%

MONTELIMAR Drôme   5D

Hôtel Cremaillère ★★★ 138 av Jean-Jaurès,
26200 Montélimar.
℡ 75 01 87 46, Fax 75 52 36 87. English spoken.
Open 01/01 to 18/12. 20 bedrooms
(all en suite). Outdoor swimming pool,
golf 5 km, garage, parking. &
Situated 1.5 km from the city centre.

■ TARIFF: (1994) Single 240–310, Double 270–310, Bk 30 (Amex, Euro/Access, Visa).

MONTIGNY-LE-ROI Hte-Marne   3C

Hôtel Moderne ★★ av de Lierneux, 52140 Montigny-le-Roi.
✆ 25 90 30 18, Fax 25 90 71 80. English spoken.
Open all year. 26 bedrooms (all en suite).
Garage, parking, restaurant. &
A friendly modern hotel in lush green countryside, where everything will be done to make your stay enjoyable. Near motorway A31 between Nancy and Dijon (exit no 8).
■ TARIFF: (1994) Single 230–250, Double 230–300, Bk 32, Set menu 82–190 (Amex, Euro/Access, Visa).

MONTLUCON Allier   5A

Hôtel Garden ★★ 12 av Marx Dormoy, 03310 Neris-les-Bains.
✆ 70 03 21 16, Fax 70 03 10 67. English spoken.
Open all year. 19 bedrooms (all en suite).
Golf 4 km, garage, parking.
Pretty hotel 3 minutes from the centre of this spa town, in the Auvergne/Berry/Creuse triangle. From Montluçon, south on the A71.
■ RESTAURANT: Panoramic view over pretty parkland. Good choice of set or à la carte menus; meals served outside in fine weather.
■ ACTIVITIES: A variety of sports, plus tourist and historical sightseeing opportunities nearby.
■ TARIFF: (1994) Single 225–275, Double 225–325, Bk 30, Set menu 75–190 (Amex, Euro/Access, Visa).
■ DISCOUNT: 5%

MONTMELIAN Savoie   6A

Hôtel Primivère ★★ 73800 Montmélian.
✆ 79 84 12 01, Fax 79 84 23 01.
English spoken.

Open all year. 42 bedrooms (all en suite).
Parking. &
This highly recommended hotel is peacefully situated beside the River Isère. South of Annecy from N6, take road to Montmélian and Quai de l'Isère. Also approached via A43 from Lyon.
■ RESTAURANT: Smart restaurant overlooking the Alps. Classical cuisine and extensive buffet.
■ ACTIVITIES: Mountain walks from hotel; bicycles, tennis and swimming pool nearby; half an hour to ski resorts.
■ TARIFF: (1994) Double 230–290, Bk 32, Set menu 56–145 (Euro/Access, Visa).
■ DISCOUNT: 10%

MONTOIRE-SUR-LE-LOIR Loir/Cher   2C

Hôtel Cheval Blanc ★★ place de la Libération, 41800 Trôo.
✆ 54 72 58 22, Fax 54 72 55 44.
Open all year. 9 bedrooms (all en suite).
Parking.
From Vendôme west on the D917 to Montoire-sur-le-Loir then Trôo.
■ RESTAURANT: Closed Mon & Tues lunch. Seafood specialities.
■ TARIFF: (1994) Double 270–290, Bk 30, Set menu 100–250 (Euro/Access, Visa).

Hôtel du Cheval Rouge ★★ 1 place Foch, 41800 Montoire-sur-le-Loir.
✆ 54 85 07 05, Fax 54 85 17 42. English spoken.
Open 01/03 to 31/01. 15 bedrooms (9 en suite). Garage, parking.
Traditional old French hotel with plenty of charm. 19 km west of Vendôme on the D917.
■ RESTAURANT: Closed Tues eve & Wed. Gourmet menus, for example: saumon fumé, foie gras de canard au naturel, panaché de ris et rognons de veau, feuillantine au chocolat.
■ ACTIVITIES: Walking and cycling.
■ TARIFF: (1994) Single 116–200, Double 130–220, Bk 28, Set menu 119–290 (Amex, Euro/Access, Visa).
■ DISCOUNT: 10% LS only.

Le Grand St-Vincent ★★ 6 rue Pasteur, 41800 Couture-sur-Loir.
✆ 54 72 42 02, Fax 54 72 41 55.
Open all year. 7 bedrooms (all en suite).
Tennis, parking. &
Stylishly renovated hotel dating back to the 18th century. From Montoire-sur-le-Loir follow river west to Couture-sur-Loir. 45 km from Tours, 35 km from Vendôme and 50 km from Le Mans.
■ RESTAURANT: Closed Mon & Tues lunch. Home-cooked French cuisine.

M

■ ACTIVITIES: Tennis 200 m. Jet ski, motorcross, water-skiing 2 km.
■ TARIFF: (1994) Single 220, Double 230–270, Bk 25, Set menu 55–120 (Euro/Access, Visa).

MONTPELLIER Hérault 5C

Hôtel Alliance Metropole ★★★★ 3 rue Clos René, 34000 Montpellier.
℃ 67 58 11 22, Fax 67 93 13 02. English spoken. Open all year. 85 bedrooms (80 en suite, 5 bath/shower only). Golf 5 km, garage, parking.
In the centre of Montpellier, built in 1898 and entirely renovated in 1990. 5 minutes' walk from la Place de la Comédie and the opera. Motorway A9 exit Montpellier-Centre towards station.
■ RESTAURANT: Closed Sat & Sun. Very good menus.
■ TARIFF: (1994) Single 430–580, Double 530–640, Bk 70 (Amex, Euro/Access, Visa).

Hôtel Parc ★★ 8 rue A Bège, 34000 Montpellier.
℃ 67 41 16 49, Fax 67 54 10 05. English spoken.

Open all year. 19 bedrooms (all en suite). Golf 4 km, parking.
Former Languedocian residence dating back to the 18th century and completely renovated. Located in the very heart of the city with garden and flowery breakfast terrace.
■ TARIFF: (1994) Single 200–350, Double 230–380, Bk 35 (Amex, Euro/Access, Visa).

Hôtel Climat de France ★★ Parc Euromédecine, rue du Caducée, 34080 Montpellier.
℃ 67 52 43 33, Fax 67 52 28 44. English spoken. Open all year. 43 bedrooms (all en suite). Outdoor swimming pool, golf 1 km, parking. &

Small, cosy and welcoming hotel. Quiet, countrified location yet not far from the city centre. Leave motorway at Montpellier-Sud exit and follow signs towards Millau, La Paillade and then Parc Euromédicine.
■ RESTAURANT: Regional and traditional cuisine with hors d'oeuvres buffet specialities. Children's menu also available.
■ ACTIVITIES: Most sports nearby; good area for sightseeing.
■ TARIFF: Double 270, Set menu 70–90 (Amex, Euro/Access, Visa).
■ DISCOUNT: 10%

MONTREUIL Pas-de-Calais 2B

Hôtel de France ★★ 2 rue du Petit Coquempot, 62170 Montreuil-sur-Mer.
℃ 21 06 05 36, Fax 21 81 22 60. English spoken.

Open 15/02 to 15/12. 14 bedrooms (10 en suite). Golf 10 km, garage, parking.
An original 16th-century coaching inn, newly renovated and decorated in individual style by the owners. The building is of historic importance and has much charm. Flowered courtyard/terrace bar, conference and function room. Located in the centre of Montreuil just off N1.
■ RESTAURANT: Closed Mon eve & Wed. Gourmet cuisine including local specialities in the restaurant plus new courtyard Crêperie.
■ ACTIVITIES: Riding and cycling nearby.
● Special rates arranged for golf.
■ TARIFF: (1994) Single 280–350, Double 280–380, Bk 35, Set menu 86–250 (Euro/Access, Visa).

Auberge La Grenouillère ★★★ La Madelaine-sous-Montreuil, 62170 Montreuil-sur-Mer.
℃ 21 06 07 22, Fax 21 86 36 36. English spoken.
Open 15/01 to 15/12. 4 bedrooms (all en suite). Golf 15 km, parking. &

Picardy-style farmhouse set on the banks of the River Canche, at the foot of the ramparts of Montreuil-sur-Mer.
■ RESTAURANT: Closed Tues & Wed. Rustic atmosphere, good food with specialities such as cuisses de grenouilles and crêpes.
■ TARIFF: (1994) Single 350, Double 350–500, Bk 40, Set menu 190–350 (Amex, Euro/Access, Visa).

Les Hauts de Montreuil ★★ 21-23 rue Pierre Le Dent, 62170 Montreuil-sur-Mer.
✆ 21 81 95 92, Fax 21 86 28 83. English spoken.

Open all year. 23 bedrooms (all en suite). Golf 12 km, parking. &
This lovely old hotel is highly recommended and offers a warm welcome in delightful surroundings.
■ RESTAURANT: Restaurant is surrounded by beautiful gardens and, dating from 1537, is one of the oldest in the town. Gastronomic cuisine, the freshly prepared dishes changing with the seasons. Own cheese and wine cellars.
■ ACTIVITIES: Perfect base for exploring the region; within easy reach are Le Touquet, the Berck beaches, Bolougne-sur-Mer with its Nausicaa aquarium and Napoleonic souvenirs and the lovely fishing port of Etaples. Within walking distance, discover the ancient town of Montreuil itself.
■ TARIFF: (1994) Double 345–435, Bk 50, Set menu 130–210 (Euro/Access, Visa).
■ DISCOUNT: 10%

MONTRICHARD Loir/Cher   2C

Hôtel de la Tête Noire ★★★ 24 rue de Tours, BP3, 41401 Montrichard.
✆ 54 32 05 55, Fax 54 32 78 37. English spoken.
Open 01/02 to 31/12. 38 bedrooms (31 en suite). Golf 17 km, parking.
A pretty hotel with comfortable rooms and a flowery terrace overlooking the river. In a

small, friendly town on the River Cher, ideal for visiting nearby Loire Valley châteaux.
■ RESTAURANT: Closed 04/01 to 02/02. Omelette du Père Louis and poulet à la tourangelle are just two of the good dishes to choose from in the attractive dining room.
■ TARIFF: (1994) Single 195–280, Double 195–320, Bk 35, Set menu 95–250 (Euro/Access, Visa).

MORNAC-SUR-SEUDRE Charente-Mar   4A

Hôtel Mornac ★★ rue des Halles, 17113 Mornac-sur-Seudre.
✆ 46 22 63 20, Fax 46 22 66 22. English spoken.
Open 01/04 to 31/10. 10 bedrooms (all en suite). Golf 5 km, parking. &
Small, quiet hotel in picturesque fishing village by River Seudre. Fully-equipped rooms. Located south of La Rochelle between Saujon and Tremblade, 10 km from Royan on D733.
■ RESTAURANT: Closed Tues & Wed LS & Oct. Smart restaurant set in a wooded park. Specialities: fish and local dishes.
■ TARIFF: (1994) Single 250–340, Double 290–340, Bk 38, Set menu 110–190 (Euro/Access, Visa).
■ DISCOUNT: 5%

MORNAS Vaucluse   5D

M

Hôtel Le Manoir ★★ av Jean Moulin, 84500 Mornas-en-Provence.
✆ 90 37 00 79, Fax 90 37 10 34. English spoken.
Open 10/02 to 11/11 & 08/12 to 10/01. 25 bedrooms (all en suite). Golf 10 km, garage, parking.
An 18th-century manor house with stylish rooms and a beautiful terrace. Exit A7 at Bollene then go south on the N7 for 10 km or take exit from Orange and go north on N7.
■ RESTAURANT: Good, local cuisine in the elegant dining room. Specialities are marinated smoked salmon in hazelnut oil, baked shellfish in clarified butter sauce and quail salmis in red wine.
■ ACTIVITIES: Visit the medieval fortress in Mornas; close by are Orange, Vaison-la-Romaine and Côte du Rhône vineyards as well as facilities for horse-riding, tennis and swimming.
■ TARIFF: (1994) Single 250–300, Double 250–320, Bk 40, Set menu 95–185 (Amex, Euro/Access, Visa).

MORTAGNE-AU-PERCHE Orne 2C

Hôtel du Tribunal ★★ 4 place du Palais,
61400 Mortagne-au-Perche.
☎ 33 25 04 77, Fax 33 83 60 83. English spoken.

Open all year. 11 bedrooms (all en suite).
Golf 15 km, garage, parking.

*Ancient building dating back to the 13th
century with lots of beams, studs and local
stone. Flower-covered terrace and bedrooms
have a garden view. Mortagne-au-Perche lies
in the 'Vieux Mortagne' region and is
renowned for its black puddings! From
Alençon east on N12.*

■ RESTAURANT: Fine food served in authentic
rustic surroundings.
■ ACTIVITIES: Horse-riding, hiking, cycling
nearby.
■ TARIFF: (1994) Double 220–320, Bk 40,
Set menu 80–160 (Euro/Access, Visa).

MORZINE-AVORIAZ Hte-Savoie 6A

Hôtel Soly ★★ Le Bourg, 74110 Morzine.
☎ 50 79 09 45, Fax 50 74 71 82. English spoken.
Open 15/12 to 20/04 & 15/06 to 15/09.
19 bedrooms (all en suite). Outdoor swimming
pool, golf 10 km, garage, parking,
restaurant. ⑯

*A quiet, typical Savoyard chalet-hotel situated
100 m from the church. Good facilities and a
beautiful situation for both summer and
winter holidays.*

■ TARIFF: Single 230, Double 295, Bk 39,
Set menu 95–140 (Amex, Euro/Access, Visa).
■ DISCOUNT: 5%

MOULINS Allier 5A

Hôtel Parc ★★ 31 av Gén Leclerc, 03000 Moulins.
☎ 70 44 12 25, Fax 70 46 79 35. English spoken.
Open 03/01 to 30/09 & 15/10 to 22/12.
28 bedrooms (all en suite). Parking. ⑯

*Traditional hotel, completely renovated,
with private parking. It is opposite the station,
between the N7 (from Nevers) and N79 to
Lyon.*

■ RESTAURANT: Closed Sat. Specialities: foie gras
frais de canard maison; magret de canard au
Sancerre rouge; escalope de saumon à l'oseille;
nougat glace coulis de framboises.
■ TARIFF: (1994) Single 190–320,
Double 200–320, Bk 36, Set menu 90–220
(Euro/Access, Visa).

Hôtel Paris Jacquemart ★★★ 21 rue Paris,
03000 Moulins.
☎ 70 44 00 58, Fax 70 34 05 39. English spoken.
Open all year. 28 bedrooms (all en suite).
Outdoor swimming pool, golf 5 km, garage,
parking.

*Situated in the centre of the town, near the
Préfecture, offering a high standard of service.*

■ RESTAURANT: Closed Sun & Mon eve. Well
regarded and well known restaurant.
■ TARIFF: (1994) Single 330–480,
Double 330–980, Bk 50, Set menu 160–440
(Amex, Euro/Access, Visa).

MULHOUSE Ht-Rhin 3D

Hôtel de Bale ★★ 19 passage Central,
68100 Mulhouse.
☎ 89 46 19 87, Fax 89 66 07 06.
English spoken.
Open all year. 32 bedrooms (20 en suite,
3 bath/shower only). Golf 8 km, parking.

*A well-kept, traditional hotel with garden and
where you will receive a warm welcome. Leave
motorway A36 at Mulhouse-Centre. The hotel
is in the town centre opposite the Banque de
France.*

■ ACTIVITIES: Good base for
sightseeing/organised tours, including 'route
du vin' and 'route des crêtes'.
■ TARIFF: (1994) Single 165–285,
Double 175–290, Bk 32 (Euro/Access, Visa).

Hôtel Bourse ★★★ 14 rue Bourse,
68100 Mulhouse.
☎ 89 56 18 44, Fax 89 56 60 51.
English spoken.
Open all year. 50 bedrooms (all en suite).
Golf 18 km, garage.

*Centre of the town near the park and very
quiet. Follow Gare-Centrale signs to the hotel.*

■ TARIFF: (1994) Single 350–380,
Double 410–470, Bk 50 (Amex,
Euro/Access, Visa).
■ DISCOUNT: 10%

Hôtel Bristol ★★★ 18 av de Colmare, 68100 Mulhouse.
☎ 89 42 12 31, Fax 89 42 50 57. English spoken.
Open all year. 65 bedrooms (all en suite).
Golf 15 km, garage, parking. &
*From A36 situated in the centre of Mulhouse.
Colour TV, conference facilities, groups
welcome. Very comfortable and well furnished.*
■ ACTIVITIES: On the edge of the Vosges
mountains and the Black Forest.
■ TARIFF: (1994) Single 250–380, Double 280–
450, Bk 35 (Amex, Euro/Access, Visa).
■ DISCOUNT: 10%

Hôtel Ile Napoléon ★★★ 68100 Mulhouse.
☎ 89 31 35 35, Fax 89 31 35 36. English spoken.
Open all year. 96 bedrooms (all en suite).
Outdoor swimming pool, garage, parking,
restaurant. &
*Open all year, large hotel has 96 rooms with all
modern conveniences, swimming pool and
garden. 10 minutes from the town near the A5
motorway that joins Germany and
Switzerland.*
■ TARIFF: (1994) Double 305–500, Bk 52
(Amex, Euro/Access, Visa).

Hôtel Inter Salvator ★★ 29 passage Centrale,
BP 1354, 68100 Mulhouse.
☎ 89 45 28 32, Fax 89 56 49 59. English spoken.
Open all year. 54 bedrooms (all en suite).
Golf 15 km, garage, parking.
*Quiet hotel offering a warm welcome, just after
the motorway exit to Mulhouse-Centre.*
■ ACTIVITIES: 2 and 5 day activity tours arranged
by hotel.
■ TARIFF: (1994) Single 260–280, Double 280–
300, Bk 35 (Amex, Euro/Access, Visa).
■ DISCOUNT: 5%

Hôtel Vosges ★★ 68290 Sewen.
☎ 89 82 00 43. English spoken.
Open 20/12 to 14/11. 19 bedrooms
(17 en suite, 2 bath/shower only). Golf 10 km,
garage, parking.
*Comfortable family-owned hotel with extensive
garden surrounded by the forests of the Vosges
mountains. 40 km from Mulhouse on the
D4666 heading towards Maseuaux, then
Ballon-d'Alsace.*
■ RESTAURANT: Closed Sun eve and Thur
Sep to Jun.
■ ACTIVITIES: In the vicinity: footpaths, bike
paths, fishing, horse-riding and winter skiing.
■ TARIFF: (1994) Single 190–270,
Double 250–290, Bk 32, Set menu 90–300
(Amex, Euro/Access, Visa).

MUNSTER Ht-Rhin 3D

Hôtel aux Deux Sapins ★★ 49 rue du 9ème
Zouaves, 68140 Munster.
☎ 89 77 33 96, Fax 89 77 03 90. English spoken.
Open all year. 25 bedrooms (all en suite).
Golf 15 km, parking, restaurant. &
On the D417 between Colmar and Gerardmer.
■ TARIFF: (1994) Double 220–320, Bk 28,
Set menu 70–200 (Amex, Euro/Access, Visa).

Hôtel Le Beau Site ★★ 3 rue Principale,
Hohrod, 68140 Munster.
☎ 89 77 31 55. English spoken.
Open 01/02 to 14/11. 14 bedrooms
(all en suite). Golf 15 km, garage, parking.
*In a quiet situation on a hillside, the hotel has
a family atmosphere and all modern facilities.
Large terrace with beautiful views. Follow
D417 from Colmar to Munster. After 3 km,
turn right and the hotel is on the left.*
■ RESTAURANT: Local specialities in typical
Alsace setting. Possibility of half-board with set
menu.
■ ACTIVITIES: In summer: mountain bike trail,
tennis, horse-riding. In winter: cross-country
and down-hill skiing, tobogganing.
■ TARIFF: (1994) Single 185, Double 265–310,
Set menu 69–120 (Euro/Access, Visa).

MUR-DE-BARREZ Aveyron 5A

Auberge de Barrez ★★ av du Carladez,
12600 Mur-de-Barrez.
☎ 65 66 00 76, Fax 65 66 07 98. English spoken.
Open 01/02 to 31/12. 18 bedrooms
(all en suite). Golf 20 km, garage, parking. &
*A modern hotel with TV lounge, billiard room
and garden. Situated amidst rugged scenery
and close to the Barrage de Sarrans.*
■ RESTAURANT: Closed Mon. Modern and
comfortable. Specialities: fromage de chèvre
aux poireaux, lapin farcie aux herbes.
■ TARIFF: (1994) Single 200, Double 220–450,
Bk 34, Set menu 64–190 (Amex,
Euro/Access, Visa).

MURAT Cantal 5A

Hôtel Les Messageries ★★ 18 av du D Louis
Mallet, 15300 Murat.
☎ 71 20 04 04, Fax 71 20 02 81. English spoken.
Open 25/12 to 25/11. 24 bedrooms
(all en suite). Outdoor swimming pool, garage,
parking. &
*A winter sports area, in the Auvergne regional
volcanic park. From A75, exit Massiac, then
head for Murat.*

M

■ RESTAURANT: Auvergne specialities include pounti, truffade and potée.
■ ACTIVITIES: Walking, abseiling, mountain-biking and winter sports nearby.
■ TARIFF: (1994) Single 210, Double 240–360, Bk 28, Set menu 75–180 (Amex, Visa).

LA MURE Isère   6A

Hôtel Murtel ★★ Côteau de Beauregard, 38350 La Mure.
℡ 76 30 96 10, Fax 76 30 91 38. English spoken.

Open all year. 40 bedrooms (all en suite). Parking, restaurant. &
South of Grenoble in the heart of the southern Alps, in La Mure, on the N85.
■ TARIFF: (1994) Double 240–260, Bk 28 (Euro/Access, Visa).

MUS Gard   5D

Aub de la Paillère ★★★ av de Puits Vieux, 30121 Mus.
℡ 66 23 78 79, Fax 66 73 79 28. English spoken. Open 10/02 to 01/01. 7 bedrooms (all en suite). Golf 15 km, parking.
A charming 17th-century house in a small village. Between N113 and A9, exit A9 towards Gallargues.
■ RESTAURANT: Closed Mon.
■ TARIFF: (1994) Single 350–480, Double 380–480, Set menu 110–230 (Amex, Euro/Access, Visa).

NANCY

Nancy, the one-time capital of Lorraine, lies on the left bank of the River Meurthe and on the Rhine-Marne canal. Its position, not far from the German border, means that, throughout its history, it has been subject to

One of the fantastic fountains on Nancy's Place Stanislas

periods of unrest and foreign influence. To one of these periods of foreign influence it owes its particular charm as one of the most elegant towns in France.

Following the war of Polish succession, which ended in 1738, Stanislas Leszcynski, the deposed king of Poland, was assigned the Duchy of Lorraine for his lifetime by his son-in-law Louis XV. Stanislas, with the help of the architect Héré and the ironworker Lamour, set about the planning and building of a new town centre. Here Stanislas still stands, his statue looking out over the Place Stanislas towards the triumphal arch which he built in honour of his royal son-in-law.

The Place Stanislas is surrounded by imposing palaces, fantastic fountains and, most impressively of all, by Lamour's gilded wrought-iron railings. Lamour's work can also be seen in the largest of the palaces, now used as the town hall. Here he designed the bannisters that flank the main staircase. Another palace which faces onto the great square is the Musée des Beaux-Arts with its wide-ranging collection of European paintings.

Beyond the triumphal arch lies the Place de la Carrière, an area which was redeveloped from a 16th-century jousting ground. Here a graceful double colonnade leads to two more palaces, the Palais du Gouvernement and the 16th-century Ducal Palace which was much restored in 1871. This now houses the Musée Historique Lorrain, a collection of exhibits devoted to local history and the customs of the area. The 14th-century Porte de la Craffe, which was until the French Revolution a prison, is now an annexe to this museum.

Just beside the Ducal Palace lies the Parc de la Pépinière where there is something for everyone. Visit the tree nursery, zoo or aquarium, play a game of crazy golf or relax in the formal rose gardens. Stanislas, the creator of these fine townscapes, is buried beside his wife's mausoleum, at the baroque church of Notre Dame de Bon-Secours in the south-eastern quarter of Nancy.

But Nancy is not just an 18th-century town, it boasts a further era of intense artistic activity. About 90 years ago, it became a centre of the Art Nouveau style. Few buildings from this period remain, but the Musée de l'Ecole de Nancy, a villa built in 1909, is well worth a visit. Inside, there are many examples of fine design and workmanship typical of the period.

Works of art of a different kind can be seen at the Musée de la Moto et du Vélo at Lunéville, about half an hour's drive from Nancy. More than 200 examples are on display tracing the early development of both the motorbike and the bicycle.

NANCY Meurthe/Moselle 3D

Hôtel Akena ★ ZAC du Saule Gaillard, 54390 Frouard.
☏ 45 92 38 38, Fax 49 32 13 33.
English spoken.
Open all year. 59 bedrooms (all en suite).
Parking. ♿

Ultra-modern hotel with all facilities at very economical prices. Rooms can accommodate 3 at same price. Frouard is 4 km from Nancy on Metz road.
■ TARIFF: (1994) Double 145–150, Bk 24 (Visa).

Hôtel Altea Thiers ★★★ 11 rue Raymond Poincaré, 54000 Nancy.
☏ 83 39 75 75, Fax 83 32 78 17. English spoken.

Open all year. 192 bedrooms (all en suite).
Golf 10 km, parking, restaurant.
Town-centre hotel opposite the railway station, sound-proofed and air-conditioned rooms. A31 exit Nancy-Centre-Ville, follow signs to Gare SNCF.
■ TARIFF: (1994) Double 375–625, Bk 55, Set menu 140 (Amex, Euro/Access, Visa).

N

Hôtel Mercure Nancy Centre ★★★ 5 rue des Carmes, 54000 Nancy.
☏ 83 35 32 10, Fax 83 32 92 49. English spoken.
Open all year. 80 bedrooms (all en suite).
Garage.
The hotel is near the historic town centre, close to the station and 100 m from Place Stanislas.
■ TARIFF: (1994) Single 350–475, Double 350–475, Bk 52 (Amex, Euro/Access, Visa).
■ DISCOUNT: 5%

NANTES Loire-Atlan 1D

Hôtel Astoria ★★★ 11 rue Richebourg, 44000 Nantes.
☏ 40 74 39 90, Fax 40 14 05 49. English spoken.
Open all year. 45 bedrooms (42 en suite).
Garage, parking. ♿
In the centre of Nantes, near the cathedral, Musée Beaux Arts and the railway station. Quiet street close to public gardens.
■ TARIFF: (1994) Single 290–320, Double 290–350, Bk 38 (Euro/Access, Visa).

Hôtel Beaujoire ★★ 15 rue Pays de Loire, Beaujoire, 44000 Nantes.
☎ 40 93 00 01, Fax 40 68 98 32. English spoken.
Open all year. 42 bedrooms (all en suite).
Golf 3 km, parking. ₫

Comfortable bedrooms and pleasant atmosphere. Easy to find near Beaujoire football stadium and close to leisure centre on the way to Angers/Paris.

■ RESTAURANT: Pretty, aptly named 'Le Jardin' restaurant has a lovely atmosphere and offers salmon, oysters and duck specialities.
■ ACTIVITIES: Tennis, swimming and football nearby.
■ TARIFF: (1994) Single 270, Double 290, Bk 30, Set menu 90–158 (Amex, Euro/Access, Visa).

Hôtel Bourgogne ★★★ 9 allée Cdt Charcot, 44000 Nantes.
☎ 40 74 03 34, Fax 40 14 03 86.
English spoken.
Open all year. 42 bedrooms (all en suite).

The hotel is situated opposite the railway station and 15 minutes from town centre, congress hall and main monuments.

■ TARIFF: (1994) Single 255–300, Double 284–340, Bk (Amex, Visa).
■ DISCOUNT: 5% Except weekends.

M

Holiday Inn Garden Court ★★★ 1 bd Martyrs Nantais, 44200 Nantes.
☎ 40 47 77 77, Fax 40 47 36 52. English spoken.
Open all year. 108 bedrooms (all en suite).
Golf 6 km, garage, parking. ₫

Located on one of the oldest isles of Nantes, Ile Beaulieu, overlooking the River Loire. From A11, take city centre exit and follow signs to Ile Beaulieu.

■ RESTAURANT: Closed Sat & Sun lunch.
■ ACTIVITIES: ● Golf package; dinner cruise visiting the Erdre castles.
■ TARIFF: (1994) Double 350–420, Bk 55, Set menu 89–120 (Amex, Euro/Access, Visa).

Hôtel Mascotte ★★ Aéroport Nantes Atlantique, 44340 Nantes.
☎ 40 32 14 14, Fax 40 32 14 13. English spoken.
Open all year. 73 bedrooms (all en suite).
Parking. ₫

10 minutes from the town centre directly in airport complex. Motorway A11.

■ TARIFF: (1994) Single 300–360, Double 340–400, Bk 40 (Amex, Euro/Access, Visa).

Hôtel Océania ★★★ Aéroport Nantes Atlantique, 44340 Bouguenais.
☎ 40 05 05 66, Fax 40 05 12 03. English spoken.

Open all year. 87 bedrooms (all en suite).
Outdoor swimming pool, tennis, parking, restaurant. ₫
On the airport complex.

■ TARIFF: (1994) Single 450–525, Double 500–570, Bk 50 (Amex, Euro/Access, Visa).

Hôtel Otelinn 45 rue Batignolles, Beaujoire, 44300 Nantes.
☎ 40 50 07 07, Fax 40 49 41 40. English spoken.
Open all year. 60 bedrooms (all en suite).
Golf 2 km, garage, parking. ₫

From Nantes follow signs to Beaujoire Stadium; the hotel is opposite.

■ RESTAURANT: Specialities: fish, poultry and grills from the Loire and Brittany.
■ ACTIVITIES: Organised visits round historic town centre.
■ TARIFF: Single 235–335, Double 255–355, Bk 35, Set menu 68–200 (Amex, Euro/Access, Visa).
■ DISCOUNT: 10%

Hôtel Paris ★★ 2 rue Boileau, 44000 Nantes.
☎ 40 48 78 79, Fax 40 47 63 75. English spoken.
Open all year. 50 bedrooms (all en suite).
Golf on site, parking.

Situated right in the town centre. All modern conveniences.

■ TARIFF: (1994) Single 200–300, Double 250–350, Bk (Amex, Euro/Access, Visa).

NANTUA Ain 6A

Hôtel Embarcadère ★★ av Lac, 01130 Nantua.
☎ 74 75 22 88, Fax 74 75 22 25. English spoken.
Open 20/01 to 30/04 & 08/05 to 20/12.
50 bedrooms (all en suite). Parking.

Cosy and comfortable. In a peaceful lake and forest setting with some wonderful views. From Paris, exit 8 off A40.

■ RESTAURANT: Good restaurant with specialities including quenelle de brochet Nantua and gratin de queues d'écrevisses.
■ ACTIVITIES: Windsurfing, canoeing, swimming nearby.
■ TARIFF: (1994) Double 240, Bk 30, Set menu 105–280 (Euro/Access, Visa).
■ DISCOUNT: 10%

Hôtel de France ★★★ 44 rue du Docteur Mercier, 01130 Nantua.
☎ 74 75 00 55, Fax 74 75 26 22.
English spoken.

Open 20/12 to 01/11. 17 bedrooms
(all en suite). Garage, parking.

*Old coaching inn offering a warm welcome.
Individually furnished bedrooms, sound-
proofed and very comfortable. On A40 from
Paris take exit 8, from Genève exit 9.*

■ RESTAURANT: Closed 01/11 to 20/12. Good
food, good wine list and excellent service.
Gratin de queues d'écrevisses and quenelle de
brochet maison are just two of the specialities.

■ ACTIVITIES: Water sports and mountain
pursuits nearby.

■ TARIFF: (1994) Single 210–265,
Double 300–405, Bk 33, Set menu 125–195
(Euro/Access, Visa).

NARBONNE Aude   5C

Hôtel de la Clape ★★ rue des Flots Bleus,
Narbonne Plage, 11100 Narbonne.
☎ 68 49 80 15, Fax 68 75 05 05. English spoken.
Open 01/04 to 30/09. 15 bedrooms (6 en suite,
9 bath/shower only). Indoor swimming pool,
outdoor swimming pool, tennis, golf 10 km,
parking. &

*Exit Narbonne-Est from motorway and take
D168 to this comfortable family hotel. Bar
specialising only in non-alcoholic beverages.
(Further discounts: 20% in April and 15% in
May.)*

■ ACTIVITIES: Children's club on beach 100 m.

■ TARIFF: (1994) Single 185, Double 185–305,
Bk 28 (Amex, Visa).

■ DISCOUNT: 10% Jun to Sep except weekends.

Hôtel Languedoc ★★★ 22 bd Gambetta,
11100 Narbonne.
☎ 68 65 14 74, Fax 68 65 81 48. English spoken.
Open all year. 39 bedrooms (all en suite).
Golf 5 km, garage. &

*Elegant hotel in the historical town of
Narbonne. Situated just a few minutes from
the station and the Narbonne-Est motorway
exit, opposite the Post Office.*

■ RESTAURANT: Closed 15/10 to 15/04.

■ TARIFF: (1994) Single 250–350,
Double 250–500, Bk 38, Set menu 90–220
(Amex, Euro/Access, Visa).

■ DISCOUNT: 10%

Novotel ★★★ quartier Plaisance, route de
Perpignan, 11100 Narbonne.
☎ 68 42 72 00, Fax 68 42 72 10. English spoken.
Open all year. 96 bedrooms (all en suite).
Outdoor swimming pool, parking,
restaurant. &

Access from either the A9 or A61, exit

*Narbonne-Sud. 5 km from town centre. Very
comfortable, with all the usual Novotel
facilities.*

■ TARIFF: (1994) Single 395–410,
Double 430–450, Bk 48, Set menu 80–150
(Amex, Euro/Access, Visa).

Hôtel Relais du Val d'Orbieu ★★★
11200 Ornaisons.
☎ 68 27 10 27, Fax 68 27 52 44.
English spoken.
Open all year. 20 bedrooms (all en suite).
Outdoor swimming pool, tennis, golf 15 km,
parking. &

*Within 15 minutes of the centre of Narbonne,
in 2 acres of wooded garden. The hotel is an
old mill which has been renovated and
combines luxury and comfort together with
charm. Take the A9 and exit Narbonne-Sud or
the A61 and exit Lezignan-Corbières.*

■ RESTAURANT: Renowned for its very good
cuisine.

■ TARIFF: (1994) Single 390–640,
Double 540–740, Bk 67, Set menu 195–395
(Amex, Euro/Access, Visa).

NAUCELLE Aveyron   5C

Hôtel du Château ★★ Castelpers, Lédergues,
12170 Requista.
☎ 65 69 22 61, Fax 65 69 25 31.

N

Open 01/04 to 01/10. 9 bedrooms (8 en suite,
1 bath/shower only). Parking.

*Attractive château with grounds bordered by
trout rivers. Forest walks and beautiful views.
12 km from Naucelle station, on the N88.*

■ RESTAURANT: Closed Tues LS.

■ ACTIVITIES: Trout fishing nearby.

■ TARIFF: (1994) Single 240–370,
Double 383–465, Bk 45, Set menu 130–260
(Amex, Euro/Access, Visa).

■ DISCOUNT: 10%

Auberge du Sénéchal ★★★ 12800 Sauveterre-de-Rouergue.
☎ 65 71 29 00, Fax 65 71 29 09. English spoken.
Open all year. 11 bedrooms (all en suite).
Indoor swimming pool, parking. &
In the middle of an unspoilt village full of medieval buildings and courtyards. Take walks in the quiet hills, and make room for the next meal!
■ RESTAURANT: The gourmet restaurant is more important than the rooms.
■ TARIFF: (1994) Single 450–650, Double 450–950, Bk 65, Set menu 95–450 (Amex, Euro/Access, Visa).

NAY Pyrénées-Atlan   4D

Auberge Chez Lazare ★★ Les Labassères, route Lys Arudy, 64800 Nay.
☎ 59 61 05 26, Fax 59 61 25 11. English spoken.
Open 08/08 to 23/07. 8 bedrooms (all en suite). Parking.
The hotel lies in beautiful countryside.
■ RESTAURANT: Closed Sun.
■ TARIFF: (1994) Double 220–240, Bk 30, Set menu 80–180 (Euro/Access, Visa).

NEAUPHLE-LE-CHATEAU Yvelines   2D

Hôtel Le Verboise ★★★ 78640 Neauphle-le-Château.
☎ 1 34 89 11 78, Fax 1 34 89 57 33.
English spoken.
Open 22/08 to 06/08. 20 bedrooms (all en suite). Tennis, golf 2 km, garage, parking.
Elegant 19th-century residence set in its own park. 20 minutes from Paris, to the north of the N12.
■ RESTAURANT: Closed Sun eve. Specialities: salade de langoustine, gaspacho de homard and barbue au jus de viande.
■ ACTIVITIES: Tennis, mountain-biking and forest walks.
■ TARIFF: (1994) Double 450–790, Bk 60 (Amex, Euro/Access, Visa).

NEMOURS Seine/Marne   2D

Hôtel Les Roches ★★ av L Pelletier, St-Pierre-lès-Nemours, 77140 Nemours.
☎ 1 64 28 01 43, Fax 1 64 28 04 27. English spoken.
Open 01/01 to 31/01 & 01/03 to 31/12.
15 bedrooms (13 en suite, 1 bath/shower only). Golf 10 km, garage, parking.
Former bistro converted into a comfortable hotel by present owners. 20 km from Paris and 12 km from Fontainebleau on N7.

■ RESTAURANT: Light and delicate traditional cuisine; regional value-for-money award.
■ ACTIVITIES: Water sports centre nearby.
■ TARIFF: (1994) Single 200–230, Double 230–270, Bk 35 (Amex, Euro/Access, Visa).

NEUFCHATEAU Vosges   3C

Hôtel St-Christophe ★★ 1 av de la Grande Fontaine, 88300 Neufchâteau.
☎ 29 94 38 71, Fax 29 06 02 09. English spoken.
Open all year. 34 bedrooms (all en suite). Parking. &
Small, recently renovated hotel situated on the main road to Dijon.
■ RESTAURANT: Comfortable restaurant with Lorraine regional specialities.
■ TARIFF: (1994) Single 260, Double 300, Bk 35, Set menu 90–200 (Euro/Access, Visa).
■ DISCOUNT: 10% By prior reservation.

NEUVILLE-AUX-BOIS Loiret   2D

L'Hostellerie ★★★ 48 pl du Général Leclerc, 45170 Neuville-aux-Bois.
☎ 38 75 50 00, Fax 38 91 86 81. English spoken.
Open all year. 34 bedrooms (all en suite). Golf 19 km, garage, parking. &
Modern hotel (1991), offering traditional hospitality and comfort. 20 km north of Orléans on D97 or from Paris, exit A10 at Artenay.
■ RESTAURANT: Closed Sun eve. Has a good reputation for excellent cuisine based on fresh, seasonal produce served with extensive choice of Loire valley wines. Children's menu also available.
■ ACTIVITIES: Table tennis and keep fit at hotel; visit to Château de Chamerolles and the perfume museum (6 km).
■ TARIFF: Single 350–600, Double 390–660, Bk 40, Set menu 85–170 (Amex, Euro/Access, Visa).

N

NEVERS Nièvre   2D

Hôtel de Diane ★★★★ 38 rue du Midi,
58000 Nevers.
☎ 86 57 28 10, Fax 86 59 45 08. English spoken.
Open 10/01 to 22/12. 30 bedrooms
(all en suite). Garage.
*In the centre of town near the station and
Loire. Cable TV. From the station take ave de
Gaulle, in front of main gate, and then second
right.*
■ RESTAURANT: Closed Sun & Mon lunch.
■ TARIFF: (1994) Single 380–440,
Double 450–490, Bk 40 (Amex,
Euro/Access, Visa).

Hôtel Loire ★★★★ quai de Médine,
58000 Nevers.
☎ 86 61 50 92. English spoken.
Open all year. 58 bedrooms (all en suite).
Golf 9 km, parking. &
*The hotel stands at the edge of the River Loire.
The restaurant and most of the rooms overlook
the river and old bridge. A quiet hotel, about
200 m from town centre and shopping
facilities. 5 minutes' drive from town railway
station. Near N7.*
■ RESTAURANT: Closed 15/12 to 10/01.
■ TARIFF: (1994) Single 330–345,
Double 400–435, Bk 38 (Amex,
Euro/Access, Visa).

NICE Alpes-Mar   6C

Hôtel Brice ★★★ 44 rue Maréchal Joffre,
06000 Nice.
☎ 93 88 14 44, Fax 93 87 38 54. English spoken.

Open all year. 61 bedrooms (all en suite).
Golf 15 km, parking. &
*In the heart of Nice, 200 m from the seaside.
Renovated, with flower garden.*
■ RESTAURANT: Good restaurant.
■ ACTIVITIES: Sauna, fitness room and solarium.

■ TARIFF: (1994) Single 363–441,
Double 520–672, Bk 40, Set menu 125 (Amex,
Euro/Access, Visa).
■ DISCOUNT: 10%

Hôtel Mercure Nice ★★★ 2 rue Halévy,
06000 Nice.
☎ 93 82 30 88, Fax 93 82 18 20. English spoken.

Open all year. 120 bedrooms (all en suite).
Garage.
*The Hotel Mercure Nice (Baie des Anges) is
beautifully situated on the Promenade des
Anglais at the corner of Albert 1 Gardens. It
has modern, spacious and air-conditioned
rooms (some non-smoking). The two suites and
all rooms are fully equipped. Buffet breakfast is
offered.*
■ TARIFF: Single 450–860, Double 500–990,
Bk 70 (Amex, Euro/Access, Visa).
■ DISCOUNT: 10%

Hôtel Harvey ★★ 18 av Suède, 06000 Nice.
☎ 93 88 73 73, Fax 93 82 53 55. English spoken.
Open 01/02 to 31/10. 62 bedrooms
(all en suite).
*Modern hotel with a classical façade, right in
the centre of Nice. Partly overlooking
pedestrian area and 100 m from the beach
and casino.*
■ TARIFF: (1994) Single 250–370, Double 300–
370, Bk 25 (Amex, Euro/Access, Visa).

Hôtel Le Prieure ★★ rue Jean Médecin,
St-Dalmas-de-Tende, 06430 Tende.
☎ 93 04 75 70, Fax 93 04 71 58. English spoken.
Open 01/05 to 31/10. 16 bedrooms
(all en suite). Golf 8 km, parking, restaurant. &
*Hotel in the Vallée-de-la-Roya. Peaceful and
agreeable. Good walking in the Parc
Mercantour.*
■ ACTIVITIES: 4X4 trails nearby.
■ TARIFF: (1994) Single 270, Double 325, Bk 33,
Set menu 90–145 (Amex, Euro/Access, Visa).

N

Occidental Nice Hôtel ★★★★ 179 bd René-Cassin, 06200 Nice.
☎ 93 83 91 92, Fax 93 21 69 57. English spoken.

Open all year. 150 bedrooms (all en suite). Outdoor swimming pool, garage, restaurant. &

Modern high-rise hotel with all amenities close to town centre, opposite Nice airport on the French Riviera. Also surprisingly close to the ski resorts of southern Alps.
■ TARIFF: (1994) Single 680–850, Double 760–950, Bk 78, Set menu 95 (Amex, Euro/Access, Visa).

Hôtel Pullman ★★★ 28 av Notre Dame, 06000 Nice.
☎ 93 13 36 36, Fax 93 62 61 69. English spoken.
Open all year. 201 bedrooms (all en suite). Outdoor swimming pool, golf 15 km, garage.

Large, air-conditioned modern hotel set in gardens, in the heart of Nice. Rooms fully equipped. Five minutes from the beach and the Promenade des Anglais. 7 km from international airport, railway station 300 m.
■ TARIFF: (1994) Single 495–830, Double 550–930, Bk 70 (Amex, Euro/Access, Visa).
■ DISCOUNT: 15% By prior arrangement.

Hôtel Splendid ★★★★ 50 bd Victor Hugo, 06048 Nice.
☎ 93 16 41 00, Fax 93 87 02 46. English spoken.
Open all year. 127 bedrooms (all en suite). Outdoor swimming pool, golf 20 km, garage. &

Family-run, air-conditioned hotel in a quiet town-centre position. Rooftop bar, terraces and only 300 m from beach.

■ RESTAURANT: Closed lunch. Traditional French cooking with local specialities.
■ ACTIVITIES: ● Hotel guests can obtain special rates at the beach, tennis club and golf club.
■ TARIFF: (1994) Single 650–700, Double 690–900, Bk 75, Set menu 135 (Amex, Euro/Access, Visa, **BT**).

Hôtel Windsor ★★★ 11 rue Dalpozzo, 06000 Nice.
☎ 93 88 59 35, Fax 93 88 94 57. English spoken.
Open all year. 60 bedrooms (all en suite). Outdoor swimming pool, golf 10 km, parking.

In the heart of Nice. From the Promenade des Anglais, close to Westminster Hotel, turn into Meyerbeer Street, take first right, then second left.

■ RESTAURANT: Closed Sun.
■ TARIFF: (1994) Single 350–525, Double 460–670, Bk 40 (Amex, Euro/Access, Visa).

NIMES Gard   5D

Hôtel L'Hacienda ★★★ Mas de Brignon, 30320 Marguerittes.
☎ 66 75 02 25, Fax 66 75 45 58. English spoken.

Open 01/03 to 31/12. 12 bedrooms (all en suite). Outdoor swimming pool, golf 10 km, garage, parking.

Exit Nîmes-Est from A9, 4 km east of Nîmes turn right on to N86. On arrival in Marguerittes follow red arrow signs.

■ RESTAURANT: Closed Sun & Mon lunch LS. Good food, nice atmosphere.
■ ACTIVITIES: Sauna, solarium, and boulodrome at hotel.
■ TARIFF: (1994) Single 350–450, Double 400–550, Bk 70, Set menu 140–320 (Euro/Access, Visa).

Hôtel Majestic ★★ 10 rue Pradier, 30000 Nîmes.
☎ 66 29 24 14, Fax 66 29 77 33. English spoken.

Open all year. 26 bedrooms (24 en suite, 2 bath/shower only). Outdoor swimming pool, tennis, golf 2 km, garage. &
Next to the train and bus stations in the town centre.
■ TARIFF: (1994) Single 190–230, Double 220–250, Bk 35 (Euro/Access, Visa).
■ DISCOUNT: 5%

Hôtel Tuileries ★★★ 22 rue Roussy, 30000 Nîmes.
📞 66 21 31 15, Fax 66 67 48 72. English spoken.
Open all year. 10 bedrooms (all en suite).
Golf 2 km, garage.
Small, new hotel in the centre of the town, situated in a quiet street near the arena and Roman monuments.
■ TARIFF: (1994) Single 260, Double 350–600, Bk 40 (Amex, Euro/Access, Visa).

Hôtel Vatel ★★★★ 140 rue Vatel, BP 7128, 30913 Nîmes.
📞 66 62 57 57, Fax 66 62 57 50.
English spoken.

Open all year. 45 bedrooms (all en suite). Indoor swimming pool, tennis, golf 3 km, parking, restaurant. &
Vatel is also a hotel management school, restaurant and keep-fit centre. From the motorway A9, take Nîmes-Ouest exit and follow Alès signs towards Sommière. At the Kennedy Avenue road crossing, go towards Sommière and take the second right.
■ TARIFF: (1994) Single 350–500, Double 450–600, Bk 45 (Euro/Access, Visa).

NIORT Deux-Sèvres   4B

Hôtel Mercure Porte Oceane 17 rue Bellune, 79000 Niort.
📞 39 24 29 29, Fax 49 28 00 90. English spoken.
Open all year. 60 bedrooms (all en suite).

Indoor swimming pool, outdoor swimming pool, golf 5 km, parking. &
Attractive, comfortable hotel located in the heart of historic Niort in an extraordinary garden setting.
■ RESTAURANT: Closed Sat & Sun lunch LS. Attractively furnished, comfortable dining room. Terrace for meals outside in summer and snack bar beside the pool.
■ ACTIVITIES: Visits to Futuroscope theme park, Poitevin marshes, Puy du Fou castle and the Bougon burial mound; very good area for exploring other nearby towns; lots of sports facilities available within easy reach.
■ TARIFF: Single 415–590, Double 495–620, Bk 50, Set menu 98–148 (Amex, Euro/Access, Visa).
■ DISCOUNT: 10% On request.

Hôtel Moulin 27 rue Espingole, 79000 Niort.
📞 49 09 07 07.
Open all year. 34 bedrooms (all en suite).
Garage, parking.
Modern hotel in town centre beside the river.
■ TARIFF: (1994) Single 240–250, Double 240–280, Bk 30 (Amex, Visa).

Hôtel Les Ruralies ★★ 79230 Prahecq.
📞 49 75 67 66, Fax 49 75 80 29.
English spoken.

Open all year. 51 bedrooms (50 en suite, 1 bath/shower only). Parking. &
Situated in peaceful area of Les Ruralies on Aquitaine A10 motorway next to Niort between exits 22 and 23.
■ RESTAURANT: Regional and country cuisine in restaurant; fast food in 'La Pergola' café.
■ TARIFF: (1994) Single 310–380, Double 310–380, Bk 30, Set menu 95–135 (Euro/Access, Visa).

N

NOE Hte-Garonne 4D

Hôtel l'Arche de Noé ★★ 2 place de la
Bascule, 31410 Noé.
☎ 61 87 40 12, Fax 61 87 06 67. English spoken.

Open all year. 20 bedrooms (15 en suite).
Tennis, parking.

*Charming, traditional hotel set in lovely
gardens and only yards from the River
Garonne. Noé is a quiet, peaceful village on the
road leading to the Pyrénées and the Atlantic.*

■ RESTAURANT: For hotel guests only, offering
traditional and regional cuisine.

■ ACTIVITIES: ● Special arrangements made for
nearby lake and river fishing.

■ TARIFF: (1994) Double 160–260, Bk 32
(Euro/Access, Visa).

NOIRMOUTIER-EN-L'ILE Vendée 1D

Hôtel Fleur de Sel ★★★ 85330 Noirmoutier-
en-l'Ile.
☎ 51 39 21 59, Fax 51 39 75 66. English spoken.

Open 11/02 to 05/11. 35 bedrooms (all en suite).
Outdoor swimming pool, tennis, parking. ᴴ

*In a quiet island location between the port and
beaches. Attractive flowered and exotic
gardens. Approach island on D948.*

■ RESTAURANT: Excellent restaurant overlooking
gardens; seafood specialities.

■ ACTIVITIES: Many local places of interest to visit.

■ TARIFF: (1994) Single 345–460,
Double 395–600, Bk 48, Set menu 135–165
(Euro/Access, Visa).

■ DISCOUNT: 10%

NOYON Oise 2B

Hôtel Le Cèdre ★★ 8 rue de l'Evêché,
60400 Noyon.
☎ 44 44 23 24, Fax 44 09 53 79. English spoken.
Open all year. 34 bedrooms (all en suite).
Golf 25 km, parking, restaurant. ᴴ

*In the heart of Noyon, where you can visit the
old Roman ramparts and houses, the hotel
stands at the foot of the 12th-century cathedral
and opposite a Renaissance palace and
medieval tower. Comfortable accomodation set
around a large cedar tree.*

■ TARIFF: (1994) Single 290, Double 350, Bk 38,
Set menu 69–180 (Amex, Euro/Access, Visa).

OBERNAI Bas-Rhin 3D

Hôtel Les Jardins d'Adalric ★★ rue du
Maréchal Koenig, 67210 Obernai.
☎ 88 49 90 90, Fax 88 49 91 80. English spoken.
Open all year. 45 bedrooms (all en suite).
Outdoor swimming pool, parking. ᴴ

*Large comfortable hotel set in a park by a
stream, in the Alsace region. From Strasbourg
follow N422 south for 23 km to Obernai's town
centre.*

■ ACTIVITIES: Boating and tennis nearby. Lovely
forest walks.

■ TARIFF: (1994) Single 260–330, Double 290–
360, Bk 38 (Amex, Euro/Access, Visa).

OLARGUES Hérault 5C

Domaine de Rieumégé ★★★ Parc Naturel du
Haut Languedoc, rte de St-Pons,
34390 Olargues.
☎ 67 97 73 99, Fax 67 97 78 52. English spoken.
Open 01/04 to 01/11. 14 bedrooms
(all en suite). Outdoor swimming pool, tennis,
golf 18 km, parking.

*From Béziers take the D14 to Olargues and
Rieumégé is 3 km along the road to St-Pons. A
17th-century hotel standing in 35 acres. Lovely
mountain scenery.*

■ RESTAURANT: Has a good reputation and offers
a variety of beautifully prepared, imaginative
dishes. Meals served on the terrace in fine
weather accompanied by a cicada chorus!

N

■ ACTIVITIES: Good area for sightseeing, fishing, hunting, canoeing and rock climbing. Only one hour from the Mediterranean beaches.
■ TARIFF: (1994) Single 318–478, Double 350–518, Bk 55, Set menu 79–220 (Euro/Access, Visa).
■ DISCOUNT: 10%

OLERON

ST-PIERRE-D'OLERON Charente-Mar   4A

Hôtel Otelinn ★★ 17310 St-Pierre-d'Oléron, Oléron.
☎ 46 47 19 92, Fax 46 47 47 19. English spoken. Open all year. 34 bedrooms (all en suite). Tennis, golf 2 km, parking, restaurant. &

Ample gardens and spacious accommodation in this island hotel.
■ TARIFF: (1994) Double 280–400, Bk 40, Set menu 85–225 (Amex, Euro/Access, Visa).

END OF OLERON RESORTS

OMONVILLE-LA-PETITE Manche   1B

Hôtel La Fossardière ★★ Hameau de la Fosse, 50440 Omonville-la-Petite.
☎ 33 52 19 83. English spoken. Open 01/03 to 15/12. 8 bedrooms (all en suite). Parking. &

In a quiet and secluded location, this comfortable hotel is just 500 m from the sea, 3 km from Port Racine, the smallest port in France, 6 km from Goury and Cap de la Hague. Just 23 km north-west of Cherbourg on D901.
■ TARIFF: (1994) Double 230–310, Bk 35 (Euro/Access, Visa).

ORANGE Vaucluse   5D

Hôtel Mas de Bouvau route de Cairanne, 84150 Violes.

☎ 90 70 94 08, Fax 90 70 95 99. English spoken. Open all year. 5 bedrooms (all en suite). Golf 5 km, parking. &

This highly recommended hotel is situated in the Mas Provençal, east of Orange. Take the D975 north-east of Orange. After approximately 13 km turn right onto the D8. The hotel is then 2 km.

■ RESTAURANT: Closed Sun eve & Mon. Very comfortable and with a good reputation for fine cuisine based on only the freshest of ingredients.
■ TARIFF: (1994) Single 270, Double 320–380, Bk 40, Set menu 125–250 (Amex, Euro/Access, Visa).

Hôtel Mas des Aigras chemin des Aigras, Russamp-Est, 84100 Orange.
☎ 90 34 81 01, Fax 90 34 05 66. English spoken.

O

Open all year. 11 bedrooms (all en suite). Outdoor swimming pool, tennis, golf 4 km, parking.

From Orange take the N7 north until you reach Chemin des Aigras crossroads and then turn left. A pretty hotel in a garden setting.
■ TARIFF: (1994) Double 350–410, Bk 50 (Euro/Access, Visa).

ORBEY Ht-Rhin   3D

Hôtel au Bois Le Sire ★★★ 20 rue Charles de Gaulle, 68370 Orbey.
℡ 89 71 25 25, Fax 89 71 30 75. English spoken.
Open 05/02 to 03/01. 36 bedrooms (all en suite). Indoor swimming pool, golf 10 km, parking. &

From Kaysersberg take N415 towards St-Die, then left to Orbey. Family-run hotel at foot of the Vosges.

■ RESTAURANT: Closed Mon LS.
■ ACTIVITIES: BMX.
■ TARIFF: (1994) Single 240–340, Double 260–360, Bk 48, Set menu 78–320 (Amex, Euro/Access, Visa).

Hôtel de la Croix d'Or ★★ 13 rue de l'Eglise, 68370 Orbey.
℡ 89 71 20 51, Fax 89 71 35 60.
English spoken.

Open 24/12 to 16/11. 19 bedrooms (16 en suite, 3 bath/shower only). Golf 10 km, parking.

This traditional family-run hotel stands on the hillside just outside the village. Orbey, situated between the Vosges and Alsace, is 12 km from Kaysersberg, birthplace of Dr Albert Schweitzer, and is a perfect base for both summer and winter holidays.

■ RESTAURANT: Closed Mon & Wed lunch. Rustic-style restaurant serving regional specialities including gibier, truite au crèmant d'Alsace, saumon fumé à l'ancienne, coq au Pinot Noir and vacherin glacé 'Croix d'Or'.
■ ACTIVITIES: Mountain-biking and rambling; ski hire/lift passes available from hotel. ● Free wine tasting nearby for RAC guests taking breakfast and evening meal at the hotel.
■ TARIFF: (1994) Double 240–280, Bk 45, Set menu 90–195 (Amex, Euro/Access, Visa).
■ DISCOUNT: 10% Not May & Jul to Sep.

Hôtel Saut de la Truite ★★ 68370 Orbey.
℡ 89 71 20 04, Fax 89 71 31 52. English spoken.
Open 01/02 to 30/11. 22 bedrooms (18 en suite). Golf 12 km, parking. &

8 km from Colmar on the N415 to Lapoutroie. Turn off to Orbey and the hotel is 1 km from Orbey.

■ RESTAURANT: Closed Wed except July & Aug. Regional specialities served in rustic surroundings.
■ ACTIVITIES: BMX and cross-country skiing nearby.
■ TARIFF: (1994) Single 200–300, Double 200–300, Bk 40, Set menu 69–200 (Euro/Access, Visa).

ORGEVAL Yvelines   2B

Hôtel Moulin d'Orgeval ★★★★ rue de l'Abbaye, 78630 Orgeval.
℡ 1 39 75 85 74, Fax 1 39 75 48 52. English spoken.
Open all year. 14 bedrooms (all en suite). Outdoor swimming pool, golf 3 km, parking.

Luxurious former abbey standing in beautiful grounds. From A13, exit at Poissy-Villennes. Turn right towards Orgeval, and look for signs.

■ RESTAURANT: Has facilities for the disabled and enjoys a very good reputation for fine cuisine.
■ TARIFF: (1994) Single 450–550, Double 600–720, Bk 50, Set menu 180–570 (Amex, Euro/Access, Visa).
■ DISCOUNT: 5%

ORLÉANS

Visit Orléans in May and you will find the town *en fête* – in celebration of France's national heroine, Joan of Arc. Known as the 'Maid of Orléans', Joan was born in 1412 at Domrémy in Lorraine. As a young woman, she began to hear heavenly voices which told her that she should lead the French army against the English. Dressing as a man, she did just that, raising the siege of Orléans on 8 May 1429. A fine statue of Joan on horseback was erected in 1855 on the Place du Martroi at the centre of the town. Scenes from her short life are depicted on the plinth. Captured and then imprisoned by the English, she was burnt at the stake in Rouen in May 1431, only two years after her triumph at Orléans. To find out more, go to the Maison de Jeanne d'Arc, a museum specialising in her life.

O

France. Built between 1020 and 1218, this Romanesque abbey is well worth a visit.

A few kilometres further lies Sully-sur-Loire with its 14th-century château, built close to the Loire and completely surrounded by water. This château, consisting of a square central block with a round tower on each corner, looks particularly splendid when it is floodlit at the time of the Sully music festival, which runs from mid June to mid July.

Further upstream you come to Gien. Here, in the château, there is a museum of hunting and falconry. The town is also well known for its decorated pottery and its hump-backed bridge across the Loire.

Finally, try to visit Briare (about 80 km from Orléans) and its informal Musée de l'Automobile, or even take a canal-boat trip across the Loire over an impressive aqueduct.

May-time pageantry in Orléans, when the life of Joan of Arc is celebrated

East of the Place Martroi stands the Cathédrale Ste-Croix, a building that has had to be much restored following its partial destruction by the Protestants in 1568. Again Joan's story is told, this time in a series of stained glass windows. She also appears outside the Hôtel de Ville, her skirted statue pierced by World War II bullets.

Walking between the Cathédrale and the Hôtel de Ville, you will pass the Musée des Beaux-Arts. Its basement glows with canvases by the French masters of the last 150 years such as Renoir, Monet and Picasso, while upstairs the collection concentrates on paintings from preceding centuries. Medieval antiquities and earlier Roman artefacts can be seen at the Hôtel Cabu, one of the finest Renaissance houses in Orléans, now used as the Musée Historique et Archéologique.

The principal Loire châteaux lie downstream from Orléans, mainly around Blois and Tours, but travel a few miles upstream and there are several places of interest to visit. At St-Benoît-sur-Loire stands one of the most impressive churches in

Onions

Known as the 'lilies of the kitchen', there are several members of the onion family that are commonly used in French cooking.

Perhaps most commonly used of all is garlic. Although raw it has a very strident flavour, when cooked the taste is much more gentle. Both chicken stuffed with garlic and soupe d'ail, garlic soup, are firm favourites.

Leeks are also used in soups. Try potage Parmentier (leek and potato soup) or garbure. This is a thick vegetable soup to which is added a piece of meat. The two are then served separately, the soup having been poured over pieces of bread. Finally, to empty the pot, the remaining contents are swilled out with a glass of wine.

Chives, with their delicate flavour, are used mainly as a garnish for soups or salads, but their presence adds much to the taste of a herb omelette.

Finally to the onion we are most familiar with in this country, the one with the richly coloured papery skin. In France, these appear everywhere cooked in soups, stews and stuffings or raw in salads. Try soupe à l'oignon, which is made with very finely sliced onions or, as a main course, onions that have been stuffed and baked.

O

ORLÉANS Loiret   2D

(See feature)

Hôtel Le Rivage ★★★ 635 rue Reine Blanche,
45160 Olivet.
℡ 38 66 02 93, Fax 38 56 31 11. English spoken.

Open 18/01 to 24/12. 17 bedrooms
(all en suite). Tennis, golf 10 km, parking,
restaurant.
*In peaceful countryside on the banks of the
River Loire, in châteaux country. There is a
shady terrace and boating. Olivet is just south
of Orléans.*
■ TARIFF: (1994) Double 350–570, Bk 45,
Set menu 155–270 (Amex, Euro/Access, Visa).

Orléans Parc Hôtel ★★★ 55 rte d'Orléans,
45380 La Chapelle-St-Mesmin.
℡ 38 43 26 26, Fax 38 72 00 99. English spoken.
Open all year. 32 bedrooms (all en suite).
Garage, parking. ⅃
*19th-century house in 8 acres, on the Loire.
A71, exit Orléans-Centre. N152 to La Chapelle-
St-Mesmin.*
■ TARIFF: (1994) Single 300–320,
Double 390–450, Bk 35 (Amex,
Euro/Access, Visa).

ORTHEZ Pyrénées-Atlan   4C

Hôtel au Temps de la Reine Jeanner ★★ 44
rue Bourg Vieux, 64300 Orthez.
℡ 59 67 00 76, Fax 59 69 09 63.
English spoken.
Open all year. 20 bedrooms (all en suite).
Golf 15 km, parking. ⅃
*Two old houses surrounding a courtyard have
been successfully converted to provide this
charming hotel.*
■ RESTAURANT: Lovely old restaurant well

known for its excellent, creative cuisine and
regional specialities.
■ ACTIVITIES: Water-skiing and rafting nearby.
■ TARIFF: (1994) Single 220–255,
Double 255–280, Bk , Set menu 85–175
(Amex, Euro/Access, Visa).

OUCQUES Loir/Cher   2D

Hôtel du Commerce ★★ 9 rue de Beaugency,
41290 Oucques.
℡ 54 23 20 41, Fax 54 23 02 88. English spoken.
Open 01/02 to 20/12. 12 bedrooms
(all en suite). Golf 5 km, garage, restaurant.
*Hotel and restaurant. The well-equipped rooms
all have a different style. 160 km from Paris on
the A10. Take exit Meungs/Loire or Blois.*
■ TARIFF: (1994) Single 210–260,
Double 240–400, Bk 40, Set menu 95–255
(Euro/Access).

OUISTREHAM Calvados   2A

Delta Hotel ★★ 37 rue Dunes,
14150 Ouistreham.
℡ 31 96 20 20, Fax 31 97 10 10.
English spoken.

Pain

*One of the simple joys of a French holiday is a
visit to a baker's shop, the* boulangerie, *to buy
your daily* pain. *Although we are apt to think
of French loaves as always being long and
thin, the word* boulangerie *comes from the
same source as the word for the popular ball
game,* boules. *At one time, apparently, French
loaves were ball-shaped, round and compact.*

*French bread is delicious when first bought
but becomes stale very quickly, so do as the
French do and buy just before the next meal or
picnic. Knowing the names of the some of the
great variety of loaves available is helpful. The
most popular of all is the* baguette *which is
what is known in this country as a French
loaf. The larger crusty version is called* gros
pain, *the thinner ones* flûtes *or* ficelles, *and
when a baguette is shaped into a circle it is
called a* couronne. *If you prefer brown bread,
try* pain bis, *and for wholemeal ask for* pain
complet *or* pain entier.

*A final note, don't be alarmed by the pricing
system because it is the price per kilo that is
quoted for some loaves rather than the price
per loaf.*

Open 01/02 to 31/12. 50 bedrooms (all en suite). Golf 6 km, parking. &

New hotel with all modern facilities. 500 m from the sandy beaches of the D-Day landings, opposite the car ferry terminal. 10 minutes from Caen, 30 km from Arromanches and Bayeux and 2 hours from Paris.

■ RESTAURANT: Has terrace overlooking the port. Fish specialities.

■ ACTIVITIES: Tennis, surfing, golf, therapy centre, casino and horse-riding within the area.

■ TARIFF: Single 220–250, Double 250–350, Bk 30, Set menu 49–135 (Amex, Euro/Access, Visa).

■ DISCOUNT: 10%

Hôtel Rivabella ★★★ 68 av du Commandant Kieffer, 14150 Ouistreham.
℡ 31 96 40 40, Fax 31 96 45 45. English spoken.
Open all year. 51 bedrooms (all en suite). Indoor swimming pool, golf 10 km, parking, restaurant. &

As well as direct access to the beach, the hotel has sea water thermal baths. 10 km north of Caen, the hotel is next to the car ferry terminal of Ouistreham, 800 metres along the beach.

■ ACTIVITIES: Wide range of sports including sand-yachting.

■ TARIFF: (1994) Single 450–600, Double 600–900, Bk 50, Set menu 120–220 (Amex, Euro/Access, Visa).

■ DISCOUNT: 10% Oct to Mar.

OYONNAX Ain   6A

Hôtel Ibis ★★ 3 rue Bichat, 01100 Oyonnax.
℡ 74 73 90 15, Fax 74 77 23 19. English spoken.
Open all year. 53 bedrooms (all en suite). Garage, parking, restaurant. &

Establishment is located in the centre of the town, near the station. Oyonnax is not very far from the motorway (approx 16 km). Exit at Nantua or St-Martin-du-Fresne. Genève 74 km.

■ ACTIVITIES: Close to lakes, forest, BMX and hiking trails. Visit the Cerdon caves and Combs museum.

■ TARIFF: (1994) Single 250–300, Double 265–320, Bk 34 (Amex, Euro/Access, Visa).

PAIMPOL Côtes-du-Nord   1A

Hôtel Bellevue ★★ Port-Clos,
22870 Ile-de-Brehat.
℡ 96 20 00 05, Fax 96 20 06 06.
Open all year. 17 bedrooms (all en suite). Garage.

Take the boat from Pointe l'Arcouest, 7 km north of Paimpol, to Port Clos on the Ile-de-Bréhat. Explore the island by bike (available at the hotel). Some rooms with sea view in this pretty hotel 'Where the boat comes in'.

■ RESTAURANT: Overlooks the terrace and harbour and specialises in seafood.

■ TARIFF: (1994) Double 360–430, Bk 40 (Euro/Access, Visa).

Hôtel Le Repaire de Kerroc'h ★★★ 29 quai Morand, Port de Plaisance, 22500 Paimpol.
℡ 96 20 50 13, Fax 96 22 07 46. English spoken.

Open 16/02 to 01/05 & 08/06 to 14/11. 13 bedrooms (all en suite). Golf 10 km, parking.

Small hotel in historic house, built by Privateer Kersanx in 1793. Rooms have views of bay and harbour. Take D786 from St-Brieuc.

■ RESTAURANT: Closed Tues & Wed lunch (Oct to Jun). Renowned for its good cuisine, specialities include lobster, roast duckling with honey and spices, braised goose liver with fruits, strawberries with mint and special assorted desserts "du Repaire".

■ TARIFF: (1994) Single 250, Double 390–580, Bk 45 (Euro/Access, Visa).

■ DISCOUNT: 10% Not including suites.

ASTOTEL
★★★

400 Rooms - 5 Hotels
"In the Heart of Paris"

❶
ASTRA OPERA
29, rue Caumartin
75009 PARIS
Tel. : (1) 42 66 15 15
Fax : (1) 42 66 98 05
FULLY AIR CONDITIONED

❷
ASTORIA OPERA
42, rue de Moscou
75008 PARIS
Tel. : (1) 42 93 63 53
Fax : (1) 42 93 30 30

❸
BERGERE OPERA
34, rue Bergère
75009 PARIS
Tel. : (1) 47 70 34 34
Fax : (1) 47 70 36 36

❹
ACADIA OPERA
4, rue Geoffroy Marie
75009 PARIS
Tel. : (1) 40 22 99 99
Fax : (1) 40 22 01 82
FULLY AIR CONDITIONED

❺
BRADFORD ELYSEES
10, Rue St-Phil. du Roule
75008 PARIS
Tel. : (1) 45 63 20 20
Fax : (1) 45 63 20 07

PARIS

PARIS I Paris   3B

Hôtel Britannique ★★★ 20 av Victoria, 75001 Paris.
℡ 1 42 33 74 59, Fax 1 42 33 82 65.
English spoken.
Open all year. 40 bedrooms (all en suite).
Located in a quiet avenue and a perfect base for sightseeing. The hotel was renovated in 1993 and the comfortable, individualised guest rooms have all modern facilities.
■ TARIFF: (1994) Single 600–720, Double 720–830, Bk 49 (Amex, Euro/Access, Visa).
■ DISCOUNT: 10%

Hôtel Le Relais du Louvre ★★★ 19 rue des Prêtres-St-Germain, L'Auxerrois, 75001 Paris.
℡ 1 40 41 96 42, Fax 1 40 41 96 44.
English spoken.

Open all year. 20 bedrooms (all en suite). Parking.
A tastefully decorated, modern hotel situated in the centre of Paris.
■ TARIFF: (1994) Single 580–750, Double 780–1400, Bk 50 (Amex, Euro/Access, Visa).

PARIS II Paris   3B

Hôtel Favart ★★★ 5 rue Marivaux, 75002 Paris.
℡ 1 42 97 59 83, Fax 1 40 15 95 58.
English spoken.
Open all year. 37 bedrooms (all en suite). &
Built in 1824, this is a quiet hotel in the centre of Paris.
■ TARIFF: (1994) Single 495–510, Double 600–620 (Amex, Euro/Access, Visa).

PARIS IV Paris   3B

Hôtel St-Louis ★★★ 75 rue St-Louis-en-l'Ile, 75004 Paris.
℡ 1 46 34 04 80, Fax 1 46 34 02 13. English spoken.

Open all year. 21 bedrooms (all en suite).
Charming, cosy hotel with lots of ambiance. Beautifully renovated to combine nostalgia of the past with modern-day comforts.
■ TARIFF: (1994) Single 670, Double 670–770, Bk 45 (Visa).

Hôtel St-Louis Marais 1 rue Charles-V, 75004 Paris.
℡ 1 48 87 87 04, Fax 1 48 87 33 26. English spoken.

Open all year. 15 bedrooms (all en suite).
Chic and charming, hotel dates from the 18th-century when it belonged to the Celestin Convent. Rooms still have their original dark wood panelled walls and beamed ceilings. Closest métro is Sully-Morland. Lots of restaurants nearby.

■ ACTIVITIES: Great area for sightseeing and visiting museums.
■ TARIFF: (1994) Single 510, Double 510–710, Bk 40 (Euro/Access, Visa).

P

Hôtel du Jeu de Paume ★★★★
54 rue St-Louis-en-l'Ile, 75004 Paris.
℡ 1 43 26 14 18, Fax 1 40 46 02 76.
English spoken.
Open all year. 32 bedrooms (all en suite).
Small, very tastefully decorated hotel on Ile-St-Louis in the middle of the Seine. Created from an old royal 'Jeu de Paume' of the 17th-century. Close to Notre Dame.
■ TARIFF: Single 795–930, Double 795–1250, Bk 75 (Amex, Euro/Access, Visa).

PARIS V Paris   3B
Hôtel Carofftel Gobelins ★★ 18 av des Gobelins, 75005 Paris.
℡ 1 45 35 80 12, Fax 1 45 35 00 57.
English spoken.
Open all year. 23 bedrooms (all en suite).
Small comfortable hotel, close to the historic Latin quarter and Montparnasse. Nearest métro is Les Gobelins. (Hotel is closed 24 & 25 Dec.)
■ TARIFF: (1994) Single 340–395, Double 380–490, Bk 35 (Amex, Euro/Access, Visa).
■ DISCOUNT: 8%

JAPANESE RESTAURANTS

SUSHI CHO
鮨長

YAKITORI
やきとり
BROCHETTES

(SUSHI-CHO ET YAKITORI)

Muette	3, rue Guichard, 75016 Paris	Tél. 42 88 20 10
Champs-Elysées	24, rue Marbeuf, 75008	Tél. 42 25 77 77
Opéra	12, rue de Port Mahon, 75002	Tél. 42 65 74 24

(SUSHI-CHO)

| Passy | 2, rue de Passy, 75016 | Tél. 46 47 66 85 |

(YAKITORI)

Saint-Honoré	34, place du Marché St-Honoré, 75001	Tél. 42 61 03 54
Saint-Germain	8, rue des Ciseaux, 75006	Tél. 46 33 69 49
Montparnasse	64, rue du Montparnasse, 75014	Tél. 43 20 27 76

PARIS VI Paris   3B
Hôtel Ferrandi ★★★ 92 rue du Cherche-Midi, 75006 Paris.
℡ 1 42 22 97 40, Fax 1 45 44 89 97.
English spoken.
Open all year. 42 bedrooms (all en suite).
Parking.
Elegant, 19th-century building in a quiet street near St-Germain-des-Prés and Montparnasse.
■ ACTIVITIES: Sightseeing.
■ TARIFF: (1994) Single 440, Double 580–980, Bk 60 (Amex, Euro/Access, Visa).
■ DISCOUNT: 5% Or 15% in Jul & Aug for stay of over 3 nights.

Hôtel Latitudes St-Germain ★★★
7-11 rue St-Benoît, 75006 Paris.
℡ 1 42 61 53 53, Fax 1 49 27 09 33.
English spoken.
Open all year. 117 bedrooms (all en suite). &
In the heart of St-Germain-des-Prés, next to Café Flore and Les Deux Magots and close to Rue Bonaparte. Parking on nearby Boulevard St-Germain.
■ TARIFF: (1994) Single 650–930, Double 650–930, Bk 65 (Amex, Euro/Access, Visa).

Hôtel Relais St-Germain ★★★ 9 carrefour de l'Odéon, 75006 Paris.
℡ 1 43 29 12 05, Fax 1 46 33 45 30.
English spoken.

Open all year. 21 bedrooms (all en suite).
Parking.
Beautifully decorated 17th-century building located in St-Germain-des-Prés. Restaurants close by.
■ TARIFF: (1994) Single 1250, Double 1450–1880 (Amex, Euro/Access, Visa).
■ DISCOUNT: 10% Aug.

PARIS VII Paris 3B

Hôtel Les Jardins d'Eiffel ★★★ 8 rue Amélie, 75007 Paris.
☏ 1 47 05 46 21, Fax 1 45 55 28 08.
English spoken.

Open all year. 80 bedrooms (all en suite).
Golf 10 km, garage, parking. &
Completely renovated hotel with sauna and garden. In a residential area close to the Eiffel Tower and Invalides.
■ ACTIVITIES: ● Guided tours by mini-bus to Euro Disney and Versailles.
■ TARIFF: (1994) Single 550–690, Double 650–810 (Amex, Euro/Access, Visa).
■ DISCOUNT: 10%

PARIS VIII Paris 3B

Hôtel Astoria-Opéra ★★★ 42 rue de Moscou, 75008 Paris.
☏ 1 42 93 63 53, Fax 1 42 93 30 30.
English spoken.
Open all year. 87 bedrooms (all en suite).
In the heart of Paris, 15 minutes from the

Opéra, the rooms have all modern-day facilities. (On presentation of this guide, first night's car park fee is free.)
■ TARIFF: Single 490–890, Double 490–890, Bk 60 (Amex, Euro/Access, Visa).

Hôtel Bradford-Elysées ★★★ 10 rue St-Philippe-du-Roule, 75008 Paris.
☏ 1 45 63 20 20, Fax 1 45 63 20 07.
English spoken.

Open all year. 48 bedrooms (all en suite).
A few steps from the Champs-Elysées and rue du Faubourg St-Honoré, a splendid building built at the beginning of the century. All rooms fully equipped. (On presentation of this guide first night's parking fee is free.)
■ TARIFF: Single 590–990, Double 590–990, Bk 60 (Amex, Euro/Access, Visa).

Hôtel Napoléon ★★★★ 40 av de Friedland, 75008 Paris.
☏ 1 47 66 02 02, Fax 1 47 66 82 33.
English spoken.
Open all year. 102 bedrooms (all en suite).
Empire-style hotel offering friendly and efficient service. Close to l'Arc de Triomphe and Champs-Elysées.
■ RESTAURANT: Closed Sat & Sun. Very good restaurant.
■ TARIFF: (1994) Single 800–1150, Double 1150–1650, Bk 95 (Amex, Euro/Access, Visa).

L'Ouest-Hôtel ★★ 3 rue de Rocher, 75008 Paris.
☏ 1 43 87 57 49, Fax 1 43 87 90 27.
English spoken.
Open all year. 53 bedrooms (all en suite).
Next to Saint-Lazare station, in the heart of the business centre, between Montmartre and the Champs-Elysées.
■ TARIFF: Single 360–480, Double 430–510, Bk 30 (Amex, Euro/Access, Visa).

P

Hôtel Résidence Monceau ★★★ 85 rue du Rocher, 75008 Paris.
☎ 1 45 22 75 11, Fax 1 45 22 30 88.
English spoken.
Open all year. 51 bedrooms (all en suite). ⌖
Comfortable hotel with spacious accommodation and gardens. Breakfast served outside when weather permits.
■ TARIFF: Double 670, Bk 48 (Amex, Euro/Access, Visa).

Hôtel Sofitel Paris Arc de Triomphe ★★★
14 rue Beaujon, 75008 Paris.
☎ 1 45 63 04 04, Fax 1 42 25 36 81.
English spoken.
Open all year. 135 bedrooms.
Located in a prestigous area, equally ideal for business or leisure. 5 minutes' walk from Charles de Gaulle station.
■ RESTAURANT: 'Le Clovis' restaurant, often mentioned in the press, offers refined cuisine in an elegant setting.
■ ACTIVITIES: Shopping, theatre, museums, cabarets, and various sports facilities in the vicinity.
■ TARIFF: (1994) Single 1410–2210, Double 1410–2210, Bk 50-95, Set menu 210 (Amex, Euro/Access, Visa).
■ DISCOUNT: 10%

PARIS IX Paris   3B

Hôtel Acadia-Opéra 4 rue Geoffroy Marie, 75009 Paris.
☎ 1 40 22 99 99, Fax 1 40 22 01 82.
English spoken.

Open all year. 36 bedrooms (all en suite).
In the heart of Paris, 5 minutes' from the Opéra, new, fully equipped hotel with air-conditioning. (On presentation of this guide first night's parking fee is free.)
■ TARIFF: (1994) Single 490–890, Double 490–890, Bk 60 (Amex, Euro/Access, Visa).

Hôtel Astra-Opéra ★★★ 29 rue Caumartin, 75009 Paris.
☎ 1 42 66 15 15, Fax 1 42 66 98 05.
English spoken.

Open all year. 83 bedrooms (all en suite).
Between the Opéra and Madeleine, in the heart of Paris, hotel has all modern-day facilities including full air-conditioning. (On presentation of this guide first night's parking fee is free.)
■ TARIFF: Single 590–990, Double 590–990, Bk 60 (Amex, Euro/Access, Visa).

Hôtel Bergère-Opéra ★★★ 34 rue Bergère, 75009 Paris.
☎ 1 47 70 34 34, Fax 1 47 70 36 36.
English spoken.

Open all year. 136 bedrooms (all en suite).
In the heart of Paris, just 5 minutes from the Opéra. Rooms are equipped with all modern-day facilities. (On presentation of this guide first night's parking fee is free.)
■ TARIFF: (1994) Single 490–890, Double 490–890, Bk 60 (Amex, Euro/Access, Visa).

P

Les Hôtels du Pré ★★★ 10 rue du P Sémard, 75009 Paris.
☎ 1 42 81 37 11, Fax 1 40 23 98 28. English spoken.

Open all year. 145 bedrooms (all en suite). Parking.

Renovated throughout, central Paris location between the Opéra, Gare du Nord and Sacré Coeur. From Autoroute du Nord exit via Porte de la Chapelle along Gare du Nord to hotel.
■ TARIFF: (1994) Single 395–425, Double 460–545, Bk 50 (Amex, Euro/Access, Visa).

PARIS X Paris   3B

Hôtel Ibis Jemmapes ★★ 12 rue Louis-Blanc, 75010 Paris.
☎ 1 42 01 21 21, Fax 1 42 08 21 40. English spoken.

Open all year. 49 bedrooms (all en suite). Parking. ♿

Conveniently situated only 5 minutes' walk from Gare du Nord station with its direct RER access to Roissy airport. By car, exit Porte de Pantin towards Paris, turn left after the bridge into bd de Lavillette and carry on until Place

du Colonel Fabien. Very good restaurants nearby.
■ TARIFF: (1994) Single 370, Double 395, Bk 37 (Amex, Euro/Access, Visa).
■ DISCOUNT: 10% Weekends only.

Promotour-Sudôtel ★★★ 42 rue des Petites Ecurres, 75010 Paris.
☎ 1 42 46 91 86, Fax 1 40 22 90 85. English spoken.

Open all year. 45 bedrooms (all en suite). Parking. ♿

Rooms recently refurbished with all possible facilities and equipment. Close to Bonne Nouvelle/Poissonnière métro and within a short walk of hundreds of restaurants!
■ ACTIVITIES: Within 5 minutes' walk of theatres and the Folies Bergères. 15 minutes from the Opéra, Sacré Coeur, Louvre and Gare du Nord.
■ TARIFF: Single 480–520, Double 650, Bk 45 (Amex, Euro/Access, Visa).
■ DISCOUNT: 10%

PARIS XII Paris   3B

Hôtel Belle Epoque ★★★ 66 rue de Charenton, 75012 Paris.
☎ 1 43 44 06 66, Fax 1 43 44 10 25. English spoken.
Open all year. 29 bedrooms (all en suite). Parking.

Built around a patio to ensure privacy and quiet, the hotel is decorated in Art Deco style and is close to the new Bastille Opera House and the Lyon railway station.
■ TARIFF: (1994) Single 530, Double 670–950, Bk 50 (Amex, Euro/Access, Visa).
■ DISCOUNT: 10%

Nouvel Hôtel ★★ 9 rue d'Austerlitz, 75012 Paris.
☎ 1 43 42 15 79, Fax 1 43 42 31 11. English spoken.

P

Open all year. 24 bedrooms (all en suite). Parking. ⟨wheelchair symbol⟩

Ideally situated between Gare de Lyon and Gare d'Austerlitz. 10 mins to Omnisport de Bercy and place de Bastille. Three stops to Etoile and two stops to the Opéra on the métro. All rooms are comfortable, fully equipped and have sound-proofing.

■ TARIFF: (1994) Single 300–360, Double 350–380, Bk 25 (Amex, Euro/Access, Visa).
■ DISCOUNT: 10%

Hôtel Le Relais de Lyon ★★★ 64 rue Crozatier, 75012 Paris.
☎ 1 43 44 22 50, Fax 1 43 41 55 12.
English spoken.

Open all year. 34 bedrooms (27 en suite, 7 bath/shower only). Garage, parking.

Located in eastern central Paris, this hotel is conveniently close to both the Bastille and the Gare de Lyon. Built in 1984, modern 5-storey building in a quiet location. Period furnishing; free garaging.

■ TARIFF: (1994) Single 415, Double 530, Bk 40 (Amex, Euro/Access, Visa).
■ DISCOUNT: 10%

PARIS XIII Paris   3B

Hôtel Arts ★★ 8 rue Coypel, 75013 Paris.
☎ 1 47 07 76 32, Fax 1 43 31 18 09.
English spoken.
Open all year. 37 bedrooms (8 en suite, 29 bath/shower only).

Comfortable hotel in a quiet residential street. Close to the Place d'Italie-Gobelins métro station.

■ TARIFF: Single 298–318, Double 336–406 (Amex, Euro/Access, Visa).

Hôtel Istria ★★ 29 rue Campagne Première, 75014 Paris.
☎ 1 43 20 91 82, Fax 1 43 22 48 45.
English spoken.

Open all year. 26 bedrooms (all en suite).

Hôtel Istria is situated in a very quiet street in artists' Montparnasse area, close to Luxembourg gardens. All rooms have a hair-dryer, direct telephone, colour TV and safe box.

■ TARIFF: (1994) Single 470–530, Double 530–580, Bk 40 (Amex, Euro/Access, Visa).
■ DISCOUNT: 10% B&B.

Hôtel Mercure Paris Montparnasse ★★★
20 rue de la Gaîté, 75014 Paris.
☎ 1 43 35 28 28, Fax 1 43 27 98 64.
English spoken.
Open all year. 185 bedrooms (all en suite). Garage. ⟨wheelchair symbol⟩

Modern hotel on the left bank, near Montparnasse TGV station and within walking distance of St-Germain-des-Prés, the Latin Quarter and Luxembourg Park. Access: Périphérique-Sud exit Pte Orléans towards Montparnasse.

■ RESTAURANT: Authentic bistro. Regional specialities plus a wide selection of dishes-of-the-day. Good wines at attractive prices.
■ ACTIVITIES: Hotel has an up-to-date information database on anything worth seeing or doing in Paris - all you have to do is ask!
■ TARIFF: (1994) Double 820, Bk 68, Set menu 125–175 (Amex, Euro/Access, Visa, **BT**⟨symbol⟩).
■ DISCOUNT: 15% Jul & Aug

P

Orléans Palace Hotel ★★★ 185 bd Brune, 75014 Paris.
☎ 1 45 39 68 50, Fax 1 45 43 65 64.

Open all year. 92 bedrooms (all en suite).
Traditional hotel with comfortable modern rooms. Piano bar with adjoining garden.
■ ACTIVITIES: Bowling, swimming pool, tennis, squash, cinema and theatre (10 minutes) jogging at Montsouris Park (5 minutes) and Euro Disney (45 minutes).
■ TARIFF: (1994) Single 496, Double 550, Bk 49 (Amex, Euro/Access, Visa).
■ DISCOUNT: 10% July & August only.

PARIS XV Paris   3B

Hôtel Arès ★★★ 7 rue du Général de Larminat, 75015 Paris.
☎ 1 47 34 74 04, Fax 1 47 34 48 56.
English spoken.

Open all year. 43 bedrooms (all en suite).
Parking.
Although close to the Eiffel Tower and the Champ de Mars, the Hôtel Arès boasts a very quiet city location. The bright, spacious rooms, some with balconies, are well furnished and have good facilities.

■ TARIFF: (1994) Single 510, Double 650, Bk 39 (Amex, Euro/Access, Visa).
■ DISCOUNT: 10%

Abaca Messidor Hôtel ★★★ 330 rue de Vaugirard, 75015 Paris.
☎ 1 48 28 03 74, Fax 1 48 28 75 17.
English spoken.
Open all year. 72 bedrooms (all en suite).
Parking.
Rooms with character and garden views in the centre of Paris, between métro stations Porte de Versailles and Convention.
■ TARIFF: (1994) Single 405–720, Double 545–900, Bk 50 (Amex, Euro/Access, Visa).

Hôtel Bailli de Suffren ★★★ 149 av Suffren, 75015 Paris.
☎ 1 47 34 58 61, Fax 1 45 67 75 82.
English spoken.
Open all year. 25 bedrooms (all en suite).
Parking.
Furnished with antiques and all rooms individually styled. Close to Eiffel Tower, Champs de Mars and Invalides. From métro, travel from the centre out on Boulogne-Pont de St-Cloud Line (10) and exit at Ségur station.
■ TARIFF: (1994) Single 580, Double 620–650, Bk 40 (Amex, Euro/Access, Visa).

Hôtel Delos ★★ 7 rue du Gén Beuret, 75015 Paris.
☎ 1 48 28 29 32, Fax 1 48 28 88 56. English spoken.

P

Open all year. 43 bedrooms (33 en suite). &
Quiet, traditional hotel with all modern conveniences. Parking nearby. From Porte de Versailles take rue de Vaugirard, rue de Cambronne and then turn left twice.
■ ACTIVITIES: Hotel can arrange reservations for theatre etc.
■ TARIFF: (1994) Single 230–360, Double 250–420, Bk 36 (Amex, Euro/Access, Visa).

Hôtel Forest Hill Paris Balard ★★★ 1 bd Victor, 75015 Paris.
☎ 1 40 60 16 16, Fax 1 40 60 03 40.
English spoken.

Open all year. 130 bedrooms (all en suite). Parking. &

Comfortable hotel close to the 'Balard' métro station. 100 m from the Aquaboulevard de Paris and Porte de Versailles Exhibition Centre.

■ RESTAURANT: Good food and a magnificent buffet can be enjoyed in 'Le Beverly' restaurant.
■ ACTIVITIES: Good sports facilities at hotel and nearby; excellent base for sightseeing.
■ TARIFF: (1994) Single 495–890, Double 595–930, Bk 65, Set menu 79–129 (Amex, Euro/Access, Visa).
■ DISCOUNT: 20%

P **Hôtel Lecourbe** ★★ 28 rue Lecourbe, 75015 Paris.
☎ 1 47 34 49 06, Fax 1 47 34 64 65. English spoken.

Open all year. 47 bedrooms (all en suite).

Elegant older hotel with an interesting history and charming, flower-filled private courtyard.

■ TARIFF: (1994) Single 400, Double 450, Bk 44 (Amex, Euro/Access, Visa).
■ DISCOUNT: 10%

Hôtel Fondary ★★ 30 rue Fondary, 75015 Paris.
☎ 1 45 75 14 75, Fax 1 45 75 84 42.
English spoken.
Open all year. 20 bedrooms (all en suite). Parking.

Traditional town centre hotel, 20 minutes from the Champs Elysées. Nearest métro: Emile Zola.

■ ACTIVITIES: Sightseeing.
■ TARIFF: (1994) Double 375–395, Bk 38 (Amex, Euro/Access, Visa).

Hôtel Lilas Blanc Grenelle ★★ 5 rue de l'Avre, 75015 Paris.
☎ 1 45 75 30 07, Fax 1 45 78 66 65.
English spoken.

Open all year. 32 bedrooms (all en suite). Golf 18 km.

Located in the centre of the 15th district. Quiet and comfortable, its 32 personalised rooms, in harmony with the artist's palette, are equipped with the latest comforts. Visitor tax included in price. SEE ADVERTISEMENT

■ ACTIVITIES: Swimming pool and tennis 2 km.
■ TARIFF: (1994) Single 350–380, Double 405–455, Bk 32 (Amex, Euro/Access, Visa).
■ DISCOUNT: 5%

PARIS XVI Paris   3B

Hôtel Baltimore ★★★★ 88 bis av Kléber, 75116 Paris.
☎ 1 44 34 54 54, Fax 1 44 34 54 44. English spoken.
Open all year. 105 bedrooms (all en suite). Garage.

Open all year with elegant décor enhanced by the work of contemporary artists. Located near the place Charles de Gaulle between place de l'Etoile and the Trocadero.

■ RESTAURANT: Closed Sat & Sun. British specialities include potted crab, Dover sole,

steak and kidney pie and apple crumble!
■ ACTIVITIES: Paris sightseeing trips by
arrangement with the Concierge. ● Hotel has
arranged special packages for golf and health
club. Also discounts in the restaurant and
hairdressers at nearby Printemps department
store. Paris sightseeing trips by arrangement
with the Concierge.
■ TARIFF: (1994) Single 1300–2500,
Double 1600–2500, Bk 115 (Amex,
Euro/Access, Visa).
■ DISCOUNT: 8%

Hôtel du Bois ★★ 11 rue du Dôme,
75116 Paris.
☎ 1 45 00 31 96, Fax 1 45 00 90 05.
English spoken.
Open all year. 41 bedrooms (all en suite).
Recently decorated and situated in quiet
pedestrian street 200 m from Arc de Triomphe.
Pay car park 100 m. Access from the
Périphérique at Pte Maillot.
■ TARIFF: (1994) Single 405–435,
Double 505–585, Bk 42 (Amex,
Euro/Access, Visa).

Hôtel Etoile Maillot ★★★ 10 rue Bois de
Boulogne, 75116 Paris.
☎ 1 45 00 42 60, Fax 1 45 00 55 89. English spoken.

Open all year. 28 bedrooms (all en suite).
Small traditional hotel combining charm and
modern facilities. Situated close to the Arc de
Triomphe and the business centre of Paris.
Métro: Line 1 Argentine station, RER Line A
Etoile station, and Line C Porte Maillot station.
■ TARIFF: (1994) Single 560–690,
Double 600–730 (Amex, Euro/Access, Visa).

Hôtel Pergolèse ★★★★ 3 rue Pergolèse,
75116 Paris.
☎ 1 40 67 96 77, Fax 1 45 00 12 11.
English spoken.

Open all year. 40 bedrooms (all en suite).
Near Champs Elysées, between Arc de
Triomphe and Palais de Congrès. Direct line to
Louvre museum and business area La Défense.
Decorated by the famous designer Rena
Dumas.
■ TARIFF: (1994) Single 850–1200,
Double 950–1500, Bk 75 (Amex,
Euro/Access, Visa).

Hôtel Hameau de Passy ★★ 48 rue de Passy,
75016 Paris.
☎ 1 42 88 47 55, Fax 1 42 30 83 72.
English spoken.
Open all year. 32 bedrooms (all en suite). ❧

P

Recently renovated hotel with small garden and private garage nearby. In a residential area between Muette and Passy métro stations and close to the Eiffel Tower.
■ TARIFF: (1994) Single 450–495, Double 500–560 (Amex, Euro/Access, Visa).

Queen's Hôtel ★★ 4 rue Bastien Lepage, 75016 Paris.
☎ 1 42 88 89 85, Fax 1 40 50 67 52.
English spoken.
Open all year. 22 bedrooms (all en suite).
In a very quiet street in the 16th district, though close to the Périphérique. Direct métro line to the Champs Elysées and St-Germain-des-Prés.
■ ACTIVITIES: Good reservations service for tours, theatre etc.
■ TARIFF: (1994) Single 320–450, Double 450–540, Bk 40 (Amex, Euro/Access, Visa).
■ DISCOUNT: 5% Sep to Jun, 10% in Jul & Aug.

Hôtel Rond Point de Longchamp ★★★ 86 rue de Longchamp, 75116 Paris.
☎ 1 45 05 13 63, Fax 1 47 55 12 80.
English spoken.

Open all year. 57 bedrooms (all en suite).
Fully renovated hotel offering all modern facilities including a bar. Ideally centrally situated in the triangle of the Champs-Elysées,

Trocadero and l'Arc de Triomphe. Leave the Périphérique at Porte Dauphine for rue de Longchamp.
■ RESTAURANT: Closed 01 to 25 Aug. The Angelina Tea Room is open for lunch and afternoon tea. Specialities are Mont-Blanc cakes and special recipe hot chocolate.
■ ACTIVITIES: Hotel will make reservations for guided tours, theatre, restaurants etc.
■ TARIFF: (1994) Single 510–790, Double 730–1000, Bk 65 (Amex, Euro/Access, Visa).
■ DISCOUNT: 10%

PARIS XVII Paris   3B

Hôtel Abrial ★★★ 176 rue Cardinet, 75017 Paris.
☎ 1 42 63 50 00, Fax 1 42 63 50 03.
English spoken.
Open all year. 80 bedrooms (all en suite).
Garage. &

A new hotel with a garden terrace, between the Champs-Elysées and Montmartre.
■ ACTIVITIES: Department stores close by.
■ TARIFF: (1994) Single 490–590, Double 550–650, Bk 45 (Amex, Euro/Access, Visa).
■ DISCOUNT: 10%

Hôtel Acacias Etoile ★★★ 11 rue Acacias, 75017 Paris.
☎ 1 43 80 60 22, Fax 1 48 88 96 40.
English spoken.

Open all year. 37 bedrooms (all en suite).
Garage.
Charming hotel located in a quiet position near the Arc de Triomphe. Private garden.
■ TARIFF: (1994) Single 400–500, Double 590–630, Bk 37 (Amex, Euro/Access, Visa).

P

Hôtel Astor ★★★ 36 rue Pierre-Demours, 75017 Paris.
☎ 1 42 27 44 93, Fax 1 40 53 91 34.
English spoken.

Open all year. 45 bedrooms (all en suite).
Indoor swimming pool, golf 5 km.
Situated between the Porte Maillot and the Champs-Elysées, the hotel offers all the privileges of staying in a peaceful street in a prestigious quarter of Paris. Very comfortable with good facilities.
■ ACTIVITIES: Health/fitness centre. Hotel will arrange sightseeing tours by boat or coach/bus as well as making reservations for theatre, shows etc or a visit to Euro Disney.
■ TARIFF: Single 495–740, Double 525–790, Bk 35 (No credit cards).
■ DISCOUNT: 15%

Hôtel Champerret Heliopolis ★★ 13 rue d'Héliopolis, 75017 Paris.
☎ 1 47 64 92 56, Fax 1 47 64 50 44.
English spoken.
Open all year. 22 bedrooms (all en suite). &
■ ACTIVITIES: Easy access to Montmartre, flea market, Champs-Elysées and the Eiffel Tower and the "Flea Boats" harbour.
■ TARIFF: Single 350–380, Double 420–490, Bk 35 (Amex, Euro/Access, Visa).
■ DISCOUNT: 8%

Hôtel Magellan ★★★ 17 rue J B Dumas, 75017 Paris.
☎ 1 45 72 44 51, Fax 1 40 68 90 36. English spoken.
Open all year. 75 bedrooms (all en suite).
Parking. &
A comfortable hotel with an enclosed garden and private parking facilities. Near the Arc de Triomphe and the Opéra. Excellent restaurants close by.
■ ACTIVITIES: ● Hotel organises tours and excursions by private mini-bus, departing from

the hotel with English-speaking guide.
■ TARIFF: (1994) Single 400–560, Double 620, Bk 35 (Amex, Euro/Access, Visa, BT🍴).
■ DISCOUNT: 10%

Hôtel de Neuville ★★★ 3 place Verniquet, 75017 Paris.
☎ 1 43 80 26 30. English spoken.

Open all year. 28 bedrooms (all en suite).
Tennis, garage.
Elegant hotel with all modern conveniences.
■ RESTAURANT: Closed Aug and weekends. Snacks, cold dishes, wine by the glass.
■ TARIFF: (1994) Single 610–720, Double 610–720, Bk 60 (Amex, Euro/Access, Visa).
■ DISCOUNT: 15%

Hôtel Ouest ★★ 165 rue de Rome, 75017 Paris.
☎ 1 42 27 50 29, Fax 1 42 27 27 40.
English spoken.
Open all year. 48 bedrooms (all en suite).
Parking.
Close to Porte Maillot conference centre, l'Opéra and the Parc Monceau. Métro: Rome, Villiers, Brochant. Easy access from RER. From the Périphérique via Porte Clichy.
■ ACTIVITIES: Sightseeing tours by boat.
■ TARIFF: (1994) Single 320–415, Double 376–426, Bk 30 (Euro/Access, Visa).
■ DISCOUNT: 10%

PARIS XVIII Paris   3B

Hôtel Mercure Paris Monmartre ★★★ 1 rue Caulaincourt, 75018 Paris.
☎ 1 42 94 17 17, Fax 1 42 93 66 14.
English spoken.
Open all year. 308 bedrooms (all en suite).
Parking. &
Modern décor and efficient service from one of the largest hotels in the Mercure Group. Close to the artistic Monmartre area of Paris, down

the hill from the Sacré-Coeur. Métro station Clichy.

■ TARIFF: (1994) Double 680–900, Bk 68 (Amex, Euro/Access, Visa).

Hôtel Utrillo ★★ 7 rue A Bruant, 75018 Paris.
☎ 1 42 58 13 44, Fax 1 42 23 93 88.
English spoken.

Open all year. 30 bedrooms (all en suite).
Situated in the centre of Montmartre near the métro stations, Abbesses and Blanche.

■ TARIFF: (1994) Single 310–360, Double 370–440, Bk 40 (Amex, Euro/Access, Visa).

■ DISCOUNT: 8% Jul & Aug.

PARIS XIX Paris   3B

Hôtel Forest Hill La Villette ★★★ 28 avenue Corentin Cariou, 75019 Paris.
☎ 1 44 72 15 30, Fax 1 44 72 15 80.
English spoken.

Open all year. 259 bedrooms (all en suite).
Parking. &

In the northern part of the city, close to the La Cité des Sciences and the stunning 'Gèode'. Next to the 'Porte de la Villette' métro station.

■ RESTAURANT: Two restaurants: a brasserie, and

a 'gastronomic' where the very special Forest Hill buffet can be found.

■ ACTIVITIES: Ideal location for sightseeing and boat trips; squash courts nearby.

■ TARIFF: (1994) Single 495–890, Double 595–930, Bk 65, Set menu 79–129 (Amex, Euro/Access, Visa).

■ DISCOUNT: 20%

PARIS XX Paris   3B

Hôtel Climat de France ★★ 2 av Prof A Lemierre, 75020 Paris.
☎ 1 43 63 16 16, Fax 1 43 63 31 32. English spoken.

Open all year. 325 bedrooms (all en suite).
Golf 2 km, garage, parking, restaurant. &

A modern hotel next to the Périphérique at Porte de Montreuill exit. Close to the A3 and A4 exits, with easy access to airports and Euro Disney. Métro station at 100 m with direct link to centre.

■ TARIFF: (1994) Double 440, Bk 35, Set menu 90–125 (Amex, Euro/Access, Visa).

■ DISCOUNT: 10%

PARIS WEST

BOULOGNE-BILLANCOURT H/Seine   3B

Hôtel Acanthe ★★★ 9 rondpoint Rhin et Danube, 92100 Boulogne-Billancourt.
☎ 1 46 99 10 40, Fax 1 46 99 00 05. English spoken.

Open all year. 34 bedrooms (all en suite). &

South-west of Paris. Hotel is 20 m from métro Boulogne, Pont de St-Cloud.

■ TARIFF: (1994) Single 580–670, Double 580–760, Bk 55 (Amex, Euro/Access, Visa).

COURBEVOIE Hts-de-Seine 3B

Hôtel Blois ★★ 85 bd St-Denis, 92400 Courbevoie.
✆ 1 47 88 28 58, Fax 1 47 88 24 80.
English spoken.
Open all year. 33 bedrooms (all en suite).
Parking.

Completely modernised hotel with fully equipped rooms. Close to the Etoile and La Défense. Cross the Seine at the Courbevoie Bridge and the hotel is visible on the opposite side.

■ TARIFF: (1994) Double 390–450, Bk 40 (Amex, Euro/Access, Visa).
■ DISCOUNT: 30% Weekends.

MEUDON Hts-de-Seine 3B

Hôtel Forest Hill ★★★ 40 av Mar de Lattre, Meudon La Forêt, Cedex, 92365 Meudon.
✆ 1 46 30 22 55, Fax 1 46 32 16 54. English spoken.

Open all year. 157 bedrooms (all en suite). Outdoor swimming pool, tennis, parking. &

Meudon is south-west of Paris, close to the Velizy Shopping Centre and with easy access to the heart of Paris via the Pont de Sèvres or the Porte de St-Cloud.

■ RESTAURANT: Excellent hot and cold buffet served in 'Les Mousquetaires'.
■ TARIFF: (1994) Single 350–520, Double 390–590, Bk 55, Set menu 79–129 (Amex, Euro/Access, Visa).
■ DISCOUNT: 20%

P

PUTEAUX Hts-de-Seine   3B

Hôtel Syjac ★★★ 20 quai de Dion Bouton, La Défense, 92800 Puteaux.
☎ 1 42 04 03 04, Fax 1 45 06 78 69.
English spoken.
Open all year. 36 bedrooms (all en suite).
Golf 5 km, parking.

Comfort and old-world elegance in new-world setting, just below La Défense. RER to La Défense or métro to Pont-de-Neuilly.

■ TARIFF: (1994) Single 550–650,
Double 650–730, Bk 55 (Amex,
Euro/Access, Visa).

RUEIL-MALMAISON Hts-de-Seine   3B

Atria Novotel Rueil ★★★ av Edouard Belin, 92501 Rueil-Malmaison.
☎ 1 47 51 41 33, Fax 1 47 51 09 29. English spoken.
Open all year. 118 bedrooms (all en suite).
Golf 1 km, parking, restaurant. &

From the ring road (towards La Défense), exit Rueil-Malmaison. 8 km from the centre of Paris, and 6 km from Versailles.

■ TARIFF: (1994) Single 530–550,
Double 560–620, Bk 50 (Amex,
Euro/Access, Visa).

ST-CLOUD Hts-de-Seine   3B

Hôtel Quorum ★★★ 2 bd République, 92210 St-Cloud.
☎ 1 47 71 22 33, Fax 1 46 02 75 64.
English spoken.
Open all year. 58 bedrooms (all en suite).
Golf 1 km, garage, parking, restaurant. &

Modern hotel with traditional charms close to the gardens of St-Cloud. To the south-west of Paris.

■ TARIFF: (1994) Single 460–520,
Double 520–580, Bk 40 (Amex,
Euro/Access, Visa).

PARIS NORTH-EAST

AULNAY-SOUS-BOIS Seine-St-Denis   3B

Hôtel de Strasbourg ★★ 43 bd de Strasbourg, 93600 Aulnay-sous-Bois.
☎ 1 48 66 60 38, Fax 1 48 66 15 71. English spoken.
Open all year. 24 bedrooms (all en suite).
Parking.

Comfortable hotel with TV lounge and bar, 10 minutes from Roissy/Charles de Gaulle airport and Villepinte exhibition centre. 300 m from high speed métro line.

P

■ TARIFF: (1994) Single 225–280, Double 225–305, Bk 33 (Amex, Euro/Access, Visa).

BAGNOLET Seine-St-Denis 3B

Novotel Paris Bagnolet ★★★ 1 av de la République, 93177 Bagnolet.
✆ 1 49 93 63 00, Fax 1 43 60 83 95.
English spoken.
Open all year. 611 bedrooms (all en suite).
Outdoor swimming pool, parking, restaurant.
Modern hotel on eastern edge of Paris, near the Hallieni métro station. Five minutes from the Cité des Sciences at La Vellette Park and ten minutes from the centre of Paris.
■ TARIFF: (1994) Single 615–630, Double 660–670, Bk 55 (Amex, Euro/Access, Visa).

LE BLANC-MESNIL Seine-St-Denis 3B

Novotel ★★★ ZI Pont Y Blon, 93153 Le Blanc-Mesnil.
✆ 1 48 67 48 88, Fax 1 45 91 08 27. English spoken.
Open all year. 143 bedrooms (all en suite).
Outdoor swimming pool, golf 5 km, párking, restaurant. ♿
Located 8 km from Porte de la Chapelle (Paris). From A3 exit Le Blanc-Mesnil or form A1 exit 5 Le Bourget. 30 km from Euro Disney.
■ TARIFF: (1994) Single 470, Double 490, Bk 50 (Amex, Euro/Access, Visa).

LE BOURGET Seine-St-Denis 3B

Hôtel Bleu Marine ★★★ Aéroport du Bourget, Zone Aviation d'Affaires, 93350 Le Bourget.
✆ 1 49 34 10 38, Fax 1 49 34 10 35. English spoken.

Open all year. 86 bedrooms (all en suite).
Golf 5 km, parking. ♿
Sound-proofed and air-conditioned, smoking and non-smoking rooms with every facility to make your stay a pleasant one. From Paris/Lille A1 take Bourget/Blanc Mesnil exit, then signs for airport and 'Zone d'Aviation d'Affaires'. Offers complimentary "carte de fidelité" entitling holder to a free night's accommodation at another Bleu Marine hotel of one's choice.
■ RESTAURANT: Traditional food plus a very good buffet which includes seafood.
■ ACTIVITIES: Fitness room with sauna at hotel. Euro Disney and Asterix theme parks within half an hour.
■ TARIFF: (1994) Double 510, Bk 48 (Amex, Euro/Access, Visa).

NOISY-LE-GRAND Seine-St-Denis 3B

Novotel Marne-La-Vallée ★★★ Porte de Paris, 2 allée Bienvenue, 93885 Noisy-le-Grand.
✆ 1 48 15 60 60, Fax 1 43 04 78 83.
English spoken.
Open all year. 142 bedrooms (all en suite).
Outdoor swimming pool, golf 15 km, parking, restaurant. ♿
From Paris, Reims, Euro Disney: A4 exit Noisy-le-Grand then Noisy-Horizon.
■ TARIFF: (1994) Single 470–500, Double 550–590, Bk 51 (Amex, Euro/Access, Visa).

PARIS SOUTH-EAST

CHARENTON Val-de-Marne 3B

Hôtel Atria Paris Charenton ★★★ 5 place des Marseillais, 94227 Charenton.
✆ 1 46 76 60 60, Fax 1 49 77 68 00.
English spoken.

P

Open all year. 133 bedrooms (all en suite). Parking. &

Situated close to the Bois de Vincennes. From the Paris ring road (Périphérique) go to Charenton-Centre. Métro station Liberté 20 m away.

■ RESTAURANT: Good à la carte choice as well as the set menus.
■ ACTIVITIES: Fitness centre opposite the hotel.
■ TARIFF: (1994) Single 550–590, Double 640–690, Bk 51, Set menu 90–115 (Amex, Euro/Access, Visa).

ST-MAURICE Val-de-Marne 3B

Hôtel Mercure ★★★ 12 rue Maréchal Leclerc, 94410 St-Maurice.
☎ 1 43 75 94 94, Fax 1 48 93 21 14.
English spoken.
Open all year. 99 bedrooms (all en suite).
Garage, parking, restaurant.
Modern, fully-equipped rooms, all with air-conditioning in a recently renovated castle by the Marne river. Family rooms also available. 3 km from Paris. From the ring road, take the Porte de Bercy exit (A4 Metz/Nancy) St-Maurice exit 3. 30 minutes from Euro Disney on the A4, Val d'Europe exit.

■ TARIFF: (1994) Single 470, Double 490, Set menu 75–95 (Amex, Euro/Access, Visa).

END OF PARIS HOTELS

Found in the town centre, near the old quarters, this traditional hotel offers a warm and friendly welcome with comfortable accommodation.

■ RESTAURANT: Closed Sun. Decorated in regional, rustic-style; specialities include magret de canard aux poires, filet mignon de veau aux morilles and seafood dishes. Meals are served on the patio in fine weather.
■ TARIFF: (1994) Single 265–285, Double 285–305, Bk 34, Set menu 75–145 (Amex, Euro/Access, Visa).
■ DISCOUNT: 20% Not Jul, Aug or weekends.

Hôtel Béarn ★★ 14 rue Las Bordes, 64420 Soumoulou.
☎ 59 04 60 09, Fax 59 04 63 33. English spoken.
Open 05/02 to 05/01. 14 bedrooms (all en suite). Golf 15 km, garage, parking.
Country hotel located near the Pyrénées. N117 east of Pau (direction: Lourdes, Tarbes).

■ RESTAURANT: Closed Sun eve & Mon LS. Specialises in regional cuisine.
■ TARIFF: (1994) Single 200–280, Double 220–310, Bk 35, Set menu 70–195 (Amex, Euro/Access, Visa).

PAUILLAC Gironde 4A

Hôtel de France et d'Angleterre ★★ 3 quai A Pichon, 33250 Pauillac.
☎ 56 59 01 20, Fax 56 59 02 31.
English spoken.
Open 10/01 to 20/12. 29 bedrooms (all en suite). Parking. &

In the heart of the Médoc region, Pauillac is 45 km from Bordeaux. The hotel has terraces and a garden, and the Château Mouton Rothschild is just a few minutes' drive away.

P

PAU Pyrénées-Atlan 4D

Hôtel Les Bains de Secours ★★
64260 Sevignacq-Meyracq.
☎ 59 05 62 11, Fax 59 05 76 56. English spoken.
Open all year. 7 bedrooms (all en suite).
Parking.
Most attractive renovated farm in the Béarn hills. From Pau, take N134 south, then D934. The hotel is just south of Rébénacq.

■ RESTAURANT: Closed Sun eve & Mon. Restaurant enjoys a good reputation for its fine regional specialities.
■ ACTIVITIES: ● Reduction at nearby health spa.
■ TARIFF: (1994) Double 270–350, Bk 38, Set menu 80–250 (Amex, Euro/Access, Visa).
■ DISCOUNT: 5%

Hôtel Le Commerce ★★ 9 bis rue Maréchal Joffre, 64000 Pau.
☎ 59 27 24 40, Fax 59 83 81 74. English spoken.
Open all year. 51 bedrooms (all en suite).
Golf 5 km, parking.

Pauillac is on the D2, on the edge of the Gironde.

■ RESTAURANT: Closed Sun eve & Mon LS. Enjoy agneau de Pauillac, regional specialities and good wines in a refined atmosphere.

■ ACTIVITIES: Hotel will organise wine tasting (groups of 10 or more), river trips, mountain bike and pony-trekking, 2-day, 4 wheel-drive vineyards excursion, flying lessons, gourmet stay in château.

■ TARIFF: (1994) Double 300–350, Bk 33, Set menu 90–290 (Amex, Euro/Access, Visa).

■ DISCOUNT: 10%

PAYRAC Lot   4B

Hôtel de la Paix ★★ N20, 46350 Payrac.
☎ 65 37 95 15, Fax 65 37 90 37.
English spoken.
Open 20/02 to 31/12. 50 bedrooms
(all en suite). Outdoor swimming pool,
parking, restaurant. &
*An old building full of character, a former
staging post totally renovated and comfortably
furnished. Almost all rooms located peacefully
at the rear of the building, which is in the
centre of the village.*

■ TARIFF: (1994) Single 215–275,
Double 235–320, Bk 287 (Amex,
Euro/Access, Visa).

Hôtel Petit Relais ★★ Calés, 46350 Payrac.
☎ 65 37 96 09, Fax 65 37 95 93. English spoken.
Open all year. 9 bedrooms (7 en suite).
Outdoor swimming pool, garage, parking. &
*In the attractive village of Payrac, between
Souillac and Rocamour.*

■ RESTAURANT: Closed Sat lunch. Modern
setting. Speciality: ragoût de gesiers au vin de
Cahors.

■ ACTIVITIES: Mountain-biking, horse-riding.
■ TARIFF: (1994) Single 190, Double 190–320,
Bk 32, Set menu 70–255 (Amex,
Euro/Access, Visa).
■ DISCOUNT: 5% LS.

PÉRIGUEUX

This busy market town is the capital of the Dordogne and, as such, makes a good centre from which to explore this attractive and interesting region. The Romans were here and Vesunna, as they called their town, was for 400 years one of the most prosperous in south-west France. To see some of the mosaic floors, statues and jewellery that survives from their occupation, go to the Musée de Périgord. Most of the Roman buildings no longer exist but a 24-m-tall tower, the Tour de Vésone, still stands close to the railway line.

Also in the Musé de Périgord are many prehistoric artefacts discovered in the numerous caves in the Dordogne region which were home to early man. A trip to the prehistoric museum at Les-Eyzies-de-Tayac and to some of the actual caves makes an extremely interesting expedition.

The most famous cave of all is the Grotte de Lascaux with its impressive prehistoric animal paintings. Unfortunately, having been open to the public since 1948, it began to deteriorate owing to the rise in temperature caused by the number of visitors. To relieve this situation a replica, now known as Lascaux II, was painstakingly constructed and opened in 1983. The entrance ticket to Lascaux II also allows you to visit the prehistoric theme park at Le Thot. Here, as well as reconstructions of prehistoric scenes, there are life-like examples of the animals that featured in the cave paintings.

At the other end of the rue St-Front from the museum, the domes and cupolas of the huge Cathédrale St-Front rise above the surrounding medieval houses. Originally built in the 12th century, it was completely renovated in the 19th century in a not

P

altogether sympathetic manner. It is, however, worth a visit as its Greek cross design is unusual in this part of Europe. Prior to 1699, St-Étienne-de-la-Cité was the cathedral church of Périgueux and its remains stand close to the Jardin des Arènes. These gardens are built on the site of a vast Roman arena which was dismantled in the 3rd century.

Périgueux has a busy market on Wednesdays and Saturdays which is held in the Place de la Chautre, outside the cathedral in the medieval part of town. Many of the houses here have been carefully restored and give a good impression of how Périgueux must have looked several hundred years ago.

To make a change from sightseeing and to imagine how the countryside appeared before the days of motor traffic, why not hire a canoe and drift quietly down the Rivers Dordogne or Vézère? This is not a particularly energetic occupation as, at the end of the day, you will be picked up and driven back upstream, instead of having to return your canoe to the starting place. If you would rather explore on foot, the booklet *Randonnées Pédestres en Périgord* would be very useful when planning your route.

P PERIGUEUX Dordogne 4B

(See feature)

Hôtel Chandelles ★★★ Antonne-et-Trigonant, 24420 Périgueux.
✆ 53 06 05 10, Fax 53 06 07 33. English spoken.
Open 01/02 to 01/01. 7 bedrooms (all en suite). Outdoor swimming pool, tennis, golf 9 km, parking.
9 km from Périgueux on the way to Limoges, this is an old farm building now turned into a small hotel.
■ RESTAURANT: Closed Mon except Jul & Aug. Classic and regional dishes based on market-fresh produce.
■ ACTIVITIES: Visits to castles and prehistoric caves.
■ TARIFF: (1994) Single 200–350, Double 280–350, Bk 40, Set menu 145–395 (Amex, Euro/Access, Visa).
■ DISCOUNT: 15%

Château du Roc Chautru Le Roc, 24640 Le Change.
✆ 53 06 17 31, Fax 53 06 17 03. English spoken.
Open all year. 11 bedrooms (all en suite). Outdoor swimming pool, tennis, golf 20 km, parking, restaurant. ఉ
Restored 19th-century château set in large grounds. From Périgueux, go east to La Change via Boulazac on the D5. Crossing the river, turn right 1 km out of La Change, where the hotel is signposted.
■ TARIFF: (1994) Double 400–700, Bk 50, Set menu 180–350 (Amex, Euro/Access, Visa).

Château de Rognac ★★ 24330 Bassillac.
✆ 53 54 40 78, Fax 53 54 53 95. English spoken.
Open 08/04 to 30/09. 12 bedrooms (all en suite). Golf 12 km, parking.
Listed château with 16th-century mill, on an 'island', 9 km north-east of Périgueux on the N21 near Périgueux/Basillac airfield.
■ RESTAURANT: Serves traditional Périgord cuisine.
■ ACTIVITIES: Near to airfield which offers some sport aeronautique! Horse-riding, tennis.
■ TARIFF: (1994) Single 252–384, Double 252–498, Bk 37, Set menu 130–285 (Euro/Access, Visa).

PERONNE Somme 2B

Hostellerie des Remparts ★★ 21 rue Beaubois, 80200 Peronne.
✆ 22 84 01 22, Fax 22 84 31 96. English spoken.
Open all year. 16 bedrooms (all en suite). Garage, parking.
East of the A1 or N17, exit at Maurepas.
■ RESTAURANT: Gastronomic cuisine. Specialities: ficelle and flamiche picarde, sandre au beurre d'anguille, blanc de raie en vinaigrette de betteraves rouges.
■ ACTIVITIES: First World War museum; cemetery, battlefield and upper Somme valley visits.
■ TARIFF: (1994) Double 190–450, Bk 35, Set menu 79–249 (Amex, Euro/Access, Visa).

PERPIGNAN Pyrénées-Or 5C

Hôtel de la Loge ★★★ pl Loge, 66000 Perpignan.
✆ 68 34 41 02, Fax 68 34 25 13. English spoken.
Open all year. 22 bedrooms (all en suite). Golf 20 km, parking.
An old Catalan-style hotel in the pedestrian district of Perpignan town centre. It is

3 minutes' walk from the République car park, which the hotel will pay for.
■ TARIFF: (1994) Single 230–320, Double 320–380, Bk 35 (Amex, Euro/Access, Visa).

PERROS-GUIREC Côtes-du-Nord   1A

Golf-Hôtel ★★ route de Kerenoc, 22560 Pleumeur-Bodou.
☎ 96 23 87 34, Fax 96 23 84 59. English spoken.
Open all year. 54 bedrooms (all en suite).
Outdoor swimming pool, tennis, golf on site, parking, restaurant. &
The hotel is ideally located on an 18-hole golf course. When leaving Perros-Guirec take the Trégastel road.
■ ACTIVITIES: Golf on the spot.
■ TARIFF: (1994) Single 315–350, Double 385–425, Bk 40, Set menu 60–180 (Amex, Euro/Access, Visa).

LA PETITE-PIERRE Bas-Rhin   3B

Hôtel La Clairière ★★★ 63 rte d'Ingwiller, 67290 La Petite-Pierre.
☎ 88 70 47 76, Fax 88 70 41 05. English spoken.

Open all year. 50 bedrooms (all en suite). Indoor swimming pool, parking. &
Hotel situated in the middle of a forest, restful and relaxing opposite a park with animals. Take E25/A4 take Sarre-Union exit on to N61. Turn left at Drulingen for La Petite-Pierre.
■ RESTAURANT: Varied menu - country cuisine.
■ ACTIVITIES: Walking, châteaux, museums.
■ TARIFF: Single 400–550, Double 400–650, Bk 48 (Amex, Euro/Access, Visa).

Hôtel au Lion d'Or ★★ 15 rue Principale, 67290 La Petite-Pierre.
☎ 88 70 45 06, Fax 88 70 45 56.
English spoken.
Open 01/02 to 25/06 & 10/07 to 04/01.

40 bedrooms (all en suite). Indoor swimming pool, tennis, parking. &
Highly recommended family hotel. In an ancient hilltop village of Northern Alsace, with rooms overlooking the valley. A4, 60 km north-west of Strasbourg.
■ RESTAURANT: Excellent cuisine and good service.
■ ACTIVITIES: Hotel has very good swimming pool/whirlpool complex.
■ TARIFF: (1994) Single 240–280, Double 350–410, Bk 48, Set menu 98–260 (Amex, Euro/Access, Visa).

Hôtel aux Trois Roses ★★ 19 rue Principale, 67290 La Petite-Pierre.
☎ 88 89 89 00, Fax 88 70 41 28. English spoken.

Open all year. 43 bedrooms (all en suite). Indoor swimming pool, tennis, parking. &
Situated in the village and facing an old castle. Exit Sarre-Union from A4, south on N61 for 10 km and then left to La Petite-Pierre.
■ RESTAURANT: Closed Sun eve & Mon.
■ TARIFF: (1994) Single 270–460, Double 330–550, Bk 65, Set menu 100–240 (Euro/Access, Visa).

Hôtel Vieux Moulin ★★ 67320 Graufthal.
☎ 88 70 17 28, Fax 88 70 11 25. English spoken.

P

Open 16/02 to 03/01. 14 bedrooms (7 en suite, 7 bath/shower only). Garage, parking. &
A lovely house in the forest with fine cooking. From the A4, exit Phaisbourg 8 km.

■ RESTAURANT: Closed Mon eve & Tue. Traditional and regional cuisine.
■ TARIFF: (1994) Double 195–347, Bk 26, Set menu 50–200 (Euro/Access, Visa).

Hôtel Vosges 67290 La Petite-Pierre.
☏ 88 70 45 05, Fax 88 70 41 13. English spoken.
Open 01/01 to 19/11 & 16/12 to 31/12.
30 bedrooms (all en suite). Golf 30 km, parking. &

Traditional hotel with sauna and solarium situated in the forested region of Alsace. 60 km from Strasbourg on A4. Turn off at Saverne take, D178 to village.

■ RESTAURANT: Established in 1924, has renowned kitchen. Specialities: foie gras frais maison, truites au bleu, coq au Riesling and gibiers.
■ ACTIVITIES: Good health/fitness facilities at hotel.
■ TARIFF: (1994) Single 250–350, Double 250–450, Bk 38, Set menu 98–270 (Euro/Access, Visa).

PEYRAT-LE-CHATEAU Hte-Vienne   5A

Auberge Bois de l'Etang 38 av de la Tour, 87470 Peyrat-le-Château.
☏ 55 69 40 19, Fax 55 69 42 93. English spoken.

P

Open 20/01 to 20/12. 28 bedrooms (16 en suite). Golf 30 km, parking.
A comfortable inn near the Vassivière lake. Peyrat-le-Château is north of Eymoutiers on D979.

■ RESTAURANT: Attractive dining room with views of the garden. Specialities include blinis with raspberry caviar, hot foie gras, escalope with apples and beef tournedos Rossini.

■ ACTIVITIES: Hire of mountain bikes, access to circuit, organised walks (groups) and tennis nearby can be booked from hotel.
■ TARIFF: (1994) Single 135–270, Double 135–295, Bk 28 (Euro/Access, Visa).

Hôtel Voyageurs ★ 87470 Peyrat-le-Château.
☏ 55 69 40 02. English spoken.

Open 01/03 to 30/09. 14 bedrooms (6 en suite, 2 bath/shower only). Garage, parking.
Hotel with secure parking and garden, 7 km from Vassivière lake between Guéret and Tulle.

■ RESTAURANT: Closed LS.
■ TARIFF: (1994) Double 160–260, Bk 30, Set menu 75–150 (Euro/Access, Visa).

PIERREFONTAINE-LES-VARANS   3D

Hôtel Franche-Comte ★★ 14 Grand rue, 25510 Pierrefontaine-les-Varans.
☏ 81 56 12 62, Fax 81 56 06 08. English spoken.
Open 15/01 to 15/12. 7 bedrooms (3 en suite). Parking.

Quiet, family-run hotel with nice garden and lovely surrounding countryside. From Besançon on the D461, then left on the D31 (40 km).

■ RESTAURANT: Closed 15/12 to 15/01. Typical Franche-Comté setting and regional dishes.
■ ACTIVITIES: Horse-riding and bicycle hire in the village; cross-country skiing in winter.
■ TARIFF: (1994) Single 120–180, Double 120–220, Bk 25, Set menu 55–180 (Visa).

PIERRELATTE Drôme   5B

Hôtel du Tricastin ★★ 1 rue Caprais Favier, 26700 Pierrelatte.
☏ 75 04 05 82. English spoken.
Open all year. 13 bedrooms (all en suite). Garage, parking.

A comfortable hotel with bar 20 km from Montélimar, motorway exit Montélimar-Sud, then take N7, 12 km to Pierrelatte town centre.

■ ACTIVITIES: Soon to be completed crocodile reserve with 200 crocodiles nearby!

■ TARIFF: (1994) Single 218, Double 238, Bk 30 (Euro/Access, Visa).

PLAN-D'ORGON Bches-du-Rhône 5D

Hôtel Flamant Rose ★★ rte St-Rémy, 13750 Plan-d'Orgon.
℡ 90 73 10 17, Fax 90 73 19 61. English spoken.

Open all year. 30 bedrooms (14 en suite, 16 bath/shower only). Outdoor swimming pool, golf 15 km, garage, parking. ំ
A large hotel with 2 swimming pools and a playground. From the A7 at Orgon, take the Cavaillon exit and follow directions to St-Remy.

■ RESTAURANT: Closed Jan & Feb. 2 large restaurants. Speciality: magret de canard. Free aperitifs to RAC guests.

■ ACTIVITIES: Bikes and tennis nearby.

■ TARIFF: (1994) Single 135–250, Double 135–350, Bk 35, Set menu 48–165 (Euro/Access, Visa, **BT**᠔).

PLANCOET Côtes-du-Nord 1D

Hôtel L'Ecrin ★★★ 20 Les Quais, 22130 Plancoët.
℡ 96 84 10 24, Fax 96 84 01 93. English spoken.
Open all year. 7 bedrooms (all en suite).
Golf 8 km, garage, parking.

More a restaurant with rooms, but exquisitely decorated and furnished. There are plenty of other activities in the region to prolong your stay if you can drag yourself away from the restaurant, 'Chez Crouzil'.

■ RESTAURANT: Closed Sun eve & Mon. Renowned for its atmosphere and fine cuisine.

Breton specialities as well as seafood, game and home-made foie gras. Monsieur Crouzil uses only choice, natural ingredients.

■ ACTIVITIES: Sauna and solarium at hotel. Good base for exploring Brittany.

■ TARIFF: (1994) Single 350–500, Double 350–700, Bk 65, Set menu 120–480 (Amex, Euro/Access, Visa).

■ DISCOUNT: 10% (RAC member card needed)

PLENEUF-VAL-ANDRE Côtes-du-Nord 1D

Château Hôtel Domaine du Val ★★★
22400 Planguenoual.
℡ 96 32 75 40, Fax 96 32 71 50. English spoken.
Open all year. 36 bedrooms (all en suite).
Indoor swimming pool, tennis, golf 4 km, parking. ំ

Imposing château in tree-lined grounds, ideal base for touring Brittany. Rooms have antique furniture. Follow signs for Château-du-Val from Planguenoual on D786 south of Pléneuf-Val-André.

■ RESTAURANT: Traditional cuisine.

■ ACTIVITIES: Fitness room, sauna, squash, balneotherapy.

■ TARIFF: (1994) Single 570–960, Double 450–840, Bk 45, Set menu 135–340 (Euro/Access, Visa).

PLOERMEL Morbihan 1D

Hôtel Le Cobh ★★★ 10 rue des Forges, 56800 Ploërmel.
℡ 97 74 00 49, Fax 97 74 07 36. English spoken.
Open all year. 13 bedrooms (all en suite).
Golf 2 km, garage, parking. ំ

An old Breton house in the centre of Ploërmel, near the magnificent church.

■ RESTAURANT: 'Cruaud' offers a warm welcome and specialises in traditional local cuisine with good value set menus.

■ ACTIVITIES: Ideal base for touring Brittany; sailing on nearby lake; ● Cookery lessons with Monsieur Cruaud on request.

■ TARIFF: (1994) Single 200–300, Double 200–330, Bk 38, Set menu 60–210 (Euro/Access, Visa).

■ DISCOUNT: 5%

Hôtel Relais du Porhoet ★★ 11 place de l'Eglise, 56490 Guilliers.
℡ 97 74 40 17, Fax 97 74 45 65. English spoken.
Open all year. 15 bedrooms (14 en suite).
Tennis, golf 13 km, parking.

In a small, Breton village, a comfortable hotel is an ideal stop-over point. Guilliers is north of Ploërmel (D766 then left onto D13).

P

■ RESTAURANT: Lots of character; offers tempting cuisine with seafood specialities.
■ ACTIVITIES: Discover the nearby forests, lakes, historical sites and coastline.
■ TARIFF: (1994) Single 180–240, Double 200–260, Bk 32, Set menu 65–200 (Amex, Euro/Access, Visa).

Auberge Table Ronde place de l'Eglise, 56430 Neant-sur-Yvel.
℃ 97 93 03 96, Fax 97 93 05 26. English spoken.
Open 18/01 to 04/09 & 13/09 to 31/12.
10 bedrooms (6 en suite, 4 bath/shower only).
Golf 10 km, garage, parking. ♿

In the middle of legendary Brocéliande Forest, tranquil Brittany, midway between the Channel and the Atlantic. From Ploërmel D766 north towards Mauron and St-Meen.

■ RESTAURANT: Closed Mon except Jul & Aug. Regional and seafood specialities in a rustic setting.
■ ACTIVITIES: Tennis and horse-riding nearby.
■ TARIFF: (1994) Single 100–175, Double 120–200, Bk 24, Set menu 58–170 (Euro/Access, Visa).

PLONEOUR-LANVERN Finistère   1C

Hôtel des Voyageurs ★★ 1 rue Jean Jaurés, 29720 Ploneour-Lanvern.
℃ 98 87 61 35, Fax 98 82 62 82. English spoken.
Open 01/12 to 31/10. 12 bedrooms (all en suite). Golf 18 km, garage, parking.
From Quimper take the Pont-l'Abbé road. After 3 km turn right and go for 11 km. The hotel is behind the church.

■ RESTAURANT: Specialities: soupe de poisson maison, homard façon du chef, brochette de lotte sauce diable, coq au vin du patron.
■ ACTIVITIES: Water sports, boating and horse-riding nearby.
■ TARIFF: (1994) Single 205–235, Double 235–275, Bk 32, Set menu 89–320 (Amex, Euro/Access, Visa).

PLOUESCAT Finistère   1A

Hôtel Caravelle ★★ 20 rue Calvaire, 29430 Plouescat.
℃ 98 69 61 75, Fax 98 61 92 61. English spoken.
Open all year. 16 bedrooms (all en suite).
Parking.
Comfortable hotel, near the centre of town, but beside the sea. 15 minutes drive from the Roscoff Ferry on the D10.

■ RESTAURANT: Restaurant is recommended for its seafood specialities.

■ ACTIVITIES: Water sports, sea fishing, bike hire and horse-riding can be booked by the hotel.
■ TARIFF: (1994) Single 185–210, Double 230–285, Bk 32, Set menu 65–250 (Amex, Euro/Access, Visa).

PLOUGASNOU Finistère   1C

Hôtel Le Ty-Pont ★★ Bourg, 29630 St-Jean-du-Doigt.
℃ 98 67 34 06. English spoken.
Open 15/03 to 31/10. 31 bedrooms (18 en suite).
15 km from Morlaix and 2 km from Plougasnou, this quiet hotel is in a large garden just 800 m from the beach.

■ RESTAURANT: Closed Sun eve & Mon LS. Specialities include seafood dishes.
■ ACTIVITIES: Trekking and cycling nearby.
■ TARIFF: (1994) Double 135–220, Bk 28, Set menu 68–180 (Euro/Access, Visa).

POITIERS

Although surrounded by rather off-putting suburbs, the heart of Poitiers retains the atmosphere of a pleasant country town. It stands on a hill between two rivers, the Clain and the Boivre, and is centred around its large market on the Place Charles-de-Gaulle.

Nearby is the church of Notre-Dame-La-Grande, its west front covered with a great variety of sculptures. Originally highly coloured, they are very typical of the local style of Romanesque architecture, of which this church is a fine example. For a view over Notre-Dame-La Grande and the rest of the old town, try to visit the Palais de Justice in the Place Lepetit and climb onto its roof. Inside this former ducal palace, take time to visit the magnificent 12th-century Grande Salle of the Dukes of Aquitaine. Here, in this great hall during the latter part of the 14th century, Jean, Duc de Berry held court in the grand manner. He, as governor of Poitiers, was very much responsible for its Renaissance flowering.

By now you may well need a cup of coffee or perhaps something stronger! There are plenty of cafés to try both close to the market and in the Place du Maréchal-

P

Leclerc. To sit and watch others going about their everyday lives is often fascinating, and for some an important part of a holiday. To watch the French at their leisure, go to the Parc de Blossac, a large area of public gardens, close to the River Clain.

There are two other churches in the centre of the town of particular interest. First, the Gothic cathedral, which is dedicated to St-Pierre, soaring above its surroundings, the height of its naves and apse emphasised by its position on sloping ground above the River Clain. Second, the 4th-century Baptistère St-Jean, supposedly the earliest church in France, which is now used as a museum. Opposite, in the Musée Ste-Croix, there is an interesting collection of farming implements as well as exhibits from early Poitiers.

Although your children may not be keen to visit yet another church or go to yet another museum, there is something to attract them in Poitiers. It is the home of Futuroscope, an incredible theme park concentrating on the moving image. Its futuristic buildings, which tower above the landscape, house a variety of cinematic experiences. There is Kinemax with its vast seven-storey-tall screen . . . Omnimax where films are projected onto a huge hemisphere . . . Cinéma Dynamique where your seat moves as well as the film . . . These are only some of the attractions. Set around a lake, there is much to see that will entertain grown-ups as well as children. If you are lucky enough to be there at dusk on a summer Saturday, there is a spectacular firework, fountain and laser show put on free for all those who have visited the park during the day.

Croissants

The name of Kulyeziski, the Pole, is not generally known in France, or anywhere else for that matter. However, like Stanislas, his influence outside his native Poland has been immense, for Kulyeziski invented the croissant.

He was in Vienna when, in 1683, the city was relieved from a devastating Turkish siege by Charles of Lorraine and the then king of Poland, John III Sobieski. The Turks fled leaving behind their stocks of coffee and Kulyeziski took advantage of this situation by opening a café. Here he sold his newly-acquired coffee accompanied by some small bread rolls, which he ordered to be made in a crescent shape to celebrate the ending of the Turkish siege.

So raise your cup of coffee each morning and drink to Kulyeziski as you enjoy your croissant, a traditional part of a French holiday breakfast. Nowadays, there are several different types of croissant available, like pain au chocolat, a chocolate-filled version which is particularly delicious. Although packets of croissants can be bought in supermarkets, it is best to buy your croissants at a local bakery where they are freshly made every day.

POITIERS Vienne 4B

(See feature)

Château Clos Ribaudière ★★★
10 place de Champ de Foire,
86360 Chasseneuil-du-Poitou.
☎ 49 52 86 66, Fax 49 52 86 32.
English spoken.

Open all year. 19 bedrooms (all en suite).
Golf 8 km, parking. &

A 19th-century château set in a riverside park and boasting exceptional décor. Take Futuroscope exit towards Chasseneuil-Centre Village.

■ RESTAURANT: Creative cuisine in lovely surroundings.
■ TARIFF: (1994) Single 300–580, Double 360–600, Bk 50 (Amex, Euro/Access, Visa).

P

Hôtel Deltasun ★★ sur l'aire du Futuroscope, 86360 Poitiers.
℡ 49 49 01 01, Fax 49 49 01 10. English spoken.

Open all year. 75 bedrooms (all en suite). Outdoor swimming pool, golf 15 km, parking. ふ
Situated in a very modern complex devoted to European cinema. Motorway A10 (Paris-Bordeaux). Exit 18, Futuroscope or N10 main road.
■ RESTAURANT: Gourmet restaurant.
■ ACTIVITIES: Golf, tennis, beach and interesting places to visit close at hand.
■ TARIFF: (1994) Single 310–380, Double 310–380, Bk 40, Set menu 90–160 (Amex, Euro/Access, Visa).

Hôtel Mondial ★★ 86240 Croutelle.
℡ 49 55 44 00, Fax 49 55 33 49. English spoken.

Open 03/01 to 22/12. 40 bedrooms (all en suite). Outdoor swimming pool, golf 12 km, parking. ふ
A motel-style hotel with the swimming pool in the centre. 10 minutes' drive from the centre of Poitiers, take exit 20 from the N10 towards Angoulême.

■ TARIFF: (1994) Single 270–450, Double 305–450, Bk 34 (Amex, Euro/Access, Visa).

POIX-DE-PICARDIE Somme 2B

Hôtel Le Cardinal ★★ place de la République, 80290 Poix-de-Picardie.
℡ 22 90 08 23, Fax 22 90 18 61. English spoken.
Open all year. 35 bedrooms (all en suite). Parking.
A 16th-century hotel situated in the centre of the town. Completely refurbished. Ideally situated en route to Beauvais, Paris and the South West of France on the N29 Amiens/Rouen.
■ RESTAURANT: Warm atmosphere and traditional French cuisine.
■ ACTIVITIES: Games room with snooker, pool and French billiards.
■ TARIFF: (1994) Single 240, Double 270, Bk 32, Set menu 85–160 (Amex, Euro/Access, Visa, BT⚡).

POMPADOUR Corrèze 4B

Auberge de la Mandrie ★★ route de la Périgueux, 19230 Pompadour.
℡ 55 73 37 14, Fax 55 73 67 13.
English spoken.
Open all year. 22 bedrooms (all en suite). Outdoor swimming pool, garage, parking. ふ
5 km from Pompadour going towards Payzac and Ségur-le-Château (D7). Comfortable hotel/restaurant in the country.
■ RESTAURANT: Closed 15/11 to 28/11. Regional and traditional cuisine.
■ TARIFF: Double 210–235, Bk 29, Set menu 62–202 (Euro/Access, Visa).

PONS Charente-Mar 4B

Hôtel Le Rustica Le Grand Village, 17800 St-Léger.
℡ 46 96 91 75. English spoken.
Open all year. 7 bedrooms.
Off the beaten track in the midst of vineyards, 5 km north-west of Pons, easy access from Bordeaux-Paris motorway. Exit Pons towards Saintes.
■ RESTAURANT: Closed Oct 2 wks/Feb 1 wk/Tue/Wed LS. Intimate, beamed restaurant with terraces. Enjoy foie gras, homard, huîtres and tournedos.
■ TARIFF: (1994) Single 120–140, Double 140–150, Bk 26, Set menu 70–250 (Euro/Access, Visa).

P

PONT-AUDEMER Eure 2A

Hôtel Les Cloches de Corneville ★★★
27500 Pont-Audemer.
☎ 32 57 01 04, Fax 32 57 10 96. English spoken.

Open 15/03 to 15/11. 13 bedrooms
(12 en suite, 1 bath/shower only). Parking.

Comfortable, country inn, where you may visit the bells of Corneville inside the property. On the N175 on the Rouen side of Pont-Audemer and just 4 km from A13.

■ RESTAURANT: Closed Mon. Speciality of confit de lapin with garlic bread is served in either the cosy, Norman-style restaurant or in the terrace restaurant overlooking the river valley.
■ ACTIVITIES: Good area for touring and sightseeing.
■ TARIFF: Single 260–380, Double 260–420, Bk 40 (Euro/Access, Visa).

Hôtel La Cremaillère ★ 27210 St-Maclou.
☎ 32 41 17 75.
Open 10/10 to 28/02 & 10/03 to 21/09.
7 bedrooms (4 en suite). Parking.

Small village hotel and restaurant, 5 km from the A13. Handy for Le Havre (30 km). 9 km north-west of Pont-Audemer, on the N175.

■ RESTAURANT: Closed Tues eve & Wed LS.
■ ACTIVITIES: Close to the beach. In reach of Deauville and Honfleur.
■ TARIFF: (1994) Single 130–170, Double 170–230, Bk 25, Set menu 65–165 (Euro/Access, Visa).

Hôtel Le Petit Coq aux Champs Campigny, 27500 Pont-Audemer.
☎ 32 41 04 19, Fax 32 56 06 25. English spoken.
Open all year. 12 bedrooms (all en suite).
Outdoor swimming pool, golf 10 km, parking.

Charming thatched property with family furnishings that really make it seem more like a cosy home. Lovely gardens and excellent facilities.

■ RESTAURANT: Fine beamed dining room with antique furniture and an old Norman fireplace. Beautifully presented cuisine with specialities including Saint-Jacques aux shii-také, pot-au-feu de fois gras aux choux croquants and salade de langouste aux pousses d'épinards à l'huile vierge, to name but a few!
■ ACTIVITIES: Good area for sightseeing, biking, visiting the Calvados distillery. Hotel is happy to assist in making arrangements.
■ TARIFF: (1994) Single 440–520, Double 595–790, Bk 53, Set menu 180–320 (Amex, Euro/Access, Visa, BT⚡).

PONT-AVEN Finistère 1C

Hôtel Roz-Aven ★★★ 11 quai Théodore Botrel, 29930 Pont-Aven.
☎ 98 06 13 06, Fax 98 06 03 89. English spoken.

Open 01/03 to 15/11. 26 bedrooms
(25 en suite, 1 bath/shower only). Golf 15 km, parking. ♿

A beautifully restored 18th-century thatched house, right on the edge of the River Aven. The hotel is reached by following signs to the harbour from the bridge.

■ RESTAURANT: Closed 16/09 to 14/06.
■ ACTIVITIES: Boat trips, kayaking.
■ TARIFF: (1994) Single 340–600, Double 340–900, Bk 42, Set menu 90–150 (Euro/Access, Visa).
■ DISCOUNT: 10%

PONT-DE-VAUX Ain 5B

Hôtel Le Raisin ★★ 01190 Pont-de-Vaux.
☎ 85 30 30 97, Fax 85 30 67 89. English spoken.
Open all year. 8 bedrooms (all en suite).
Golf 10 km, garage, parking.

Traditionally furnished hotel in a quiet village near the river and close to the A6 motorway. In between Tournus and Mâcon on the D933.

■ RESTAURANT: Restaurant is decorated in local

P

style. Good regional food with specialities of volailles de Bresse, crêpes parmentier and a very inviting dessert trolley.

■ ACTIVITIES: Boats for hire, fishing and tennis nearby.

■ TARIFF: (1994) Single 230–250, Double 250–300, Bk 35, Set menu 100–300 (Amex, Euro/Access, Visa).

PONT-DU-GARD Gard 5D

Hôtel de la Castellas ★★★ Grand'rue, Collias, 30210 Pont-du-Gard.
✆ 66 22 88 88, Fax 66 22 84 28. English spoken. Open 06/03 to 06/01. 14 bedrooms (all en suite). Outdoor swimming pool, tennis, golf 7 km, parking, restaurant.

Delightful, mellow stone hotel in the old Provence village of Collias. Charming little garden/arbor. Equally charming, individually decorated bedrooms and bathrooms. Remoulins west to Pont-du-Gard and Collias.

■ TARIFF: (1994) Single 395–580, Double 430–620, Bk 50, Set menu 160–360 (Amex, Euro/Access, Visa).

PONT-L'ABBE Finistère 1C

Hôtel de Bretagne ★★ 24 place de la République, 29120 Pont-l'Abbé.
✆ 98 87 17 22, Fax 98 82 89 34. English spoken. Open all year. 18 bedrooms (all en suite). Golf 18 km, parking.

A charming family hotel quietly situated and just a few minutes from the Bay of Audierne.

■ RESTAURANT: Closed Mon LS. Specialises in seafood.

■ TARIFF: (1994) Single 230–290, Double 270–360, Bk 36, Set menu 110–380 (Amex, Euro/Access, Visa).

Hôtel Château de Kernuz ★★
29120 Pont l'Abbé.
✆ 98 87 01 59, Fax 98 66 02 36. English spoken.

Open 01/04 to 30/09. 19 bedrooms (all bath/shower only). Outdoor swimming pool, tennis, golf 15 km, parking.

16th-century manor in the middle of a private park. 1 km from Pont-l'Abbé towards Plomeur.

■ RESTAURANT: 2 dining rooms with seafood specialities.

■ ACTIVITIES: ● Fishing and boat trips available with or without guide - special price for RAC clients.

■ TARIFF: (1994) Single 370–450, Double 370–450, Bk 35, Set menu 150 (Euro/Access, Visa).

■ DISCOUNT: 5%

PONT-L'EVEQUE Calvados 2A

Hôtel Le Clos Saint-Gatien ★★★ Saint-Gatien-des-Bois, 14130 Pont-l'Evêque.
✆ 31 65 16 08, Fax 31 65 10 27. English spoken.
Open all year. 56 bedrooms (all en suite). Indoor swimming pool, outdoor swimming pool, tennis, golf 2 km, parking, restaurant. ♿

Prize-winning hotel conversion from former 17th-century working farm, which is set in gardens and has on-site sport and health amenities. 18 km from the A13 Paris to

Le Lion d'Or

10 minutes from Deauville and the sea, close to Honfleur.

Pleasant hotel with open-air swimming pool in charming Pont-l'Evêque on the banks of the River Touques.

See under Pont-l'Evêque

P

Cherbourg motorway. Take the Deauville exit, then Honfleur.
■ TARIFF: (1994) Single 280–450, Double 280–850, Bk 50, Set menu 98–240 (Amex, Euro/Access, Visa).
■ DISCOUNT: 10%

Hôtel Le Lion d'Or ★★ 14130 Pont-l'Evêque.
✆ 31 65 01 55, Fax 31 65 05 64. English spoken.
Open all year. 26 bedrooms (all en suite).
Outdoor swimming pool, golf 2 km, parking.
Pleasant hotel, standing at the crossroads in Pont-l'Evêque and close to the river. A short drive from Deauville and the sea.
SEE ADVERTISEMENT.
■ RESTAURANT: Has a good reputation and specialities include sole Normande, magret de canard au cidre and tripes à la mode de Caen.
■ ACTIVITIES: Well situated for visits to Deauville and Honfleur.
■ TARIFF: Single 200–260, Double 260–350, Bk 33, Set menu 98.50–160 (Amex, Euro/Access, Visa).
■ DISCOUNT: 10%

PONT-SUR-YONNE Yonne   2D

Hôtel L'Ecu ★ 3 rue Carnot, 89140 Pont-sur-Yonne.
✆ 86 67 01 00. English spoken.
Open 01/01 to 25/01 & 25/02 to 31/12.
7 bedrooms (3 en suite, 4 bath/shower only).
Golf 7 km, parking.
Old coaching inn 12 km north of Sens.
■ RESTAURANT: Closed Mon eve & Tues. Good reputation and very popular.
■ TARIFF: (1994) Single 90–160, Double 160–280, Bk 30 (Amex, Euro/Access, Visa).

PONTARLIER Doubs   3D

Hôtel Bon Repos ★★ 25160 Les Grangettes.
✆ 81 69 62 95. English spoken.
Open 20/12 to 20/10. 16 bedrooms (9 en suite, 2 bath/shower only). Garage, parking.
Highly recommended. Comfortable and friendly. Close to Lac de St-Point and in beautiful, quiet countryside. From Pontarlier go south on N57 then D437 towards Lac St-Point. At the lake (5 km) keep right along the west side of the lake for Les Grangettes.
■ RESTAURANT: Closed Tues & Wed eve LS.
■ ACTIVITIES: Lots to do on and around the lake. Near enough to winter ski too!
■ TARIFF: (1994) Single 138–213, Double 156–229, Bk 28, Set menu 66–162 (Amex, Euro/Access, Visa).

PONTIVY Morbihan   1C

Hôtel Le Vieux Moulin ★★ 56930 St-Nicolas-des-Eaux.
✆ 97 51 81 09, Fax 97 51 83 12.
Open 01/03 to 31/01. 10 bedrooms (all en suite). Golf 5 km, parking.
Set beside the River Blavet. From Pontivy take the D768 towards Baud, then turn right on to the D1.
■ RESTAURANT: Closed Sun eve & Mon lunch. Specialities include St-Jacques à la Bretonne and filet de canard aux myrtilles.
■ ACTIVITIES: Boating, horse-riding and tennis nearby; beach 30 minutes; lots to see.
■ TARIFF: (1994) Double 260–280, Bk 29, Set menu 67–162 (Visa).

PONTORSON Manche   1D

Hôtel Montgomery ★★★ rue Couesnon, 50170 Pontorson.
✆ 33 60 00 09, Fax 33 60 37 66. English spoken.

P

Open 08/04 to 02/11. 32 bedrooms (all en suite). Garage, parking.
Historic 16th-century mansion. Off N175 and N176 9 km from Mont-St-Michel.
■ RESTAURANT: Gourmet restaurant specialities: fish and agneau de pré-salé from St-Michel Bay.
■ ACTIVITIES: ● Bicycles free of charge to guests with RAC guide.
■ TARIFF: (1994) Single 245–345, Double 245–460, Bk 49, Set menu 128–196 (Amex, Euro/Access, Visa).

PORNIC Loire-Atlan   1D

Hôtel La Flotille ★★ pointe St-Gildas, 44770 Préfailles.
✆ 40 21 61 18, Fax 40 64 51 72. English spoken.
Open all year. 26 bedrooms (all en suite).
Indoor swimming pool, golf 8 km, garage, parking. ♿

Modern, friendly hotel with sea views. North of Pornic on D13 towards Préfailles.

■ RESTAURANT: Seafood is a speciality.
■ ACTIVITIES: Fishing and water sports nearby.
■ TARIFF: (1994) Set menu 95–270 (Amex, Euro/Access, Visa).

Hôtel Relais St-Gilles ★★ 7 rue F de Mun, 44210 Pornic.
℡ 40 82 02 25. English spoken.
Open 01/04 to 10/10. 29 bedrooms
(22 en suite, 4 bath/shower only). Golf 1 km.
A 19th-century posthouse, close to Pornic Castle. In a quiet location but not far from the lively harbour, ancient burial ground and health spa.

■ RESTAURANT: Closed LS.
■ TARIFF: (1994) Double 230–350, Bk 32, Set menu 95–115 (Euro/Access, Visa).

PORT-LA-NOUVELLE Aude   5C

Hôtel Méditerranée ★★★ BP 92, 11210 Port-la-Nouvelle.
℡ 68 48 03 08, Fax 68 48 53 81.
English spoken.

Open all year. 31 bedrooms (all en suite). Garage, parking.
A fine modern building which is ideally situated on the seafront, facing the beach, as well as being in the centre of town.

■ RESTAURANT: Restaurant overlooks sea and beach. Specialities: poissons, bouillebaisse, cassolette de baudroie, coquillages, fricassé de poulet aux langoustines sauce whisky.
■ ACTIVITIES: ● Sea fishing trips by catamaran - 2 half days for 350F inclusive.
■ TARIFF: Single 180–390, Double 200–490, Bk 35, Set menu 60–290 (Amex, Euro/Access, Visa).
■ DISCOUNT: 10% LS.

POUILLY-EN-AUXOIS Côte-d'Or   3C

Hôtel Château de Ste-Sabine ★★★
Ste-Sabine, 21320 Pouilly-en-Auxois.
℡ 80 49 22 01, Fax 80 49 20 01.
English spoken.

Open all year. 16 bedrooms (12 en suite, 4 bath/shower only). Outdoor swimming pool, golf 15 km, garage, parking. ⅋
Beautiful castle from the 18th century overlooking wildlife park. Tastefully decorated rooms. Special half-board tariffs available. Halfway between Paris and Lyon, by the A6 motorway, Pouilly-en-Auxois exit.

■ RESTAURANT: Gourmet restaurant, stone vaulted dining rooms - inventive and refined cuisine - fresh seasonal produce.
■ ACTIVITIES: Tennis (5 mins), mountain bikes for hire, ballooning, boat trips on Burgundy canals (must be booked), wine tasting, châteaux, churches and monuments.
■ TARIFF: (1994) Single 300–560, Double 300–560, Bk 50, Set menu 150–280 (Visa).
■ DISCOUNT: 8%

POUILLY-SUR-LOIRE Nièvre   2D

Hôtel Le Relais Fleuri ★★★ 2 av de la Tuileric, 58150 Pouilly-sur-Loire.
℡ 86 39 12 99, Fax 86 39 14 15. English spoken.
Open 15/02 to 15/01. 9 bedrooms
(all en suite). Golf 4 km, garage, parking. ⅋
Traditional hotel with lots of atmosphere. Overlooking the Loire with sun terrace and flower-filled gardens. Situated in the village.

■ RESTAURANT: Very pretty dining room with enchanting view. Creative cuisine and a fine selection of wines.
■ ACTIVITIES: Canoeing, sailing, hiking/walking.
■ TARIFF: (1994) Double 250–300, Bk 35, Set menu 99–250 (Amex, Euro/Access, Visa).

LE POULDU Finistère   1C

Hôtel Armen ★★★ 29360 Le Pouldu.
✆ 98 39 90 44, Fax 98 39 98 69. English spoken.

Open 24/04 to 27/09. 38 bedrooms
(all en suite). Golf 20 km, garage, parking.
*800 m from the sea, this traditional family
hotel offers a warm welcome. Signposted from
the D24 and D49 into Le Pouldu.*
■ RESTAURANT: Good menu with seafood
specialities.
■ ACTIVITIES: Sailing, tennis and horse-riding
nearby.
■ TARIFF: (1994) Single 240–350,
Double 270–430, Bk 45, Set menu 80–230
(Amex, Euro/Access, Visa).

POUZAUGES Vendée   1D

Auberge de la Bruyère ★★ 18 rue du Dr
Barbanneau, 85700 Pouzauges.
✆ 51 91 93 46, Fax 51 57 08 18. English spoken.
Open all year. 28 bedrooms (all en suite).
Indoor swimming pool, parking.
*New hotel on a hillside with wonderful views of
countryside. From Nantes, take N137, turn off
to D960 bis at Chantonnay following signs for
Pouzauges and Bressuire. From the centre of
Pouzauges, drive towards La Pommeraie. The
hotel is 300 m beyond the church.*
■ RESTAURANT: Closed Sat & 2nd Sun eve Oct to
Mar. Enjoy panoramic views, seafood and
regional cuisine. In summer, eat on the lovely
terrace overlooking Pouzauges.
■ TARIFF: (1994) Single 250–290,
Double 305–390, Bk 38, Set menu 80–165
(Amex, Euro/Access).
■ DISCOUNT: 10% LS.

PRATS-DE-MOLLO-LA-PRESTE   5C

Hôtel Ribes 66230 Prats-de-Mollo-la-Preste.
✆ 68 39 71 04, Fax 68 39 78 02.

Open 01/04 to 31/10. 25 bedrooms (3 en suite,
14 bath/shower only).
*Splendid views at an altitude of 1130 m.
10 minutes from Prats-de-Mollo-la-Preste
nature reserve. 15 minutes from medieval
village. Access: A9 Le Boulou, then D115 Prats-
de-Mollo, then D115A to La Preste.*
■ RESTAURANT: Closed 1/11 to 31/3. Panoramic
views over the River Tech valley. Good
reputation for its country cooking.
■ ACTIVITIES: Trout fishing, walking, excursions.
■ TARIFF: (1994) Single 140–260,
Double 140–300, Bk 25 to 39, Set menu 76
(Euro/Access, Visa).
■ DISCOUNT: 10% Full & half-board.

PRIVAS Ardèche   5B

Hôtel Le Panoramic Escrinet ★★ 07000 Privas.
✆ 75 87 10 11, Fax 75 87 10 34. English spoken.

Open 15/03 to 15/11. 20 bedrooms
(all en suite). Outdoor swimming pool, garage,
parking. &
*Small family hotel/restaurant with garden and
wonderful views. Located at Col de l'Escrinet,
between Privas and Aubenas on N104.*
■ RESTAURANT: Closed 15/11 to 15/03. Ravioles
au foie gras, mignons de boeuf au parfum de
chèvre and other tempting home-made dishes
can be enjoyed in this peaceful, panoramic
setting.
■ TARIFF: (1994) Single 250–320,
Double 280–350, Bk 38, Set menu 120–290
(Amex, Euro/Access, Visa).

LE-PUY-EN-VELAY

The market town of Le-Puy-en-Velay
occupies one of the strangest sites in
France, lying as it does at the centre of an

area shaped originally by volcanic activity. Two pinnacles of lava rock dominate the town.

On the highest stands the immense statue of Notre-Dame-de-France, built in 1860 from canon captured during the Crimean war. On the other, there is the 11th-century chapel of St-Michel-d'Aiguilhe. If you have the energy, a climb up either of them will be rewarded with panoramic views of this unique area.

LE PUY-EN-VELAY Hte-Loire   5A

(See feature)

Hôtel Brivas ★★ av Charles Massot, 43750 Vals-près-le-Puy.
☎ 71 05 68 66, Fax 71 05 65 88. English spoken. Open all year. 60 bedrooms (all en suite). Tennis, golf 5 km, parking, restaurant. Ᏹ
Two minutes from centre of Le Puy-en-Velay, in a pleasant and tranquil quarter, with ample parking.
■ TARIFF: (1994) Single 250, Double 280, Bk 32, Set menu 90–160 (Amex, Euro/Access, Visa).

PUY-L'EVEQUE Lot   4D

Hôtel La Source Bleue ★★★ Moulin de Leygues, 46700 Touzac.
☎ 65 36 52 01, Fax 65 24 65 69. English spoken. Open 01/04 to 31/12. 12 bedrooms (all en suite). Outdoor swimming pool, golf 15 km, parking. Ᏹ
An 11th-century mill on the River Lot, in beautiful surroundings. Rooms of character and comfort.
■ RESTAURANT: Closed Wed. Good food with specialities of terrine maison de foie gras, pot au feu de canard à l'ancienne and côtes d'agneau à la crème de gingembre.
■ ACTIVITIES: Sauna; fishing and sailing nearby.
■ TARIFF: (1994) Single 270, Double 270–450, Bk 35, Set menu 140–220 (Amex, Euro/Access, Visa).

Hôtel Le Vert ★★ Mauroux, 46700 Puy-l'Evêque.
☎ 65 36 51 36, Fax 65 36 56 84. English spoken. Open 12/02 to 26/11. 7 bedrooms (all en suite). Outdoor swimming pool, golf 8 km, parking.
Charming, welcoming, small hotel in a typical 400-year-old farmhouse. Rooms carefully designed and individually decorated. The

P

village is south of Puy amongst the Cahors vinyards and close to the River Lot.
■ RESTAURANT: Closed Thur & Fri lunch. Traditional restaurant opening on to terrace. Specialities: foie gras, magret de canard.
■ ACTIVITIES: Bikes and scooters at hotel. Arrangements made for tours and a variety of sporting activities.
■ TARIFF: (1994) Single 230–340, Double 270–340, Bk 35, Set menu 100–150 (Amex, Euro/Access, Visa).

QUIMPER

The River Odet, looking towards the cathedral

In the far west of France, in the Finistère *département*, is Quimper – often considered to be the cultural capital of Brittany. Visit its huge Gothic Cathedral, stroll through the narrow cobbled streets or shop in its modern market hall. Everywhere you go, the locally-made Breton pottery for which Quimper is famous is on sale. Here, too, at the end of July, one of the largest folk festivals in Europe is held, ending with an amazing parade through the town.

QUIMPER Finistère   1C

(See feature)

Hôtel Le Griffon ★★★ 131 route de Bénodet, 29000 Quimper.
☎ 98 90 33 33, Fax 98 53 06 67. English spoken. Open all year. 50 bedrooms (all en suite). Indoor swimming pool, golf 10 km, parking, restaurant. Ᏹ
Contemporary establishment on the outskirts of town 10 minutes' drive from the beaches. Motorway N165.

■ TARIFF: (1994) Single 250–350,
Double 300–480, Bk 48 (Amex, Euro/Access,
Visa).

Hôtel Mascotte ★★ rue Théodore Le Hars,
29000 Quimper.
✆ 98 53 37 37, Fax 98 90 31 51. English spoken.
Open all year. 63 bedrooms (all en suite).
Golf 10 km, garage, restaurant. ⅁
*Located in the centre of town, close to the old
town. Quimper is on the N165.*
■ TARIFF: (1994) Single 300–400,
Double 340–480, Bk 40 (Amex,
Euro/Access, Visa).

Novotel Quimper ★★★ 2 rue du Poher,
29000 Quimper.
✆ 98 90 46 26, Fax 98 53 01 96. English spoken.
Open all year. 92 bedrooms (all en suite).
Outdoor swimming pool, golf 10 km, parking,
restaurant. ⅁
*2 minutes by car from Quimper centre. D785
over River Odet, Pont de Poulguilnan, straight
on past Centre Commercial Le Continent.*
■ TARIFF: (1994) Single 410, Double 460–480,
Bk 50 (Amex, Euro/Access, Visa).

Hôtel Tour d'Auvergne ★★ 13 rue Réguaires,
29000 Quimper.
✆ 98 95 08 70, Fax 98 95 27 31. English spoken.
Open all year. 42 bedrooms (38 en suite).
Golf 10 km, parking.
*Situated in town centre, free private car park
closed at night.*
■ RESTAURANT: Closed Sun 10/10-30/04 Sat eve
1/11-3. Overlooking patio full of flowers.
■ ACTIVITIES: Horse-riding (8 km), tennis courts
and swimming pool (4 km).
■ TARIFF: (1994) Double 410–515, Bk ,
Set menu 125–195 (Amex, Euro/Access, Visa).
■ DISCOUNT: 10% LS.

RAMBOUILLET Yvelines   2D

Hôtel Abbaye les Vaux de Cernay ★★★★
78720 Cernay-la-Ville.
✆ 1 34 85 23 00, Fax 1 34 85 20 95. English spoken.
Open all year. 58 bedrooms (all en suite).
Outdoor swimming pool, tennis, golf 15 km,
parking.
*An 800-year-old abbey set in parkland. 12 km
east of Rambouillet on N306 towards Paris.
Just before Cernay-la-Ville fork left then turn
left to Abbaye.*
■ RESTAURANT: Excellent cuisine, based on
dishes created by the renowned Antonin
Carême.

■ TARIFF: (1994) Single 390–850,
Double 490–1050, Bk 75 (Amex,
Euro/Access, Visa).

RANCOURT Somme   2B

Hôtel Le Prieuré ★★★ 80360 Rancourt.
✆ 22 85 04 43, Fax 22 85 06 69.
English spoken.

Open all year. 28 bedrooms (all en suite).
Garage, parking.
*Beautiful, imposing hotel. Well placed in the
midst of this historic region. Found on the N17
midway between Bapaume and Péronne, just
a few minutes' drive from the Bapaume exit on
the motorway from Calais.*
■ RESTAURANT: Atmospheric brick and stone
interior. Specialities: pigeon aux queues de
boeuf et jus de volaille; ris de veau au beurre
de champagne.
■ ACTIVITIES: On war cemetery circuit, very
popular with British visitors.
■ TARIFF: (1994) Single 260, Double 260–290,
Bk 28, Set menu 65–240 (Amex,
Euro/Access, Visa).
■ DISCOUNT: 5%

Q

RECQUES-SUR-HEM Pas-de-Calais 2B

Château du Cocove ★★★ av de Cocove, 62890 Recques-sur-Hem.
℄ 21 82 68 29, Fax 21 82 72 59. English spoken.
Open 26/12 to 24/12. 24 bedrooms
(all en suite). Golf 7 km, garage, parking. &

An 18th-century château built set in 23 acres of beautiful parkland. Charming atmosphere and very good facilities. Leave A26 at exit 2, Nordausques.

■ RESTAURANT: Gastronomic restaurant with lovely views and excellent regional cuisine.
■ ACTIVITIES: Golf practice pitch, table tennis, sauna and wine shop at hotel.
● TARIFF: (1994) Double 435–690, Bk 45, Set menu 115–335 (Amex, Euro/Access, Visa).

ILE DE RE

ARS-EN-RE Charente-Mar 4A

Hôtel Le Martray ★★ 17590 Ars-en-Ré, Ile de Ré.
℄ 46 29 40 04, Fax 46 29 41 19.
English spoken.

R

Open 01/04 to 02/11. 14 bedrooms
(all en suite). Parking.

Enjoys a lovely position, facing the beach, on the west side of the island at narrowest point just before Ars-en-Ré. Comfortable rooms, some with sea view and balcony/verandah.

■ RESTAURANT: Seafood specialities served in the restaurant or on the vine-covered terrace.
■ ACTIVITIES: Cycling and sailing near hotel; tennis 3 km, tours of the island.
● TARIFF: (1994) Single 320–370, Double 320–370, Bk 40, Set menu 110–200 (Amex, Euro/Access, Visa).

END OF ILE DE RE RESORTS

REIMS Marne 3A

Hôtel Bristol ★★ 76 pl Drouet d'Érlon, 51100 Reims.
℄ 26 40 52 25, Fax 26 40 05 08. English spoken.
Open all year. 40 bedrooms (all en suite).
Parking.

Fully renovated, traditional hotel in the centre of this charming city.

■ ACTIVITIES: Cinemas and the cathedral are within walking distance.
■ TARIFF: (1994) Single 220–250, Double 260–285, Bk 26 (Amex, Euro/Access, Visa).
■ DISCOUNT: 10% Or free breakfast.

Hôtel Cheval Blanc ★★★★ 51400 Sept-Saulx.
℄ 26 03 90 27, Fax 26 03 97 09. English spoken.
Open 23/02 to 31/01. 25 bedrooms
(all en suite). Tennis, golf 20 km, garage, parking, restaurant.

In lovely grounds with a river running through, a hotel that's been run by the same family for 150 years. From Reims N44 south then D37 to Sept-Saulx.

■ TARIFF: (1994) Single 340–800, Double 380–980, Bk 50, Set menu 180–360 (Amex, Euro/Access, Visa).

Grand Hôtel de l'Univers ★★ 41 bd Foch, 51100 Reims.
℄ 26 88 68 08, Fax 26 40 95 61. English spoken.
Open all year. 42 bedrooms (all en suite).
Parking. &

Quiet and comfortable 1930s-built hotel in the centre of town opposite the station.

■ RESTAURANT: Closed Sun eve.
■ TARIFF: (1994) Single 210–280, Double 250–310, Bk 30, Set menu 85–160 (Amex, Euro/Access, Visa).

Hôtel Libergier ★★ 20 rue Libergier, 51100 Reims.
℄ 26 47 28 46, Fax 26 88 65 81. English spoken.
Open all year. 17 bedrooms (all en suite).
Golf 17 km, parking.

Comfortably furnished small traditional hotel close to Reims Cathedral.

■ TARIFF: (1994) Single 230–260, Double 260–330, Bk 35 (Amex, Euro/Access, Visa).

Hôtel La Maison du Champagne ★★ 2 rue du Port, 51360 Beaumont-sur-Vesle.
℄ 26 03 92 45, Fax 26 03 97 59. English spoken.
Open all year. 13 bedrooms (9 en suite, 1 bath/shower only). Golf 10 km, garage, parking.

From Reims south-east on N44, 10 km to Beaumont-sur-Vesle.

■ RESTAURANT: Closed Sun eve.
■ ACTIVITIES: Visits/tours to wine cellars and the surrounding area.
■ TARIFF: (1994) Single 110–200, Double 160–250, Bk 30, Set menu 70–220 (Amex, Euro/Access, Visa).

Hôtel Mercure Reims Cathédrale ★★★
31 bd P Doumer, 51100 Reims.
📞 26 84 49 49, Fax 26 84 49 84. English spoken.
Open all year. 124 bedrooms (all en suite). Garage.

Take Reims-Cathédrale exit from A4 motorway. 5 minutes from town centre and the cathedral.

■ RESTAURANT: Closed Sat & Sun lunch. Champagne setting and cuisine. Views over the River Marne.
■ ACTIVITIES: Exercise room at hotel; swimming pool and go-karting nearby. Visits to all the wonderful sights of Reims as well as a champagne cellar.
■ TARIFF: (1994) Single 360–430, Double 330–465, Bk 50, Set menu 90–120 (Amex, Euro/Access, Visa).

New Hôtel Europe ★★★ 29 rue Buirette,
51100 Reims.
📞 26 47 39 39, Fax 26 40 14 37. English spoken.
Open all year. 54 bedrooms (all en suite).
Golf 12 km, parking. ♿

Only 2 mins from the A4 and A26, this hotel is situated in the town centre. Pleasant garden, peaceful surroundings, comfortable rooms.

■ ACTIVITIES: ● Good discounts on a variety of activities and services including green fees, theatre/cinema tickets and car hire, with the hotel's complimentary 'Carte Clef d'Or'.
■ TARIFF: (1994) Single 325–355, Double 370–405, Bk 38 (Amex, Euro/Access, Visa).

Hôtel Paix ★★★ 9 rue Buirette, 51100 Reims.
📞 26 40 04 08, Fax 26 47 75 04. English spoken.
Open all year. 105 bedrooms (all en suite).
Outdoor swimming pool, golf 8 km, garage.

Attractive, recently built hotel in the centre of Reims. Comfortable rooms with warm, relaxing décor, pool terrace and garden. Between railway station and cathedral.

■ RESTAURANT: The rustic-style 'Taverne de Maitre Kanter' offers a wide range of dishes in comfortable surroundings.
■ TARIFF: (1994) Single 400–550, Double 400–600, Bk 50 (Amex, Euro/Access, Visa).

REMIREMONT Vosges 3D

Hôtel du Cheval de Bronze ★★ 59 rue Ch de Gaulle, Bd 57, 88202 Remiremont.
📞 29 62 52 24, Fax 29 62 34 90. English spoken.
Open all year. 36 bedrooms (24 en suite).
Golf 20 km, garage, restaurant.

Old coaching inn in centre of town. Small private garden/courtyard. 25 km south of Epinal, in the Vosges.

■ TARIFF: (1994) Double 150–330, Bk 30, Set menu 84–195 (Amex, Euro/Access, Visa).

Hôtel de la Poste ★★ 67 rue Ch de Gaulle, Bd 57, 88202 Remiremont.
📞 29 62 55 67, Fax 29 62 34 90. English spoken.
Open all year. 21 bedrooms (19 en suite).
Golf 20 km, garage. ♿

An old hotel in picturesque town at the foot of the Vosges.

■ RESTAURANT: Classic and regional cuisine with an excellent wine cellar.
■ TARIFF: (1994) Double 255–345, Bk 30, Set menu 84–195 (Amex, Euro/Access, Visa).

RENNES

Brittany is a very popular seaside holiday destination with British tourists. Arriving in France at any of the ports east of Cherbourg, or indeed coming off the Channel Tunnel train, a stopover at Rennes is a possibility whether you are going to the north or south coast of Brittany. Rennes, which has been the capital of Brittany since 1213, is not a typical Breton town, having been almost completely burnt down in 1720. The fire, started by a drunken carpenter, raged for a whole week destroying more than a thousand houses. A small portion of the medieval town survives close to La Porte Mordelaise, which is all that remains of the town ramparts. This ceremonial arch was traditionally passed through by the Dukes and Duchesses of Brittany on their way to be crowned in the nearby Cathedral of St-Sauveur. The two towers of the cathedral escaped the fire but the rest had to be rebuilt.

The town that was constructed after the fire is of classical design. Broad streets intersect at right angles and are flanked by

R

One of the few half-timbered buildings in Rennes to survive the disastrous fire of 1720

beautifully proportioned houses, some of which are reconstructions following the devastation of World War II.

The Palais de Justice is the only important building in the town to have survived both the fire and war damage. If gilded interiors are of interest to you, a visit here is a must. Each room surpasses its predecessor in splendour, until finally you reach the most splendid of them all, the Grande Chambre. The ceiling is crimson and gold and the walls are hung with modern tapestries showing episodes from Brittany's past.

To discover more of the history of this area, visit the Musée de Bretagne which has a particularly interesting audiovisual display of life in Brittany at the turn of the century. Housed in part of the old university, it shares a building with the Musée des Beaux-Arts. Here, as well as a collection of drawings by Leonardo da Vinci, there is a part of the museum devoted particularly to Breton art.

Like many French towns, Rennes is well served by public gardens, a fine example of which is the Jardin du Thabor, just across the River Vilaine from the old university. Once part of the gardens of the abbey of St-Melanie, this 25-acre site has a botanical garden, a children's garden and a miniature zoo amongst its attractions.

Rennes is at its busiest during the early part of July when an extensive festival of music and drama is held in the town. Called the *Festival des Tombées de la Nuit,* it celebrates Breton culture, which is of particular interest to the British visitor since we share many of our Celtic legends with the people of Brittany. The well-loved story of King Arthur exists here in much the same form as it does in Cornwall. In the Fôret de Paimpont (about 30 km west of Rennes), you can taste the clear waters at either La Fontaine de Barenton, known as Merlin's Spring, or at La Fontaine de Jouvenance, near to Merlin's supposed burial place.

RENNES Ille/Vil 1D

(See feature)

Hôtel Garden ★★ 3 rue Duhamel, 35000 Rennes.
☎ 99 65 45 06, Fax 99 65 02 62. English spoken. Open all year. 24 bedrooms (16 en suite, 6 bath/shower only). Golf 8 km, parking. *Centrally placed for seeing Rennes and the surrounding countryside.*
■ TARIFF: (1994) Single 145–260, Double 180–280, Bk 30 (Amex, Euro/Access, Visa).

Hôtel Mascotte ★★★ espace Performance, 35769 St-Grégoire.
☎ 99 23 78 78, Fax 99 23 78 33. English spoken. Open all year. 48 bedrooms (all en suite). Indoor swimming pool, parking, restaurant. ⴲ
Hotel is part of the Espace Business Area at Rennes/St-Grégoire lying between the N137 and N175 northern by-pass towards St-Malo.
■ TARIFF: (1994) Single 300–410, Double 300–450, Bk 42 (Amex, Euro/Access, Visa).

Hôtel Otelinn ★★ 6 av St-Vincent, St-Grégoire, 35760 Rennes.
☎ 99 68 76 76, Fax 99 68 83 01. English spoken. Open all year. 51 bedrooms (all en suite). Golf 5 km, parking. ⴲ
Well-appointed rooms with colour television. On the Rennes/St-Malo road.
■ RESTAURANT: Closed 25 Dec.
■ TARIFF: (1994) Single 258–268, Double 278–288, Bk 32, Set menu 80–180 (Amex, Euro/Access, Visa).

REVEL Tarn 5C

Château de Garrevaques
81700 Garrevaques.
☎ 63 75 04 54, Fax 63 70 26 44. English spoken. Open 01/04 to 01/12. 9 bedrooms (all en suite). Outdoor swimming pool, tennis, golf 20 km, garage, parking.
This turretted, 15th-century château was refurbished in the 19th century and is now modernised as an exclusive hotel, where you are made to feel like privileged house guests. From central Revel take the D1 towards Montégut and turn right opposite the police station on the D79 to Garrevaques.
■ RESTAURANT: Private table d'hôte; specialities include cassoulet, truite and foie gras.
■ ACTIVITIES: Billiards lounge, visit to reproduction furniture makers in Revel.

■ TARIFF: (1994) Single 400–450, Double 600–700, Set menu 150–300 (Amex, Visa).
■ DISCOUNT: 10% Minimum stay of 3 days.

REVILLE Manche 1B

Hôtel au Moyne de Saire ★★ Village de l'Eglise, 50760 Réville.
☎ 33 54 46 06, Fax 33 54 14 99. English spoken. Open 01/02 to 04/01. 11 bedrooms (4 en suite, 4 bath/shower only). Golf 10 km, parking. *Small and comfortable, hotel is in a quiet setting with garden and bar and just 5 minutes from the beach. 3 km from St-Vaast on the Barfleur road.*
■ RESTAURANT: Closed Sun LS. Warm atmosphere and good food. Seafood specialities as well as foie gras, fillet of beef in port wine sauce, veal kidneys with mustard seed and Normandy pancakes.
■ ACTIVITIES: Horse-riding, mountain-biking, windsurfing, sailing, tennis and deep-sea diving nearby.
■ TARIFF: (1994) Single 130–270, Double 170–270, Bk 30, Set menu 80–195 (Euro/Access, Visa).

RIBEAUVILLE Ht-Rhin 3D

Hôtel La Pepinière ★★★ rte de Ste-Marie-aux-Mines, 68150 Ribeauvillé.
☎ 89 73 64 14, Fax 89 73 88 78. English spoken. Open 14/04 to 30/11. 21 bedrooms (all en suite). Garage, parking. ⴲ
A traditional, chalet-style hotel, in the middle of the forest. On the Ribeauvillé to Ste-Marie-aux-Mines road.
■ RESTAURANT: Closed Tues & Wed lunch. Panoramic views.
■ TARIFF: (1994) Single 220–350, Double 340–450, Bk 42, Set menu 110–380 (Euro/Access, Visa).
■ DISCOUNT: 10% LS.

Hôtel Tour ★★ 1 rue Mairie, 68150 Ribeauvillé.
☎ 89 73 72 73, Fax 89 73 38 74. English spoken. Open 01/03 to 01/01. 35 bedrooms (all en suite). Tennis, golf 12 km, garage, parking.
Attractive old hotel in centre of medieval village.
■ TARIFF: (1994) Single 260–340, Double 290–420, Bk 38 (Euro/Access, Visa).

Hôtel Les Vosges ★★★ 2 Grand rue, 68150 Ribeauvillé.
☎ 89 73 61 39, Fax 89 73 34 21. English spoken.

R

Open 01/03 to 01/02. 18 bedrooms
(all en suite). Golf 10 km, parking.
*Small hotel/restaurant in old village at foot of
mountains. From N83 go west on D106.*
■ RESTAURANT: Closed Mon & Tues lunch.
French cuisine, with specialities of foie gras
and seafood dishes, served in a cosy
atmosphere.
■ TARIFF: (1994) Single 290, Double 340–470,
Bk 50, Set menu 160–380 (Amex,
Euro/Access, Visa).

RIBERAC Dordogne   4B

Hôtel de France ★★ rue M Dufraisse,
24600 Ribérac.
☎ 53 90 00 61, Fax 53 91 06 05. English spoken.
Open all year. 20 bedrooms (16 en suite,
3 bath/shower only). Parking.
*An old post house converted into a
comfortable, cosy hotel. In the centre of
Ribérac near the place Général de Gaulle and
in the heart of the Périgord region.*
■ RESTAURANT: Good food in traditional dining
room.
■ ACTIVITIES: Canoeing/kayaking (summer) and
horse-riding nearby.
■ TARIFF: (1994) Single 160–200,
Double 170–250, Bk 28, Set menu 68–270
(Amex, Euro/Access, Visa).
■ DISCOUNT: 2%

RICHELIEU Indre/Loire   2C

Hôtel Puits Dore ★★ 24 place du Marché,
37120 Richelieu.
☎ 47 58 10 59, Fax 47 58 24 39. English spoken.
Open 01/02 to 15/12. 17 bedrooms
(14 en suite). Golf 20 km, garage, parking.
*A 17th-century Logis de France hotel, situated
in the centre of the market place. From
Châtellerault take D749 north-west to
Richelieu.*
■ RESTAURANT: Being enlarged for 1995, hotel
will offer a gourmet restaurant and a pizzeria.
■ ACTIVITIES: Sauna, solarium and massage at
hotel. Good sports facilities nearby.
■ TARIFF: (1994) Single 145–280,
Double 145–425, Bk 30, Set menu 99–165
(Euro/Access, Visa).
■ DISCOUNT: 10%

RIOM Puy-de-Dôme   5A

Hôtel Mikège ★★ 40 pl J-B Laurent,
63200 Riom.
☎ 73 38 04 12, Fax 73 38 05 08. English spoken.

Open 10/01 to 20/12. 15 bedrooms
(all en suite). Golf 3 km, garage, parking.
*Sound-proofed hotel in the part pedestrianised
lower part of town. Riom has a rich heritage
and is at the entrance to the National Volcanic
Nature Park. Take the Riom exit from the A71.*
■ ACTIVITIES: Hotel will be pleased to advise you
on visits, activities, restaurants.
■ TARIFF: (1994) Single 190–210,
Double 220–250, Bk 30 (Euro/Access, Visa).

RIQUEWIHR Ht-Rhin   3D

Hôtel Le Schoenenbourg ★★★ rue du
Schoenenbourg, 68340 Riquewihr.
☎ 89 49 01 11, Fax 89 47 95 88. English spoken.
Open all year. 45 bedrooms (all en suite).
Golf 10 km, garage, parking. &
*Modern hotel with a peaceful setting near
vineyards. Just 100 yards from old Riquewihr,
a medieval town.*
■ RESTAURANT: Closed Wed. Restaurant is next
door to the hotel. Fine food and panoramic
views.
■ ACTIVITIES: Sauna, solarium, gym.
■ TARIFF: (1994) Single 300–500,
Double 385–550, Bk 47 (Euro/Access, Visa).

ROANNE Loire   5B

Hôtel Ibis ★★ 53 bd Ch de Gaulle, au Côteau,
42120 Roanne.
☎ 77 68 36 22, Fax 77 71 24 99. English spoken.

Open all year. 67 bedrooms (all en suite).
Outdoor swimming pool, golf 6 km, parking,
restaurant. &

*The hotel is south of Roanne, towards Lyon
and St-Etienne.*

■ TARIFF: (1994) Single 280–300,
Double 290–320, Bk 34, Set menu 60–98
(Amex, Euro/Access, Visa).

Hôtel Primevère ★★ rte de Lyon, 42120 Roanne.
☏ 77 62 84 84, Fax 77 62 02 09. English spoken.

Open all year. 42 bedrooms (2 en suite,
40 bath/shower only). Golf 8 km, parking. &

*Comfortable modern hotel in quiet country
setting, 10 minutes from the centre of Roanne.
Take N7 towards Lyon.*

■ RESTAURANT: Buffet offering hors d'oeuvres,
mixed salads, cheese and desserts including
regional specialities.

■ TARIFF: Single 230–270, Double 230–270,
Bk 30, Set menu 85–102 (Amex,
Euro/Access, Visa).

■ DISCOUNT: 10%

ROCAMADOUR Lot   5A

Hôtel Pages ★★ route de Payrac, 46350 Calés.
☏ 65 37 95 87, Fax 65 37 91 57. English spoken.

Open 03/02 to 15/10 & 28/10 to 03/01.
20 bedrooms (all en suite). Outdoor swimming
pool, parking.

*Recently renovated, a quiet, relaxing hotel in
the countryside, on the outskirts of Calés.
D673, route de Payrac.*

■ RESTAURANT: Closed 15 to 28 Oct & Jan.
Traditional, rustic-style dining room. Regional
specialities such as magret de canard aux baies
de cassis and suprême de truite sauce crème
romarin.

■ ACTIVITIES: Hiking and mountain-biking.

■ TARIFF: (1994) Single 170–300,
Double 180–450, Bk 30, Set menu 75–230
(Euro/Access, Visa).

■ DISCOUNT: 10%

Hôtel Lion d'Or ★★ 46500 Rocamadour.
☏ 65 33 62 04, Fax 65 33 72 54.
English spoken.

Open 09/04 to 02/11. 35 bedrooms
(all en suite). Parking. &

*The hotel is in the centre of this medieval city,
an old building, but with modern amenities
and fine views across the canyon.*

■ RESTAURANT: Panoramic view from restaurant
with specialities including foie gras, truffes,
cèpes and confits canard et oie.

■ ACTIVITIES: Good area for rambling.

■ TARIFF: (1994) Single 160–180,
Double 200–250, Bk , Set menu 59–210
(Euro/Access, Visa).

R

Hôtel Panoramic ★★ 46500 Rocamadour.
℡ 65 33 63 06, Fax 65 33 69 26. English spoken.

Open 15/02 to 11/11. 21 bedrooms
(16 en suite, 5 bath/shower only). Outdoor
swimming pool, parking.

*Traditional hotel with large, sunny terrace
facing the Causses Mountains and wonderful
views of historic Rocamadour. Quiet setting.*

■ RESTAURANT: Closed Fri except school
holidays. Specialities: foie gras, cèpes, truffes,
truite, escargots and cabécou de Rocamadour.
■ ACTIVITIES: Horse-riding, hiking, canoeing
down the Dordogne river.
■ TARIFF: Double 230–290, Bk 35,
Set menu 67–198 (Amex, Euro/Access, Visa).

Domaine de la Rhue ★★★ La Rhue,
46500 Rocamadour.
℡ 65 33 71 50, Fax 65 33 72 48. English spoken.

Open 01/04 to 15/10. 12 bedrooms
(all en suite). Outdoor swimming pool,
parking. &

*A lovely, peaceful hotel. Formerly the stables of
a château, now beautifully converted. Situated
in the countryside just outside the town. 7 km
NW of Rocamadour on the D673, then N140
towards Brive for 1 km. Hotel can then be
found on the road to the left.*

■ ACTIVITIES: Horse-riding, canoeing, cycling,
hot-air ballooning.
■ TARIFF: (1994) Double 370–570, Bk 42
(Euro/Access, Visa).
■ DISCOUNT: 10% LS.

LA ROCHE-POSAY Indre/Loire   4B

Hôtel La Promenade ★★★ 37290 Yzeures-
sur-Creuse.
℡ 47 94 55 21, Fax 47 94 46 12. English spoken.

Open all year. 15 bedrooms (all en suite).
Golf 4 km, parking.

*Comfortable 18th-century old post house with
original open fireplaces and beams. From A10,
take Châtellerault-Nord exit heading for La
Roche-Posay. The village is 4 km further on the
D750.*

■ RESTAURANT: Closed Tues lunch. Fresh daily
produce is transformed into delicious meals,
carefully prepared by Madame Bussereau, the
owner.
■ TARIFF: (1994) Single 225–265,
Double 240–295, Bk 35, Set menu 149–295
(Euro/Access, Visa).

LA ROCHE-SUR-YON Vendée   4A

Hôtel Logis de la Couperie ★★ 85000 La
Roche-sur-Yon.
℡ 51 37 21 19, Fax 51 47 71 08.
English spoken.
Open all year. 7 bedrooms (all en suite).
Golf 7 km, garage, parking.

*An 18th-century manor house with antique
furniture and featuring a grand staircase in
the main hall. Close to the town centre; good
car parking facilities. From the N160 take the
D948 to La Roche-sur-Yon.*

■ ACTIVITIES: Hiking and horse-riding.
■ TARIFF: (1994) Single 265–420,
Double 285–470, Bk 38 (Amex,
Euro/Access, Visa).

R

Hôtel Marie Stuart ★★ 86 rue Louis Blanc,
85000 La Roche-sur-Yon.
☎ 51 37 02 24, Fax 51 37 86 37. English spoken.
Open all year. 14 bedrooms (all en suite).
Golf 4 km.

*Friendly and comfortable, a town centre,
family-run hotel dating from the 1800s, in the
heart of picturesque Vendée.*

■ RESTAURANT: Lots of ambience and good food.
■ TARIFF: (1994) Single 229, Double 279, Bk 32,
Set menu 69–210 (Amex, Euro/Access, Visa).

Hôtel Le Point du Jour ★★ 7 rue Gutenberg,
85000 La Roche-sur-Yon.
☎ 51 37 08 98, Fax 51 46 22 44. English spoken.
Open all year. 25 bedrooms (22 en suite,
3 bath/shower only). Golf 3 km, parking. ᕼ

*Family hotel 1 km from town centre. From
Nantes, head for the town centre.*

■ RESTAURANT: Closed Sun eve LS. Country and
traditional cuisine.
■ TARIFF: (1994) Single 190–230,
Double 210–280, Bk 28, Set menu 58–230
(Amex, Euro/Access, Visa).

ROCHEFORT Charente-Mar   4A

Hôtel Commerce ★ rue Gén Bruncher,
17450 Fouras-les-Bains.
☎ 46 84 22 62, Fax 46 84 14 50. English spoken.
Open 15/02 to 15/11. 12 bedrooms (8 en suite,
2 bath/shower only).

*The hotel is in the centre of the Fouras-les-
Bains peninsula 50 m from the main beach.
Peaceful, homely environment. From
Rochefort N137 towards La Rochelle. Approx
15 km from Rochefort take left turn on to D937
to Fouras.*

■ RESTAURANT: Traditional cuisine.
■ TARIFF: (1994) Double 135–300, Bk 28,
Set menu 85–140 (Euro/Access, Visa).

Hôtel Le Soubise ★★ 62 rue de la République,
17780 Soubise.
☎ 46 84 92 16, Fax 46 84 91 35.
English spoken.
Open 01/02 to 30/09 & 01/11 to 15/01.
24 bedrooms (20 en suite,
4 bath/shower only). Golf 15 km, parking.

*Le Soubise is close to the sea and just 5 km
from Rochefort. From there, follow signs to Ile
d'Oleron and turn right over the bridge after
toll gate.*

■ RESTAURANT: Closed Sun eve & Mon LS. Rustic
setting. Specialities: foie gras, marinated
salmon. A full range of local fish, shellfish and
other regional dishes.

■ TARIFF: (1994) Double 140–360, Bk 35,
Set menu 95–165 (Euro/Access, Visa).
■ DISCOUNT: 15% LS only.

LA ROCHELLE Charente-Mar   4A

Hôtel Le Relais de Benon ★★★
17170 Courçon.
☎ 46 01 61 63, Fax 46 01 70 89.
English spoken.

Open all year. 30 bedrooms (all en suite).
Outdoor swimming pool, tennis, parking. ᕼ

R

*Set in 5 acres of parkland in the middle of the
Aunis forest; modern, comfortable and very
peaceful. Situated between Niort and La
Rochelle on the main N11 and 20 minutes'
drive from the sea.*

■ RESTAURANT: Spacious dining room
overlooking the forest. Hors d'oeuvre buffet,
grill, regional dishes including seafood, foie
gras maison and steak flambé. Home-made
pastries are also a speciality.
■ ACTIVITIES: 8 tennis courts, table tennis, volley
ball at hotel; horse-riding and boating nearby.
■ TARIFF: (1994) Single 330–360,
Double 410–420, Bk 45, Set menu 85–230
(Amex, Euro/Access, Visa).
■ DISCOUNT: 10%

Hôtel du Commerce ★★ 6 place de Verdun, 17000 La Rochelle.
☎ 46 41 08 22, Fax 46 41 74 85.
English spoken.
Open 20/01 to 23/12. 63 bedrooms
(49 en suite). Golf 7 km.
*Located in the centre of old town, opposite
cathedral and car park.*
■ RESTAURANT: Closed Fri lunch & Sat 01/10 to
28/02.
■ TARIFF: (1994) Double 135–305, Bk 30,
Set menu 72–155 (Amex, Euro/Access, Visa).

Hôtel Le Savary ★★ 2 rue Alsace-Lorraine, 17000 La Rochelle.
☎ 46 34 83 44, Fax 46 43 83 44.
English spoken.
Open all year. 35 bedrooms (all en suite).
Golf 5 km, parking.
*Quiet comfortable hotel, welcomes families
and is near the sea. Situated between Tours
and Bordeaux on the A10, turning off at
Poitiers heading for Niort on the N11.*
■ TARIFF: (1994) Double 220–300, Bk 30
(Euro/Access, Visa).
■ DISCOUNT: 15% Between 01/10 & 31/03.

Hôtel St-Nicolas ★★ 13 rue Sardinerie, 17000 La Rochelle.
☎ 46 41 71 55, Fax 46 41 70 46. English spoken.
Open all year. 79 bedrooms (all en suite).
Golf 5 km, garage. &
*Charming, renovated mansion in the heart of
the old town. Close to the pedestrian precinct
and a few minute's walk from the ancient
harbour. Indoor garden; locked, open or
covered garage available.*
■ TARIFF: (1994) Single 275–370,
Double 310–405, Bk 36 (Amex,
Euro/Access, Visa).

R

ROCROI Ardennes   3A

Hôtel du Commerce ★★ pl A Briaud, 08230 Rocroi.
☎ 24 54 11 15.
Open all year. 9 bedrooms (7 en suite).
Parking, restaurant.
*The hotel is situated in the main square of the
town.*
■ ACTIVITIES: Windsurfing and boating on
nearby lake (8 km); visits to the old
fortifications and museum commemorating the
Battle of Rocroi.
■ TARIFF: (1994) Single 140–160,
Double 140–210, Bk 19, Set menu 60–180
(Euro/Access, Visa).

RODEZ Aveyron   5C

Hôtel Eldorado ★★ rte d'Espalion, 12740 Sébazac.
☎ 65 46 99 77, Fax 65 46 99 80. English spoken.
Open all year. 22 bedrooms (all en suite).
Parking. &
*A new hotel, 5 km north of Rodez on the D904
(off the D988).*
■ RESTAURANT: Closed Sun eve.
■ TARIFF: (1994) Single 250, Double 280, Bk 35,
Set menu 90–180 (Amex, Euro/Access, Visa).
■ DISCOUNT: 10%

ROISSY Val-d'Oise   2B

Hôtel Altea ★★★ allée du Verger, 95700 Roissy-en-France.
☎ 1 34 29 40 00, Fax 1 34 29 00 18.
English spoken.
Open all year. 202 bedrooms (all en suite).
Golf 5 km, parking. &
*From Roissy/Charles de Gaulle airport, follow
the signs to the town. There is a free shuttle
from the hotel to the airport.*
■ RESTAURANT: Selection of appetizers from the
buffet. Speciality is home-made duck liver.
Dessert buffet includes meringue cake filled
with creamy bergamot.
■ ACTIVITIES: Tennis nearby. Euro Disney
30 km, Parc Asterix 20 km.
■ TARIFF: (1994) Single 640–740,
Double 640–740, Bk 65, Set menu 72–139
(Amex, Euro/Access, Visa, **BT✆**).

Hôtel de Louvres ★★ 94 rue de Paris, 95380 Louvres.
☎ 1 34 72 44 44, Fax 1 34 72 42 42.
English spoken.

Open all year. 40 bedrooms (all en suite).
Golf 10 km, garage, parking. &
*Near Charles de Gaulle airport. Just north of
Paris on the A1, take exit 7 (Louvres). Direct*

métro into Paris (30 mins) close to hotel.
■ RESTAURANT: Light meals only plus buffet breakfast.
■ ACTIVITIES: Parc Asterix is just 5 minutes' drive and Euro Disney 20 minutes. Also close by: Château de Chantilly and Van Gogh Museum.
■ TARIFF: (1994) Single 265, Double 280, Bk 30 (Amex, Euro/Access, Visa).
■ DISCOUNT: 10% Minimum stay 3 nights.

ROMANECHE-THORINS Saône/Loire 5B

Hôtel les Maritonnes ★★★ route de Fleurie, 71570 Romaneche-Thorins.
✆ 85 35 51 70, Fax 85 35 52 64.
English spoken.

Open 31/01 to 15/12. 21 bedrooms (all en suite). Outdoor swimming pool, golf 15 km, parking.
In the heart of the Beaujolais area, in a spendid setting of greenery and flowers. Motorway exit: Belleville coming from Lyon, Mâcon-Sud from Paris.
■ RESTAURANT: Closed Mon & Tues lunch. Classic French cuisine served in most attractive, rustic surroundings.
■ ACTIVITIES: Wine tasting, visit to wine museum.
■ TARIFF: (1994) Single 380–400, Double 400–500, Bk 55 (Amex, Euro/Access, Visa).

RONCHAMP Hte-Saône 3D

Hôtel Le Ronchamp ★★★ route de Belfort, 70250 Ronchamp.
✆ 84 20 60 35, Fax 84 63 58 46. English spoken.
Open all year. 20 bedrooms (all en suite). Parking.
Small hotel on the N19, north-west of Belfort.
■ TARIFF: (1994) Single 280, Double 310, Bk 35 (Amex, Euro/Access, Visa).

ROQUEBRUNE-CAP-MARTIN 6C

Hôtel Deux Frères ★★ pl 2 Frères, 06190 Roquebrune-Cap-Martin.
✆ 93 28 99 00, Fax 93 28 99 10. English spoken.
Open 10/12 to 01/11. 10 bedrooms (all en suite). Golf 4 km, parking. ქ
Hotel with bar and terrace. At a height of 300 m in the centre of the 10th-century village of Roquebrune, with lovely views of the mountains, bay and harbour of Monte Carlo. Access motorway A8.
■ RESTAURANT: Closed Thur & Fri lunch. Gastronomic cuisine. Specialities: lamb, duck, foie gras.
■ ACTIVITIES: A host of activities in nearby Monte-Carlo, including parachuting and hang-gliding.
■ TARIFF: (1994) Single 385, Double 495, Bk 40 (Amex, Euro/Access, Visa).

Hôtel Vista Palace ★★★★ Grande Corniche, 06190 Roquebrune-Cap-Martin.
✆ 92 10 40 00, Fax 93 35 18 94. English spoken.

Open all year. 68 bedrooms (all en suite). Outdoor swimming pool, golf 5 km, garage, parking. ქ
De-luxe apartments perched 1,000 feet above the sea overlooking Monte Carlo and Cap Martin. 8-acre landscaped Mediterranean gardens, helicopter pad and boutique.
■ RESTAURANT: Gourmet restaurant; restaurant for business meals, functions and dances; summer restaurant beside swimming pool.
■ ACTIVITIES: Workout centre with excellent facilities including squash is free to guests. Tennis nearby.
■ TARIFF: (1994) Double 1200–2400, Bk 100, Set menu 200–560 (Amex, Euro/Access, Visa).

Hôtel Westminster ★★ 14 av L Laurent, 06190 Roquebrune-Cap-Martin.
✆ 93 35 00 68, Fax 93 28 88 50. English spoken.

R

Open 15/02 to 15/11. 30 bedrooms
(25 en suite, 5 bath/shower only). Tennis,
golf 10 km, garage, parking.

*On a private road, with air-conditioned rooms
which face the the sea and have balconies.
Large garden, and beaches directly below the
hotel. 800 m from Monaco towards Menton.*

■ RESTAURANT: Closed lunch.
■ TARIFF: (1994) Single 240–335,
Double 280–450, Bk 30 (Amex,
Euro/Access, Visa).
■ DISCOUNT: 5% 15/07 to 15/10.

ROSCOFF Finistère   1A

Hôtel d'Angleterre ★ 28 rue Albert Demun,
29211 Roscoff.
☎ 98 69 70 42, Fax 98 69 75 16. English spoken.

Open 01/04 to 15/10. 40 bedrooms
(11 en suite, 2 bath/shower only). Golf 10 km.

*An old manor near the church in town centre.
Warm and comfortable with a pretty garden.*

■ RESTAURANT: Closed Sun eve. Family cuisine
as well as seafood specialities.
■ ACTIVITIES: Good sports facilities and beach
within easy reach of hotel.
■ TARIFF: (1994) Double 150–260, Bk 30,
Set menu 70–145 (Amex, Euro/Access, Visa).
■ DISCOUNT: 5% Full or half-board only.

La Cigale route de Botmeur, 29690 La Feuillee.
☎ 98 99 62 17. English spoken.
Open all year. 8 bedrooms. Parking.

*Small hotel with washbasins in all rooms.
From Roscoff ferry drive from Morlaix on D785
to Huelgoat (D764) turn left at second La
Feuillée sign.*

■ ACTIVITIES: Sports facilities in the park.
■ TARIFF: (1994) Single 150, Double 180–200
(No credit cards).

Hôtel Les Tamaris ★★ rue Edouard Corbière,
29680 Roscoff.
☎ 98 61 22 99, Fax 98 69 74 36. English spoken.
Open 01/04 to 15/10. 27 bedrooms
(all en suite). &

*From Brittany Ferries terminal drive towards
town centre. Follow esplanade past church
and on to sea-front by 'Toutes Directions' sign.
Once you can see the sea the hotel is also in
sight. Some rooms with sea views.*

■ TARIFF: (1994) Single 190–300,
Double 210–320, Bk 32 (Euro/Access, Visa).

Hôtel Thalasstonic ★★★ av V Hugo,
29680 Roscoff.
☎ 98 29 20 20, Fax 98 61 22 73. English spoken.
Open 15/02 to 31/12. 54 bedrooms
(all en suite). Golf 10 km, parking,
restaurant. &

*Between the beach and town centre. From the
church, take the road towards Santec for
700 m.*

■ TARIFF: (1994) Single 395, Double 435, Bk 45,
Set menu 140 (Amex, Euro/Access, Visa).

ROUEN Seine-Marit   2A

Hôtel Astrid 121 rue Jeanne d'Arc,
76000 Rouen.
☎ 35 71 75 88, Fax 35 88 53 25. English spoken.
Open all year. 40 bedrooms (all en suite).
Parking.

In the centre of the town opposite the station.

■ TARIFF: (1994) Single 280–320,
Double 340–380 (Amex, Euro/Access, Visa).

Hôtel La Bertelière ★★★ St-Martin-du-Vivier,
76160 Rouen.
☎ 35 60 44 00, Fax 35 61 56 63. English spoken.

Open all year. 44 bedrooms (all en suite).
Tennis, golf 5 km, parking. &

Warm and comfortable hotel just 10 minutes

R

from the centre of Rouen. Rooms are fully equipped. From Rouen take the N28 towards Amiens for 10 km and exit at Bihorel/St-Martin-du-Vivier (D43). Turn right on D443 into La Chapitre and hotel is on the right just over the cross-roads.

■ RESTAURANT: Closed Sat & Sun eve. 'Le Jardin d'Hiver' restaurant for romantics and gourmets, and the alternative 'L'Auberge' overlooks the garden. Both offer Normandy specialities.
■ ACTIVITIES: ● Free use of pool and tennis courts 5 minutes away and 50% reduction on green fees at nearby golf course.
■ TARIFF: (1994) Single 300–385, Double 400–435, Bk 50 (Amex, Euro/Access, Visa).

Hôtel de Bordeaux ★★ 9 place de la République, 76000 Rouen.
℡ 35 71 93 58, Fax 35 71 92 15. English spoken. Open all year. 48 bedrooms (all en suite). Parking.
In the centre of Rouen, between the River Seine and the cathedral. Good facilities in all rooms and private underground parking.
■ TARIFF: (1994) Single 195–280, Double 215–330, Bk 30 (Amex, Euro/Access, Visa).
■ DISCOUNT: 10%

Hôtel Dieppe ★★★ pl B Tissot, 76000 Rouen.
℡ 35 71 96 00, Fax 35 89 65 21. English spoken. Open all year. 41 bedrooms (all en suite). Golf 5 km.
Typical traditional hotel, fully renovated, founded and managed by the Guerer family since 1880. Excellent town-centre location in a district noted for art and painting.
■ RESTAURANT: Delectable Normandy gourmet specialities including caneton à la Rouennaise.
■ TARIFF: Single 415–485, Double 475–585, Bk 40, Set menu 135–195 (Amex, Euro/Access, Visa).
■ DISCOUNT: 10%

Hôtel Québec ★★ 18 rue Québec, 76000 Rouen.
℡ 35 70 09 38, Fax 35 15 80 15.
Open 04/01 to 23/12. 38 bedrooms (30 en suite, 4 bath/shower only). Golf 5 km, parking.
In the centre of Rouen, on the right bank, just a few minutes from the cathedral.
■ TARIFF: (1994) Single 165–255, Double 205–310, Bk 30 (Amex, Euro/Access, Visa).
■ DISCOUNT: 10%

Château de Rosay 27790 Rosay-sur-Lieure.
℡ 32 49 66 51, Fax 32 49 70 77. English spoken.

Open all year. 24 bedrooms (all en suite). Outdoor swimming pool, golf 25 km, parking.
Built in 1611 the château has been entirely renovated and lies in the Lyons Forest, famous for its beeches. From Rouen take N14 for 32 km to Ecouis then turn left onto the D2 heading towards Lyons-la-Foret.
■ TARIFF: (1994) Single 350–670, Double 390–670, Bk 50 (Amex, Visa).

Hôtel Le Vert Bocage ★★ rte de Paris, 76520 Franqueville-St-Pierre.
℡ 35 80 14 74, Fax 35 80 55 73. English spoken. Open all year. 19 bedrooms (all en suite). Parking.
From Rouen take the N14 towards Paris/Pontoise, and the hotel is on the left, 2 km before Rouen-Boos airport.
■ RESTAURANT: Closed Mon Nov to Mar. Traditional cuisine with many specialities.
■ TARIFF: (1994) Single 230–250, Double 250–270, Bk 25, Set menu 98–200 (Euro/Access, Visa).
■ DISCOUNT: 10%

R

ROYAN Charente-Mar　　　　　4A

Hôtel Beau Rivage ★★ 9 façade Foncillon, 17200 Royan.
℡ 46 39 43 10, Fax 46 38 22 50. English spoken. Open all year. 22 bedrooms (all en suite). ♿
The hotel is located beside the Palais de Congrès, opposite the beach at Foncillon.
■ ACTIVITIES: Tennis, sea water therapy, golf and horse-riding nearby.
■ TARIFF: (1994) Double 260–390, Bk 34 (Euro/Access, Visa).

Hôtel Beauséjour ★★ 32 av Grande Conche, 17200 Royan.
℡ 46 05 09 40. English spoken.

Open all year. 14 bedrooms (all en suite).
Golf 5 km.
Outdoor dining terrace in this hotel just 100 m from Royan's main beach.
■ RESTAURANT: Closed lunch LS. Dining on the terrace.
■ TARIFF: (1994) Single 235–305, Double 240–310, Bk 30 (Euro/Access, Visa).

Family Golf Hôtel ★★★ 28 bd Garnier, 17200 Royan.
☎ 46 05 14 66, Fax 46 06 52 56. English spoken.
Open 09/04 to 30/09. 33 bedrooms (all en suite). Golf 5 km, parking.
In the middle of the long beach of Royan, near the yachting harbour and fishing harbour.
■ TARIFF: (1994) Single 350–380, Double 390–500, Bk 40 (Euro/Access, Visa).

Grand Hotel de Pontaillac ★★★ 195 av Pontaillac, 17200 Royan.
☎ 46 39 00 44, Fax 46 39 04 05. English spoken.
Open 01/05 to 30/09. 42 bedrooms (all en suite). Golf 4 km, garage, parking.
Sea-front hotel, halfway along Pontillac beach, with pleasant shady garden. Follow the coast road from the centre of Royan.
■ TARIFF: (1994) Single 350–420, Double 430–540, Bk 43 (Euro/Access, Visa).

Hôtel Résidence de Rohan ★★★ Parc des Feés, route de St-Palais, 17640 Royan.
☎ 46 39 00 75, Fax 46 38 29 99. English spoken.
Open 01/04 to 15/11. 41 bedrooms (all en suite). Tennis, golf 4 km, parking.
Old house opening on to the beach of Vaux-Nauzan, just at the end of the garden. From the centre of Royan go towards the beach at Pontaillac and St-Palais-sur-Mer (D25).
■ ACTIVITIES: Horse-riding; ● 20% reduction on green fees.
■ TARIFF: (1994) Single 300–600, Double 300–650, Bk 49 (Amex, Euro/Access, Visa).
■ DISCOUNT: 15%

Hôtel La Saintonge ★★ 14 rue Gambetta, 17200 Royan.
☎ 46 05 78 24. English spoken.
Open all year. 14 bedrooms (11 en suite, 3 bath/shower only). Golf 5 km, parking.
Royan lies on the coast and this quiet hotel is only 50 m from the beach. From the A10 going north, turn left towards coast on N150 to Royan.
■ TARIFF: (1994) Double 180–340, Bk 33 (Euro/Access, Visa).

ROYE Somme 2B

Hôtel Central ★★ 36 rue Amiens, 80700 Roye.
☎ 22 87 11 05, Fax 22 87 42 74. English spoken.
Open all year. 8 bedrooms (all en suite). Garage, parking.
Small hotel in the centre of town. From the A1 Lille/Paris motorway, take the exit marked Roye following the D930 and the hotel is 2 km from leaving the main road.
■ RESTAURANT: Closed Sun eve & Mon. Neo-classical style restaurant specialising in very good regional dishes and seafood.
■ TARIFF: (1994) Single 230–280, Double 260–320, Bk 28, Set menu 85–200 (Amex, Euro/Access, Visa).

Motel des Lions ★★ route Rosières, 80700 Roye.
☎ 22 87 20 61, Fax 22 87 24 83. English spoken.

Open all year. 43 bedrooms (all en suite). Parking. ♿
Set in the countryside, hotel is quiet and peaceful. Leave A1 at exit 12 and hotel at Roye is about 300 m.
■ RESTAURANT: Specialities: ficelle Picarde, mignons de veau, jambonette de volaille, profiteroles au chocolat, sabayon de fruits frais.
■ TARIFF: (1994) Single 290, Double 320, Bk 40, Set menu 90–180 (Amex, Euro/Access, Visa).
■ DISCOUNT: 10%

RUE Somme 2B

Hôtel Lion d'Or ★★ rue Barrière, 80120 Rue.
☎ 22 25 74 18, Fax 22 25 66 63. English spoken.
Open all year. 16 bedrooms (all en suite). Golf 10 km, parking.
Located in the centre of town, beside a public car park, between Abbeville and the beaches.
■ RESTAURANT: Closed Sun eve LS.
■ TARIFF: (1994) Single 240–270, Double 300, Bk 35, Set menu 80–200 (Euro/Access, Visa).

R

SABLE-SUR-SARTHE Sarthe   2C

Hôtel Escu du Roy ★★ 20 rue Léon Legludic, 72300 Sable-sur-Sarthe.
℡ 43 95 90 31, Fax 43 92 33 69. English spoken.
Open all year. 11 bedrooms (all en suite). Golf 5 km, garage. ⅃

Large, comfortable house in the town centre and opposite the port (River Sarthe).

■ RESTAURANT: Closed Sun eve. Friendly and refined air-conditioned restaurant. Carefully prepared dishes are based on fresh products.

■ ACTIVITIES: Saulges caves, the earthenware pottery at Raireries and the medieval village of Ste-Suzanne are all within easy reach.

■ TARIFF: (1994) Single 180–220, Double 220–270, Bk , Set menu 69–220 (Euro/Access, Visa).

■ DISCOUNT: 5%

LES SABLES-D'OLONNE Vendée   1D

Hôtel Antoine ★★ 60 rue Napoléon, 85100 Les Sables-d'Olonne.
℡ 51 95 08 36. English spoken.
Open 01/03 to 20/10. 19 bedrooms (all en suite). Golf 5 km, garage, restaurant.

Close to beaches and port, this hotel has a pretty garden. Prices are on a demi-pension basis.

■ TARIFF: (1994) Single 245–275, Double 490–550, Bk 30 (Visa).

Chalet St-Hubert ★ 20 route de Jard, 85520 St-Vincent-sur-Jard.
℡ 51 33 40 33. English spoken.

Open all year. 10 bedrooms (7 en suite). Parking.

On the road from Longeville to Jard-sur-Mer, the hotel is near the sea.

■ RESTAURANT: Specialises in seafood.

■ TARIFF: (1994) Single 180–225, Double 190–225, Bk 25, Set menu 75–298 (Euro/Access, Visa).

SABLES-D'OR-LES-PINS   1D

Hôtel Au Bon Accueil ★★ Sables-d'Or-les-Pins, 22240 Fréhel.

℡ 96 41 42 19, Fax 96 41 57 59. English spoken.
Open 01/04 to 30/09. 38 bedrooms (32 en suite, 6 bath/shower only). Golf 2 km, garage, parking. ⅃

A large comfortable bed and breakfast hotel with lift. On the main avenue of Fréhel, it stands in its own grounds and is close to the beach. Good restaurants nearby.

■ ACTIVITIES: Children's activities, table tennis. Horse-riding, tennis, cycling and good walks nearby.

■ TARIFF: (1994) Single 180–250, Double 210–340, Bk 35 (Euro/Access, Visa).

■ DISCOUNT: 5%

Hôtel Le Manoir St-Michel ★★ La Carquois, Les Sables-d'Or-les-Pins, 22240 Fréhel.
℡ 96 41 48 87, Fax 96 41 41 55. English spoken.
Open 01/04 to 02/11. 20 bedrooms (all en suite). Golf 1 km, parking. ⅃

16th-century manor house in extensive grounds with lake and views to the sea. Tranquil and charming. Satellite TV. North of Sables-d'Or towards Cap-Fréhel.

■ TARIFF: (1994) Single 250–380, Double 280–550, Bk 40 (Euro/Access, Visa).

SAIGNES Cantal   5A

Château de Trancis ★★★ 15210 Ydes.
℡ 71 40 60 40, Fax 71 40 62 13. English spoken.

Open 01/04 to 30/09. 7 bedrooms (all en suite). Outdoor swimming pool, golf 20 km, parking.

Luxurious Italian Renaissance-style château, owned and run by Innes and Fiona Fennell. Situated in secluded parkland with terraces and lovely views. From the D922 going towards Mauriac, at Bort-les-Orgues take the D15 to Saignes.

■ RESTAURANT: Gastronomic delights are served by candlelight to guests of Château de Trancis.

■ TARIFF: (1994) Double 500–950 (Euro/Access, Visa).

S

ST-AFFRIQUE Aveyron 5C

Hôtel Moderne ★★ 54 av Alphonse Pezet, 12400 St-Affrique.
✆ 65 49 20 44, Fax 65 49 36 55. English spoken.
Open 20/01 to 20/12. 28 bedrooms (all en suite). Garage, parking. &

Comfortable, inviting hotel, which houses a permanent art exhibition. Rooms are decorated in warm colours and have recently been refurbished. St-Affrique is due west of Roquefort.

■ RESTAURANT: Closed 7/10 to 14/10. Renowned for its delicious local cuisine, Roquefort cheese and fine regional wines.
■ ACTIVITIES: Cycling, tennis, swimming, river sports (including white-water rafting) and bungee jumping all available nearby.
■ TARIFF: Single 200–320, Double 250–390, Bk 32, Set menu 75–260 (Amex, Euro/Access, Visa).

ST-ALBAN-SUR-LIMAGNOL Lozère 5A

Hôtel Centre 48120 St-Alban-sur-Limagnole.
✆ 66 31 50 04. English spoken.
Open all year. 20 bedrooms (9 en suite). Outdoor swimming pool, tennis, golf 2 km, parking, restaurant. &

Quiet spot, 1000 m up in the Margeride mountains. Just off the main road between St-Flour and Mende.

■ ACTIVITIES: Plenty of outdoor pursuits including walking, fishing, mushroom picking and winter skiing.
■ TARIFF: (1994) Single 100–250, Double 130–325, Bk 25 (Amex, Euro/Access, Visa).

ST-AMAND-MONTROND Cher 5A

Hôtel L'Amandois ★★ 7 rue Henri Barbusse, 18200 St-Amand-Montrond.
✆ 48 63 72 00, Fax 48 96 77 11. English spoken.
Open all year. 27 bedrooms (all en suite). Parking, restaurant. &

The hotel is in the town centre. St-Amand is a wooded area in central France. Good shopping. Prehistoric and Gallo-Roman remains. From A71 motorway go east on to N144 to St-Amand Montrond.

■ TARIFF: (1994) Single 270, Double 320, Bk 33, Set menu 74–120 (Amex, Euro/Access, Visa).

Hôtel Le Noirlac ★★ 215 rte de Bourges, 18200 St-Amand-Montrond.
✆ 48 96 80 80, Fax 48 96 63 88. English spoken.

Open all year. 44 bedrooms (all en suite). Outdoor swimming pool, tennis, parking. &

A new, quiet and welcoming hotel. From N144 towards Bourge, take A71 exit and hotel is 2 km from the town centre.

■ RESTAURANT: Spacious, serving traditional menus using locally-grown produce. Meals served on the terrace during summer.
■ ACTIVITIES: Visits to: Abbaye de Noirlac (2 km), Château de Meillant (8 km) and Château d'Ainay-le-Vieil (10 km).
■ TARIFF: (1994) Single 255, Double 295, Bk 32, Set menu 90–190 (Amex, Euro/Access, Visa).

Hôtel Poste ★★ 9 rue du Dr Vallet, 18200 St-Amand-Montrond.
✆ 48 96 27 14, Fax 48 96 97 74. English spoken.
Open 12/02 to 05/01. 22 bedrooms (18 en suite). Golf 25 km, garage, parking.

16th-century building in the centre of the town. Quiet, comfortable rooms. 45 km south of Bourges. Leave the A7 at junction 8.

■ RESTAURANT: Closed Mon LS.
■ TARIFF: (1994) Single 230–280, Bk 35, Set menu 100–235 (Euro/Access, Visa).

ST-ANDRE-LES-ALPES Alpes-Hte-Prov 6C

Hôtel Le Clair Logis ★★ rte de Digne, 04170 St-André-les-Alpes.
✆ 92 89 04 05. English spoken.
Open 01/03 to 31/10. 12 bedrooms (all en suite). Garage, parking.

A chalet hotel 400 m out of town overlooking Lac de Castillon and the Verdon valley. N202 from Nice, N85 from de Digne to Bareme then N202 from Bareme to St-André-les-Alpes.

■ RESTAURANT: Traditional food including regional specialities. Varied choice of set menus and à la carte. Good wine list.
■ ACTIVITIES: Hang-gliding and parascending in Verdon; kayaking, rafting, hydrospeed, sailing,

S

water-skiing; fishing in nearby rivers, mountain walks.

■ TARIFF: (1994) Single 170–220, Double 220–280, Bk 35, Set menu 68–180 (Amex, Euro/Access, Visa).

ST-ANTHEME Puy-de-Dôme 5B

Hôtel Voyageurs ★★ place de l'Aubeguin, 63660 St-Anthème.
℡ 73 95 40 16, Fax 73 95 80 94. English spoken.
Open 01/01 to 31/10 & 21/12 to 31/12.
32 bedrooms (all en suite). Outdoor swimming pool, tennis, golf 1 km, garage. &
Hotel is in the centre of this little mountain village which lies 20 km east of Ambert on D996.
■ RESTAURANT: Closed Sun eve & Mon.
Specialities: pâté de canard aux pistaches à l'oseille; canard à l'orange; soufflé glacé au Grand Marnier chocolat chaud.
■ ACTIVITIES: Lovely walks, mountain-biking, lake, tennis and horse-riding nearby.
■ TARIFF: (1994) Single 176–186, Double 227–247, Bk 30, Set menu 53–163 (Euro/Access, Visa).

ST-BRIEUC Côtes-du-Nord 1D

Hôtel du Champ de Mars ★★ 13 rue du champs de Mars, 22000 St-Brieuc.
℡ 96 33 60 99, Fax 96 33 60 05. English spoken.
Open 03/01 to 26/12. 21 bedrooms (all en suite). Golf 10 km. &
Completely refurbished, both inside and out. In the centre of town, opposite a park.
■ TARIFF: (1994) Single 220–250, Double 240–280, Bk 30 (Amex, Euro/Access, Visa).

ST-CERE Lot 5A

Hôtel Ric ★★★ route de Leyme, 46400 St-Céré.
℡ 65 38 04 08, Fax 65 38 00 14.
Open 01/03 to 01/01. 6 bedrooms (all en suite). Outdoor swimming pool, golf 3 km, parking, restaurant.
Hotel-restaurant in the middle of a forest overlooking the Dordogne Valley. 3 km from St-Céré on the D48.
■ TARIFF: (1994) Double 300–350, Bk 40, Set menu 100–250 (Visa).

ST-CIRQ-LAPOPIE Lot 4D

Hôtel La Pelissaria ★★★ 46330 St-Cirq-Lapopie.
℡ 65 31 25 14, Fax 65 30 25 52. English spoken.
Open 01/04 to 15/11. 7 bedrooms (all en suite). Garage, parking.
An old hotel in this medieval village. From Cahors go east towards Tour-de-Faure, to St-Cirq-Lapopie.

■ RESTAURANT: Closed Thur and Fri.
■ TARIFF: (1994) Double 410–640, Bk 48, Set menu 200 (Euro/Access, Visa).

ST-CLAUDE Jura 6A

Hôtel St-Hubert ★★ 39200 St-Claude.
℡ 84 45 10 70, Fax 84 45 64 76. English spoken.

Open all year. 30 bedrooms (all en suite).
Tennis, golf 4 km, garage, parking.
A modern hotel within a short walk of cathedral.
■ RESTAURANT: Closed 1/10 to 7/10 & 20/12 to 3/01.
■ ACTIVITIES: ● 30% reduction on green fees at St-Claude Golf Course.
■ TARIFF: (1994) Single 225–315, Double 225–395, Bk 30 (Euro/Access, Visa).

ST-CYPRIEN Pyrénées-Or 5C

Hôtel Le Mas d'Huston ★★★ St-Cyprien-Plage, 66750 St-Cyprien.
℡ 68 37 63 63, Fax 68 37 64 64. English spoken.

Open 01/01 to 31/01 & 01/03 to 31/12.
50 bedrooms (all en suite). Outdoor swimming pool, tennis, golf on site, parking, restaurant. &
Very attractive, light and spacious golf-hotel with lovely gardens.

S

■ ACTIVITIES: Water sports school in summer.
● Special golf packages available.
■ TARIFF: Single 335–535, Double 550–770
(Amex, Euro/Access, Visa).

ST-CYR-SUR-MER Var   6C

Grand Hôtel ★★★ 24 av du Port, Les Lecques,
83270 St-Cyr-sur-Mer.
℡ 94 26 23 01, Fax 94 26 10 22.
English spoken.

Open 14/04 to 15/10. 58 bedrooms
(51 en suite). Outdoor swimming pool, tennis,
golf 3 km, parking.
*The hotel sits high in a large flower-filled and
wooded park just 200 m from the sandy beach
with clear views across the whole bay. From St-
Cyr follow Les Lecques beach signs.*
■ RESTAURANT: A good choice of menus, with
the accent on Mediterranean cuisine, can be
enjoyed in a panoramic setting.
■ TARIFF: (1994) Single 325–630,
Double 385–885, Bk 55, Set menu 160 (Amex,
Euro/Access, Visa).

ST-DIZIER Hte-Marne   3C

Hôtel Le Gambetta ★★★ 62 rue Gambetta,
52100 St-Dizier.
℡ 25 56 52 10, Fax 25 56 39 47. English spoken.
Open all year. 63 bedrooms (all en suite).
Golf 15 km, garage, parking. ₺
■ RESTAURANT: Closed Sun eve.
■ TARIFF: (1994) Single 210–290,
Double 270–390, Bk 35 (Amex,
Euro/Access, Visa).

ST-EMILION Gironde   4B

Hôtel Logis des Remparts ★★★ rue Guadet,
33330 St-Emilion.
℡ 57 84 70 43, Fax 57 74 47 44. English spoken.
Open 08/01 to 21/12. 15 bedrooms
(all en suite). Parking.

*Stone-built hotel with pretty terraces in a
medieval town overlooking the Dordogne
Valley. Comfortably furnished, fully equipped
rooms with private parking. 30 km from
Bordeaux on the N89 to Libourne then 8 km
on the D243.*
■ TARIFF: (1994) Double 298–580, Bk 48
(Euro/Access, Visa).

ST-ETIENNE Loire   5B

Hôtel Ibis ★★ 35 pl Massenet,
42000 St-Etienne.
℡ 77 93 31 87, Fax 77 93 71 29. English spoken.
Open all year. 85 bedrooms (all en suite).
Golf 15 km, garage, parking, restaurant. ₺
*The hotel is situated to the north of St-Etienne
en route to Roanne (A72).*
■ TARIFF: (1994) Single 295–300,
Double 320–330, Bk 33 (Amex,
Euro/Access, Visa).

Hôtel Midi ★★★ 19 bd Pasteur,
42000 St-Etienne.
℡ 77 57 32 55, Fax 77 59 11 43. English spoken.
Open 01/09 to 31/07. 33 bedrooms
(all en suite). Garage, parking. ₺
*A comfortable business hotel near the Bellevue
Hospital south of St-Etienne.*
■ TARIFF: (1994) Single 275–310,
Double 310–380, Bk 36 (Amex,
Euro/Access, Visa).

ST-FLORENTIN Yonne   3C

Hôtel Grande Chaumière ★★★ 3 rue des
Capucins, 89600 St-Florentin.
℡ 86 35 15 12, Fax 86 35 33 14. English spoken.
Open 17/01 to 01/09 & 09/09 to 20/12.
11 bedrooms (all en suite). Parking.
*Charming, comfortable hotel with lovely
gardens. 25 km north of Auxerre.*
■ RESTAURANT: Closed Wed. Enjoys a good
reputation for its food and wine.
■ ACTIVITIES: Good walking country.
■ TARIFF: (1994) Single 300–650,
Double 450–750, Bk 50, Set menu 130–480
(Amex, Euro/Access, Visa).

ST-FLOUR

St-Flour lies some 80 km to the south of
Clermont-Ferrand in an area of outstanding
natural beauty. Before starting out to
explore the surrounding countryside, enjoy

S

wandering around this hillside town with its 14th-century cathedral. An austere building from the outside, it has a bare but beautifully vaulted interior and is famous for its 15th-century Black Christ. Visit the town on a Saturday and the place d'Armes outside the cathedral comes alive with a colourful market. Also on the place d'Armes is the Hotel de Ville housing the Musée de la Haute-Auvergne, an interesting collection dedicated to the way of life and traditions of this rural area of France.

Each direction taken from St-Flour has much to offer. To the east are the Montagnes de Margeride and also the Forêt de la Margeride. Stop first at the Ecomuseum of Ruynes-en-Margeride where there are displays showing life on a 19th-century farm, life in a 1930s school, and a

Fromage

Sampling the different cheeses that are produced locally is yet another great pleasure that awaits the holidaymaker in France. Cheese may be served at the end of a meal, as part of an hors d'œuvre or in a cooked sauce.

The cheeses of the Auvergne are made from milk which has a particular flavour due to the volcanic pastures on which the cows are grazed. The most common of all is Cantal which is also known as Fourme de Cantal. Said by some to be the French equivalent of Cheddar, it may look similar but it has a much stronger tangy taste. A cheese similar in looks and taste, but less common, is Salers.

Arguably the finest cheese of the Auvergne is St-Nectaire which has been made in this area since the Middle Ages. It is a flat cheese weighing about 1 1/2 kilos with a mottled crust and a distinctive nutty flavour.

Lovers of blue cheese should try Bleu d'Auvergne. Its taste is similar to that of Roquefort but, because it is made from cows' rather than goats' milk, it is pleasantly milder.

There are so many cheeses to try and they can, perhaps, best be enjoyed outside, whilst admiring the countryside from which they spring. What could be more delicious than a picnic of bread and cheese washed down with a glass or two of local wine?

display describing the construction of the Garabit viaduct in 1884. Gustave Eiffel, best remembered for his Parisian tower, designed this impressive structure which spans the nearby River Truyére.

South-west of Garabit, the Truyére widens out into a lake formed by a dam, the Barrage de Grandvet. Although artificial, the lake, with its many inlets, adds to the wild grandeur of this sparsely populated area. On a rocky hill above the lake stands the romantic Château d'Alleuze now in ruins, a pleasant spot for a picnic. Beyond the barrage, the river enters a series of gorges, both above and below the next dam, the Barrage de Sarrans. Chaudes-Aigues, which lies on a tributary of the Truyére just above the first series of gorges, is an interesting little town with its hot spring (82°) gushing out of a well into the street. This natural hot water is collected by the townsfolk for household tasks and used to centrally heat some of the houses.

Starting again from St-Flour and going west, you come to the Parc Régional de Volcans d'Auvergne, a distinctive landscape formed by volcanic action. From the top of the Plomb du Cantal, at 1855 m, the views are superb. But don't worry, you don't have to walk all the way! A cable car from Super Lioran takes you to within a short distance of the summit. If you would rather drive to a viewpoint, take the hairpin bends to Puy Mary. For more information about volcanoes, visit the specialist museum in the Château St-Étienne at Aurillac.

Amidst the spectacular scenery, the area is dotted with delightful villages and small towns of which Salers, about 60 km west of St-Flour, is a fine example. Its houses are built out of lava stone and are particularly well preserved. The town is especially lively in July when the Renaissance festival is held. In June a medieval fair is held in St-Flour and in August, at the height of the tourist season, there is a street theatre festival held in Aurillac. But if you prefer the quiet of the countryside, you can always find lots of out-of-the-way places to visit off the main tourist routes.

S

ST-FLOUR Cantal 5A

(See feature)

Grand Hôtel de l'Europe ★★ 12 cours Spy-des-Ternes, 15100 St-Flour.
℡ 71 60 03 64, Fax 71 60 03 45. English spoken.
Open 24/01 to 07/01. 45 bedrooms
(43 en suite). Outdoor swimming pool, garage, parking.

This comfortable hotel is situated in the city near shops and museum. Coming from the north, motorway from Clermont-Ferrand to St-Flour is free of charge.

■ RESTAURANT: Traditional dining room with panoramic view over the old town and La Margeride. Classical food based on regional specialities. Hotel also has a brasserie and bar.
■ ACTIVITIES: Mountain bikes, 4-wheel drive vehicles, pony-trekking and tennis can be organised from the hotel.
■ TARIFF: Double 150–350, Bk 35, Set menu 78–255 (Euro/Access, Visa).
■ DISCOUNT: 10% Nov to Apr (ask about full board).

Grand Hôtel des Voyageurs ★★ 25 rue du Collège, 15100 St-Flour.
℡ 71 60 34 44, Fax 71 60 00 21. English spoken.
Open 01/04 to 30/10. 33 bedrooms
(25 en suite). Garage.

Relaxing, tranquil hotel with a pretty, flower-filled terrace; in the heart of medieval St-Flour.

■ RESTAURANT: Creative, regional cuisine taking advantage of fresh, local products. Try chou farci au canard confit et jus de persil, one of chef M. Quinonero's specialities.
■ ACTIVITIES: Swimming and horse-riding nearby; good walks; museum and other sights to see.
■ TARIFF: (1994) Single 150–260, Double 360, Bk 36, Set menu 88–220 (Euro/Access, Visa).

S **Hôtel Les Messageries** ★★ 23 av Charles de Gaulle, 15100 St-Flour.
℡ 71 60 11 36, Fax 71 60 46 73.
Open all year. 17 bedrooms (all en suite).
Outdoor swimming pool, garage, parking.

Very quiet, yet only 5 minutes from town centre. South of Clermont-Ferrand on A75, in the 'ville basse' not far from the station.

■ RESTAURANT: Regional specialities (note: the restaurant is closed Friday and Saturday in winter).
■ ACTIVITIES: Sauna.
■ TARIFF: (1994) Single 190–375, Double 190–395, Bk 35, Set menu 78–350 (Visa).

Auberge La Providence ★★ 1 rue Château d'Alleuze, 15100 St-Flour.
℡ 71 60 12 05, Fax 71 60 33 94.
Open all year. 10 bedrooms (all en suite).
Garage, parking. ⅙

Restored, peaceful old inn, on the pilgrim road to St-Jacques-de-Compostelle.

■ RESTAURANT: Closed Mon lunch.
■ TARIFF: (1994) Single 220–250, Double 250–280, Bk 30, Set menu 78–150 (Amex, Euro/Access, Visa).

Hôtel St-Jacques ★★ 8 place de la Liberté, 15106 St-Flour.
℡ 71 60 09 20, Fax 71 60 33 81. English spoken.
Open 15/01 to 15/11. 28 bedrooms
(all en suite). Outdoor swimming pool, garage, parking, restaurant. ⅙

Close to the station at lower end of the town, access from the N9.

■ TARIFF: (1994) Single 240–280, Double 240–390, Bk 35, Set menu 85–220 (Euro/Access, Visa).

ST-GAUDENS Hte-Garonne 4D

Hostellerie de Cèdres ★★★ à Villeneuve-de-Rivière, 31800 St-Gaudens.
℡ 61 89 36 00, Fax 61 88 31 04. English spoken.
Open all year. 24 bedrooms (all en suite).
Outdoor swimming pool, tennis, golf 18 km, parking. ⅙

17th-century manor house in a wooded setting with lovely gardens. 1 hour from Toulouse and 30 minutes from the Spanish border on the N117.

■ RESTAURANT: Closed Dec.
■ TARIFF: (1994) Single 350–650, Double 410–690, Bk 60, Set menu 110–260 (Euro/Access, Visa).

ST-GENIEZ-D'OLT Aveyron 5C

Hôtel Poste ★★ 3 pl Charles de Gaulle, 12130 St-Geniez-d'Olt.
℡ 65 47 43 30, Fax 65 47 42 75.
English spoken.
Open 09/04 to 15/11. 50 bedrooms
(all en suite). Outdoor swimming pool, tennis, garage, parking, restaurant.

In the Lot Valley, a quiet hotel set in attractive gardens. From Rodez take D988 north-east to St-Geniez-d'Olt.

■ ACTIVITIES: Canoeing, kayaking and horse-riding nearby.
■ TARIFF: (1994) Single 215, Double 268–298, Bk 38, Set menu 89–135 (Euro/Access, Visa).

ST-GERMAIN-EN-LAYE Yvelines 2B

Hôtel La Cazaudehore et La Forest ★★★★
1 av Prés Kénnédy, 78100 St-Germain-en-Laye.
☎ 1 34 51 93 80, Fax 1 39 73 73 88.
English spoken.
Open all year. 30 bedrooms (all en suite).
Golf 1 km, parking.
Stylish hotel located in the heart of the St-Germain Forest. 1.5 km from the town (towards Pontoise) and 20 km from Paris.
■ RESTAURANT: Closed Mon. Refined cuisine in a lovely setting. Meals are served in the garden in fine weather. Specialities include foie gras and gigot de lotte rôtie.
■ TARIFF: (1994) Single 730, Double 930, Bk 75 (Euro/Access, Visa).

Hôtel Forest Hill ★★★ 10 rue Yvan Tourgueneff, 78380 Bougival.
☎ 39 18 17 16, Fax 39 18 15 80. English spoken.

Open all year. 175 bedrooms (all en suite). Outdoor swimming pool, golf 3 km, parking. ♿
To the west of Paris, in a pleasant green setting on the banks of the Seine. The hotel is close to La Défense business centre, Versailles Château and St-Germain. Bougival lies close to the N13, about 4 km on the Paris side of central St-Germain.
■ RESTAURANT: 'Les Mousquetaires' has views over the river and offers a magnificent buffet.
■ ACTIVITIES: Tennis and jogging trail nearby.
■ TARIFF: (1994) Single 450–650, Double 490–650, Bk 55, Set menu 79–129 (Amex, Euro/Access, Visa).
■ DISCOUNT: 20%

ST-GUENOLE/PENMARC'H Finistère 1C

Hôtel Sterenn ★★★ Plage de la Joie, 29760 Penmarc'h.
☎ 98 58 60 36, Fax 98 58 71 28. English spoken.
Open 09/04 to 08/10. 16 bedrooms (all en suite). Outdoor swimming pool, golf 20 km, parking.
A modern hotel next to the beach and with stunning views to Penmarc'h. From Quimper follow signs to Pont l'Abbé and then to Penmarc'h-St-Guénolé.
■ RESTAURANT: Closed 09/10 to 08/04. Air-conditioned restaurant with panoramic view of La Pointe de Penmarc'h. Traditional and gourmet cuisine with many specialities, including seafood.
■ ACTIVITIES: Water sports, fishing, cycling, hiking trails, horse-riding and sailing lessons all available nearby.
■ TARIFF: (1994) Single 250–300, Double 250–430, Bk 38, Set menu 80–250 (Amex, Euro/Access, Visa).
■ DISCOUNT: 15%

ST-HILAIRE-DU-HARCOUET Manche 1D

Hôtel Cygne ★★ rue Waldeck, Rousseau, 50600 St-Hilaire-du-Harcouet.
☎ 33 49 11 84, Fax 33 49 53 70. English spoken.
Open all year. 20 bedrooms (all en suite). Garage, parking. ♿
Hotel of character with all modern facilities and offering a warm welcome.
■ RESTAURANT: Has a good reputation and specialises in fish. Excellent cellar.
■ ACTIVITIES: Horse-riding and tennis nearby.
■ TARIFF: (1994) Single 185–230, Double 235–300, Bk 32 (Amex, Euro/Access, Visa).

ST-HILAIRE-ST-MESMIN Loiret 2D

Hôtel L'Escale du Port-Arthur ★★ 205 rue de l'Eglise, St-Hilaire-St-Mesmin, 45160 Orléans.
☎ 38 76 30 36, Fax 38 76 37 67. English spoken.
Open 20/01 to 31/12. 20 bedrooms (all en suite). Golf 6 km, parking. ♿
Charming hotel on the banks of the River Loire. On the D951, 7 km south-west of Orléans, towards Blois via Clery-St-André.
■ RESTAURANT: The dining rooms overlook the river and meals are served on the terrace in fine weather. Specialities: foie gras, coquilles Saint-Jacques and poissons de rivière.
■ ACTIVITIES: Boating, fishing, way-marked walks, swimming, tennis and horse-riding nearby.

S

■ TARIFF: (1994) Single 140–270, Double 270–310, Bk 32, Set menu 100–210 (Amex, Euro/Access, Visa).
■ DISCOUNT: 10% LS.

ST-HIPPOLYTE Ht-Rhin 3D

Hôtel aux Ducs de Lorraine ★★★ 16 route du Vin, 68590 St-Hippolyte.
✆ 89 73 00 09, Fax 89 73 05 46. English spoken.
Open 01/03 to 30/11 & 15/12 to 10/01.
40 bedrooms (all en suite). Golf 18 km, garage, parking.

Elegant hotel with period atmosphere on outskirts of the village. Wonderful views of mountains and vineyards.

■ RESTAURANT: Closed Sun eve & Mon. Louis XV-style. Specialities include raviolis d'écrevisses, escalopes de foie d'oie au gingembre and noisettes de chevreuil aux pleurotes.
■ ACTIVITIES: Excellent walking country.
■ TARIFF: (1994) Single 290–460, Double 350–700, Bk 55, Set menu 100–300 (Euro/Access, Visa).

Hôtel Parc ★★★ 6 rue du Parc, 68590 St-Hippolyte.
✆ 89 73 00 06, Fax 89 73 04 30. English spoken.

S Open all year. 42 bedrooms (all en suite). Indoor swimming pool, tennis, golf 20 km, garage, parking. &

A traditional hotel located on the outskirts of the village and bordering the Route du Vin.

■ RESTAURANT: Closed Mon. Warm, relaxed atmosphere with regional specialities.
■ TARIFF: (1994) Single 220–260, Double 260–450, Bk 45, Set menu 85–260 (Amex, Euro/Access, Visa).

ST-JAMES Manche 1D

Normandie Hôtel ★★ pl Bagot, 50240 St-James.
✆ 33 48 31 45, Fax 33 48 59 45. English spoken.

Open 12/01 to 24/12. 13 bedrooms (5 en suite, 8 bath/shower only). Garage, parking, restaurant.

Family-run business in a quiet street with seafood a speciality. 23 km north of Fourgères on the D998 and within striking distance of the Normandy beaches and Mont St-Michel (24 km).

■ TARIFF: (1994) Single 180, Double 185–260, Bk 35, Set menu 68–220 (Euro/Access, Visa).

ST-JEAN-DE-LUZ Pyrénées-Atlan 4C

Hôtel Agur ★★ 96 rue Gambetta, 64500 St-Jean-de-Luz.
✆ 59 26 21 55. English spoken.
Open 15/03 to 15/11. 19 bedrooms (all en suite). Golf 2 km, parking.

Modern hotel situated in town centre not far from the beach. Family rooms and studio flats available. English speaking proprietor. Leave A63 at St-Jean-de-Luz (nord) and follow signs to Centre Ville and Plage for 2 km.

■ TARIFF: (1994) Single 245–315, Double 285–340, Bk 33 (Amex, Euro/Access, Visa).
■ DISCOUNT: 10% LS.

Hôtel Bakea ★★ 64700 Biriatou.
✆ 59 20 76 36, Fax 59 20 58 21. English spoken.
Open all year. 8 bedrooms (4 en suite, 4 bath/shower only). Golf 5 km, parking.

Situated at the foot of the Pyrénées in the village of Biriatou, 4 km from the seaside, offering a shaded terrace with panoramic view. From St-Jean-de-Luz take N10 south. At Béhobie follow the signs to Biriatou.

■ RESTAURANT: Closed Wed lunch LS.
■ TARIFF: (1994) Single 200–250, Double 300–350, Bk 50, Set menu 150–240 (Amex, Euro/Access, Visa).

Hôtel de Chantaco ★★★★ Golf de Chantaco, route d'Ascain, 64500 St-Jean-de-Luz.
✆ 59 26 14 76, Fax 59 26 35 97. English spoken.
Open 01/04 to 30/11. 24 bedrooms (all en suite). Outdoor swimming pool, tennis, golf on site, parking. &

In the heart of the lush green Basque countryside, just opposite Chantaco golf course. A century-old wisteria hugs the patio archways, stately trees shade the terraces with flower-fragrant gardens. South of St-Jean on the D918 towards Ascain.

■ RESTAURANT: Renowned for its excellent cuisine.
■ ACTIVITIES: ● Free use of golf clubs and

trolleys at the 18-hole Chantaco course, one of the oldest in the area.
■ TARIFF: (1994) Single 600–1100, Double 800–1500, Bk 75, Set menu 160–290 (Amex, Euro/Access, Visa).

Hôtel Chez Antoinette ★★ Hendaye village, 64700 Hendaye.
☎ 59 20 08 47, Fax 59 48 11 64. English spoken. Open 01/04 to 31/10. 20 bedrooms (12 en suite, 4 bath/shower only). Golf 10 km, parking.
Small hotel offering a warm welcome. Southwest of St-Jean-de-Luz, off the N10, and close to sea, mountains and Spanish border.
■ RESTAURANT: Small restaurant with good, classic cuisine and Basque specialities.
■ ACTIVITIES: Sailing school nearby.
■ TARIFF: (1994) Double 180–250, Bk 30, Set menu 125–165 (Euro/Access, Visa).

Grand Hôtel de la Poste ★★★ 83 rue Gambetta, 64500 St-Jean-de-Luz.
☎ 59 26 04 53, Fax 59 26 42 14. English spoken. Open all year. 34 bedrooms (30 en suite).
■ TARIFF: (1994) Single 235–360, Double 360–425, Bk 35 (Amex, Euro/Access, Visa).
■ DISCOUNT: 10% LS.

Hôtel Madison ★★★ 25 bd Thiers, 64500 St-Jean-de-Luz.
☎ 59 26 35 02, Fax 59 51 14 76. English spoken.

Open all year. 25 bedrooms (all en suite). Golf 2 km, parking.
100 m from the beach and the centre of town.
■ ACTIVITIES: Sauna and gymnasium.
■ TARIFF: (1994) Single 275–380, Double 300–450, Bk 38 (Amex, Euro/Access, Visa).
■ DISCOUNT: 8%

Hôtel Parc Victoria ★★★★ 5 rue Cépé, 64500 St-Jean-de-Luz.
☎ 59 26 78 78, Fax 59 26 78 08. English spoken. Open 15/03 to 15/11. 12 bedrooms (all en suite). Outdoor swimming pool, golf 3 km, parking. &

Only a few steps away from the bay and beach of St-Jean-de-Luz, this beautiful white hotel is surrounded by trees and flower-filled gardens. Each room has antique furniture and marble bathroom.
■ RESTAURANT: Closed April & Nov.
■ TARIFF: (1994) Single 800–1100, Double 900–1200, Bk 68 (Amex, Euro/Access, Visa).

Hôtel La Réserve ★★★ rondpoint de St-Barbe, 64500 St-Jean-de-Luz.
☎ 59 26 04 24, Fax 59 26 11 74. English spoken. Open all year. 60 bedrooms (all en suite). Outdoor swimming pool, tennis, garage, parking. &
Comfortable hotel with large gardens, sea views and mini-golf. Short, pretty walk from town centre and main beach.
■ RESTAURANT: Offers a good choice of regional and seafood dishes.
■ ACTIVITIES: Sea fishing, 4x4 trips, helicopter flights available nearby.
■ TARIFF: (1994) Single 500–800, Double 600–1500, Bk 55, Set menu 150–250 (Amex, Euro/Access, Visa).
■ DISCOUNT: 5% Jul & Aug.

ST-JEAN-DE-MONTS Vendée   4A

Auberge de la Chaumière ★★
103 av d'Orouet, lieu-dit Orouet, 85160 St-Jean-de-Monts.
☎ 51 58 67 44, Fax 51 58 98 12. English spoken.

S

Open 01/04 to 30/09. 38 bedrooms (all en suite). Outdoor swimming pool, tennis, golf 6 km, garage, parking. &
Orouet is 6 km south of St-Jean-de-Monts towards Les Sables-d'Olonne.
■ RESTAURANT: Fish and meat specialities.
■ TARIFF: (1994) Single 200–250, Double 200–400, Bk 35, Set menu 98–230 (Amex, Euro/Access, Visa).
■ DISCOUNT: 10% LS.

Hôtel L'Espadon ★★ 8 av Forêt, 65160 St-Jean-de-Monts.
☏ 51 58 03 18, Fax 51 59 16 11. English spoken.

Open all year. 27 bedrooms (all en suite). Tennis, golf 1 km, garage, parking. &
Modern rooms with balconies and all conveniences. Close to both the beach and the town centre. On the Altantic coast, 10 km south of Nantes on the D758.
■ RESTAURANT: Closed 15/11 to 01/03.
■ TARIFF: (1994) Single 270–320, Double 270–320, Bk 38, Set menu 75–180 (Amex, Euro/Access, Visa).

Hôtel Mercure Le Sloï ★★★ av des Pays de Monts, 85160 St-Jean-de-Monts.
☏ 51 59 15 15, Fax 51 59 91 03. English spoken.

Open 06/03 to 06/11. 44 bedrooms (all en suite). Outdoor swimming pool, golf on site, garage, parking, restaurant. &
Located outside the hustle-bustle of the resort, between the golf course and the spa, 300 m from the beach in a pine forest.
■ ACTIVITIES: ● 15% green fee reduction.
■ TARIFF: (1994) Single 390–620, Double 410–660, Bk 50, Set menu 89–150 (Amex, Euro/Access, Visa).

Hôtel Robinson ★★ 28 bd Gén Leclerc, 65160 St-Jean-de-Monts.
☏ 51 59 20 20, Fax 51 58 88 03. English spoken.
Open all year. 83 bedrooms (72 en suite, 11 bath/shower only). Indoor swimming pool, golf 1 km, garage, parking. &
Comfortable hotel with garden and terrace. Close to town centre and 900 m from beach. Half-board, full-board and weekend breaks also available.
■ RESTAURANT: Modern restaurant with a good reputation for its refined regional cuisine.
■ ACTIVITIES: Cycling and windsurfing nearby.
■ TARIFF: Single 210–330, Double 210–350, Bk 35, Set menu 73–220 (Amex, Euro/Access, Visa).

ST-JEAN-LE-THOMAS Manche   1D

Hôtel Bains ★★ 8 allée Clémenceau, 50530 St-Jean-le-Thomas.
☏ 33 48 84 20, Fax 33 48 66 42. English spoken.

Open 01/04 to 02/11. 30 bedrooms (27 en suite, 1 bath/shower only). Outdoor swimming pool, golf 17 km, parking.
In the bay of Mont-St-Michel, which is illuminated at night, and halfway between Granville and Avranches. The hotel has been run by the family for 4 generations. Close to the 1,000-year-old village of St-Jean-le-Thomas (which was Eisenhaeuer's headquarters in the war), on the D911.
■ RESTAURANT: Closed Wed 03/10 to 02/11. Traditional restaurant specialising in creative country cooking. Dishes include huîtres au cidre, brochette à lotte au beurre de rhum and ris de veau à l'orange.
■ ACTIVITIES: Visits to Mont-St-Michel and Tombelaine; boat trips to Jersey and Guernsey.
■ TARIFF: (1994) Double 152–324, Bk 31, Set menu 66–175 (Amex, Euro/Access, Visa).
■ DISCOUNT: 10% Restaurant only.

S

Hôtel Marquis de Tombelaine ★★
50530 Champeaux.
☎ 33 61 85 94, Fax 33 61 21 52.

Open 01/03 to 14/09 & 01/11 to 15/02.
6 bedrooms (all en suite, 1 bath/shower only).
Parking. &

Just across the bay from Mont-St-Michel, which is visible from the hotel. Essentially, the hotel is a good restaurant with rooms.

■ RESTAURANT: Closed Tue eve & Wed. Rustic dining room with seafood specialities of plateau fruits de mer, bouillabaise du pêcheur and huîtres chaudes au cidre.
■ ACTIVITIES: Good area for walkers, sea-lovers and fresh-air fiends!
■ TARIFF: (1994) Double 140–280, Bk 25, Set menu 98.50–350 (Euro/Access, Visa).

ST-JEAN-PIED-DE-PORT Pyr-Atlan   4C

Hôtel Ipoutchania ★★ Ascarat, 64220 St-Jean-Pied-de-Port.
☎ 59 37 02 34, Fax 59 37 36 95. English spoken.
Open 01/01 to 14/11 & 16/12 to 31/12.
12 bedrooms (all en suite). Tennis, parking.

A family hotel in a quiet, rustic setting with a shady terrace and comfortable rooms. Situated in Ascarat on the road between St-Jean-Pied-de-Port (1.5 km) and St-Etienne-de-Baigorry. (If booked in advance, written confirmation of booking is advised).

■ RESTAURANT: Closed 15/11 to 15/12. Basques specialities: cervelles aux cèpes, truite aux girolles, médaillons de foie gras à l'Armagnac.
■ ACTIVITIES: Pigeon shooting behind the hotel.
■ TARIFF: (1994) Double 200, Bk 35, Set menu 70–140 (No credit cards).

ST-LARY-SOULAN Htes-Pyrénées   4D

Hôtel de la Neste ★★ 65170 St-Lary-Soulan.
☎ 62 39 42 79, Fax 62 39 58 77. English spoken.
Open 01/06 to 30/09 & 15/12 to 01/05.

21 bedrooms (all en suite). Golf 28 km, parking. &

A modern hotel in this well-known winter sports resort. In the Aure valley, at the gateway to Aragon, Spain.

■ RESTAURANT: Restaurant is air-conditioned and offers seafood and local specialities.
■ ACTIVITIES: Close to lakes, nature reserve and national park. Most sports including skiing, fishing and canoeing within a short distance.
■ TARIFF: (1994) Single 230–260, Double 250–300, Bk 35, Set menu 68–145 (Euro/Access, Visa).
■ DISCOUNT: 5%

ST-LAURENT-EN-GRANDVAUX Jura   6A

Hôtel du Commerce ★★ 2 rue de Genève, 39150 St-Laurent-en-Grandvaux.
☎ 84 60 11 41.
Open 20/12 to 18/04 & 04/05 to 11/11.
13 bedrooms (10 en suite). Garage, parking.

The hotel is on the N5 towards Paris and from Lons-le-Saunier east on the N78.

■ RESTAURANT: Closed Mon LS.
■ TARIFF: (1994) Single 140–220, Double 150–270, Bk 28, Set menu 70–200 (Euro/Access, Visa).

Hôtel Moulin des Truites Bleues ★★★
39150 St-Laurent-en-Grandvaux.
☎ 84 60 83 03, Fax 84 60 87 23. English spoken.

Open all year. 20 bedrooms (all en suite). Golf 25 km, parking, restaurant.

This extraordinary collection of buildings, dating from the 2nd century with a 17th-century mill, now provides the setting for a spectacular hotel. Built on a wooded hillside beside a waterfall, you will find high quality cuisine and service. North of St-Laurent on the N5 towards Champagnole.

■ TARIFF: (1994) Double 450–725, Bk 60, Set menu 140–380 (Amex, Euro/Access, Visa).

S

Auberge du Herisson ★★ 39150 Ilay.
☎ 84 25 58 18. English spoken.
Open 01/02 to 30/11. 16 bedrooms
(11 en suite). Parking.

A small, comfortable inn in typical Jura style. Ilay is a hamlet set in an area surrounded by lakes and waterfalls. 10 km from St-Laurent-en-Grandvaux.

■ RESTAURANT: Regional cuisine with sea and freshwater fish specialities.
■ ACTIVITIES: Walking/hiking and exploring the beautiful countryside.
■ TARIFF: (1994) Single 180, Double 140–295, Bk 38, Set menu 69–220 (Euro/Access, Visa).

ST-MALO Ille/Vil   1D

Hôtel Alba ★★★ 17 rue des Dunes,
35400 St-Malo.
☎ 99 40 37 18, Fax 99 40 96 40. English spoken.

Open 10/02 to 15/11 & 20/12 to 03/01.
22 bedrooms (all en suite). Golf 15 km, parking.

A comfortable, charming hotel overlooking the sea. Good Breton restaurants in town. Follow signs for Thermes Marins.

■ TARIFF: (1994) Double 300–680, Bk 45 (Amex, Euro/Access, Visa).
■ DISCOUNT: 10% RAC members.

Hôtel Atlantis ★★★ Tropee, 35400 St-Malo.
☎ 99 56 09 26, Fax 99 56 41 65. English spoken.
Open all year. 55 bedrooms (all en suite).
Golf 15 km, garage, parking. &

Comfortable hotel just a short walk from town and situated on the seafront. Renovation in 1994.

■ TARIFF: Single 350–440, Double 370–550, Bk 44 (Amex, Euro/Access, Visa).

Hôtel Bristol Union 4 pl Poissonnerie,
35400 St-Malo.
☎ 99 40 83 36. English spoken.
Open 01/02 to 30/11. 27 bedrooms
(all bath/shower only). Golf 10 km.

In the heart of the old town, a pleasant, comfortable hotel.

■ TARIFF: (1994) Single 230–345, Double 230–345, Bk 30 (Euro/Access, Visa).

Hôtel Broceliande ★★★ 43 chaussée du Sillon, 35400 St-Malo.
☎ 99 20 62 62, Fax 99 40 42 47. English spoken.

Open 01/01 to 14/11 & 15/12 to 16/11.
12 bedrooms (all en suite). Golf 7 km, garage, parking.

Period brick and stone built house with traditionally furnished rooms on the seafront. Direct access to the beach. Family apartment also available. The hotel is midway between the old town and the thermal sea baths overlooking the wide beach.

■ ACTIVITIES: Swimming pool, water sports, horse-riding, tennis, and cycling all available in the vicinity.
■ TARIFF: (1994) Double 300–500, Bk 45 (Amex, Euro/Access, Visa).

Hôtel La Cité ★★★ 26 rue Ste-Barbe, BP77, 35412 St-Malo.
☎ 99 40 55 40, Fax 99 40 10 04. English spoken.
Open all year. 41 bedrooms (all en suite).
Golf 10 km, garage, parking. &

Inside the town wall. Enter by the main gate Porte St-Vincent, turn right, near the ramparts. The hotel was built in 1990 in an 18th-century architectural style. Quiet and very

*comfortable, many rooms with a sea view and
the beach just 50 m away.*
■ TARIFF: (1994) Single 350–500,
Double 450–520, Bk 40 (Amex,
Euro/Access, Visa).

Hôtel Elizabeth ★★★ 2 rue des Cordiers,
35400 St-Malo.
☎ 99 56 24 98, Fax 99 56 39 24. English spoken.
Open all year. 17 bedrooms (all en suite).
Golf 12 km, garage.
*Refined and comfortable small apartments.
Stylish furnishing in Louis X111 to XV settings.
Porte-St-Louis 2nd road on the right.*
■ TARIFF: (1994) Single 280–525, Double 325–
525, Bk 47 (Amex, Euro/Access, Visa).
■ DISCOUNT: 20% LS.

Grand Hôtel Thermes ★★★ St-Malo-Est et
Parame, 35400 St-Malo.
☎ 99 40 75 75, Fax 99 40 76 00. English spoken.

Open 29/01 to 31/12. 189 bedrooms
(all en suite). Indoor swimming pool,
golf 20 km, garage, parking. ♿
*Large, comfortable hotel overlooking the beach.
Follow signs for Thermes Marins to find the
hotel. A11 motorway to Rennes, then follow the
N137 64 km to St-Malo.*
■ RESTAURANT: Closed Jan. Good, creative
cuisine. Sample fried kidneys of veal with
bacon and cider, monkfish slices and potato
cake stuffed with clams, or a dessert of hot
orange crêpe flamed in brandy.
■ ACTIVITIES: Water therapy centre, horse-riding,
tennis, sailing, boat trips to Channel Islands,
Mont-St-Michel etc.
■ TARIFF: (1994) Single 240–615,
Double 370–1270, Bk 60, Set menu 125–270
(Amex, Euro/Access, Visa).

Hôtel La Korrigane ★★★ 39 rue Le Pomellec,
35400 St-Malo.
☎ 99 81 65 85, Fax 99 82 23 89. English spoken.

Open 01/02 to 31/12. 10 bedrooms
(16 en suite, 4 bath/shower only). Parking.
*19th-century period house in its own gardens
situated in a quiet residential area close to
ferry terminal.*
■ ACTIVITIES: Bar, tea room, several excellent
restaurants nearby.
■ TARIFF: (1994) Single 350–600,
Double 400–700, Bk 55 (Amex,
Euro/Access, Visa).
■ DISCOUNT: 8% Except Jul, Aug & public
holidays.

Hôtel Mascotte ★★ 76 chaussée du Sillon,
35400 St-Malo.
☎ 99 40 36 36, Fax 99 40 18 78. English spoken.
Open all year. 88 bedrooms (all en suite).
Garage, restaurant. ♿
*Facing the beach 5 minutes' drive from the city
walls and the old town. N137 towards the sea.*
■ TARIFF: (1994) Single 300–420,
Double 340–500, Bk 40 (Amex,
Euro/Access, Visa).

Hôtel Mercure ★★★ 2 chaussée du Sillon,
35400 St-Malo.
☎ 99 56 84 84, Fax 99 56 45 73.
English spoken.
Open all year. 70 bedrooms (all en suite).
Garage. ♿
*Facing the sea, 2 minutes' walk from the old
town. Contemporary construction with all
glass façade. Take N137 from Rennes towards
the sea to St-Malo.*
■ TARIFF: (1994) Single 360–820,
Double 420–820, Bk 50 (Amex,
Euro/Access, Visa).

S

Hôtel Quic en Groigne ★★ 8 rue d'Estrées, 35400 St-Malo.
☏ 99 40 86 81, Fax 99 40 11 64.
English spoken.

Open all year. 15 bedrooms (all en suite). Garage.

In the walled city, the hotel, situated near the beaches, welcomes you to a calm and comfortable atmosphere. The shipping terminal for passengers from Portsmouth is within a few minutes' walk of the hotel.
■ TARIFF: (1994) Single 280–340, Double 340–450, Bk 40 (Euro/Access, Visa).

Hôtel La Rance ★★ 15 quai Sebastopol, 35400 St-Malo.
☏ 99 81 78 63, Fax 99 81 44 80.
English spoken.
Open all year. 11 bedrooms (all en suite). Golf 15 km, parking.

A delightful hotel overlooking the bay and only 5 minutes from the ferry terminal. Follow signs for the Tower of Solidor (museum about Cape Horn) and hotel is close by.
■ ACTIVITIES: ● 20% reduction on 3-day green fee at certain courses.
■ TARIFF: (1994) Single 300–410, Double 300–470, Bk 42 (Amex, Euro/Access, Visa).

Hôtel La Villefromoy ★★★ 7 bd Hebert, 35400 St-Malo.
☏ 99 40 92 20, Fax 99 56 79 49.
English spoken.
Open 15/03 to 15/11. 20 bedrooms (all en suite). Golf 15 km, parking. ⑆

In a residential district on the edge of the long beach at St-Malo. Modern comfort with Victorian-style furnishings. The promenade is close by.

■ TARIFF: (1994) Single 400–600, Double 480–1300, Bk 55 (Amex, Euro/Access, Visa).

ST-MARTIAL-VIVEYROLS Dordogne   4B

Hostellerie Les Aiguillons ★★★
24320 St-Martial-Viveyrols.
☏ 53 91 07 55, Fax 53 90 40 97.
English spoken.

Open 01/03 to 31/12. 8 bedrooms (all en suite). Outdoor swimming pool, parking. ⑆

Small, family-run hotel offering comfortable rooms.

■ RESTAURANT: Closed Sun eve & Mon LS. Cosy

S

restaurant with seasonal menus. Meals served on the terrace in fine weather.
- ACTIVITIES: Sauna at hotel; tennis, horse-riding, fishing, walking and mountain-biking all close at hand.
- TARIFF: (1994) Double 350, Bk 35, Set menu 125–195 (Euro/Access, Visa).
- DISCOUNT: 10% Full and half-board.

ST-MARTIN-EN-BRESSE Saône/Loire   3C

Hôtel au Puits Enchante ★★
71620 St-Martin-en-Bresse.
℡ 85 47 71 96, Fax 85 47 74 58.
English spoken.
Open all year. 14 bedrooms (12 en suite, 2 bath/shower only). Golf 5 km, parking.

Surrounded by lovely countryside, this family-run hotel is in the centre of the little village of St-Martin-en-Bresse. Take the D35 from the N73 to St-Martin.

- RESTAURANT: Closed Sun eve & Tues. Traditional dishes of Burgundy, including freshwater fish specialities.
- ACTIVITIES: Horse-riding nearby.
- TARIFF: (1994) Double 160–270, Bk 36, Set menu 95–210 (Euro/Access, Visa).

ST-MARTIN-LA-MEANNE Corrèze   5A

Hôtel Voyageurs ★★ place de la Mairie, 19320 St-Martin-la-Meanne.
℡ 55 29 11 53, Fax 55 29 27 70. English spoken.

Open all year. 8 bedrooms (all en suite). Garage, parking. &

A small hotel near the Dordogne gorges. Comfortable and full of character. On D18, 8 km north of Argentat.

- RESTAURANT: Delightful old traditional dining room. Specialities: foie gras, magrets, fresh river fish and home-made pastries.
- ACTIVITIES: Swimming pool and tennis in the village; opportunities for hiking, cycling and fishing close by.
- TARIFF: (1994) Single 230–240, Double 230–300, Bk 29, Set menu 85–190 (Euro/Access, Visa).

ST-NAZAIRE Loire-Atlan   1D

Hôtel La Boissière ★★ 70 avenue de Mindin, 44250 St-Brévin-les-Pins.
℡ 40 27 21 79, Fax 40 39 11 88.
English spoken.
Open 01/04 to 10/10. 23 bedrooms (21 en suite, 2 bath/shower only). Golf 16 km, garage, parking, restaurant.

More in the style of a large residential house than a hotel, in architecture and atmosphere. From St-Nazaire go south over the bridge. Turn immediately right to St-Brévin-les-Pins.

- TARIFF: (1994) Single 220–280, Double 235–395, Bk 30 (Euro/Access, Visa).

ST-OMER Pas-de-Calais   2B

Hostellerie St-Hubert ★★★★ 1 rue du Moulin, 62570 Hallines.
℡ 21 39 77 77, Fax 21 93 00 86.
English spoken.
Open all year. 9 bedrooms (all en suite). Golf 8 km, garage, parking.

Attractive château, situated in a green park and renovated at the end of the 19th century in La Belle Epoque style. Hallines is ten minutes' drive south-west of St-Omer.

- RESTAURANT: Closed Sun eve & Mon.
- TARIFF: (1994) Single 350–500, Double 400–800, Bk 45, Set menu 170–320 (Euro/Access, Visa).

ST-PAUL-DE-VENCE Alpes-Mar   6C

S

Hôtel Messugues ★★★
06570 St-Paul-de-Vence.
℡ 93 32 53 32, Fax 93 32 94 15.
English spoken.
Open 01/04 to 31/10. 15 bedrooms (18 en suite). Outdoor swimming pool, golf 8 km, parking. &

Quiet, peaceful hotel with lovely pool area. Set in unspoilt countryside just outside the village of St-Paul.

- ACTIVITIES: All the amenities of the Côte d'Azure just a few km away.
- TARIFF: Double 450–650, Bk 50 (Amex, Euro/Access, Visa).

Adhôtel Les Vergers de St-Paul ★★★
940 route de la Colle, 06570 St-Paul-de-Vence.
☎ 93 32 94 24, Fax 93 32 91 07. English spoken.

Open all year. 19 bedrooms (all en suite).
Outdoor swimming pool, golf 15 km, parking.
*This family hotel, set in the beautiful
countryside surrounding St-Paul, is a haven if
you hate the noise and bustle of the coast. The
hotel can be found just after the village La
Colle-sur-Loup, 900 m before St-Paul-de-
Vence. Motorway exit for Cagnes-sur-Mer.*
- RESTAURANT: Closed eve 24/12 to 31/12.
- TARIFF: Single 380–600, Double 460–650,
Bk 50, Set menu 160–180 (Amex,
Euro/Access, Visa).
- DISCOUNT: 5%

ST-PAUL-TROIS-CHATEAUX Drôme 5D

Hôtel L'Esplan ★★★ place Médiéval de
l'Esplan, 26130 St-Paul-Trois-Châteaux.
☎ 75 96 64 64, Fax 75 04 92 36. English spoken.
Open 06/01 to 19/12. 36 bedrooms
(all en suite). Golf 4 km, garage, parking,
restaurant.
*Renovated building combining traditional
and contemporary achitecture/styles. The
bedrooms are very modern in design. Garden
and terraces. Medieval town with easy access,
22 km from A7 motorway. From Avignon take
the Montelimar-Sud exit to Bollerie and from
there head towards Suze-la-Rousse on the D94.*
- TARIFF: (1994) Single 280–350,
Double 310–380, Bk 35, Set menu 108–248
(Amex, Euro/Access, Visa).

Auberge des Quatre-Saisons ★★★
26130 St-Restitut.
☎ 75 04 71 88, Fax 75 04 70 88.
English spoken.
Open 01/02 to 01/01. 10 bedrooms
(all en suite, all bath/shower only).
Golf 25 km, parking.

*Lovely old building with comfortable antique-
furnished rooms. St-Restitut is a medieval
village lying just south-east of St-Paul and a
short distance from the main routes to the
south coast.*
- RESTAURANT: Closed Sat lunch and Jan. Warm,
inviting dining room. Specialities: carré
d'agneau aux herbe de Provence, truffes du
Tricastin.
- ACTIVITIES: Horse-riding, swimming pool and
tennis nearby; Ardèche gorges and Grignan
château within easy reach.
- TARIFF: (1994) Single 290–390,
Double 300–450, Bk 40, Set menu 130–195
(Amex, Euro/Access, Visa).

ST-PEE-SUR-NIVELLE Pyrénées-Atlan 4C

Hôtel Nivelle ★★ 64310 St-Pée-sur-Nivelle.
☎ 59 54 10 27, Fax 59 54 19 82. English spoken.
Open 15/03 to 15/01. 30 bedrooms
(all en suite). Golf 10 km, parking.
*Family-run Logis de France hotel, in the centre
of this pretty, rural village, just 5 minutes from
the lake. Take St-Jean-de-Luz exit from N10.*
- RESTAURANT: Basque and regional specialities
include pipérade, chipiron and confit de
canard.
- ACTIVITIES: Boating, trout fishing and
mountain-biking nearby.
- TARIFF: (1994) Single 190–260,
Double 200–350, Bk 35, Set menu 90–150
(Amex, Euro/Access, Visa).
- DISCOUNT: 10% LS.

ST-POL-SUR-TERNOISE Pas-de-Calais 2B

Hôtel Lion d'Or ★★ 74 rue d'Hesdin,
62130 St-Pol-sur-Ternoise.
☎ 21 03 10 44, Fax 21 41 47 87. English spoken.
Open all year. 20 bedrooms (all en suite).
Garage, parking.
*A small hotel on the N39 Béthune to Amiens
road.*
- RESTAURANT: Very popular.
- TARIFF: (1994) Single 220–280,
Double 240–300, Bk 35, Set menu 76–200
(Amex, Euro/Access, Visa).

ST-QUAY-PORTRIEUX Côtes-du-Nord 1D

Hôtel Lucotel ★★ Parc Lannec, rue des
Fontaines, 22290 Lanvollon.
☎ 96 70 01 17, Fax 96 70 08 84. English spoken.
Open all year. 20 bedrooms (all en suite).
Tennis, golf 5 km, garage, parking. ♿
*A modern hotel in a leafy setting just a short
distance from the sea.*

S

■ RESTAURANT: Seafood specialities: poêlée de Saint-Jacques, raie aux poireaux.
■ ACTIVITIES: Crazy golf at the hotel.
■ TARIFF: (1994) Single 190–230, Double 260–320, Bk 33, Set menu 75–220 (Amex, Euro/Access, Visa).
■ DISCOUNT: 10% 01/09 to 08/07.

ST-QUENTIN Aisne   2B

Hôtel Mémorial ★★★ 8 rue Comédie, 02100 St-Quentin.
☎ 23 67 90 09, Fax 23 62 34 96. English spoken.

Open all year. 18 bedrooms (all en suite). Parking.

Small hotel in the town centre not far from the town hall. 35 km north of Laon on the A26 Calais to Reims motorway.

■ TARIFF: (1994) Single 280, Double 280–530, Bk 40 (Amex, Euro/Access, Visa).
■ DISCOUNT: 10%

ST-RAPHAEL Var   6C

Hôtel Sol e Mar ★★★ rte Corniche d'Or, 83700 St-Raphaël.
☎ 94 95 25 60, Fax 94 83 83 61.
English spoken.
Open 01/04 to 15/10. 47 bedrooms

(all en suite). Outdoor swimming pool, golf 3 km, parking, restaurant.
Adjacent to sea and beach, with exceptional views. On the N98, between St-Raphaël and Cannes.

■ ACTIVITIES: ● Special price for a wide range of activities including golf, scuba diving and sea trips.
■ TARIFF: (1994) Single 400–630, Double 470–640, Bk 50, Set menu 145–210 (Amex, Euro/Access, Visa).

ST-REMY-DE-PROVENCE   5D

Hôtel Castelet des Alpilles ★★★ pl Mireille, 13210 St-Rémy-de-Provence.
☎ 90 92 07 21, Fax 90 92 52 03.
English spoken.

Open 01/04 to 31/10. 18 bedrooms (17 en suite). Golf 8 km, parking.

In a restful garden, with the shade of a century-old cedar tree. The rooms face south towards the Alpilles range, some with terrace. The hotel is 300 m from the centre of St-Rémy towards 'Les Antiques les Baux'.

■ RESTAURANT: Closed Mon & Tues lunch.
■ TARIFF: (1994) Single 220–370, Double 335–460, Bk 42, Set menu 125–185 (Amex, Visa).

Hôtel Le Mas des Carassins ★★★ 1 chemin Gaulois, 13210 St-Rémy-de-Provence.
☎ 90 92 15 48. English spoken.
Open 15/03 to 15/11. 10 bedrooms (all en suite). Golf 8 km, parking.

In the Provençal countryside, hotel is at the foot of the Alpilles hills and 10 mins from town centre. There is a large garden. From the A7 go west on the D99 to St-Rémy-de-Provence.

■ TARIFF: (1994) Single 340–440, Double 380–520, Bk 48 (Euro/Access, Visa).

S

Hôtel Mas d'Aigret ★★★
13520 Les Baux-de-Provence.
📞 90 54 33 54, Fax 90 54 41 37. English spoken.

Open 25/02 to 04/01. 16 bedrooms
(all en suite). Outdoor swimming pool,
golf 2 km, parking.

*A former farm house, dating back to 1630 and
set in 4 acres of gardens at the foot of the
ruined château. Rumoured to have been the
home of a 17th-century troglodyte. Tastefully
and comfortably renovated, with most rooms
having their own terrace or balcony. 9 km
south of St-Rémy.*

■ RESTAURANT: Closed Wed lunch. Restaurant is
carved into solid rock. Has a good reputation
for its regional cuisine.
■ ACTIVITIES: Excellent area for sightseeing,
visiting ruins (some dating back to 20 BC) and
taking advantage of the nearby sports and
leisure facilities.
■ TARIFF: (1994) Double 350−850, Bk 70,
Set menu 90−350 (Amex, Euro/Access, Visa).

Hôtel Soleil ★★ 13 av Pasteur,
13210 St-Rémy-de-Provence.
📞 90 92 00 63, Fax 90 92 61 07.
Open 01/03 to 15/11. 18 bedrooms
(all en suite). Outdoor swimming pool,
golf 12 km, garage, parking.

*Pleasant hotel with gardens and terrace. From
St-Rémy centre follow signs for Les Baux. After
tourist office, turn left back on yourself into av
Pasteur. Hotel on right.*

■ ACTIVITIES: BMX.
■ TARIFF: (1994) Single 270−310,
Double 270−355, Bk 34 (Amex,
Euro/Access, Visa).

Host. du Vallon de Valruge ★★★★
13210 St-Rémy-de-Provence.
📞 90 92 04 40, Fax 90 92 44 01. English spoken.

Open all year. 53 bedrooms (all en suite).
Indoor swimming pool, outdoor swimming
pool, tennis, golf 8 km, garage, parking. &
*Luxurious hotel with a restful atmosphere set
in the enchanting landscape of the Alpilles.
Apartments also available.*

■ RESTAURANT: Excellent cuisine.
■ ACTIVITIES: Good sporting facilities.
■ TARIFF: (1994) Single 600−700,
Double 760−960, Bk 90, Set menu 220−430
(Amex, Euro/Access, Visa).

ST-SYMPHORIEN-LE-CHATEAU   2D

Château d'Esclimont ★★★★
28700 St-Symphorien-le-Château.
📞 37 31 15 15, Fax 37 31 57 91. English spoken.

Open all year. 53 bedrooms (all en suite).
Outdoor swimming pool, tennis, golf 17 km,
parking, restaurant.

*A superb 16th-century château with moat,
lake, landscaped gardens and 150 acres of
woodland park. From Paris take A11 and exit
at Ablis, 6 km after on N10 turn right.*

■ ACTIVITIES: Fishing, boating, cycling at the
château; horse-riding, pleasure flights, hot-air
ballooning and golf can be arranged.

■ TARIFF: (1994) Single 685–1165, Double 820–2020, Set menu 320–495 (Amex, Visa).

ST-TROPEZ Var   6C

Hôtel Byblos ★★★★ av P Signac, 83991 St-Tropez.
☎ 94 97 00 04, Fax 94 97 40 52. English spoken.

Open 01/03 to 31/10. 102 bedrooms (all en suite). Outdoor swimming pool, golf 9 km, garage, parking.

Just a few steps away from the place des Lices, in the shadow of the Citadel. Hotel has excellent facilities including a beauty parlor. Each fully-equipped room has its own personal character, and some a jaccuzzi.

■ RESTAURANT: Fresh, authentic Provençal cuisine can be enjoyed in the restaurant 'Les Arcades', which overlooks the swimming pool.
■ ACTIVITIES: Turkish bath and disco.
■ TARIFF: (1994) Single 700–2380, Double 1080–2380, Bk 120 (Amex, Euro/Access, Visa).

Hôtel La Ferme d'Augustin ★★★ Plage de Tahiti, St-Tropez, 83350 Ramatuelle.
☎ 94 97 23 83, Fax 94 97 40 30. English spoken.
Open 25/03 to 17/10. 34 bedrooms (all en suite). Outdoor swimming pool, golf 20 km, parking.

Just 5 minutes from St-Tropez, a grand hotel in a garden. Traditionally furnished deluxe rooms looking out over the sea, countryside or park, with breakfast in room, garden or on the terrace. Secure parking.

■ ACTIVITIES: Pool with hydromassage system.
■ TARIFF: (1994) Single 580–1600, Double 620–1800, Bk 75 (Amex, Euro/Access, Visa).

Hôtel Lou Troupelen ★★★ chemin des Vendanges, 83990 St-Tropez.
☎ 94 97 44 88, Fax 94 97 41 76. English spoken.

Open 07/04 to 01/11. 45 bedrooms (all en suite). Golf 15 km, parking.

Excellent location, 400 m walk from the town centre. Quick and easy access to the beaches. Quiet garden.

■ TARIFF: (1994) Single 320, Double 380–490, Bk 45 (Amex, Euro/Access, Visa).

Hôtel du Treizain ★★★★ Domaine du Treizain, 63990 St-Tropez-Gassin.
☎ 94 97 70 08, Fax 94 97 67 25. English spoken.

Open 15/04 to 15/10. 16 bedrooms (all en suite). Outdoor swimming pool, golf 3 km, parking.

Very pretty hotel with wonderful views over the bay of St-Tropez. Well-equipped, comfortable rooms, sun terrace, bar and sauna.

■ RESTAURANT: Light meals only (salads, omelettes, spaghetti etc) are served near the bar, on the poolside terrace.
■ ACTIVITIES: Tennis and sailing 500 m, a wealth of things to do and see in nearby St-Tropez and the surrounding area.
■ TARIFF: (1994) Single 400–500, Double 550–1200 (Amex, Euro/Access, Visa).

ST-VAAST-LA-HOUGUE Manche   1B

S

Hôtel France et Fuchsias ★★ 50550 St-Vaast-la-Hougue.
☎ 33 54 42 25, Fax 33 43 46 79. English spoken.
Open 21/02 to 05/01. 32 bedrooms (28 en suite). Golf 18 km.

Family-run hotel. Pretty, provincial-style building with beautiful gardens.

■ RESTAURANT: Closed Mon LS. Terrace restaurant opening on to garden. Normandy cuisine, with the emphasis on fish and country dishes, some of the produce coming from the family farm. Specialities: choucroute de la mer au beurre blanc, feuilleté de pommes tièdes à la crème de Calvados.

■ ACTIVITIES: Bicycle hire; chamber music in the hotel gardens (1800-1900 hrs) during last 10 days of August (free entry).
■ TARIFF: (1994) Double 140–400, Bk 42, Set menu 75–240 (Amex, Euro/Access, Visa).

Hôtel La Granitière ★★★ 64 bis du Maréchal Foch, 50550 St-Vaast-la-Hougue.
✆ 33 54 58 99, Fax 33 20 34 91. English spoken.

Open 01/04 to 15/02. 11 bedrooms (8 en suite). Golf 8 km, garage, parking.
An impressive granite building with marble floors, rich wall coverings and splendid objets d'art. There are also some unusual stained glass windows. The rooms are spacious and elegant, offering comfort and refinement.
■ RESTAURANT: Closed Tues LS. Décor in the style of a royal hunting lodge with splendid seafood specialities.
■ ACTIVITIES: Bicycles can be hired.
■ TARIFF: (1994) Single 140–280, Double 280–500, Bk 38, Set menu 110–190 (Amex, Euro/Access, Visa).
■ DISCOUNT: 10%

ST-VERAN Htes-Alpes   6A

Hôtel Châteaurenard ★★ 05350 St-Veran.
✆ 92 45 85 43, Fax 92 45 84 20.
English spoken.
Open all year. 20 bedrooms (all en suite).
Parking. ♿
The hotel at 2040 m overlooks the historic village of St-Veran, the highest in Europe, in the Queyras regional nature park. The village is famous for its traditional architecture, sundials and sculptors. The Queyras is famous for its climate (alpine/Mediterranean with over 300 days of sun a year). St-Veran is reached via Guillestre from Briançon, Gap or Turin. (Low season discounts.)

■ RESTAURANT: Traditional French cooking using locally produced beef, goats and ewes milk and cheese, fresh and smoked lamb, cured ham, blueberries and apples.
■ ACTIVITIES: In winter: skiing, dog sleighs, snow-shoe walking. The rest of the year: mountaineering, alpine walking, mountain-biking, horse-riding, hang/paragliding, boating, discovering the flora and fauna.
■ TARIFF: (1994) Single 290–355, Double 335–355, Bk 35, Set menu 85–110 (Euro/Access, Visa).

ST-YRIEIX-LA-PERCHE

If you think you would enjoy getting to know a small French market town, try staying in St-Yrieix-la-Perche. Sited high on a hillside in the triangle of land between Limoges, Périgueux and Brive, it makes a good centre for touring. Narrow streets and small squares huddle close to the handsome church of St-Yrieix. Inside, look for the saint's reliquary, a black wooden head covered with a silver mask. St-Yrieix is also well known for its small rum-flavoured sponge cakes known as *madeleines*, and for its kaolin quarries which provided the original raw material for the famous porcelain factories in Limoges.

ST-YRIEIX-LA-PERCHE Hte-Vienne   4B

(See feature)

Hostellerie La Tour Blanche ★★ 74 bd de l'Hôtel-de-Ville, 87500 St-Yrieix-la-Perche.
✆ 55 75 18 17, Fax 55 08 23 11. English spoken.
Open all year. 11 bedrooms (all en suite).
Outdoor swimming pool, tennis, golf 1 km, parking. ♿

Family restaurant with rooms. From Limoges, D704 direction Périgueux.

■ RESTAURANT: Closed 15/02 to 15/03. A good choice of home-cooked, high quality meals.

■ ACTIVITIES: Fishing and horse-riding nearby.

■ TARIFF: (1994) Single 205, Double 240, Bk 28, Set menu 79–177 (Euro/Access, Visa).

STE-FOY-LA-GRANDE Dordogne 4B

Hôtel Le Jardin d'Eyquem ★★★ 24230 St-Michel-de-Montaigne.
℄ 53 24 89 59, Fax 53 61 14 40. English spoken.

Open 01/03 to 30/11. 5 bedrooms (all en suite). Outdoor swimming pool, parking. ♿

An old house, typical of the region, now sympathetically restored and offering 5 very comfortable apartments. Member of Châteaux et Hôtels Indépendents. 18 km from St-Emilion in the heart of the vineyards. From Ste-Foy, go west and turn right for St-Michel-de-Montaigne off the D936.

■ ACTIVITIES: Short wine tasting sessions, visits to wine cellars and sporting activities close by.

■ TARIFF: (1994) Single 395–525, Double 470–600, Bk 40 (Euro/Access, Visa).

■ DISCOUNT: 5%

STE-MAURE-DE-TOURAINE 2C

Host Hauts de Ste-Maure ★★★ 2 av Charles de Gaulle, 37800 Ste-Maure-de-Touraine.
℄ 47 65 50 65, Fax 47 65 60 24. English spoken.
Open 02/01 to 21/12. 19 bedrooms (all en suite). Outdoor swimming pool, tennis, golf 1 km, garage, parking. ♿

This newly-renovated, comfortable posthouse has stood on the Paris to Madrid road (N10) for many centuries.

■ RESTAURANT: Closed Sun & Mon lunch LS. Tempting dishes are prepared by the

proprietor's son. Specialities: potato shells with tarragon butter; braised pigeon; monkfish with ginger.

■ ACTIVITIES: Hotel has a vintage car collection. Good area for touring, sightseeing and visiting private châteaux and cellars. 20 minutes' from Futurescope.

■ TARIFF: (1994) Double 280–380, Bk 40, Set menu 108–240 (Amex, Euro/Access, Visa).

■ DISCOUNT: 10%

STE-MAXIME Var 6C

Hôtel Villa Tricoli Impasse du Temps Perdu, San-Peire, 83380 Les Issambres.
℄ 94 49 65 32, Fax 94 49 68 20. English spoken.

Open all year. 10 bedrooms (all en suite). Golf 6 km, parking. ♿

Small privately owned hotel in quiet street. Stylish, even romantic! 600 m from beach. Just along the coast from Ste-Maxime, turn after the port entrance in Les Issambres and look for hotel signpost.

■ ACTIVITIES: Arrangements made for water sports, golf, tennis and excursions on request.

■ TARIFF: (1994) Single 200–335, Double 260–430, Bk 45 (No credit cards).

■ DISCOUNT: 10%

S

Hôtel de la Poste ★★★ 7 bd F Mistral, 83120 Ste-Maxime.
☎ 94 96 18 33, Fax 94 96 41 68. English spoken. Open 20/05 to 20/10. 24 bedrooms (all en suite). Outdoor swimming pool, golf 2 km, restaurant.
The hotel is located in the middle of Ste-Maxime, opposite the post office. Only 100 m from a fine sandy beach and the port. Breakfast is served on a terrace overlooking the swimming pool and solarium, surrounded by a small garden.
■ TARIFF: (1994) Single 300–500, Double 400–590, Bk 45 (Amex, Euro/Access, Visa).

STE-MENEHOULD Meuse 3A

Hôtel Commerce ★ 55120 Aubreville.
☎ 29 87 40 35, Fax 29 87 43 69.
Open 20/10 to 30/09. 10 bedrooms (4 en suite, 2 bath/shower only). Garage, parking.
Peaceful and traditional family-run Logis de France hotel. Leave A4 at Ste-Menehould exit and Aubreville is about 15 km east of the town of Ste-Menehould.
■ RESTAURANT: Home-cooked dishes using fresh, country produce.
■ ACTIVITIES: Good area for walking and biking; horse-riding (2 km) and Verdun First World War battlefield (25 km).
■ TARIFF: (1994) Single 130–200, Double 150–220, Bk 25, Set menu 65–120 (Euro/Access, Visa).

STES-MARIES-DE-LA- MER 5D

Hôtel L'Etrier Camarguais ★★★ 13460 Stes-Maries-de-la-Mer.
☎ 90 97 81 14, Fax 90 97 88 11. English spoken. Open 01/04 to 30/11. 27 bedrooms (all en suite). Outdoor swimming pool, tennis, parking.
Ranch-style hotel, typical of the region. Offers comfortable rooms in the garden or near the pool. Situated 2 km before Stes-Maries-de-la-Mer, by the route d'Arles.
■ RESTAURANT: Attractive restaurant and bar near the swimming pool. Fresh seafood and local specialities.
■ ACTIVITIES: Horse-riding nearby.
■ TARIFF: (1994) Single 540, Double 540–980, Bk 50 (Amex, Euro/Access, Visa).

Hôtel Mas des Roseaux 13460 Stes-Maries-de-la-Mer.
☎ 90 97 86 12, Fax 90 97 70 84. English spoken.

Open 01/04 to 31/10. 16 bedrooms (all en suite). Outdoor swimming pool, parking.
Small, comfortable hotel which aims to please. Large rooms with terrace; garden. 900 m from the town and 1 km from the beach. Booking is advised.
■ ACTIVITIES: Horse-riding and sailing nearby.
● Free mountain bikes at hotel.
■ TARIFF: (1994) Single 350–500, Double 400–600 (Amex, Euro/Access, Visa).

SAINTES Charente-Mar 4B

Hôtel Bleu Nuit ★★ 1 rue Pasteur, 17100 Saintes.
☎ 46 93 01 72, Fax 46 74 43 80. English spoken. Open all year. 35 bedrooms (all en suite). Golf 10 km, garage, parking. ♿
Take Saintes-Centre exit from A10. Hotel is 30 m before the Tourist Information Office.
■ TARIFF: Single 180–210, Double 210–250, Bk 30 (Amex, Euro/Access, Visa).

Hôtel Climat de France ★★ route de Royan, 17100 Saintes.
☎ 46 97 20 40, Fax 46 92 22 54. English spoken. Open all year. 36 bedrooms (all en suite). Outdoor swimming pool, golf 3 km, parking, restaurant. ♿
From station, head towards Royan and from motorway (exit 25) towards Royan (about 1 km after motorway exit).
■ TARIFF: (1994) Double 260–270, Bk 32, Set menu 80–120 (Amex, Euro/Access, Visa).
■ DISCOUNT: 10%

Hôtel au Terminus ★★ 2 rue J Moulin, 17100 Saintes.
☎ 46 74 35 03, Fax 46 97 24 47. English spoken. Open 16/01 to 22/12. 28 bedrooms (all en suite). Golf 4 km, garage.
Delightful, traditional 1920s building, recently modernised. Opposite the Gare SNCF, the hotel has little or no train noise and is run by an Irish/French couple who give a warm personal welcome.
■ TARIFF: (1994) Single 200–275, Double 200–370, Bk 30 (Amex, Euro/Access, Visa).

SALAUNES Gironde 4A

Hôtel Les Ardillières ★★★ rte de la Lacanau, 33160 Salaunes.
☎ 56 58 58 08, Fax 56 58 51 01. English spoken.

S

Open all year. 40 bedrooms (all en suite). Outdoor swimming pool, tennis, golf 5 km, parking. &

In beautiful grounds on the N215 towards Lacanau.

■ RESTAURANT: Rustic style restaurant specialities: mille feuille de foie gras; oeufs brouillés aux cèpes; parfait glace chocolat.
■ ACTIVITIES: Outdoor health facilities, bicycle track, large park. Châteaux 10 km.
■ TARIFF: (1994) Single 300–385, Double 350–385, Bk 35, Set menu 110–350 (Amex, Visa).
■ DISCOUNT: 5%

SALBRIS Loir/Cher   2D

Hôtel Parc ★★★ 8 av d'Orléans, 41300 Salbris.
℡ 54 97 18 53, Fax 54 97 24 34. English spoken.
Open all year. 27 bedrooms (23 en suite, 4 bath/shower only). Golf 1 km, garage, parking.

Charming, comfortable hotel, just one-and-a-half hours from Paris. In a beautiful parkland setting between Orléans and Bourges.

■ RESTAURANT: Good food and wines at very reasonable prices. Specialities include gibiers and champignons in season.
■ TARIFF: (1994) Single 200–400, Double 220–450, Bk 42, Set menu 90–200 (Amex, Euro/Access, Visa).
■ DISCOUNT: 8%

SALERS Cantal   5A

Hôtel Le Bailliage ★★ rue Notre Dame, 15410 Salers.
℡ 71 40 71 95, Fax 71 40 74 90. English spoken.
Open all year. 30 bedrooms (all en suite). Outdoor swimming pool, golf 15 km, garage, parking.

Spacious bedrooms in this charming hotel in

one of France's prettiest small towns. On the D680 west of Murat and south-east of Mauriac.

■ RESTAURANT: Auvergne specialities in restaurant overlooking garden: potée auvergnate; feuilleté au bleu d'Auvergne.
■ ACTIVITIES: ● Accommodation for 7 days including cross-country and ski pass: 2030F.
■ TARIFF: (1994) Single 180–220, Double 260–380, Bk 38 (Amex).

Hostellerie de la Maronne ★★★ Le Theil, 15140 Salers.
℡ 71 69 20 33, Fax 71 69 28 22. English spoken.

Open 03/04 to 05/11. 25 bedrooms (all en suite). Outdoor swimming pool, tennis, golf 25 km, parking. &

A traditional Auvergne house dating from the 19th century. 4 km east of the D922, on the D37.

■ RESTAURANT: Good restaurant with specialities of foie gras chaud au caramel de porto et choux vert étuvé, poitrine de pigeon rôti au vin and gâteau tiède aux marrons et chocolat.
■ ACTIVITIES: Sight-seeing and rambling; fishing and horse-riding nearby.
■ TARIFF: (1994) Single 350–450, Double 350–550, Bk 40 (Amex, Euro/Access, Visa).

Hôtel des Remparts ★★ esplanade de Barrouze, 15410 Salers.
℡ 71 40 70 33, Fax 71 40 75 32. English spoken.
Open 01/12 to 20/10. 31 bedrooms (29 en suite, 2 bath/shower only). Parking.

Substantial hotel overlooking the valley. Salers is a medieval city on the D680 west of Murat and south-east of Mauriac. (The Château de la Bastide, also in Salers, is owned by the same family.)

■ RESTAURANT: Panoramic view. Auvergne specialities: la truffade, le pounti aux pruneaux, la liogue.

S

■ ACTIVITIES: Walking, fishing, mountain-biking, archery, cross-country skiing.
■ TARIFF: Single 190–200, Double 240–330, Bk 34, Set menu 65–130 (Euro/Access, Visa).

SALIES-DE-BEARN Pyrénées-Atlan 4C

Hôtel du Golf ★★ 64270 Salies-de-Béarn.
✆ 59 65 02 10, Fax 59 38 05 84. English spoken.
Open all year. 33 bedrooms (all en suite).
Outdoor swimming pool, tennis, golf on site, parking, restaurant. &

Hotel can be accessed via D30 running south from junction 3 of the A64 towards Salies.

■ TARIFF: (1994) Single 175–250, Double 210–300, Bk 25, Set menu 70–150 (Euro/Access, Visa).

SALON-DE-PROVENCE B-du-Rhône 5D

Hôtel Angleterre ★★ 98 cours Carnot, 13300 Salon-de-Provence.
✆ 90 56 01 10, Fax 90 56 71 75. English spoken.
Open all year. 26 bedrooms (all en suite).
Garage, parking.

Newly renovated hotel traditionally furnished with fully-equipped rooms. In the town centre. Between Aix-en-Provence and Arles, close to the A7.

■ TARIFF: (1994) Single 215–245, Double 245–295, Bk 30 (Amex, Euro/Access, Visa).
■ DISCOUNT: 10%

Hôtel Le Mas du Soleil ★★★★ 38 chemin St-Come, 13300 Salon-de-Provence.
✆ 90 56 06 53, Fax 90 56 21 52. English spoken.

Open all year. 10 bedrooms (all en suite).
Outdoor swimming pool, golf 10 km, parking. &

In a very quiet area, 5 minutes from the centre of Salon-de-Provence with its castle and

Nostradamus House. Patio, garden. Near the hospital on the road to Avignon.

■ RESTAURANT: Closed Sun eve & Mon.
■ ACTIVITIES: ● Reduced green fees at golf course.
■ TARIFF: (1994) Single 480–600, Double 650–850, Bk 50, Set menu 160–350 (Amex, Euro/Access, Visa).

Domaine de Roquerousse ★★ rte d'Avignon, 13300 Salon-de-Provence.
✆ 90 59 50 11, Fax 90 59 53 75. English spoken.
Open all year. 30 bedrooms (all en suite).
Outdoor swimming pool, tennis, golf 7 km, parking.

Peacefully set in 1000 acres in the heart of Provence, attractive, stone-built hotel with comfortable rooms and lovely gardens. 4 km from Salon, towards Avignon.

■ RESTAURANT: Closed 24/12 eve & 25/12. Country cuisine served on shady terrace or in 150-year-old dining room once used for breeding silkworms. Typical 'Provence' atmosphere.
■ ACTIVITIES: Gym, boules; mountain-biking, walking and hunting.
■ TARIFF: (1994) Single 240–420, Double 270–470, Bk 48, Set menu 75–150 (Amex, Euro/Access, Visa).

SARLAT-LA-CANEDA Dordogne 4B

Hôtel Edward 1er ★★★ 5 rue St-Pierre, 24540 Monpazier.
✆ 53 22 44 00, Fax 53 22 57 99. English spoken.

S

Open 01/05 to 15/11. 13 bedrooms (all en suite). Outdoor swimming pool, golf 20 km, parking. &

In the heart of Monpazier, one of Europe's oldest walled towns, this restored château offers all modern comforts with character, set in a region steeped in history.

■ TARIFF: (1994) Single 370–670, Double 500–1000, Bk 65 (Amex, Euro/Access, Visa).

Hostellerie de Meysset ★★★ lieu-dit Argentauleau, 24200 Sarlat.
✆ 53 59 08 29, Fax 53 28 47 61. English spoken.
Open 14/04 to 30/09. 26 bedrooms (all en suite). Tennis, golf 10 km, parking.
Situated 2 km north of Sarlat in parkland. Take D47 in the direction of Périgueux.

■ RESTAURANT: Closed 14 to 27 Apr & Wed lunch.
■ TARIFF: (1994) Single 304–334, Double 390–430, Bk 45, Set menu 100–250 (Amex, Euro/Access, Visa).

Hôtel Relais du Touron ★★ Le Touron, 24200 Carsac-Aillac.
✆ 53 28 16 70. English spoken.
Open 01/04 to 14/11. 12 bedrooms (all en suite). Outdoor swimming pool, golf 3 km, parking. &

Hotel has a friendly atmosphere and stands in a large park on the outskirts of Sarlat. From Sarlat go south on the D704 to Carsac-Aillac.

■ RESTAURANT: Closed Tues lunch & Wed HS, lunch LS. Regional and traditional cuisine.
■ ACTIVITIES: Fishing and canoeing on the Dordogne.
■ TARIFF: (1994) Single 245–300, Double 265–375, Bk 35, Set menu 90–265 (Amex, Euro/Access, Visa, **BT**).
■ DISCOUNT: 5% Half-board only.

Hôtel de Selves ★★★ 93 avenue de Selves, 24200 Sarlat.
✆ 53 31 50 00, Fax 53 31 23 52. English spoken.
Open 10/02 to 09/01. 40 bedrooms (all en suite). Indoor swimming pool, outdoor swimming pool, golf 6 km, garage. &

200 m from the old town, a very comfortable, modern hotel with a lovely garden, satellite television, air-conditioning and sauna.

■ ACTIVITIES: Tennis, horse-riding and canoeing nearby; ideal base for visiting Les Eyzies, Le Quercy and the châteaux of the Dordogne valley.
■ TARIFF: (1994) Single 360–460, Double 420–520, Bk 45 (Amex, Euro/Access, Visa).

SAULGES Mayenne 2C

Hôtel L'Ermitage ★★★ 53340 Saulges.
✆ 43 90 52 28, Fax 43 90 56 61. English spoken.

Open 01/03 to 31/01. 36 bedrooms (all en suite). Outdoor swimming pool, tennis, golf 20 km, garage, parking. &

A picturesque, quiet hotel in the heart of the Mayenne countryside. Excellent facilities and lovely gardens.

■ RESTAURANT: Closed Feb. 'Winter garden' décor. Enjoys a good reputation and specialises in regional dishes. Meals are served outside on the terrace in summer.
■ ACTIVITIES: Fitness room, croquet, sauna.
■ TARIFF: (1994) Single 270–400, Double 300–480, Bk 50, Set menu 98–300 (Amex, Euro/Access, Visa).

SAUMUR Maine/Loire 2C

Hôtel Anne d'Anjou ★★★ 32 quai Mayaud, 49400 Saumur.
✆ 41 67 30 30, Fax 41 67 51 00. English spoken.
Open all year. 50 bedrooms (all en suite). Tennis, golf 15 km, garage, parking. &

Between the River Loire and the Château of Saumur, this 18th-century building overlooks the river. Charming illuminated interior courtyard.

■ RESTAURANT: Imaginative menu using fresh local produce.
■ TARIFF: (1994) Single 270–640, Double 350–640, Bk 48 (Amex, Euro/Access, Visa).

Hôtel Cheval Blanc ★★ 2 rue des Marines, 49160 St-Martin-de-la-Place.
✆ 41 38 42 96, Fax 41 38 42 62. English spoken.
Open 05/02 to 05/01. 12 bedrooms (11 en suite, 1 bath/shower only). Golf 8 km, parking. &

Take the 952 from Saumur towards Angers, for

S

6 km. The hotel is in the village of St-Martin, opposite the church.

■ RESTAURANT: Gourmet restaurant. Specialities: foie gras, saumon fumé, assiette du pêcheur aux trois sauces, magret de canard au citron.
■ ACTIVITIES: Fishing, tennis and horse-riding close by.
■ TARIFF: (1994) Single 215, Double 215–300, Bk 30, Set menu 90–250 (Euro/Access, Visa).

Hôtel Loire ★★★ rue Vieux Port, 49400 Saumur.
℡ 41 67 22 42, Fax 41 67 88 80. English spoken. Open all year. 45 bedrooms (all en suite). Golf 15 km, garage, parking.
Situated on the island of Offard, overlooking the Loire. The hotel is very quiet and comfortable.
■ RESTAURANT: Restaurant has splendid view of the Château of Saumur. Specialities: terrine de poisson de Loire; cuisse de canard aux oignons confits.
■ ACTIVITIES: Hire of canoes and mountain bikes and access to nearby sports complex.
■ TARIFF: Single 305–365, Double 360–575, Bk 48 (Amex, Euro/Access, Visa).
■ DISCOUNT: 10%

Hôtel St-Pierre ★★★ 8 rue Haute-St-Pierre, 49400 Saumur.
℡ 41 50 33 00, Fax 41 50 38 68. English spoken. Open all year. 14 bedrooms (all en suite). Tennis, golf 5 km, garage, parking. &
Stylish, luxurious 17th-century hotel in the renovated, historic town centre. Quiet rooms with designer bathrooms. Saumur is in the Loire Valley and can be reached on either side of the river from Tours, on the N152 and the D7.
■ ACTIVITIES: Horse-riding nearby.
■ TARIFF: (1994) Single 300–365, Double 525–690, Bk 47 (Amex, Euro/Access, Visa).
■ DISCOUNT: 8%

SAUSSET-LES-PINS Bches-du-Rhône 5D

Hôtel Paradou-Méditerranée ★★★ Le Port, 13960 Sausset-les-Pins.
℡ 42 44 76 76, Fax 42 44 78 48. English spoken. Open all year. 42 bedrooms (all en suite). Outdoor swimming pool, parking. &
A modern hotel overlooking the sea in Sausset-les-Pins, just 15 km from Marseille airport, on the Côte d'Azur with its pine trees and rocky bays. From the A55 take Carry-le-Rouet exit and follow the signs to Sausset-les-Pins.

■ RESTAURANT: Closed Sat lunch.
■ TARIFF: (1994) Single 360–450, Double 380–550, Bk 45, Set menu 130–180 (Amex, Euro/Access, Visa).

SAVERNE Bas-Rhin 3B

Hôtel Chez Jean ★★ 3 rue de la Gare, 67700 Saverne.
℡ 88 91 10 19, Fax 88 91 27 45. English spoken. Open 10/01 to 22/12. 25 bedrooms (all en suite). Garage, parking.
The hotel is in an old convent, situated near the town centre.
■ RESTAURANT: Closed Sun eve & Mon. Two restaurants.
■ TARIFF: (1994) Single 295–320, Double 320–350, Bk 38, Set menu 95–220 (Amex, Euro/Access, Visa).

SCHIRMECK Bas-Rhin 3D

Château de Barembach ★★★ 5 rue du Maréchal de Lattre, 67130 Schirmeck.
℡ 88 97 97 50, Fax 88 47 17 19. English spoken. Open all year. 15 bedrooms (all en suite). Tennis, garage, parking.
Small but elegant 19th-century château used as the owners' private home until 1983. Surrounded by mountains and forests, it has a terrace and pretty flower garden. General Patton made the château his headquarters in 1944. 40 km west of Strasbourg on A35/N392.
■ RESTAURANT: Excellent light cuisine, good choice of menus. Specialities include carpaccio of spice-marinated monkfish and salmon, roast kidney of veal fricassée with fresh mushrooms, butter-fried breast of guinea fowl and fillet of sole in Champagne.
■ ACTIVITIES: Horse-riding, fishing, skiing, cycling; sightseeing visits to museums and vineyards.

S

TARIFF: (1994) Single 385–665,
Double 475–825, Bk 55, Set menu 145–398
(Amex, Euro/Access, Visa).
■ DISCOUNT: 10% LS (1/11 to 1/4).

Hôtel La Rubanerie ★★ La Claquette,
67570 Rothau.
☎ 88 97 01 95, Fax 88 47 17 34. English spoken.

Open all year. 16 bedrooms (all en suite).
Outdoor swimming pool, parking. &
*Situated 35 minutes from Strasbourg, beside a
river in a large park. This traditional house
offers spacious, comfortable rooms with charm
and distinction.*
■ RESTAURANT: Closed Sun & Mon lunch.
■ TARIFF: (1994) Single 270–405,
Double 305–430, Bk 40, Set menu 140–260
(Amex, Euro/Access, Visa).

SECLIN Nord   2B

Auberge du Forgeron ★★★ 17 rue Roger
Bouvry, 59113 Seclin.
☎ 20 90 09 52, Fax 20 32 70 87.
English spoken.

Open all year. 18 bedrooms (15 en suite,
3 bath/shower only). Golf 8 km, parking. &

*Comfortable and cosy rooms of character.
Proximity to autoroutes A27 and A25. A1 exit
no 19.*
■ RESTAURANT: Closed Sun. Excellent food and
wine.
■ TARIFF: (1994) Single 250–450,
Double 280–450, Bk 40 (Amex,
Euro/Access, Visa).

SEES Orne   2C

Hôtel Ile de Sées ★★ à Mace, 61500 Sées.
☎ 33 27 98 65, Fax 33 28 41 22.
English spoken.

Open 15/03 to 15/01. 16 bedrooms
(all en suite). Tennis, parking.
*Attractive, peaceful hotel situated just south of
N138/N158 junction.*
■ RESTAURANT: Closed Sun eve & Mon.
Traditional restaurant offering classic and
regional cuisine.
■ ACTIVITIES: Good area for visiting châteaux
and other places of interest.
■ TARIFF: (1994) Single 280, Double 340, Bk 38,
Set menu 98–170 (Euro/Access, Visa).

SENLIS Oise   2B

Auberge de Fontaine ★★ 22 Grande rue,
60300 Fontaine-Châalis.
☎ 44 54 20 22, Fax 44 60 25 38.
English spoken.
Open all year. 9 bedrooms (all en suite).
Golf 8 km, parking. &

*In the centre of the village of Fontaine-Châalis,
a few kilometres from Senlis. N330 south-east
of Senlis and then D126 to Fontaine-Châalis.*
■ RESTAURANT: Closed Mon eve and Wed.
■ TARIFF: (1994) Double 275–320, Bk 40,
Set menu 115–190 (Euro/Access, Visa).

S

Château de Raray ★★★★ Domaine de Raray, 60810 Raray.
☎ 44 54 70 61, Fax 44 54 74 97.
English spoken.

Open all year. 10 bedrooms (all en suite). Tennis, golf on site, parking.
17th-century château. Location for 'Beauty and the Beast' film. Senlis exit from A1, then third exit right on to D932A after toll, towards Compiègne. Right in Villeneuve-sur-Verbérie, then D100.
■ RESTAURANT: Gourmet restaurant.
■ TARIFF: (1994) Single 700, Double 850, Bk 60 (Euro/Access, Visa).

SENS Yonne   2D

Hôtel Pavillon Bleu ★★ 89330 Villevallier.
☎ 86 91 12 17, Fax 86 91 17 74.
Open 01/02 to 31/12. 18 bedrooms (13 en suite, 5 bath/shower only). Parking, restaurant.
Pleasantly located back from the N6 and close to the river. From Sens, south on the N6.
■ TARIFF: (1994) Single 150–195, Double 150–195, Bk 30, Set menu 78–195 (Amex, Euro/Access, Visa).

SERRE-CHEVALIER Htes-Alpes   6A

Hôtel Plein Sud ★★★ Chantmerle, 05330 Serre-Chevalier.
☎ 92 24 17 01, Fax 92 24 10 21.
English spoken.
Open 17/06 to 17/09 & 16/12 to 16/04.
1612 bedrooms (42 en suite). Indoor swimming pool, outdoor swimming pool, golf 16 km, garage, parking.
In the village of Chantmerle on N91, 5 km from Briançon. Every comfort in this resort-centre hotel.

■ ACTIVITIES: BMX, horse-riding, hang-gliding and a host of other activities nearby.
■ TARIFF: (1994) Single 300–410, Double 360–510, Bk 45 (Euro/Access, Visa).

SETE Hérault   5C

Hôtel Imperial ★★★ pl E Herriot, 34200 Sète.
☎ 67 53 28 32, Fax 67 53 37 49. English spoken.

Open all year. 40 bedrooms (all en suite). Parking.
Good standard and value for money. 100 m from beaches and 1 km from town centre and shops. (Restaurant is due to be opened in 1995.)
■ ACTIVITIES: Nearby casino, piano bar, bike hire and horse-riding.
■ TARIFF: (1994) Single 245–345, Double 425–500, Bk 35 (Amex, Euro/Access, Visa).

SEYNE Alpes-Hte-Prov   6C

Le Relais de la Forge 04460 Selonnet.
☎ 92 35 16 98. English spoken.
Open 01/01 to 15/11 & 15/12 to 31/12.
15 bedrooms (10 en suite). Parking, restaurant. ♿

S

*In a peaceful mountain setting by a footpath
and 20 minutes from Lake Serre Ponçon. From
Seyne take the D900 north and turn left to
Selonnet.*
- TARIFF: (1994) Single 150–220,
Double 170–250, Bk 26, Set menu 72–165
(Amex, Euro/Access, Visa).

SEYSSEL Ain   6A

Hôtel du Rhône ★★ Rive-droite,
01420 Seyssel.
☎ 50 59 20 30. English spoken.

Open all year. 12 bedrooms (8 en suite,
4 bath/shower only). Golf 15 km, garage,
parking.
*Recommended family-run hotel, delightfully
situated on the banks of the Rhône. From A40
motorway go southwards on the D991 to
Seyssel.*
- RESTAURANT: Closed Wed. Good food in lovely
surroundings.
- TARIFF: (1994) Single 110–125,
Double 170–260, Bk 35, Set menu 90–140
(Amex, Euro/Access, Visa).

SISTERON Alpes-Hte-Prov   6C

Grand Hôtel du Cours ★★★ pl de l'Eglise,
04200 Sisteron.
☎ 92 61 04 51, Fax 92 61 41 73.
English spoken.
Open 01/03 to 30/11. 50 bedrooms
(all en suite). Garage, parking. &
*Situated in the middle of this historic town,
hotel is beautifully presented and offers
comfortable rooms with modern facilities. Bar
and tea room. Sisteron, the Gateway to
Provence, is on the A51.*
- ACTIVITIES: A host of sporting activities
nearby, including the new swimming centre,

only 5 minutes' walk away. Good area for
cultural visits and sightseeing.
- TARIFF: Single 220–330, Double 270–430,
Bk 40 (Amex, Euro/Access, Visa).

SOMMIERES Gard   5D

Auberge du Pont-Romain ★★★ 2 rue Emile
Jamais, 30250 Sommières.
☎ 66 80 00 58, Fax 66 80 31 52. English spoken.
Open 15/03 to 15/01. 19 bedrooms
(17 en suite, 2 bath/shower only). Outdoor
swimming pool, golf 20 km, parking. &
*Leave N110 at Lunel and go 12 km to
Sommières.*
- RESTAURANT: Closed Wed LS. Good restaurant
with creative, seasonal specialities.
- TARIFF: (1994) Single 210–380,
Double 265–420, Bk 45, Set menu 155–225
(Amex, Euro/Access, Visa).

SORGES Dordogne   4B

Hôtel de la Mairie ★★ 24420 Sorges.
☎ 53 05 02 05, Fax 53 05 39 27.
English spoken.
Open all year. 27 bedrooms (all en suite).
Outdoor swimming pool, parking. &
*Sorges is in the centre of the foie gras and
truffles area. This family-run hotel is on the
N21 between Périgueux and Thiviers.*
- RESTAURANT: Comfortable restaurant offering
classical and modern cuisine using fresh, local
produce. Specialities: veal sweetbreads with
truffles; breast of duck with foie gras and
truffles. Meals served on the terrace when
weather permits.
- ACTIVITIES: ● From 1 December to 28 February
hotel offers truffle-hunting expeditions and
courses on the making of paté de foie gras.
- TARIFF: (1994) Single 220–260,
Double 220–315, Bk 35, Set menu 75–250
(Amex, Euro/Access, Visa).

S

SOUILLAC Lot 4B

Auberge du Puits ★ 5 pl du Puits,
46200 Souillac.
☎ 65 37 80 32, Fax 65 37 07 16. English spoken.
Open 01/01 to 01/11. 20 bedrooms
(all en suite). Parking. &

From Brive, N20 south to Souillac. In Souillac
turn right after the post office and hotel is
located in a lovely square.
■ RESTAURANT: Closed Sun eve & Mon LS. Local
specialities.
■ TARIFF: (1994) Double 130–250, Bk 30,
Set menu 70–250 (Euro/Access, Visa).

Inter-Hôtel Le Quercy ★★ rue de la Recège,
46200 Souillac.
☎ 65 37 83 56, Fax 65 37 07 22. English spoken.
Open 15/03 to 15/12. 25 bedrooms
(all en suite). Outdoor swimming pool,
golf 20 km, garage, parking.

A modern B&B hotel close to town centre with
good restaurant next door. Most rooms have
balconies. Good spot for exploring region.
35 km from Brive, 70 km from Cahors.
■ TARIFF: (1994) Single 240–260,
Double 250–300, Bk 32 (Euro/Access, Visa).

Hôtel La Vieille Auberge ★★ rue de la
Recège, 46200 Souillac.
☎ 65 32 79 43, Fax 65 32 65 19. English spoken.
Open all year. 20 bedrooms (all en suite).
Indoor swimming pool, outdoor swimming
pool, garage, parking.

A comfortable, well-equipped hotel. All rooms
have video. N20, D703.
■ RESTAURANT: Closed Sun eve & Mon 01/11 to
01/04. Restaurant appears in the main gourmet
food guides. Quercy-Périgord specialities.
■ ACTIVITIES: Fitness room and solarium at hotel.
Many places of interest to visit plus canoeing,
kayaking, cycling, mountain-biking, horse-
riding, walking and tennis in the vicinity.
■ TARIFF: (1994) Single 220–285,
Double 240–350, Bk 35 (Amex,
Euro/Access, Visa).

SOURZAC-MUSSIDAN Dordogne 4B

Hôtel Le Chaufourg-en-Périgord
24400 Sourzac.
☎ 53 81 01 56, Fax 53 82 94 87. English spoken.
Open all year. 9 bedrooms (all en suite).
Outdoor swimming pool, golf 25 km, parking.

4 km from Mussidan on N89 overlooking the
River Isle in a region steeped in history,
châteaux, fine foods and wines. This 17th-
century family residence offers elegant

comfort, charm, and some truly exceptional
gardens.
■ TARIFF: (1994) Double 700–1300, Bk 65
(Amex, Euro/Access, Visa).

LA SOUTERRAINE Creuse 4B

Hôtel de la Porte St-Jean ★★ 2 rue des Bains,
23300 La Souterraine.
☎ 55 63 90 00, Fax 55 63 77 27. English spoken.
Open all year. 32 bedrooms (3 en suite,
28 bath/shower only). Garage, restaurant. &

The hotel restaurant is in the centre of La

465 Boulevard Labrasse
62780 Stella-Plage
Tel: 21 94 60 86   Fax: 21 94 10 11

Charming hotel just a few minutes'
walk from the sea and delightful
surrounding countryside.

5 minutes' drive from the
resort of Le Touquet.

Good regional food.

See under
Stella-Plage

S

Sauterraine in a pedestrian area and is very quiet. Historical surroundings. N20 from Limoges, northwards, then right onto N145 to La Souterraine.

■ TARIFF: (1994) Single 155–269, Double 155–289, Bk 34, Set menu 84–199 (Amex, Euro/Access, Visa, **BT***).

STELLA-PLAGE Pas-de-Calais   2B

Hôtel des Pelouses ★★ 465 bd Labrasse, 62780 Stella-Plage.
℄ 21 94 60 86, Fax 21 94 10 11.
Open 01/02 to 31/12. 30 bedrooms (15 en suite, 3 bath/shower only). Golf 4 km, parking.

A modern hotel 5 km from Le Touquet in Stella-Plage. Between Le Touquet and Berck-Plage on the D940. SEE ADJACENT ADVERTISEMENT.

■ RESTAURANT: Well prepared, varied cuisine. Specialities include moules farcies and pavé de boeuf.
■ TARIFF: (1994) Single 150–260, Double 220–300, Bk 25, Set menu 65–160 (Euro/Access, Visa).
■ DISCOUNT: 5% On presentation of this book.

STRASBOURG

Stasbourg's Gothic cathedral

The Rhine is not generally thought of as a French river but, between Basle in Switzerland and Karlsruhe in Germany, the French border runs for about 150 km along its length. Here, where the main river is joined by the River Ill, lies Strasbourg – the only French port on the Rhine. Very much a city of barges, a boat trip around the old town can be a good starting point for an exploration of this thriving community.

Historically a European city of great importance, it was here that Gutenberg pioneered his printing press in the late 15th century. His statue stands at the centre of the old town in the square named after him. On the west side of the Place Gutenberg is the Hôtel de Commerce, a fine Renaissance building which now houses the tourist office. Look down the rue Mercière for a splendid view of the Cathédrale de Notre-Dame, whose west front towers above the surrounding houses. Climb the 328 steps up the spire for a view that takes in the roof tops of the old town, the River Rhine with its connecting waterways and, away to the east, the Black Forest. Two of Strasbourg's main tourist attractions lie inside this magnificent building, one is the 13th-century carved Pilier des Anges and the other the 19th-century astronomical clock.

As well as an abundance of pavement cafés in this area, there are plenty of museums. The Musée des Arts Décoratifs, the Musée

Foie Gras

Translated into English, the French words foie gras become 'fat liver', not in Britain a very appetising thought, but in France these words describe a great and expensive delicacy. Foie gras comes from poultry, generally speaking geese, that have been force-fed with maize in order to enlarge the goose's liver but this also makes it bright yellow. Until Louis XIV made the eating of foie gras fashionable, it was thought of as a dish only suitable for peasants to eat.

Alsace, of which Strasbourg is the capital, is one of the major centres for the production of foie gras. From September onwards, the geese are ready to be slaughtered and their livers removed. Some livers weigh as much as 4 kg, but the taste of lighter ones is thought by many to be superior.

As well as eating foie gras in restaurants, you may want to buy a tin or two to take home. When buying tins look carefully at the labelling. By law pâté de foie gras must be at least 80% goose liver, while mousse de foie gras only has to contain 55%. You may also see tins of foie d'oie which is liver from an ordinary, not force-fed, goose.

S

des Beaux-Arts and the Musée Archéologique are all housed in one building, the Palais Rohan. But if one had to choose only one museum to visit in Strasbourg, it might be the Musée d'Art Moderne with its collection of paintings by Monet, Picasso, Klimt and Klee, amongst many others.

A walk through the area known as La Petite France gives an impression of 16th-century Strasbourg, but the reality was probably somewhat different from what we see here today. These houses that were traditionally lived in by fishermen, tanners and millers are now all flower-bedecked and perfectly restored. However, with its riverside setting, this is an extremely pleasant part of the city in which to wander.

Strasbourg is perhaps best known as the city of the European Parliament, housed in the flag-fronted Palais de l'Europe that so frequently features as backdrop to television news reports on the European Union. To explore beyond the familiar rank of national flags, join a guided tour of the building and institution. Directly across the avenue de l'Europe from the Palais is the Parc de l'Orangerie, a vast and beautiful public park created in the nineteenth century. This has a mini-zoo and free summer concerts (also in Parc des Contades) but, perhaps more noteworthily, a spectacular community of nesting storks.

Strasbourg is very much a city of concerts and there are several international festivals held here each year. June is the month for classical music, July the month for jazz and then, in September, the music is contemporary. So choose the timing of your visit with care and, if miming or clowning is more of interest to you, come in November.

STRASBOURG Bas-Rhin   3D

(See feature)

Hôtel Altea Pont de l'Europe ★★★ Par du Rhin, 67000 Strasbourg.
℡ 88 61 03 23, Fax 88 60 43 05. English spoken.
Open all year. 93 bedrooms (all en suite).
Parking. &

In Strasbourg follow directions to Offenburg. Just before the bridge, near the border, turn right

into a large park where the hotel is located.
- RESTAURANT: Has a large, shady terrace and offers cuisine 'Bourgeoise' and fish specialities.
- ACTIVITIES: Water sports and riding centres nearby.
- TARIFF: (1994) Single 380–450, Double 380–480, Bk 50, Set menu 75–150 (Amex, Euro/Access, Visa).

Bonôtel de France ★★ 59 rte de Rhin, 67000 Strasbourg.
℡ 88 60 10 52, Fax 88 60 22 77. English spoken.

Open all year. 70 bedrooms (all en suite). Indoor swimming pool, outdoor swimming pool, tennis, parking. &
Prominent hotel close to the Rhine. From the centre of Strasbourg follow signs to Germany and Kehl. The hotel stands on the left, directly opposite the Office du Tourisme, just before the frontier (the Pont du Europe over the Rhine).

Hôtel du Dragon ★★★ 2 rue de l'Ecarlate, 67000 Strasbourg.
℡ 88 35 79 80, Fax 88 25 78 95. English spoken.
Open all year. 32 bedrooms (all en suite).
Golf 6 km. &
In a quiet street of the old city near La Petite France, 17th-century house converted into a stylish hotel. Some rooms with view of the cathedral. Small garden. Many restaurants within walking distance. Approach the hotel via quai St-Nicolas.
- TARIFF: (1994) Single 435–565, Double 475–610, Bk 54 (Amex, Euro/Access, Visa).

Hôtel Europe ★★★ 38 rue Fosses des Tanneurs, 67000 Strasbourg.
℡ 88 32 17 88, Fax 88 75 65 45. English spoken.
Open all year. 60 bedrooms (all en suite).
Garage. &
Full of charm and character, 15th-century posthouse next to the pedestrian area of La Petite France. Houses a unique 1/50 scale

model of Strasbourg Cathedral in the reception hall. Straight access from motorway exit Place des Halles.

■ ACTIVITIES: ● Free bicycles.
■ TARIFF: (1994) Single 290–450, Double 370–500, Bk 40 (Amex, Euro/Access, Visa).

Hilton Hôtel av Herranschmidt, 67000 Strasbourg.
☎ 88 37 10 10, Fax 88 36 89 27. English spoken. Open all year. 246 bedrooms (all en suite). Parking. ♿

Hotel is located opposite the Music and Convention Centre, near the highway exits and minutes away from the European institutions and city centre.

■ RESTAURANT: Closed Aug. Enjoy gastronomic cuisine in 'La Maison du Boeuf' or traditional dishes in 'Le Jardin'.
■ ACTIVITIES: Tennis, golf, horse-riding; excursions to Haut-Koenigsbourg Castle, the Vosges and Black Forest mountains and old villages with typical Alsacian architecture.
■ TARIFF: Single 415–1120, Double 430–1120, Bk 85 (Amex, Euro/Access, Visa).

Hôtel du Rhin ★★ 7-8 place de la Gare, 67000 Strasbourg.
☎ 88 32 35 00, Fax 88 23 51 92. English spoken.

Open all year. 61 bedrooms (54 en suite). Parking. ♿

In the town centre opposite the station (the hotel has sound-proofed rooms). Underground parking available. From the A35, take the Centre Ville exit just after the Gare Centrale.

■ TARIFF: (1994) Single 200–340, Double 200–360, Bk 30 (Euro/Access, Visa).

Hôtel des Rohan ★★★ 17 rue du Maroquin, 67000 Strasbourg.
☎ 88 32 85 11, Fax 88 75 65 37. English spoken. Open all year. 36 bedrooms (all en suite). Golf 15 km, garage, parking.

From the ring road take the exit place de L'Etoile and follow Centre-Ville and parking-Gutenberg signs. Porters are available at the hotel from 7 am to 8 pm.

■ TARIFF: (1994) Single 350–540, Double 350–595, Bk 50 (Amex, Euro/Access, Visa).

Hôtel aux Trois Roses ★★ 7 rue de Zurich, 67000 Strasbourg.
☎ 88 36 56 95, Fax 88 35 06 14. English spoken. Open all year. 33 bedrooms (all en suite). Parking. ♿

In the centre of Strasbourg, on the banks of the Ill. Near the Cathedral. Private car park. Exit motorway A4 at place de l'Etoile towards Centre-Ville and Krutenau.

■ TARIFF: (1994) Single 280–410, Double 380–465, Bk 55 (Amex, Euro/Access, Visa).

TALLOIRES Hte-Savoie   6A

Hôtel Beau Site ★★★ 74290 Talloires.
☎ 50 60 71 04, Fax 50 60 79 22. English spoken. Open 18/05 to 12/10. 29 bedrooms (all en suite). Tennis, golf 3 km, parking.

Excellent location in a park, directly adjoining the east shores of Lake Annecy. Very quiet. Superb views of the lake and mountains. On D509A.

■ RESTAURANT: Gastronomic cuisine and panoramic views.
■ ACTIVITIES: Swimming, fishing and boating literally on the doorstep.
■ TARIFF: (1994) Single 280–300, Double 400–720, Bk 50 (Amex, Euro/Access, Visa).

Hôtel La Charpenterie ★★ 74290 Talloires.
☎ 50 60 70 47, Fax 60 60 79 07. English spoken.
Open 12/02 to 12/12. 18 bedrooms (all en suite). Golf 3 km, parking.

Warm and welcoming chalet-style hotel with lovely views. Accommodation caters for couples or families, each room having its own private balcony. On the east shore of the lake, 10 km from Annecy.

■ RESTAURANT: Wood-clad, typical Savoyard-style dining room with panoramic views. Fresh lake fish specialities.

S

■ ACTIVITIES: Water sports, fishing and winter sports close by.
■ TARIFF: (1994) Single 205–400, Double 245–440, Bk 40, Set menu 105–165 (Amex, Euro/Access, Visa).
■ DISCOUNT: 10%

Hôtel Le Cottage Fernand Bise ★★★★ route du port, 74290 Talloires.
℄ 50 60 71 10, Fax 50 60 77 51. English spoken.
Open 01/04 to 31/10. 35 bedrooms (all en suite). Outdoor swimming pool, golf 2 km, garage, parking, restaurant. ♿
An extremely comfortable hotel, with views of the lake.

■ ACTIVITIES: ● Accommodation plus golf package available.
■ TARIFF: (1994) Single 500–1100, Double 500–1100, Bk 65, Set menu 180–270 (Amex, Euro/Access, Visa).

THEOULE-SUR-MER Alpes-Mar 6C

Hôtel Mas Provençal ★★ 10 av du Trayas, 06590 Théoule.
℄ 93 75 40 20, Fax 93 75 44 83. English spoken.

Open all year. 27 bedrooms (all en suite). Outdoor swimming pool, tennis, golf 10 km, parking, restaurant.
5 km from Théoule, on the Corniche d'Or road, the hotel is situated in the red rocks of the Esterel, close to the harbour and sandy beaches.
■ TARIFF: (1994) Single 270–420, Double 340–540, Bk 35 (Amex, Euro/Access, Visa).

Hôtel Miramar Beach ★★★ 47 av de Miramar, Miramar, 06590 Théoule-sur-Mer.
℄ 93 75 41 36, Fax 93 75 44 83. English spoken.
Open all year. 60 bedrooms (all en suite). Indoor swimming pool, outdoor swimming pool, tennis, golf 7 km, garage, parking. ♿

Between Cannes and St-Raphaël with private beach and heated (and in winter covered) swimming pool. Restaurant and all bedrooms air-conditioned. Tennis court and beauty/health centre. Satellite TV with 22 stations.

■ RESTAURANT: Panoramic views from the restaurant which serves traditional French cuisine.

THIERS Puy-de-Dôme 5A

Eliôtel ★★ route de Maringues, Pont de Dore, 63920 Thiers.
℄ 73 80 10 14. English spoken.
Open all year. 13 bedrooms (all en suite). Golf 2 km, parking.
4 miles from the centre of the medieval town of Thiers, on the N89 towards Clermont-Ferrand.
■ RESTAURANT: Closed Sat & Sun eve.
■ ACTIVITIES: Nearby leisure park with windsurfing, pedalos, fishing, 9-hole golf course and sandy beaches.
■ TARIFF: (1994) Double 260, Bk 32, Set menu 85–210 (Amex, Euro/Access, Visa).

THIONVILLE Moselle 3B

Hôtel Saint-Hubert ★★ 2 rue de la Convention, 57100 Thionville.
℄ 82 51 84 22, Fax 82 53 99 61. English spoken.
Open all year. 45 bedrooms (all en suite). Golf 12 km, parking. ♿
Spacious, modern comforts are on offer in this hotel which has sound-proofed rooms. In the centre, by the bank of the Moselle River. 27 km north of Metz on the A31 motorway, follow directions to the town centre and then after crossing the Moselle Bridge, the hotel is in front of you.

T

■ TARIFF: (1994) Single 270–300, Double 300–330 (Amex, Euro/Access, Visa).

THONON-LES-BAINS Hte-Savoie 6A

Hôtel L'Arc en Ciel ★★ 18 place de Crête, 74200 Thonon-les-Bains.
☎ 50 71 90 63, Fax 50 26 27 47. English spoken. Open all year. 40 bedrooms (all en suite). Outdoor swimming pool, golf 9 km, garage, parking. ♿

Between Genève and Evian, the hotel is in the centre of Thonon and overlooks Lac Léman. The rooms have balconies.

■ RESTAURANT: Closed Nov.
■ TARIFF: (1994) Single 310–450, Double 350–550, Bk 38, Set menu 75–220 (Amex, Euro/Access, Visa).

Hôtel L'Ombre des Marronniers ★ 17 pl de Crête, 74200 Thonon-les-Bains.
☎ 50 71 26 18, Fax 50 26 27 47. English spoken. Open all year. 18 bedrooms (11 en suite, 4 bath/shower only). Golf 9 km, parking.

Pleasant situation, 5 minutes' walk from town centre of pretty Thonon, on Lac Léman.

■ RESTAURANT: Closed Nov.
■ TARIFF: (1994) Single 160–250, Double 250–280, Bk 29, Set menu 75–250 (No credit cards).

THORENC Alpes-Mar 6C

Auberge Les Merisiers ★ avenue du Belvédère, 06750 Thorenc.
☎ 93 60 00 23, Fax 93 60 00 17. English spoken. Open all year. 12 bedrooms (11 en suite, 1 bath/shower only). Golf 15 km.

Charming country inn, renovated and run by a young Anglo-French couple. In the heart of 'La Suisse Provençale'- a good base for all outdoor activities. Take the N85 from Grasse, turn right after 12 km and follow signs.

■ RESTAURANT: Refined, regional cuisine served in rustic-style surroundings, complete with an ancient fireplace. Specialities include stuffed sardines, foie gras and home-smoked salmon.
■ ACTIVITIES: ● Various activities including skiing and hang-gliding can be arranged with 10% reduction.
■ TARIFF: (1994) Double 200–250, Bk 30, Set menu 83–99 (Euro/Access, Visa).

THUEYTS Ardèche 5B

Hôtel des Marronniers ★★ place du Champ de Mars, 07330 Thueyts.
☎ 75 36 40 16, Fax 75 36 48 02. English spoken. Open 01/03 to 31/12. 19 bedrooms (16 en suite). Outdoor swimming pool, parking.

Classical hotel in verdant surroundings with terraced garden. In the centre of the town close by the N102. From Aubenas 20 km west on N102.

■ RESTAURANT: Attractive, light and airy. Father and son offer house and local specialities.
■ ACTIVITIES: BMX, tennis and fishing nearby.
■ TARIFF: (1994) Single 170–250, Double 210–260, Bk 29, Set menu 85–185 (Visa).

THURY-HARCOURT Calvados 2A

Relais de la Poste ★★★ 2 route de Caen, 14220 Thury-Harcourt.
☎ 31 79 72 12, Fax 31 39 53 55. English spoken.

Open all year. 11 bedrooms (8 en suite, 3 bath/shower only). Indoor swimming pool, tennis, golf 7 km, garage, parking.

Very French hotel with creepers covering the walls around shuttered windows. Pleasant rooms and apartments. On the river. Good for fishing and walking. South from Caen on D562 to Thury-Harcourt.

■ RESTAURANT: Closed Sun eve & Mon LS. Seafood, especially shellfish, specialities.

T

■ ACTIVITIES: Horse-riding, BMX and canoeing nearby.
■ TARIFF: (1994) Single 250–420, Double 250–620, Bk 42, Set menu 135–400 (Amex, Euro/Access, Visa).
■ DISCOUNT: 10% LS.

TOULON Var   6C

Hôtel La Corniche ★★★ 17 Littoral Frédérick Mistral, 83000 Toulon.
☎ 94 41 35 12, Fax 94 41 24 58. English spoken.
Open all year. 22 bedrooms (all en suite).
Garage, parking. &
Simple stylish décor, recently renovated, each room now air-conditioned. From Toulon, head for Le Mourillon and Les Plages, hotel overlooks the Port Saint-Louis.
■ RESTAURANT: The 'Bistro' and 'Oyster Bar' restaurants are renowned for their good food.
■ TARIFF: (1994) Single 320–440, Double 320–580, Bk 40, Set menu 100–180 (Amex, Euro/Access, Visa, BT𝄽).

Hôtel Promotour ★★ Les Espaluns, 83160 La Valette.
☎ 94 08 38 08, Fax 94 08 48 60. English spoken.

Open all year. 42 bedrooms (all en suite).
Outdoor swimming pool, golf 3 km, garage, parking, restaurant. &
Pleasant hotel with rooms overlooking garden and swimming pool. Special rates for families. From Toulon, exit 5 from A57 towards Nice.
■ TARIFF: (1994) Double 280, Bk 35, Set menu 65–105 (Amex, Euro/Access, Visa).
■ DISCOUNT: 10%

New Hôtel Tour Blanche ★★★
83000 Toulon.
☎ 94 24 41 57, Fax 94 22 42 25. English spoken.
Open all year. 92 bedrooms (all en suite).
Outdoor swimming pool, golf 15 km, parking, restaurant. &

Just below Mt Faron, only a few minutes from the harbour and town centre. Large swimming pool in lovely gardens. Conference facilities, spectacular views over bay.
■ TARIFF: (1994) Single 395–395, Double 395–395, Bk 50 (Amex, Euro/Access, Visa, BT𝄽).

TOULOUSE Hte-Garonne   4D

Hôtel Albion ★★ 28 rue Bachelier, 31000 Toulouse.
☎ 61 63 60 36, Fax 61 62 66 95. English spoken.
Open all year. 27 bedrooms (all en suite).
Garage. &
Modern hotel with breakfast service in the rooms. 5 minutes from the station and near to the airport shuttle.
■ TARIFF: (1994) Single 250, Double 270, Bk 30 (Amex, Euro/Access, Visa).

Auberge de France 2 rue Alex Coutet, 31000 Toulouse.
☎ 61 44 86 44, Fax 61 43 90 31. English spoken.
Open all year. 43 bedrooms (all en suite).
Golf 10 km, parking. &
Situated in the south-west of Toulouse, halfway between the race course and the leisure centre.
■ RESTAURANT: Classic and regional cuisine.
■ ACTIVITIES: Park and aquatic centre close by.
■ TARIFF: Double 189–270, Bk 32, Set menu 59–145 (Amex, Euro/Access, Visa).
■ DISCOUNT: 30%

Hôtel Le Barry ★★ rue du Barry, 31150 Gratentour.
☎ 61 82 22 10, Fax 61 82 22 38.
Open all year. 22 bedrooms (all en suite).
Outdoor swimming pool, golf 8 km, parking. &
From Toulouse take the A62 north, exit at St-Jory. A pleasant hotel in Gratentour.
■ RESTAURANT: Closed 15/08 to 31/08.
■ TARIFF: (1994) Single 265–330, Double 295–330, Bk 30, Set menu 85–130 (Amex, Euro/Access, Visa).

Hôtel Jean-Mermoz ★★★ 50 rue Matabiau, 31000 Toulouse.
☎ 61 63 04 04, Fax 61 63 15 64. English spoken.
Open all year. 53 bedrooms (all en suite).
Garage. &
Modern, air-conditioned hotel, right in the centre of town but in a quiet location within a small, pretty garden. Friendly atmosphere. Just off the bd de Strasbourg, on the place Jeanne-d'Arc and near the station.

T

■ ACTIVITIES: Guided tours of the city; organised visit to Aerospatiale.
■ TARIFF: (1994) Double 450–690, Bk 50 (Amex, Euro/Access, Visa).

Hôtel Trianon ★★ 7 rue Lafaille, 31000 Toulouse.
☏ 61 62 74 74. English spoken.
Open all year. 30 bedrooms (all en suite). &
A new hotel with all modern facilities in the town centre.

■ ACTIVITIES: This hotel has become the meeting place for local wine buffs and is the venue for many a wine tasting session. Hotel guests seem to join in!
■ TARIFF: (1994) Single 195, Double 210–230, Bk 30 (Amex, Euro/Access, Visa).
■ DISCOUNT: 10%

LE TOUQUET Pas-de-Calais   2B

Hôtel Grand ★★★★ 4 bd de la Canche, 62520 Le Touquet-Paris-Plage.
☏ 21 06 88 88, Fax 21 06 87 87. English spoken.

Open all year. 135 bedrooms (all en suite). Indoor swimming pool, golf 3 km, parking, restaurant. &
Quietly situated on the River Canche, the hotel has everything to offer and is within walking distance of the town and beaches. Apartments and suite also available. Conference and business facilities. 35 km from Boulogne on N940. (British reservation office Globe Hotels Ltd: Tel 0372 467 462; Fax 0372 470 032.)

■ ACTIVITIES: ● Excellent choice of activities can be organised, ranging from sailing and golf to guided tours and pleasure flights.
■ TARIFF: (1994) Single 560–760, Double 760–960, Bk 65 (Amex, Euro/Access, Visa).

Hôtel Manoir ★★★
62520 Le Touquet-Paris-Plage.
☏ 21 05 20 22, Fax 21 05 31 26. English spoken.

Open 01/02 to 31/12. 42 bedrooms (all en suite). Outdoor swimming pool, tennis, golf on site, parking.
The hotel is situated in the forest estate of Le Touquet, right opposite its own golf courses. Coming from Boulogne-sur-Mer, turn left at first set of traffic lights in Le Touquet and hotel is on the right.

■ RESTAURANT: Closed Jan.
■ ACTIVITIES: ● Free green fees from 16/10 to 16/03, preferential rates at other times.
■ TARIFF: (1994) Single 585–805, Double 770–955, Set menu 130–195 (Amex, Euro/Access, Visa).

Hôtel Le Picardy ★★★★ av Mar Foch, 62520 Le Touquet-Paris-Plage.
☏ 21 06 85 85, Fax 21 06 85 00. English spoken.
Open all year. 88 bedrooms (all en suite). Indoor swimming pool, tennis, golf 2 km, parking, restaurant. &
Surrounded by lush gardens, a modern, beautifully designed hotel with excellent facilities.

■ ACTIVITIES: Jacuzzi, solarium, fitness room.
■ TARIFF: (1994) Double 590–1500, Bk 60, Set menu 120 (Amex, Euro/Access, Visa).

Westminster Hôtel ★★★★ 5 av du Verger, 62520 Le Touquet.
☏ 21 05 48 48, Fax 21 05 45 45. English spoken.
Open all year. 115 bedrooms (all en suite). Indoor swimming pool, golf 1 km, garage, parking. &
A hotel of great tradition and with a good reputation. Situated between the town and forest, 500 m from the beach and 150 m from the Convention Centre. Large entrance hall, cosy lounges and American bar.

■ RESTAURANT: Closed Tues eve & lunch.
■ TARIFF: (1994) Single 580–980, Double 680–1080, Bk 65 (Amex, Euro/Access, Visa).

T

TOURNON-SUR-RHONE Ardèche 5B

Hôtel Château ★★★ 12 quai M Sequin, 07300 Tournon-sur-Rhône.
☏ 75 08 60 22, Fax 75 07 02 95. English spoken.
Open 01/01 to 31/10 & 16/11 to 31/12.
14 bedrooms (all en suite). Garage.

Just two minutes from the motorway exit, a good hotel-restaurant in the centre of this town on the banks of the Rhône.

■ RESTAURANT: Closed Sat lunch & 1 to 15/11. Comfortable with good food.
■ TARIFF: (1994) Single 290, Double 320–360, Bk 40, Set menu 110–295 (Amex, Euro/Access, Visa).

TOURNUS Saône/Loire 5B

Hôtel de Greuze ★★★★ 5 rue A Thibaudet, 71700 Tournus.
☏ 85 51 77 77, Fax 85 51 77 23. English spoken.
Open all year. 23 bedrooms (all en suite).
Golf 20 km, parking. &

Classical, completely renovated hotel offering comfortable rooms and apartments with authentic period furniture. 1 km from Tournus exit off A6.

■ RESTAURANT: Restaurant has a well-deserved reputation in the area, offering fine cuisine and a warm welcome.
■ TARIFF: Single 560–1080, Double 730–1230, Bk 95 (Amex, Euro/Access, Visa).

Hôtel Le Rempart ★★★ 2 av Gambetta, 71700 Tournus.
☏ 85 51 10 56, Fax 85 51 77 22.
English spoken.
Open all year. 37 bedrooms (all en suite).
Golf 18 km, garage, parking, restaurant. &

This highly recommended hotel, formerly a 15th-century guardhouse on the ramparts of the town wall, has been renovated to a high standard and is fully air-conditioned. Take Tournus exit from A6/N6 and head towards town centre.

■ TARIFF: (1994) Single 320–690, Double 380–980, Bk 50, Set menu 159–399 (Amex, Euro/Access, Visa).

Hôtel Le Sauvage ★★★ pl du Champ de Mars, 71700 Tournus.
☏ 85 51 14 45, Fax 85 32 10 27.
English spoken.
Open all year. 30 bedrooms (all bath/shower only). Golf 10 km, garage.

An hotel with the charm of the olden days and the comfort of nowadays. Leave the A6 at the Tournus exit, follow signs to town centre.

■ RESTAURANT: Friendly setting with gourmet and regional cooking accompanied by the best Burgundy wines. Specialities include escargots and Bresse-bred chicken dishes.
■ TARIFF: (1994) Single 300–330, Double 400–430, Bk 40, Set menu 85–250 (Amex, Euro/Access, Visa).

TOURS Indre/Loire 2C

Hôtel Balzac ★★ 47 rue Scellerie, 37000 Tours.
☏ 47 05 40 87, Fax 47 20 82 30. English spoken.
Open all year. 20 bedrooms (18 en suite).
Golf 5 km.

Quiet atmosphere, near the theatre in the town centre.

■ TARIFF: Single 175–255, Double 205–285, Bk 30 (Amex, Euro/Access, Visa).

Château de Beaulieu ★★★ 67 rue de Beaulieu, 37300 Joué-les-Tours.
☏ 47 53 20 26, Fax 47 53 84 20. English spoken.
Open all year. 19 bedrooms (all en suite).
Tennis, golf 4 km, parking.

4 km south-west of Tours, access from D86 then D207. Beautiful 17th-century manor house set in lovely grounds.

■ RESTAURANT: Closed 24 Dec eve. Gastronomic cuisine and excellent wines.
■ TARIFF: (1994) Double 370–750, Bk 48, Set menu 195–420 (Amex, Euro/Access, Visa).

Hôtel Chantepie ★★ 6 rue Poincaré, 37300 Joué-les-Tours.
☏ 47 53 06 09, Fax 47 67 89 25.
English spoken.
Open 06/01 to 03/12. 28 bedrooms (26 en suite). Golf 4 km, parking.

Quietly situated in the middle of the Loire Valley, 5 km south-west of Tours on N10 towards Chinon. Closed over Christmas.

■ TARIFF: (1994) Single 269, Double 269–289, Bk 28 (Euro/Access, Visa).

T

Hôtel Cygne ★★ 6 rue Cygne, 37000 Tours.
☎ 47 66 66 41, Fax 47 20 18 76. English spoken.

Open all year. 19 bedrooms (3 en suite, 12 bath/shower only). Golf 5 km, garage.

A charming 18th-century hotel located in a quiet street in the town centre near the theatre, castle and cathedral. Five minutes from the station.

■ ACTIVITIES: Visits to nearby châteaux; horse-riding and swimming close at hand.
■ TARIFF: (1994) Single 190–300, Double 210–300, Bk 27 (Amex, Euro/Access, Visa).

Hôtel de l'Espace ★★★★ Bretonnières, Joué-les-Tours, 37300 Tours.
☎ 47 67 54 54, Fax 47 67 54 70. English spoken.
Open all year. 74 bedrooms (all en suite). Indoor swimming pool, golf 5 km, parking. &

10 minutes from the town centre, hotel offers trilingual reception and full air-conditioning. Take the Joué-les-Tours exit from the D751 Chinon road.

■ RESTAURANT: Closed Sun LS. Good, seasonal menus based on market fresh produce.
■ TARIFF: (1994) Single 400–440, Double 530–580, Bk 50 (Amex, Euro/Access, Visa).

Manoir de Foncher 37510 Villandry.
☎ 47 50 02 40. English spoken.
Open 01/04 to 30/09. 2 bedrooms (1 en suite). Golf 6 km, parking.

Private house receiving guests in the Loire Valley. Fine example of 15th-century architecture. Pleasant and comfortable. For families of 2 to 4 people. 16 km west of Tours, D7 to Savonnières Bridge, the right bank of Cher river.

■ TARIFF: (1994) Double 550 (No credit cards).

Hôtel Mercure ★★★ Tours Centre, 4 pl Thiers, 37000 Tours.
☎ 47 05 50 05, Fax 47 20 22 07. English spoken.

Open all year. 120 bedrooms (all en suite). Golf 6 km, garage, parking. &
■ RESTAURANT: 'Les Muses' offers regional and contemporary specialities.
■ ACTIVITIES: Aqua/gym club, swimming pool and lake nearby; discover the historic town.
■ TARIFF: (1994) Single 350–550, Double 390–550, Bk 50 (Amex, Euro/Access, Visa).
■ DISCOUNT: 15%

T

Château de la Loire ★★ 12 rue Gambetta,
37000 Tours.
℡ 47 05 10 05, Fax 47 20 20 14. English spoken.
Open 15/02 to 15/12. 31 bedrooms
(all en suite). Golf 10 km, garage. &

*In a quiet area near the old town and the
Town Hall, offering a warm atmosphere. Rue
Gambetta is just off rue Nationale.*

■ TARIFF: (1994) Single 185–280,
Double 200–280, Bk 35 (Amex,
Euro/Access, Visa).

■ DISCOUNT: 10%

Hôtel Mirabeau ★★ 69 bis bd Heurteloup,
37000 Tours.
℡ 47 05 24 60, Fax 47 05 31 09. English spoken.
Open all year. 25 bedrooms (all en suite).
Garage, parking.

*19th-century building in the town centre.
Period furnishings and almost overlooking the
Mirabeau Bridge over the Loire. From the A10
motorway, take exit 12 to Tours-Centre.*

■ TARIFF: (1994) Single 220–250,
Double 250–310, Bk 37 (Euro/Access, Visa).

Novotel Tours Sud ★★★ ZAC de la
Vrillonnerie, N 10, 37170 Chambray-les-Tours.
℡ 47 27 41 38, Fax 47 27 60 03. English spoken.

Open all year. 127 bedrooms (all en suite).
Outdoor swimming pool, golf 6 km,
parking. &

*Located 5 km from the centre of Tours.
Towards Poitiers by the A10/N10.*

■ TARIFF: (1994) Single 395–420, Double 450–
470, Bk 48 (Amex, Euro/Access, Visa).

Le Quart ★★★★ 37230 Luynes prés Tours.
℡ 47 555 170, Fax 47 555 749. English spoken.
Open all year. 4 bedrooms (all en suite).
Golf 12 km, garage, parking. &

*In châteaux country. Restored farmhouse,
more a guesthouse than hotel, full of character*

*with period furniture and modern bathrooms.
12 km west of Tours on the N152 to the village
of Luynes, then follow the signs to 'Le Quart'.*

■ TARIFF: (1994) Single 350, Double 450–850,
Bk 50 (No credit cards).

Hôtel Royal ★★★ 65 av Grammont,
37000 Tours.
℡ 47 64 71 78, Fax 47 05 84 62. English spoken.
Open all year. 50 bedrooms (all en suite).
Golf 12 km, garage, parking. &

*Situated in the centre of Tours in the heart of
the Loire valley. Suites are decorated in the
style of Louis XV and XVI.*

■ TARIFF: (1994) Single 322, Double 382, Bk 38
(Amex, Euro/Access, Visa, BT).

Hôtel de la Ville ★★ pl Marie,
37270 Montlouis-sur-Loire.
℡ 47 50 84 84, Fax 47 45 08 43. English spoken.
Open all year. 29 bedrooms (25 en suite,
4 bath/shower only). Parking.

*From the centre of Tours take the rue des
Tanneurs/bd d'Orléans along the river,
heading east along D751 for about 12 km to
Montlouis. At the place Courtemanche, turn
right to centre of Montlouis, and then follow
signs.*

■ RESTAURANT: Closed 24 & 25 Dec.
■ TARIFF: (1994) Single 210–280,
Double 210–350, Bk 30, Set menu 85–220
(Euro/Access, Visa).

TREMOLAT Dordogne   4B

Hôtel Le Panoramic ★★ rte du Cingle de
Trémolat, 24510 Trémolat.
℡ 53 22 80 42, Fax 53 22 47 86.
English spoken.

Open 15/04 to 15/11. 24 bedrooms
(18 bath/shower only). Parking.

*Unique hotel with panoramic views of the
Dordogne and Cingle of Trémolat by the river*

T

in a quiet sunny position. Garden and private parking, unique Perigourdine architecture.

■ RESTAURANT: Traditional restaurant offering country cooking and typical Périgord cuisine. Specialities: foie gras au torchon, confit de canard, poisson de rivière.

■ ACTIVITIES: Water sports, swimming pool, canoeing, water-skiing, sailing, walking and cycling (cycle hire from the hotel) all within the area.

■ TARIFF: (1994) Single 170–340, Double 170–340, Bk 37, Set menu 59–160 (Visa).

■ DISCOUNT: 10%

LE TREPORT Seine-Marit   2B

Hôtel Gare ★★ 20 pl Gare, 76260 Eu.
☎ 35 86 16 64, Fax 35 50 86 25. English spoken.
Open all year. 22 bedrooms (19 en suite).
Tennis, parking.

This hotel has art deco interior and all rooms have modern facilities. A 3 km walk through the forest will take you to the sea. Eu is south-east of Le Tréport.

■ RESTAURANT: Closed Sun eve. Fish specialities and traditional cuisine.

■ TARIFF: (1994) Single 200–250, Double 230–280, Bk 32, Set menu 80–180 (Amex, Euro/Access, Visa).

Hôtel Royal Albion ★★★ 1 rue de la Mer, 76910 Mesnil-Val.
☎ 35 86 21 42, Fax 35 86 78 51. English spoken.

Open all year. 20 bedrooms (all en suite). Garage, parking.

Former 19th-century manor house, now renovated, standing in 7-acre parkland. From Le Tréport head west towards Dieppe on D940, to Mesnil-Val and the beach.

■ TARIFF: (1994) Double 350–450, Bk 45 (Amex, Euro/Access, Visa).

■ DISCOUNT: 10% LS.

LA TRINITE-SUR-MER Morbihan   1C

Hôtel Domaine du Congre ★★ D781, St-Philibert, 56470 La Trinité-sur-Mer.
☎ 97 55 00 56, Fax 97 55 19 77. English spoken.
Open 10/02 to 15/11 & 23/12 to 27/12.
25 bedrooms (all en suite). Outdoor swimming pool, tennis, golf 12 km, parking.

2 km from the beach and yacht harbour, comfortable hotel with good facilities.

■ RESTAURANT: Restaurant specialises in grills, with seafood to order.

■ ACTIVITIES: Cycling, sailing, boat trips to islands and sightseeing (Carnac is just 7 km away).

■ TARIFF: Double 280–350, Bk 34, Set menu 85 (Amex, Visa).

TROUVILLE-SUR-MER Calvados   2A

Hôtel Beach ★★★ 1 quai Albert, 14360 Trouville-sur-Mer.
☎ 31 98 12 00, Fax 31 87 30 29. English spoken.
Open 05/02 to 31/12. 110 bedrooms (all en suite). Outdoor swimming pool, golf 10 km, garage, restaurant. ♿

In the heart of Trouville, facing the sea and close to the town centre. Directly linked to the casino and health centre. 2-hour drive from Paris on A13, then N177 to Trouville.

■ TARIFF: (1994) Single 320–590, Double 440–680, Bk 45, Set menu 140–160 (Amex, Euro/Access, Visa).

Hôtel Mercure ★★★ 14360 Trouville-sur-Mer.
☎ 31 87 38 38, Fax 31 87 35 41. English spoken.
Open all year. 80 bedrooms (all en suite).
Golf 6 km, parking. ♿

Town centre hotel close to beach and casino.

■ RESTAURANT: Closed Jan.

■ ACTIVITIES: Horse-riding, go-karting.

■ TARIFF: (1994) Single 390–640, Double 390–610, Bk 56, Set menu 98–150 (Amex, Euro/Access, Visa).

■ DISCOUNT: 10%

T

TROYES

Troyes, former capital of the ancient province of Champagne, lies on the River Seine about 150 km south-east of Paris. Well known in the Middle Ages for its markets and fairs, its prosperity since the 16th century has been based on the hosiery trade. Even today, more than half the

Vibrant stained glass in Troyes's Eglise Ste-Madeleine

town's workers are employed in this industry, and their traditional craft is celebrated at the Musée de la Bonneterie (the hosiery museum).

Surprisingly, despite frequent town fires in the Middle Ages, many timber-framed houses have survived, particularly in the area around the pedestrianised rue Champeaux. Especially evocative is the tiny courtyard halfway down the rue de Chats, the cour du Mortier d'Or. These streets and alleyways remain remarkably unchanged and, if you can imagine the smells of 500 years ago, you can gain a good impression of what the town was like when Henry V of England came here early in the 15th century. Following the Treaty of Troyes in 1420, he was recognised as heir to the French throne and married Catherine of France.

They were married in the Église St-Jean, which still stands as do many other ancient churches. This is not as surprising as the survival of the timber-framed houses because churches, which in medieval times symbolised the wealth of the community, were generally built of stone. Although the Cathédrale St-Pierre-et-St-Paul, like quite a number of Gothic churches, is unfinished, what we see today is quite splendid. The pale local stonework contrasts effectively with the vibrant stained glass windows. The cathedral's treasure is also on show, a rich display of the art of many different craftsmen, including goldsmiths, embroiderers and illustrators.

Another church worth mentioning is the Basilique St-Urbain, built in the 13th century by Pope Urban IV who was a native of Troyes. Like the cathedral, this church is particularly noted for its stained glass and its huge windows are the main feature of the interior. Outside, flying buttresses abound.

Troyes is also a city of museums. The vivid colours of the traditional stained glass are repeated at the Musée d'Art Moderne, where an impressive private collection of paintings from the last 150 years forms the nucleus of the exhibition. The Pharmacie, another museum and one which

Champagne

No other wine has quite the same image and taste of luxury as champagne, the classic celebratory drink. So what is it that makes champagne so special?

Wine becomes sparkling when it is bottled before fermentation is complete. The still-active agents of fermentation cause the sugar to turn into alcohol and carbon dioxide, and when the bottle is finally opened it is this carbon dioxide that provides the famous 'fizz'. But this explanation holds true for all sparkling wines and does not really answer the question 'What makes champagne so special?'

Obviously the answer is 'Its taste!' This taste comes from the particular grapes that are grown in the Champagne region. Because of the cold, damp climate of this part of northern France, the grapes here retain a higher degree of acidity than their riper southern relatives. Coupled with the chalky soil on which they are grown, this gives rise to champagne's particular light flavour.

But the real secret of its taste lies in its assemblage, the art of mixing different wines to achieve the desired blend, known by the French word cuvée. A vintage champagne is a mixture of wines from only one year. It follows that its taste may well differ from year to year, depending on the grape-growing conditions. A non-vintage blend is made from wines of different harvests, so if you find one which you enjoy, stick with it for it will always be blended to achieve a similar taste.

concentrates on an unusual subject, is a well-preserved medical laboratory, housed in the 18th-century Hôtel-Dieu.

If you tire of museums and churches, a trip into the surrounding countryside is sure to refresh you. Not many cities lie as close to a national park as Troyes – only 16 km away is the lake at the centre of the Parc Régional de la Forêt d'Orient and its boundary is only 5 km from the city centre. Sailing is permitted on this lake and there is also a bird sanctuary to visit.

TROYES Aube 3C

(See feature)

Hôtel de la Poste ★★★★ 35 rue E Zola, 10000 Troyes.
☎ 25 73 05 05, Fax 25 73 80 76. English spoken.

Open all year. 28 bedrooms (all en suite).
In the centre of this historic town, Hôtel de la Poste offers modern-day comforts and excellent cuisine. Close to museums, churches and pedestrian streets.

■ RESTAURANT: Closed Sun eve & Mon.
■ TARIFF: (1994) Single 420–750, Double 450–900, Bk 50 (Amex, Euro/Access, Visa).

Hôtel Relais St-Jean ★★★ 51 rue Paillot de Montabert, 10000 Troyes.
☎ 25 73 89 90, Fax 25 73 88 60. English spoken.
Open all year. 22 bedrooms (all en suite).
Golf 20 km, parking. &

Situated in the heart of the historical 16th-century pedestrian area of Troyes, hotel was opened in 1989 and offers beautifully conceived, ultra-modern and air-conditioned surroundings with facilities to match. Next door to a restaurant and with direct 24-hour

access to Aristide Briand underground car park. Coming into Troyes, follow signs to Centre Ville and then the car park.
■ ACTIVITIES: ● Hotel offers loan of mountain bikes, free entry to disco and 25% discount on entry to a leisure park.
■ TARIFF: (1994) Single 430–590, Double 470–650, Bk 55 (Amex, Euro/Access, Visa, BT).
■ DISCOUNT: 5%

Auberge de la Scierie ★★★ à la Vove S, 10160 Aix-en-Othe.
☎ 25 46 71 26, Fax 25 46 65 69. English spoken.

Open 01/03 to 31/01. 13 bedrooms (all en suite). Outdoor swimming pool, parking, restaurant. &
Old inn in the champagne country near a river. N60 west of Troyes for 23 km, then left onto D374.
■ TARIFF: (1994) Double 350, Bk 40, Set menu 130–220 (Amex, Euro/Access, Visa).

LES ULIS Essonne 2D

Hôtel Mercure ★★★ 3 Rio Solado, Courtaboeuf, 91952 Les Ulis.
☎ 1 69 07 63 96, Fax 1 69 07 92 00.
English spoken.
Open all year. 108 bedrooms (all en suite).
Outdoor swimming pool, tennis, golf 12 km, parking, restaurant. &

Modern hotel in a pleasant, shady park and within easy access of Paris (20 km). Take Ulis/Courtaboeuf exit coming from the west, or

T

coming from the south,
Ulis/Courtaboeuf/Versailles exit from A10.

■ ACTIVITIES: Sports facilities at hotel; many interesting châteaux to visit nearby.
■ TARIFF: (1994) Double 450–550, Bk 54 (Amex, Euro/Access, Visa).

UZERCHE Corrèze 5A

Hôtel Teyssier ★★ rue Pont-Turgot, 19140 Uzerche.
☎ 55 73 10 05, Fax 55 98 43 31. English spoken.
Open 19/01 to 06/12. 17 bedrooms (9 en suite, 1 bath/shower only). Garage, parking.
A charming family-run hotel overlooking the Vézère from flowered terraces.
■ RESTAURANT: Closed Wed LS. Highly regarded gourmet restaurant offering authentic regional cuisine.
■ ACTIVITIES: Canoeing, horse-riding.
■ TARIFF: (1994) Single 145–350, Double 180–350, Bk 35, Set menu 120–500 (Amex, Euro/Access, Visa).

VAISON-LA-ROMAINE Vaucluse 5D

Hôtel Les Aurics ★★ rte Avignon, 84110 Vaison-la-Romaine.
☎ 90 36 03 15. English spoken.
Open 01/04 to 11/11. 14 bedrooms (all en suite). Outdoor swimming pool, golf 2 km, parking.
An old building typical of Provence with a beautiful view of vineyards. From Vaison-la-Romaine take D977 to Avignon. The hotel is 2 km from Vaison-la-Romaine and Séguret.
■ TARIFF: (1994) Single 240–260, Double 240–300, Bk 28 (Amex, Euro/Access, Visa).

Hôtel Le Beffroi ★★★ rue de l'Evêché BP85, Ville Médiévale, 84110 Vaison-la-Romaine.
☎ 90 36 04 71, Fax 90 36 24 78. English spoken.
Open 16/03 to 14/11 & 16/12 to 14/02. 22 bedrooms (all en suite). Golf 1 km, garage, parking.
Dating from the 16th and 17th centuries, the hotel has been converted from two houses. In the centre of the ancient town with stunning views and terraced gardens.
■ RESTAURANT: Closed as hotel & Mon/Tues/Fri lunch. Renowned for its excellent food and fine wines.
■ ACTIVITIES: Mini-golf, horse-riding, mountain bikes; good location for walking and hiking.
■ TARIFF: (1994) Single 300–495, Double 410–595, Bk 45, Set menu 98–185 (Amex, Euro/Access, Visa).

Le Logis du Château ★★ Les Hauts de Vaison, 84110 Vaison-la-Romaine.
☎ 90 36 09 98, Fax 90 36 10 95. English spoken.
Open 01/04 to 31/10. 45 bedrooms (all en suite). Outdoor swimming pool, tennis, golf 1 km, parking. ⑤
Get away from it all. Panoramic views, silence and tranquillity. Follow signs for 'Cité Médiévale'.
■ RESTAURANT: Traditional cuisine. Specialities: terrine Provençale au genièvre, chausson d'escargots aux champignons, pieds et paquets d'agneau Provençaux.
■ TARIFF: (1994) Single 235–330, Double 250–360, Bk 38, Set menu 95–158 (Euro/Access, Visa).

Hôtel St-Marc ★★ 26170 Mollans-sur-Ouvèze.
☎ 75 28 70 01, Fax 75 28 78 63. English spoken.

Open 15/03 to 15/11. 30 bedrooms (all en suite). Outdoor swimming pool, tennis. ⑤
Hotel is set in lovely countryside, near the river and at the foot of the picturesque village. Comfortable rooms, good facilities and large garden with shaded terrace. East of Vaison-la-Romaine via Entrechaux.
■ RESTAURANT: Traditional Provençal style restaurant with large verandah. Regional specialities using local produce.
■ ACTIVITIES: Lots of sporting activities, sightseeing and wine tasting opportunities nearby.
■ TARIFF: (1994) Single 260–280, Double 310–390, Bk 48, Set menu 125 (Euro/Access, Visa).

VAL-THORENS Savoie 6A

Hôtel Trois Vallées ★★★ Grande rue, 73440 Val-Thorens.
☎ 79 00 01 86, Fax 79 00 04 08. English spoken.

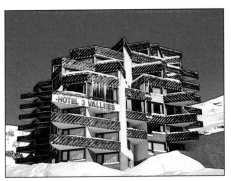

Open 25/10 to 15/05. 28 bedrooms (18 en suite). Parking.

In the centre of the resort, close to the ski lift and 200 m from the Ski School and Tourist Office.

■ RESTAURANT: Full buffet breakfast and a four-course gourmet dinner in the evenings.
■ ACTIVITIES: ● Fully-inclusive ski packages available.
■ TARIFF: (1994) Single 250–500, Double 280–550, Bk 50 (Euro/Access, Visa).

VALBONNE Alpes-Mar   6C

Hôtel Mercure ★★★ rue A Caquot, 06560 Valbonne.
☎ 92 96 04 04, Fax 92 96 05 05. English spoken.

Open all year. 104 bedrooms (all en suite). Outdoor swimming pool, golf 5 km, parking, restaurant. &

Pink, provincial style hotel with a swimming pool set in a wooded science park. Between Nice and Cannes take the Antibes and Sophia Antipolis exit from the A8.

■ TARIFF: (1994) Single 410–520, Double 410–620, Bk 60 (Amex, Euro/Access, Visa).

VALENCE

Flowers for sale in Valence's sunny market

When you reach Valence there is a definite feeling that you have now arrived in the Midi, as the French call the south of France. The division between north and south comes imperceptibly somewhere between Lyon, 150 km to the north, and Valence.

Lying on the east bank of the Rhône, the town has been inhabited since Roman times. Although there are no remains of Roman buildings to visit, a theatre is known to exist under houses near the Eglise St-Jean. This church, which has a well preserved Romanesque tower, is in the most ancient part of the town. Between here and the Cathédrale St-Apollinaire lies the heart of old Valence with its narrow streets, known as *côtes*. St-Apollinaire is a 17th-century copy, on the same site, of the original 11th-century Romanesque cathedral wrecked during the wars of religion. More bad luck followed when the reconstructed tower was burnt down in 1838 and again had to be rebuilt.

The most famous house in Valence is the Maison des Têtes, a short walk up the Grande rue from the cathedral. Built in 1532, it is so called because of its row of sculptured heads which decorate the building at first floor level. Maison Dupré-Latour, in the rue Pérollerie, is another grand house with a spiral staircase and carved porch.

The municipal museum, housed in the bishop's palace next to the cathedral, has

V

mosaics from Roman times to admire as well as French furniture from the 16th to the 19th century and a collection of contemporary art. Across the Avenue Gambetta from the museum is the Champ de Mars with views over the Parc Jouvet and the River Rhône to Mont Crussol, whose ruined cliff-topped castle overlooks the town. If you feel energetic, you could walk up to the Château de Crussol from the car park just behind the huge white statue of the Virgin Mary.

For more panoramic views over the surrounding countryside, drive from St-Péray, on the other side of Mont Crussol, to St-Romain-de-Lerps. There is an orientation table here to help you name the many mountains you can see from the special observation platforms. If you continue on to Tournon and its twin town, on the other side of the Rhône, Tain-l'Hermitage, you will find yourself amongst some of the oldest and most famous vineyards in

Nougat

Montélimar is 40 km to the south of Valence and is recognised internationally as the home of nougat. This rich sweetmeat was invented in the 17th century, not long after the introduction of the almond tree to France by Olivier de Serres. Often described as the father of French agriculture, Serres was born at Villeneuve-de-Berg, across the Rhône from Montélimar, and it was here that the first almond trees were planted. The climate proved to be just right and it was not long before the almond became an important part of both the economy and the landscape of the region.

The other basic ingredients of nougat were also readily to hand – honey from Provence and eggs from local hens. Nougat was originally made in farmhouse kitchens throughout the area and it remained a cottage industry until about 90 years ago, when the first factory was set up. One of the early manufacturers, Chabert and Guillot, still exists in Montélimar. You can visit their premises to see how nougat is made as well as to taste it. Buy it to eat straight away or, if you can restrain yourself, bring some home to share with your friends!

France. This is a good place to stock up with fine wines because even the most ordinary ones are of a very high quality. To sample what is available, visit the Cave Coopérative des Vins Fins in Tain l'Hermitage.

If you enjoy railway travel, take a trip on the narrow-gauge steam railway which runs from Tournon to Lamastre. The journey takes two hours and follows the River Doux upstream through wooded gorges. If you have used Valence as a stopping-off place en route to the Mediterranean, a diversion from the motorway south of Montélimar will bring you to yet more impressive gorges – this time on the River Ardèche.

VALENCE Drôme   5B

(See feature)

Park Hôtel ★★ 22 rue J Bouin, 26000 Valence.
✆ 75 43 37 06, Fax 75 42 43 55. English spoken.
Open all year. 21 bedrooms
(all bath/shower only). Garage, parking.
New building, all modern facilities, situated at foot of old town. Restaurant nearby.
■ TARIFF: Single 250–280, Double 250–280, Bk 28 (Amex, Visa).

VALENCIENNES Nord   2B

Grand Hôtel ★★★ 8 pl de la Gare, 59300 Valenciennes.
✆ 27 46 32 01, Fax 27 29 65 57. English spoken.
Open all year. 98 bedrooms (all en suite).
Golf 15 km.
You will receive a warm welcome at this large, classic hotel opposite the station. Modern, well-equipped rooms. Snacks available. Lounges for meetings or business meals.
■ RESTAURANT: Gastronomic restaurant.
■ TARIFF: (1994) Single 350–540, Double 390–650, Bk 50, Set menu 97–210 (Amex, Euro/Access, Visa).
■ DISCOUNT: 10%

VALGORGE Ardèche   5D

Hôtel Le Tanargue ★★ 07110 Valgorge.
✆ 75 88 98 98, Fax 75 88 96 09.
Open 10/03 to 03/01. 25 bedrooms
(all en suite). Tennis, golf 3 km, garage, parking. &
Set in the heart of a small village in the Ardèche, in a shady park, at the foot of the

V

mountains. Valgorge is 22 km from the D104, through Largentière on the D5.

■ RESTAURANT: Closed 03/01 to 10/03. Regional Cevennes cuisine and good local wines.
■ TARIFF: (1994) Double 245–350, Bk 38, Set menu 92–185 (Euro/Access, Visa).

VALLON-PONT-D'ARC Ardèche   5D

Hôtel du Tourisme ★★ 6 rue du Miarou, 07150 Vallon-Pont-d'Arc.
☎ 75 88 02 12, Fax 75 88 12 90. English spoken.
Open 01/02 to 15/12. 29 bedrooms (all en suite). Golf 4 km, parking.

Family-owned and run since 1937, hotel with friendly atmosphere in village centre but just 100 m from open countryside.

■ RESTAURANT: Specialities include charcuteries maison, omelette aux truffles, civet de cailles and poulet aux écrevisses. Cosy dining room and large terrace with lovely views.
■ ACTIVITIES: Cycling, white-water rafting.
■ TARIFF: (1994) Double 260–405, Bk 30, Set menu 85–165 (Euro/Access, Visa).

VALOGNES Manche   1B

Hôtel de l'Agriculture ★ 16 rue Léopold Delisle, 50700 Valognes.
☎ 33 95 02 02, Fax 33 95 29 33. English spoken.
Open all year. 36 bedrooms (17 en suite, 1 bath/shower only). Golf 15 km, garage, parking.

A pretty, creeper-clad building with many fine features inside. From the Valognes central square, head towards the station (Carteret road), turn second left.

■ RESTAURANT: Closed 01/01 to 15/1 & 21/09 to 04/10. Attractive stone-clad, beamed dining room. Specialities: homard grillé farci; soupe de poisson; ris de veau poêlé à la Normande.
■ ACTIVITIES: Sightseeing, sporting facilities within easy reach.
■ TARIFF: (1994) Single 107–274, Double 139–274, Bk 29, Set menu 75–174 (Euro/Access, Visa).

Grand Hôtel du Louvre ★ 28 rue des Religieuses, 50700 Valognes.
☎ 33 40 00 07, Fax 33 40 13 73. English spoken.
Open 06/01 to 01/12. 22 bedrooms (12 en suite, 1 bath/shower only). Garage, parking, restaurant.

An old coaching inn in the centre of town 20 km south of Cherbourg on N13.

■ TARIFF: (1994) Single 130–250, Double 160–265, Bk 26, Set menu 64–135 (Euro/Access, Visa).

Hôtel Haut Gallion ★★ rte Cherbourg, 50700 Valognes.
☎ 33 40 40 00, Fax 33 95 20 20. English spoken.
Open 09/01 to 19/12. 40 bedrooms (all en suite). Golf 15 km, parking. &

Very modern rooms (2 for disabled people). Valognes is 22 km from Cherbourg on the N13. The hotel is close to the town centre on the main road.

■ TARIFF: (1994) Double 265, Bk 34 (Amex, Euro/Access, Visa).

VALRAS-PLAGE Hérault   5C

Hôtel Albizzia ★★ 12 bd du Chemin Creux, 34350 Valras-Plage.
☎ 67 37 48 48, Fax 67 37 58 10. English spoken.
Open all year. 28 bedrooms (all en suite). Outdoor swimming pool, golf 20 km, parking. &

Recently-built and located just 200 m from a fine-sand beach. Via the A9 coming from Montpellier, take Béziers-Est exit. Coming from Narbonne, take Béziers-Oest exit.

■ TARIFF: (1994) Single 230–380, Double 250–400, Bk 37 (Amex, Euro/Access, Visa).

Hôtel Méditerranée ★★ 32 rue Charles Thomas, 34350 Valras-Plage.
☎ 67 32 38 60, Fax 67 32 30 91. English spoken.
Open 01/04 to 31/10. 12 bedrooms (all en suite). Garage, parking.

Close to the beach, in the centre of Valras.

■ RESTAURANT: Closed Mon. Offers seafood and other regional specialities.
■ TARIFF: (1994) Double 240–270, Bk 30, Set menu 80–250 (Amex, Euro/Access, Visa).

VANNES Morbihan   1D

Hôtel France ★★ 57 av V Hugo, 56000 Vannes.
☎ 97 47 27 57, Fax 97 42 59 17. English spoken.
Open all year. 25 bedrooms (21 en suite, 4 bath/shower only). Golf 10 km, parking.

Charming hotel with garden terrace. Rooms with full facilities including some large family rooms. Near the railway station and the centre of this historical town.

■ TARIFF: (1994) Single 150–300, Double 160–320, Bk 35 (Euro/Access, Visa).
■ DISCOUNT: 10% LS.

Hôtel Mascotte ★★ avenue Jean Monnet, 56000 Vannes.
☎ 97 47 59 60, Fax 97 47 07 54. English spoken.

V

Open all year. 65 bedrooms (all en suite).
Garage, restaurant. &

In the centre of town very close to the Bay of Morbihan. Motorway N165.

■ TARIFF: (1994) Single 300–400,
Double 340–480, Bk 40 (Amex,
Euro/Access, Visa).

Hôtel San Francisco ★★★ au Port,
56780 Ile-aux-Moines.
℡ 97 26 31 52, Fax 97 26 35 59.
English spoken.
Open all year. 8 bedrooms (all en suite).
Golf 8 km.

Charming, quiet hotel overlooking the harbour on the Ile-aux-Moines, which lies in the Golfe du Morbihan. Lovely island for biking and walking. Cars prohibited. South-west of Vannes.

■ RESTAURANT: Closed Wed eve & Thur winter.
Pleasant dining room with seafood specialities.
■ ACTIVITIES: Hotel can organise biking, boating and fishing.
■ TARIFF: Double 265–510, Bk 45 (Amex,
Euro/Access, Visa).
■ DISCOUNT: 5% LS.

VENCE Alpes-Mar 6C

Hôtel Closerie des Genêts ★ 4 impasse M
Maurel, 06140 Vence.
℡ 93 58 33 25. English spoken.
Open all year. 10 bedrooms (all en suite).

Charming, family-run establishment with lovely garden. In town centre, 100 m from Tourist Office.

■ RESTAURANT: Closed Sun eve. Pretty restaurant overlooking the garden. Fresh, seasonal cuisine.
■ ACTIVITIES: Good location for walking and touring. Swimming pool 200 m.
■ TARIFF: (1994) Single 160–180,
Double 200–260, Bk 25, Set menu 130–180
(Euro/Access, Visa).
■ DISCOUNT: 10% LS.

Hôtel La Roseraie ★★ rte Col de Vence,
06140 Vence.
℡ 93 58 02 20, Fax 93 58 99 31.
English spoken.
Open all year. 12 bedrooms (all en suite).
Outdoor swimming pool, parking.

This charming former manor house is walking distance from the centre of Vence. All the sunny bedrooms are furnished in Provençal style and look out over the garden and swimming pool.

■ TARIFF: (1994) Double 380–480, Bk 45
(Amex, Euro/Access, Visa).

VENDEUIL Aisne 2B

Auberge de Vendeuil ★★ N44,
02800 Vendeuil.
℡ 23 07 85 85, Fax 23 07 88 58. English spoken.

Open all year. 22 bedrooms (all en suite).
Golf 10 km, parking. &

Bordering woodland and close to the Oise Valley, a quiet and charming country hotel. On the N44 between St-Quentin and La Fère.

■ RESTAURANT: Creative cuisine.
■ TARIFF: (1994) Single 285, Double 335, Bk 45,
Set menu 90–190 (Amex, Euro/Access, Visa).

VENDOME Loir/Cher 2C

Hôtel Capricorne ★★ 8 bd de Tremault,
41100 Vendôme.
℡ 54 80 27 00, Fax 54 77 30 63. English spoken.
Open 01/01 to 15/12 & 29/12 to 31/12.
31 bedrooms (all en suite). Golf 15 km, garage,
parking. &

A new hotel in the town centre. Shady garden and terrace. From Tours take N10 northwards to Vendôme, then follow the signs to 'Gare SNCF'.

V

■ RESTAURANT: Closed Christmas period.
■ ACTIVITIES: Guided tours, boat trips, wine tasting.
■ TARIFF: (1994) Single 190–269, Double 190–300, Bk 34, Set menu 60–240 (Amex, Euro/Access, Visa).
■ DISCOUNT: 8%

Hôtel Vendôme ★★★ 15 Fg Chartrain, 41100 Vendôme.
℃ 54 77 02 88, Fax 54 73 90 71. English spoken.
Open 05/01 to 20/12. 35 bedrooms (all en suite). Golf 15 km, garage. &
On the N10 north of Tours.
■ RESTAURANT: Comfortable and contemporary.
■ TARIFF: Single 210–325, Double 280–395, Bk 50, Set menu 68–160 (Euro/Access, Visa).

VERDUN Meuse   3A

Hostellerie Coq Hardi ★★★ 8 av de la Victoire, 55100 Verdun.
℃ 29 86 36 36, Fax 29 86 09 21. English spoken.

Open all year. 33 bedrooms (all en suite). Garage. &
Situated in the town centre near the Meuse river, this hotel has many interesting features.
■ RESTAURANT: Closed Fri. Charming restaurant offering gourmet cuisine and an excellent cellar.
■ TARIFF: (1994) Single 390–480, Double 450–970, Bk 60, Set menu 198–450 (Amex, Euro/Access, Visa).

VERGEZE Gard   5D

Hôtel La Passiflore ★★ 1 rue Neuve, 30310 Vergèze.
℃ 66 35 00 00, Fax 66 35 09 21. English spoken.
Open all year. 11 bedrooms (10 en suite, 1 bath/shower only). Parking. &
A lovely restored farmhouse in the heart of Perrier Spring village, 5 km from the Nîmes to

Montpellier A9 motorway, exit Gallargues.
■ RESTAURANT: Closed Mon & 22/10 to 04/12. Specialities: soupe de poisson à la Setoise; maigret de canard au confit d'oignon.
■ TARIFF: (1994) Double 195–300, Bk 35, Set menu 130 (Amex, Euro/Access, Visa).
■ DISCOUNT: 10%

VERNET-LES-BAINS Pyrénées-Or   5C

Hôtel Angleterre ★ av Burnay, 66820 Vernet-les-Bains.
℃ 68 05 50 58. English spoken.
Open 02/05 to 06/11. 20 bedrooms (11 en suite).
Modern rooms, in an attractive old building decorated with 18th-century Catalan furniture. Large garden with old trees and plenty of birds. English owner. Vernet-les-Bains is on the D116 off the N116, 44 km west of Perpignan.
■ ACTIVITIES: ● Reduced rate jeep rides to the Canigou and other panoramic mountain viewpoints.
■ TARIFF: (1994) Single 120–200, Double 140–220, Bk 30 (Visa).

Hôtel Châtaigneraie ★ Sahorre, 66360 Vernet-les-Bains.
℃ 68 05 51 04.
Open 01/05 to 01/10. 10 bedrooms (8 en suite). Parking.
Hotel with peaceful gardens situated in an unspoilt mountain valley 3 km from Vernet-les-Bains on the D27. Take the N116 from Perpignan and turn onto the D116 to the village.
■ RESTAURANT: Traditional and regional cooking in pleasant surroundings.
■ ACTIVITIES: Good walking/hiking area; tennis and swimming pool 3 km. ● Jeep rides to nearby canyon at reduced rates.
■ TARIFF: (1994) Single 170–215, Double 170–255, Bk 29.50 (Visa).

Hôtel Comte Guifred de Conflent ★★★ av Thermes, 66820 Vernet-les-Bains.
℃ 68 05 51 37, Fax 68 05 64 11. English spoken.
Open 01/01 to 30/11. 10 bedrooms (all en suite).
Small hotel annexed to a catering school. Located in the town centre which is on the D116 off the N116.
■ RESTAURANT: Meals can be taken outdoors in the garden in summer.
■ TARIFF: (1994) Single 290–390, Double 360–460, Bk 35 (Amex, Euro/Access, Visa).

V

VERNEUIL-SUR-AVRE Eure   2C

Hostellerie Le Clos ★★★★ 98 rue Ferte Vidame, 27130 Verneuil-sur-Avre.
℃ 32 32 21 81, Fax 32 32 21 36. English spoken.

Open 01/02 to 31/12. 11 bedrooms (all en suite). Tennis, golf 7 km, parking. &

English-style manor house, tastefully furnished with terrace overlooking lovely gardens. Fine regional cuisine. On N12, 110 km east of Paris.

■ RESTAURANT: Closed Mon. Fine, regional cuisine served in an elegant dining room.
■ ACTIVITIES: Bicycle treks with picnic provided.
■ TARIFF: (1994) Single 600–800, Double 600–950, Bk 80, Set menu 170–320 (Amex, Euro/Access, Visa).

Hôtel Moulin de Balines ★★ 27130 Balines.
℃ 32 32 03 48, Fax 32 60 11 22.
English spoken.
Open all year. 12 bedrooms (all en suite).
Golf 4 km, parking, restaurant.

Former mill standing in 25 acres, with two rivers and two lakes. Comfortable and quiet. 4 km east of Verneuil, towards Paris, just to the right off the N12.

■ ACTIVITIES: Fishing, boating, archery, close to tennis courts.
■ TARIFF: (1994) Double 350–400, Bk 50, Set menu 135–185 (Amex, Euro/Access, Visa).

VERNON Eure   2B

Hôtel Arianotel ★★ 2 rue des Acacias, 27950 St-Marcel-Vernon.
℃ 32 21 55 56, Fax 32 51 11 18.
English spoken.
Open all year. 37 bedrooms (2 en suite, 35 bath/shower only). Parking, restaurant. &

New-look hotel built in the Norman style which is light and modern. Claude Monet's house and gardens are nearby at Giverny. Take the

Vernon exit from the A13 motorway. The house is 2 km from the centre on the N15 road to Rouen, on the right.

Château de la Corniche ★★★ 5 route de la Corniche, 78270 Rolleboise.
℃ 1 30 93 21 24, Fax 1 30 42 27 44.
English spoken.
Open 06/01 to 20/12. 38 bedrooms (all en suite). Outdoor swimming pool, tennis, golf 18 km, parking.

Château de la Corniche is set on the banks of the Seine. Motorway A13, exit 13 coming from Paris or exit 15 from Rouen.

■ RESTAURANT: Closed Sun eve. Renowned for its fine cuisine.
■ ACTIVITIES: Bikes for hire at hotel; visit to Giverny and Monet's gardens (8 km).
■ TARIFF: (1994) Single 250–350, Double 350–750, Bk 60, Set menu 150–350 (Amex, Euro/Access, Visa).

VERSAILLES Yvelines   2D

Hôtel Akena ★ rue Jacquand, 78310 Cotenières.
℃ 1 34 61 00 33, Fax 1 34 61 22 30.
English spoken.
Open all year. 77 bedrooms (all en suite).
Golf 3 km, parking. &

Good value hotel with a functional design. Price includes up to three people. From Versailles, follow N10 towards Rambouillet and at Trappes turn off at Forum.

■ TARIFF: (1994) Double 145, Bk 22 (Euro/Access, Visa).

Novotel ★★★ 4 bd St-Antoine, 78150 Le Chesnay.
℃ 1 39 54 96 96, Fax 1 39 54 94 40. English spoken.
Open all year. 105 bedrooms (all en suite).
Golf 4 km, garage, restaurant. &

Five minutes from the Palace of Versailles. From the A13 exit Versailles-Ouest/Notre-Dame/Le Chesnay or, from the A86, exit Versailles-Centre. Charge for indoor parking.

■ TARIFF: (1994) Single 530, Double 550, Bk 55 (Amex, Euro/Access, Visa).

Hôtel Résidence du Berry ★★★ 14 rue Anjou, 78000 Versailles.
℃ 1 39 49 07 07, Fax 1 39 50 59 40. English spoken.
Open all year. 38 bedrooms (all en suite).
Golf 3 km.

Located in the centre of Versailles, 5 minutes' walk from the Château and the railway station to Paris.

V

■ TARIFF: (1994) Single 380–400, Double 380–430, Bk 40 (Amex, Euro/Access, Visa).

Château Hôtel Tremblay ★★★ place de l'Eglise, 78490 La Tremblay-sur-Mauldre.
℡ 1 34 87 92 92, Fax 1 34 87 86 27. English spoken.
Open 31/12 to 31/07 & 01/09 to 20/12.
30 bedrooms (all en suite). Golf on site, parking.

275-year-old château with private golf course, set in 90 acres of parkland, 32 km west of Paris. From Versailles, N12 in the direction of Dreux, exit first left after Pontchartrain on to D13 to Le Tremblay-sur-Mauldre.

■ RESTAURANT: Closed Sun eve. Well regarded restaurant. Fish specialities and 'grandmother's pastries'. Excellent home-made foie gras.
■ ACTIVITIES: Many châteaux and houses to visit apart from Versailles also France-Miniature and lots to do locally for the sportif.
■ TARIFF: (1994) Single 550–1150, Double 600–1200, Bk , Set menu 190–290 (Amex, Euro/Access, Visa).

■ RESTAURANT: Renowned, elegant restaurant specialising in traditional, seafood and country cuisine.
■ ACTIVITIES: Canoeing, race course and Reims within easy reach. ● Green fee at nearby 18-hole golf course 100F/day.
■ TARIFF: (1994) Single 300–600, Double 300–800, Bk 60, Set menu 160–400 (Amex, Euro/Access, Visa).

VERVINS Aisne   3A

Hôtel Le Clos du Montvinage ★★ 8 rue Albert Ledent, 02580 Etréaupont.
℡ 23 97 91 10, Fax 23 97 48 92. English spoken.
Open 26/12 to 08/08 & 23/08 to 23/12.
20 bedrooms (all en suite). Tennis, golf 7 km, garage, parking. &

Charm and tranquillity on the banks of the Oise. From Vervins north on the N2 for 7 km to Etréaupont.

■ RESTAURANT: Closed Sun eve & Mon lunch. Specialities include veal sweetbreads with cèpes and champagne sauce, venison steak with bilberries and chanterelles, home-made iced chocolate cake with fruit.
■ ACTIVITIES: Nearby rock-climbing, canoeing and horse-riding. ● Good sports facilities at hotel including bikes free of charge.
■ TARIFF: (1994) Single 280–400, Double 325–435, Bk 47, Set menu 85–225 (Amex, Euro/Access, Visa).

Hôtel Tour du Roy ★★★ 45 rue du Gén Leclerc, 02140 Vervins.
℡ 23 98 00 11, Fax 23 98 00 72. English spoken.
Open all year. 15 bedrooms (all en suite).
Tennis, golf 6 km, parking. &

A splendid manor house, steeped in history, overlooking the old city of Vervins. Interior features include hand-painted bathrooms and stained-glass windows. Rooms overlook terraces, park or landscaped square. On N2 in the centre of Vervins.

LE VEURDRE Allier   5A

Hôtel Pont-Neuf ★★ Fg de Lorette, 03320 Le Veurdre.
℡ 70 66 40 12, Fax 70 66 44 15. English spoken.

Open 15/01 to 15/12. 36 bedrooms (all en suite). Outdoor swimming pool, tennis, golf 15 km, garage, parking. &

An oasis in the middle of France, with a private garden and on the edge of the Allier river, 20 km from the largest oak forest in Europe. Access from N7: D978 from St-Pierre-le-Moutier. From A71: exit Bourges and Montmarault.

■ RESTAURANT: Closed Sun eve LS. 2 pretty, traditional rooms with specialities of saumon fumé maison, foie gras and jambon bourbonnais.

V

■ ACTIVITIES: Magny-Cours and Lurcy-Levis motor race tracks, fishing and hiking trails all nearby.
■ TARIFF: (1994) Single 235–295, Double 240–320, Bk 38 (Amex, Euro/Access, Visa).

VEZELAY Yonne   3C

Hôtel Poste et Lion d'Or ★★★ pl du Champ de Foire, 89450 Vézelay.
☎ 86 33 21 23, Fax 86 32 30 92. English spoken.

Open 01/04 to 15/11. 39 bedrooms (all en suite). Garage, parking.
Former post house at the foot of the Vézelay hill, (11th-and-12th-century romanesque basilica). Traditional hotel, with comfortable welcoming rooms.
■ RESTAURANT: Closed Mon & Tues lunch. Specialities: escargots de Bourgogne; filets de sandre aux cèpes; ris de veau aux morilles.
■ TARIFF: (1994) Single 290–580, Double 320–580, Bk 42, Set menu 115–300 (Amex, Euro/Access, Visa).

VIALAS Lozère   5D

Hôtel Chantoiseau ★★★ 48220 Vialas.
☎ 66 41 00 02, Fax 66 41 04 34. English spoken.
Open 08/04 to 11/11. 15 bedrooms (all en suite). Outdoor swimming pool, golf 20 km, parking.
A 17th-century house on the outskirts of Vialas. Vialas is on the D998, east of Génolhac.
■ RESTAURANT: Excellent cuisine and an excellent choice of wines.

■ TARIFF: (1994) Single 380–420, Double 420–500, Bk 50, Set menu 130–700 (Amex, Euro/Access, Visa).

VICHY

Vichy is famous for its spa water and lies about 50 km north of Clermont-Ferrand, on the River Allier. Its waters, which were known to the Romans, are bottled and exported worldwide. If you would like to 'take the waters', visit the Palais in the shady Parc des Sources. Here there are several different types to try. The least unpleasant comes from the Célestin spring and it is the only one available in bottles. If, however, you prefer to improve your health by enjoying water sports, head for the river where a dam bridge has been built to create the Lac d'Allier.

Artichokes

Driving south from the Channel ports at the start of a French summer holiday, the presence of fields of sunflowers on either side of the road seems especially significant. They, like you, are turning their heads towards the sun. Arrive at Roscoff and you are met with a rather different sight, for the roads are lined with fields of globe artichokes. Of the many varieties grown in France, these, the Camus de Bretagne, *are probably the most famous.*

The young thistle-like heads can be eaten raw, but some people prefer them cooked. Boil for about 25 minutes in salted water and then serve with melted butter. Children love them mostly because you eat them with your fingers, breaking off each leaf and savouring the small edible piece at the base. At the centre lies the heart which is especially succulent, but take care to avoid the hairy flower that grows out of it. There is an appealing ritual to eating artichokes but, if you enjoy the taste but not the palaver, the hearts can be cut out after cooking and served in salad or in a sauce.

When eating out, try artichaut à la bretonne, *where the artichokes are chopped, simmered in oil and butter and then served with cider and onions; or* artichaut favorite, *where the artichokes are stuffed with asparagus then coated with a cheese sauce before being browned.*

V

VICHY Puy-de-Dôme 5A

(See feature)

Château de Maulmont ★★★ St-Priest-Bramefant, 63310 Randan.
℡ 70 59 03 45, Fax 70 59 11 88.
English spoken.
Open 16/01 to 31/12. 29 bedrooms
(25 en suite, 4 bath/shower only). Indoor swimming pool, outdoor swimming pool, golf 13 km, parking.
Built on the site of a 12th-century fortress for the sister of King Louis Philippe, this elegant château offers different categories of accommodation including 3 apartments with luxury bathroom & jacuzzi (sleeps four), 3 'character' rooms, in the towers, 5 fully-equipped luxury rooms and some standard rooms. Randan is on the D1093 south of Vichy, then left on to the D59 to hotel.

■ RESTAURANT: Oak-panelled dining room: traditional French cuisine. Cosy brasserie area converted from the old château kitchen: light meals and snacks.

■ ACTIVITIES: ● Horse riding in the grounds, discounts on beauty/keep fit sessions in Vichy and discounts on green fees at golf club.

■ TARIFF: (1994) Single 275–800, Double 350–900, Bk 45, Set menu 130–240 (Amex, Euro/Access, Visa, **BT**).

Château de la Rigon ★★ 70 rue Adrien Cavy, 03700 Bellerive-sur-Allier.
℡ 70 59 86 46, Fax 70 31 21 66.
English spoken.
Open 01/02 to 20/12. 10 bedrooms
(all en suite). Indoor swimming pool, golf 2 km, garage, parking.
A charming 18th-century residence, 2 km south-west of Vichy and set in an 8-acre park with hundred-year-old trees.

■ TARIFF: (1994) Single 250–300, Double 250–350, Bk 30 (Amex, Euro/Access, Visa).

Hôtel Trianon ★★ 9 rue Desbrest, 03200 Vichy.
℡ 70 97 95 96, Fax 70 97 61 14.
English spoken.
Open 07/01 to 24/12. 36 bedrooms
(24 en suite). Golf 3 km.
Conveniently situated in a quiet, shady street near the centre of Vichy. Follow signs to 'Gare SNCF'.

■ TARIFF: (1994) Single 175–195, Double 185–250, Bk 27 (Amex, Euro/Access, Visa).

VIEILLEVIE Cantal 5C

Hôtel Terrasse ★★ 15120 Vieillevie.
℡ 71 49 94 00, Fax 71 49 92 23. English spoken.
Open 01/04 to 01/11. 32 bedrooms
(27 en suite, 5 bath/shower only). Outdoor swimming pool, tennis, parking. &
Charming hotel on the banks of the River Lot, in the heart of the countryside. The village of Vieillevie is 15 km from Conques.

■ RESTAURANT: Friendly and attractive; meals served on a shady terrace in good weather. Speciality: civet de lotte.

■ ACTIVITIES: Fishing, canoeing, rafting, climbing and BMX nearby.

■ TARIFF: (1994) Double 150–260, Bk 35, Set menu 67–180 (Amex, Euro/Access, Visa).

VIENNE Isère 5B

Château des 7 Fontaines ★★★ Les 7 Fontaines, Seyssuel, 38200 Vienne.
℡ 74 85 25 70, Fax 74 31 74 47. English spoken.
Open 01/02 to 30/11. 15 bedrooms (all en suite). Tennis, golf 15 km, garage, parking.
In the Rhône valley, on the hills of Vienne, this country house hotel offers comfort and relaxation with the added benefit of a fitness centre. 15 minutes from Lyon.

■ TARIFF: (1994) Double 295–350, Bk 30 (Amex, Euro/Access, Visa).

VIERZON Cher 2D

Hôtel Continental ★★★ rte Paris, 18100 Vierzon.
℡ 48 75 35 22, Fax 48 71 10 39. English spoken.

Open all year. 37 bedrooms (30 en suite, 4 bath/shower only). Golf 2 km, garage, parking, restaurant. &
Quiet, spacious bedrooms, charming atmosphere. Leave motorway at Vierzon-Nord exit, hotel 1 km.

■ TARIFF: (1994) Single 130–225, Double 155–300, Bk 28 (Amex, Euro/Access, Visa).

V

Hôtel Arche ★★ Forum République,
18100 Vierzon.
☎ 48 71 93 10, Fax 48 71 83 63. English spoken.

Open all year. 40 bedrooms (all en suite).
Golf 2 km, garage, parking. &
In the centre of Vierzon with panoramic view of Berry canal, a modern and comfortable hotel.

■ RESTAURANT: Closed Sun.
■ TARIFF: (1994) Single 198–300,
Double 223–350, Bk 28, Set menu 55–75
(Amex, Euro/Access, Visa).

VIEUX-MAREUIL Dordogne   4B

Château de Vieux Mareuil ★★★
24340 Vieux-Mareuil.
☎ 53 60 77 15, Fax 53 56 49 33.
English spoken.

Open 01/03 to 15/01. 14 bedrooms
(all en suite). Outdoor swimming pool, garage,
parking. &
A 15th-century château with beautiful surroundings and comfortable rooms.

■ RESTAURANT: Very good cuisine.
■ TARIFF: (1994) Single 500–1000,
Double 550–1000, Bk 60, Set menu 120–320
(Amex, Euro/Access, Visa).

Hôtel L'Etang Bleu ★★★ 24340 Vieux-
Mareuil.
☎ 53 60 92 63, Fax 53 56 33 20. English spoken.
Open 15/02 to 15/01. 11 bedrooms
(all en suite). Parking, restaurant.

A lakeside hotel in extensive wooded grounds. Traditional French country furnishings and regional cuisine. On the D93, 2 km from Vieux-Mareuil.

■ TARIFF: (1994) Double 300–320, Bk 35,
Set menu 85–300 (Amex, Euro/Access, Visa).

VILLEDIEU-LES-POELES Manche   1B

Manoir de l'Acherie ★★ 50800 Ste-Cécile.
☎ 33 51 13 87, Fax 33 61 89 07. English spoken.
Open all year. 14 bedrooms (all en suite).
Golf 20 km, parking. &

Small hotel of character in the Normandy countryside. From Villedieu 3 km on the N175. Turn right on to D554.

■ RESTAURANT: Closed Mon. Rustic dining room with an open fire in winter. Regional cuisine with specialities including soufflé de langoustines sur salade and tarte Normande flambée au Calvados.
■ ACTIVITIES: Excellent walking/hiking country.
■ TARIFF: (1994) Single 220–300,
Double 250–330, Bk 38, Set menu 85–210
(Euro/Access, Visa).

Hôtel St-Pierre et St-Michel ★★ 12 pl de la
République, 50800 Villedieu-les-Poêles.
☎ 33 61 00 11, Fax 33 61 06 52. English spoken.
Open all year. 23 bedrooms (21 en suite).
Garage, parking.

Charming hotel dating from 1850, located in the town centre. Between St-Lô and Avranches. Within reach of Bayeux and Mont-St-Michel.

■ RESTAURANT: Closed 04/01 to 27/01.
■ TARIFF: (1994) Double 240–320, Bk 30,
Set menu 95–215 (Euro/Access, Visa).

VILLEFORT Lozère   5D

Hôtel La Regordane ★★ à la Garde-Guérin,
Prévenchères, 48800 Villefort.
☎ 66 46 82 88. English spoken.
Open 01/04 to 31/10. 16 bedrooms (9 en suite,
1 bath/shower only). Golf 1 km, restaurant.

Beautiful stone buildings around a terrace, in the centre of a medieval village. On the D906, 6 km north-east of Villefort.

V

■ TARIFF: (1994) Double 185–275, Bk 29, Set menu 90–165 (Euro/Access, Visa).

VILLEFRANCHE-DE-LAURAGAIS   5C

Hôtel de France ★★ 106 rue République, 31290 Villefranche-de-Lauragais.
✆ 61 81 62 17. English spoken.
Open 02/02 to 03/07 & 26/07 to 15/01.
20 bedrooms (10 en suite, 5 bath/shower only). Garage.
A 19th-century inn, having easy access to the A61 for Toulouse.
■ RESTAURANT: Closed Mon.
■ TARIFF: (1994) Single 145–175, Double 165–220, Bk 20, Set menu 70–140 (Amex, Euro/Access, Visa).

VILLEFRANCHE-DE-ROUERGUE   5C

Hôtel Relais de Farrou ★★★ au Farrou, 12200 Villefranche-de-Rouergue.
✆ 65 45 18 11, Fax 65 45 32 59. English spoken.

Open all year. 26 bedrooms (all en suite).
Outdoor swimming pool, tennis, garage, parking. &
Modern comfort in a former coaching inn. Set in the countryside 3 minutes from Villefranche-de-Rouergue. South of Figéac on D922.
■ RESTAURANT: Closed Sun eve & Mon LS.
Imaginative, creative cuisine. Specialities: les escalopines de foie gras de canard poêlées au muscat de Mireval; civet de homard au vieux Banyuls; ris d'agneau aux morilles.
■ ACTIVITIES: Very good sports/health facilities at hotel; arrangements made for canoeing, pony-trekking and rides in horse-drawn carriage.
■ TARIFF: (1994) Single 270–355, Double 315–545, Bk 42, Set menu 112–350 (Euro/Access, Visa).

VILLEFRANCHE-SUR-MER   Alpes-Mar   6C

Hôtel Provençal ★★ 4 av mar Joffre, 06230 Villefranche-sur-Mer.
✆ 93 01 71 42, Fax 93 76 96 00.
English spoken.
Open all year. 45 bedrooms (all en suite).
Golf 15 km, garage.
Central position 150 m from harbour. Comfortable and peaceful with some rooms overlooking sea.
■ RESTAURANT: Closed 01/11 to 23/12. Air-conditioned Provençal-style dining room with a good reputation.
■ ACTIVITIES: Excursions.
■ TARIFF: (1994) Single 210–400, Double 210–440, Bk 40, Set menu 75–125 (Amex, Euro/Access, Visa).

Hôtel Versailles ★★★ av Princesse Grace, 06230 Villefranche-sur-Mer.
✆ 93 01 89 56, Fax 93 01 97 48.
English spoken.
Open 31/12 to 31/10. 49 bedrooms (all en suite). Outdoor swimming pool, golf 15 km, parking. &
Most attractive hotel. Light, air-conditioned rooms with balconies overlooking the sea. Take coast road eastwards from Nice.
■ RESTAURANT: Closed Mon LS. Enjoy fine food and panoramic views over the bay. Specialities include foie gras de canard à l'Hennessy, panaché de la mer aux petits légumes and tournedos aux morilles.
■ ACTIVITIES: French billiards; tennis and water sports nearby.
■ TARIFF: (1994) Single 570–590, Double 590–650, Set menu 140–250 (Amex, Euro/Access, Visa).

VILLEFRANCHE-SUR-SAONE   Rhône   5B

Hôtel Plaisance ★★★ 96 av Libération, 69652 Villefranche-sur-Saône.
✆ 74 65 33 52, Fax 74 62 02 89.
English spoken.
Open 02/01 to 24/12. 68 bedrooms (all en suite). Golf 8 km, garage, parking.
The hotel is situated in the centre of the town, in front of a square. A gourmet restaurant, 'La Fontaine Bleue', is opposite. Villefranche is the capital of the Beaujolais area, a starting point for excursions into the Beaujolais vineyards.
■ TARIFF: (1994) Single 310–365, Double 320–400, Bk 47 (Amex, Euro/Access, Visa).

V

VILLENEUVE-SUR-LOT Lot/Garonne 4D

Hostellerie du Plantie ★★ route de
Castelmoron, 47110 Le Temple-sur-Lot.
℃ 53 84 37 48, Fax 53 84 76 32. English spoken.

Open all year. 10 bedrooms (all en suite).
Outdoor swimming pool, tennis, golf 8 km,
parking. &

*A restored farmhouse in 25 acres of wooded
grounds alongside the River Lot. From
Villeneuve-sur-Lot, D911 west to Le Temple-sur-
Lot then turn to Castelmoron for 800 m.*

■ RESTAURANT: Good food served in lovely
surroundings.
■ ACTIVITIES: Good sporting facilities nearby;
organised trips on request.
■ TARIFF: (1994) Single 300–320,
Double 340–360, Bk 38, Set menu 90–180
(Euro/Access, Visa).
■ DISCOUNT: 5%

Hôtel La Résidence ★★ 17 av Lazare Carnot,
47300 Villeneuve-sur-Lot.
℃ 53 40 17 03, Fax 53 01 57 34. English spoken.
Open all year. 18 bedrooms (13 en suite).
Golf 10 km, garage, parking.
■ TARIFF: (1994) Single 120–235,
Double 120–280, Bk 28 (Euro/Access, Visa).

VILLERS-COTTERETS Aisne 2B

Hôtel Le Regent ★★★ 26 rue du Général
Mangin, 02600 Villers-Cotterêts.
℃ 23 96 01 46, Fax 23 96 37 57. English spoken.
Open all year. 17 bedrooms (all en suite).
Garage, parking. &

*Charming 18th-century post house in the
centre of the town. Elegant, period atmosphere
with modern comfort.*

■ ACTIVITIES: Bike hire and indoor and outdoor
swimming pools nearby.
■ TARIFF: (1994) Single 155–310, Double 310–
370, Bk 29 (Amex, Euro/Access, Visa).

VIMOUTIERS Orne 2A

Hôtel Escale du Vitou ★★ rte Argentan,
61120 Vimoutiers.
℃ 33 39 12 04, Fax 33 36 13 34. English spoken.
Open all year. 17 bedrooms (all en suite).
Outdoor swimming pool, tennis, golf 25 km,
parking.

*Comfortable, Normandy-style hotel. On the
road, south, towards Argentan.*

■ RESTAURANT: Closed Sun eve & Mon.
■ TARIFF: (1994) Double 180–250, Bk 28,
Set menu 68–195 (Euro/Access, Visa).

VITTEL Vosges 3C

Hôtel d'Angleterre ★★★ 162 rue de Charmey,
88800 Vittel.
℃ 29 08 08 42, Fax 29 08 07 48. English spoken.
Open all year. 61 bedrooms (all en suite).
Golf 1 km, parking. &

*A recently renovated hotel with all modern
conveniences, a lift, private parking and
gardens near the casino and spa in Vittel.*

■ RESTAURANT: Traditional cuisine.
■ ACTIVITIES: ● Discounts at local thermal spa
and bike hire.
■ TARIFF: (1994) Single 320–370,
Double 380–460, Bk 42, Set menu 120–160
(Amex, Euro/Access, Visa).

VOVES Eure/Loir 2D

Hôtel Quai Fleuri ★★★ 15 rue Texier-Gallas,
28150 Voves.
℃ 37 99 15 15, Fax 37 99 11 20. English spoken.
Open 05/01 to 20/12. 17 bedrooms
(all en suite). Golf 15 km, garage, parking. &

*A renovated former mill, set in wooded
parkland between Chartres and Orléans.
Terrace overloking the park.*

■ RESTAURANT: Closed Sun eve, all public hols eve.
Specialities: tourte au escargots; noix de Saint-
Jacques au safron; magret de canard aux morilles.
■ ACTIVITIES: Fitness centre; French billiards,
games room, mountain-bike hire.
■ TARIFF: (1994) Single 295–700,
Double 315–700, Bk 34, Set menu 79–250
(Amex, Euro/Access, Visa).
■ DISCOUNT: 10%

WIMEREUX Pas-de-Calais 2B

Hôtel Centre ★★ 78 rue Carnot,
62930 Wimereux.
℃ 21 32 41 08, Fax 21 33 82 48. English spoken.
Open all year. 25 bedrooms (22 en suite).
Golf 2 km, garage, parking.

V

From Boulogne-sur-Mer, follow the coast road and Wimereux is 5 km to the north. The hotel is in the main street.

■ RESTAURANT: Closed Mon.
■ TARIFF: (1994) Single 215, Double 295, Bk 30, Set menu 95–160 (Euro/Access, Visa).

Hôtel Paul et Virginie ★★ 19 rue Gén de Gaulle, 62930 Wimereux.
☎ 21 32 42 12, Fax 21 87 65 85. English spoken.
Open 20/01 to 13/12. 15 bedrooms
(11 en suite, 4 bath/shower only). Golf 1 km, parking.
Quiet hotel just north of Boulogne-sur-Mer. Wimereux is on the N940 and the hotel is signposted in the town.

■ RESTAURANT: Specialises in seafood.
■ TARIFF: (1994) Single 185–265, Double 185–375, Bk 32, Set menu 95–250 (Amex, Euro/Access, Visa).

WISSANT Pas-de-Calais   2B

Hôtel Normandy ★ 2 pl de Verdun, 62179 Wissant.
☎ 21 35 90 11, Fax 21 82 19 08. English spoken.
Open 01/02 to 20/12. 30 bedrooms
(11 en suite, 8 bath/shower only). Golf 13 km, parking, restaurant.
A family hotel, built in the 18th century. Lounge, garden, restaurant and rooms with sea view. Wissant is between Boulogne and Calais. Take exit 8 or 9 from A16 and hotel is opposite the church in the village centre.
■ TARIFF: (1994) Single 190–270, Double 210–330, Set menu 90–165 (Euro/Access, Visa).

WISSEMBOURG Bas-Rhin   3B

Hôtel Alsace ★★ 16 rue Vauban, 67160 Wissembourg.
☎ 88 94 98 43, Fax 88 94 19 60. English spoken.
Open all year. 41 bedrooms (all en suite).
Tennis, garage, parking. ᕦ
In a typical Alsatian town, surrounded by forest and vineyards. This new hotel overlooks the river.

■ TARIFF: (1994) Single 220–245, Double 250–276, Bk 29 (Amex, Euro/Access, Visa).

W

Photograph acknowledgements

CDT Pas de Calais - Page 18
CRT Normandie - 22
CRT de Bretagne - 24, 26, 27, 29
CRT Loire-Atlantique - 31, 34
OT de Pornic - 33
CRT Poitou-Charentes - 36, 37
CDT d'Aqitaime - 38, 39
Frédéric Oree/Photothèque Pyrénées Roussillon - 41
CRT Languedoc-Roussillon - 42
F Laharragne/CRT L-R - 44
B Touillon - 51
Ville d'Angers - 73
OT Auxerre - 84
Patrick Blanc - 169
OT Langres - 180
Christine Delpal - 187
Ville de Nancy - 208
B Voisin - 219
CRT Alsace - 297
Yve Flatard - 308
G Testand - 311

GLOSSARY

Glossary of French food terms to help you round the tempting menus shown in this guide and in other restaurants you may visit.

agneau, *lamb*

agneau de pré-salé, *lamb pastured in salt meadows (particularly on Atlantic coast), giving it a special flavour*

aigrette, *fritter, usually savoury*

ail, *garlic*

aïoli, *garlic flavoured mayonnaise*

amer, amère, *bitter*

andouille, *type of pork sausage*

anguille, *eel*

anis, *aniseed flavoured aperitif*

AOC, appellation (d'origine) contrôlée), *system of quality control applied to wine and cheese*

Armagnac, *brandy*

assiette du pêcheur, *mixed fish platter*

autruche, *ostrich*

aux cheveux d'Ange, *layered*

baie, *berry*

ballotine, *type of meat/poultry loaf*

Banyuls, *strong, sweet red wines from the Grenace grape*

barbue, *brill*

baudroie, *monkfish*

betterave, *beetroot*

beurre, *butter*

beurre blanc, *reduction of shallots and wine or vinegar, whipped up with butter*

blanquette de *-, *something cooked in white sauce*

blini, *small thick Russian pancake*

boeuf, *beef*

bouillabaisse, *fish soup*

bourride, *fish stew*

brandade (à la), *served with salt, olive oil and cream sauce*

brochet, *pike*

brochette, *kebab, food cooked on a skewer*

brouillade aux truffes, *scrambled eggs with truffles*

Cabécou, *soft round cheese*

caille, *quail*

calamar/calmar/calmaret, *squid, inkfish*

Calvados, *apple brandy from Normandy*

canard, *duck*

caneton, *duckling*

canette, *female duckling*

carré d'agneau, *rack of lamb*

carte menu, *fixed price meal*

carte/menu gastronomique, *gourmet menu*

cassis, *blackcurrant*

cassolette, (or cassette) *small portion of food for hors d'oeuvre or dessert*

cassoulet, *haricot beans and meat stew*

cèpes, *boletus (type of mushroom)*

cervelles, *brains, usually calf's*

champignon, *mushroom*

chanterelle, *variety of mushroom*

chaource, *soft creamy cheese with fruity flavour from Champagne*

charcuterie, *cooked pork products*

Chardonnay, *variety of white grape used for wine-making*

chaud, *hot*

chausson, *puff pastry turnover with savoury or sweet filling*

(en) chemise, *(in) pastry/pancake or similar*

(aux) cheveux d'Ange, *layered*

chèvre, *goat; goat's milk cheese*

chevreuil, *roe deer; venison*

chiffonade, *thin ribbons of green vegetables added to soup*

chipirons (Basque), *squid*

chou, *cabbage*

chou de mer, chou marin, *sea kale*

chou vert, *green cabbage*

choucroute, *pickled white cabble (Sauerkraut)*

cidre, *cider*

citron, *lemon*

citron vert, *lime*

civet de, *rich stew of (hare, venison)*

cochon (de lait), *(suckling) pig*
colin, *hake*
confit, *meat cooked and preserved in stone pot*
confit de canard, *conserve of duck*
confit de poule, *conserve of chicken*
coq, *chicken*
coquillages, *shellfish*
coquilles Saint-Jacques, *scallops*
coulis, *strong clear broth/sauce*
court bouillon, *broth for poaching fish, made from vegetables, herbs and white wine*
crème, *cream*
un crème, a white coffee
crêpe, *pancake*
croustillant, *crisp, crunchy*
cru (classé), *vineyard (of special quality)*
cuisse, *thigh, drumstick*
daube, *braised meat, poultry, game, fish, served with vegetables*
diable, *hot wine and vinegar sauce*
eau douce, *fresh water*
écrevisse, *crayfish, freshwater prawn*
encornet, *squid*
encre, *ink (of squid, octopus)*
épicé, *spicy*
épinard, *spinach*
escalope, *thin slice of meat/fish*
escargot, *snail*
étuvé, *stewed, braised, steamed*
farci, *stuffed*
fenouil, *fennel*
féra, *highly prized Savoy lake salmon*
fermier, *farm-made/reared*
à la fermière, *meat or fish cooked with mixed vegetables*
feuillantine, *small light pastry*
feuilleté, *made of flaky pastry*
ficelle normande/picarde, *pancake stuffed with cream/ cheese and ham/mushrooms*
figue, *fig*
filet de boeuf, *filet of beef*
flamber, *to flame with spirit or fortified wine*
flamiche, *type of tart*
foie gras, *liver of force-fed goose or duck*
fondu, *melted*
(au) four, *baked*

frais, fraîche, *fresh, cool*
fraise, *strawberry*
framboise, *raspberry*
fricassé, *sautéed fish or meat finished in a cream sauce*
froid, *cold*
fromage, *cheese*
fruits de mer, *seafood*
fumé, *smoked*
gazpacho, *Andalusian cold soup made from tomatoes, peppers, onion, cucumber, garlic, olive oil*
gelée, *aspic*
genièvre, *juniper berry; liqueur made from same*
gésier, *gizzard (of poultry)*
gibier, *game*
gigot d'agneau, *leg of lamb*
gingembre, *ginger*
girolle, *type of mushroom*
glace, *ice-cream*
glacé, *frozen; iced; glazed*
gougère, *cheese-flavoured choux pastry ring*
grenouille, *frog*
grillade, *grilled meat or fish*
herbes, *herbs*
homard, *lobster*
huître, *oyster*
jambon, *ham*
jambonette, *dried salted meat in shape of a ham*
jus, *juice*
lapin, *rabbit*
langouste, *crayfish*
langoustine, *Dublin Bay prawn, scampi*
lapereau, *young rabbit*
lard, *pork fat, bacon*
légumes, *vegetables*
lotte, *monkfish, burbot*
lotte de mer, *monkfish*
loup (de mer), *bar, sea bass*
magret de canard, *breast of fattened duck served rare*
maison, *of the establishment, home-made*
marcassin, *young wild boar*
marron, *chestnut*

matelote, *stew of freshwater fish in wine*

menthe, *mint*

merlu/merluche merluzza, *hake*

miel, *honey*

mignon (filet mignon), *small fillet steak*

mille-feuille, *thin layers of flaky pastry with sweet or savoury filling*

mirabelle, *small gold plum from Alsace; liqueur of same*

mode, à la mode de, *in the manner of*

mont-blanc, *chestnut cream dessert*

morille, *morel, type of mushroom*

moule, *mussel*

mousseron, *highly estemmed St-George mushroom*

Munster, *cheese from Alsace with strong smell and spicy flavour*

Muscat, *wine made from muscat grape*

(à la) normande, *with cream and Calvados/cider/apples*

noix, *topside (of veal); walnut*

oeuf, *egg*

oeufs brouillés, *scrambled eggs*

oie, *goose*

oseille, *sorrel*

palombe, *wild pigeon*

panaché, *mixed (un panaché = a shandy)*

panaché de la mer, *mixed seafood*

papillotte, *meat/fish baked in foil/greaseproof*

parfait, *rich mousse/cream, flavoured with chocolate, coffee etc*

parmentier, *with potatoes*

pavé, *thick slice of beef steak*

du pays, *local*

perche, *perche*

persil, *parsley*

pigeonneau, *young pigeon*

Pinot Noir, *black grape from which great Burgundy wines are made*

pipérade, *omelette/scrambled eggs with tomatoes, peppers, onions*

pistache, *pistachio nut*

pistou, *basil (pesto sauce)*

plateau, *platter, tray*

pleurote, *highly prized mushroom*

poêlé, *pot-roasted on bed of vegetables*

poêlon de, *cooked in (earthenware) casserole*

poireau, *leek*

poisson, *fish*

poisson bleu, *fresh-caught fish plunged in boiling vinegar bouillon resulting in bluish hue*

poitrine, *breast*

poivre, *pepper*

pomme, *apple*

pomme de terre, *potato*

potage, *soup*

potée, *thick meat and vegetable soup*

poularde, *fattened hen; roasting chicken*

poulet, *chicken*

pounti, *hash of bacon and Swiss chard*

produits de mer, *sea food*

(à la) provençale, *cooked with tomatoes, garlic, onions, olives, anchovies, aubergines etc*

quenelle, *type of light mousse-cum-dumpling, served lightly poached*

queue (de boeuf), *oxtail*

raclette, *Alpine potato and melted cheese speciality prepared at table, usually served with salamis etc*

raie, *ray, skate*

réserve, *term indicating age of Armagnac, Calvados, Cognac etc.*

ris, *sweetbreads*

Roquefort, *strong sheep's-milk blue cheese*

romarin, *rosemary*

rôti, *roasted*

rouget, *red mullet*

rouille, *spicy mayonnaise with red pepper and garlic*

sabayon/zabaglione, *warm egg yolk and Marsala wine dessert*

Saint-Jacques, *short for coquille Saint-Jacques, scallop*

Saint-Pierre, *John Dory fish whose dark spots on either side of the back are said to be the thumb marks of Saint Pierre*

en saison, *in season*

salers, *large, cylindrical Auvergne cheese*

salmis, *game or poultry dish part-roasted then finished in wine sauce*

Sancerre, *wine-growing region*

sandre, *pike-perch*

saumon, *salmon*

saupiquet, *piquant wine and vinegar sauce*

sauvage, *wild*

selle, *saddle (of lamb)*

soja, *soya bean*

sole, *sole*

supioun, suppion, sépiole, *cuttlefish*

suprême, *(breast and wing) filet*

table d'hôte, *meal of several courses at fixed price*

terrine, *(pâté) baked in covered earthenware dish*

terroir, *country, rural*

thym, *thyme*

tiède, *luke warm, tepid*

torchon, *cloth, napkin*

tournedos, *small round filet steak*

tournedos Rossini, *small round filet steak with truffles*

tourte, *pie*

tripes à la mode de Caen, *ox tripe and trotters cooked in cider*

tripoux, *heavily seasoned stuffed veal or lamb tripe*

truffade, *potato cake with Cantal cheese*

truffe, *prized underground fungus; chocolate sweet*

truffé, *garnished/studded/stuffed with truffles*

truite, *trout*

vacherin, *Alpine cheese*

veau, *veal*

viande, *meat*

vin, *wine*

vin jaune, *yellow wine made in Franche-Comté region from Savagnin grape*

vinaigre, *vinegar*

volaille, *poultry, chicken*

à la volonté, *as much as you like*

à la vosgienne, *in the style of Vosges (mountain region of Lorraine and Alsace)*

INDEX

This index covers the Fringes of France, Useful Information and Hotel Directory. Places shown in **bold type** are headings used in the Hotel Directory under which towns are grouped.

Abbeville 64
Abondance 64
Abreschviller 64
Agay 64
Agde 43, 65
Agen 65
Agincourt, Battle of 16
Agon-Coutainville 66
L'Aigle 66
Aiguebelette 66
Aigues-Mortes 43, 66
l'Aiguille, rock 17
Aiguillon 66
Aiguines 66
Aïnhoa 67
Aire-sur-l'Adour 67
Aire-sur-La-Lys 67
Aix-en-Provence 67
Aix-en-Othe (**Troyes**) 307
Aix-Les-Bains 68
Ajaccio 52, 142
Alabaster Coast, the 16
Albert 69
Albi 69
alcohol 56
Alençon 69
Aleria 52
allowances 60, 61
L'Alpe-d'Huez 70
Altkirch 70
Ambert 71
Ambialet 71
Amboise 71
Amélie-les-Bains 71
Amiens 72
Anduze 72
Angers 72
Anglet (**Biarritz**) 102
Angoulême 74
Annecy 74
Annonay 76
Antibes 50, 76
Apocalypse Tapestry 72
Apt 77

Arbois 77
Arcachon 38, 77, 106
Ardres 78
Argentan 78
Argentat 78
Argenton-sur-Creuse 78
Arles 4, 79
Arles-sur-Rhône (**Arles**) 79
Armentieres 80
Arras 81
Arreau 82
Arromanches 20
Ars-en-Ré 254
artichokes 318
Arudy 82
Aubenas 83
Aubreville (**Ste-Menehould**) 288
Auch 83
Audierne 83
Aulnay-sous-Bois 236
Aumale 83
Auribeau-sur-Siagne (**Grasse**) 167
Aurillac 83
Autun 83
Auxerre 84
Avallon 84
Avène-les-Bains 84
Avignon 85
Avranches 86
Ayen 86
Azay-le-Rideau 87

Badefols 87
Bagneres-de-Bigorre 87
Bagneres-de-Luchon 87
Bagnoles-de-l'Orne 88
Bagnolet 236
Bagnols-sur-Ceze 88
Bailleul 89
Balines (**Verneuil-sur-Avre**) 316
Bandol 46, 89
Banyuls-dels-Aspres (**Le Boulou**) 41, 108
Bapaume 89
Bar-sur-Aube 90
Barbentane 90
Barbotan-les-Thermes 90
Bardot, Brigitte 48
Barfleur 90

Barneville-Carteret 91
Bassillac (**Périgueux**) 239
Bastia 52
Baugé 91
La Baule 31, 91
Baumes-les-Dames 92
Les Baux-de-Provence (**St-Rémy-de-Provence**) 283
Bayenghem-les-Seninghem (**Lumbres**) 187
Bayeux 92
Bayeux, tapestry 21
Bayonne 39, 94
Beaugency 94
Beaujeu 95
Beaulieu-sur-Mer 95
Beaumont-sur-Sarthe 96
Beaumont-sur-Vesle (**Reims**) 254
Beaune 96
Beausoleil (**Monte-Carlo**) 199
Beauvais 98
Bellegarde-sur-Valserine 98
Bellerive-sur-Allier (**Vichy**) 318
Belleville-sur-Saone 98
Bénédictine, liqueur 17
Bénodet 98
Bergerac 99
Bergues 100
Bernex (**Evian-les-Bains**) 155
Besançon 100
Bessé-sur-Braye 101
Béthune 101
Beynac 102
Béziers 42, 102
Biarritz 39, 102
Bidarray 103
bird watching 26
Biriatou (**St-Jean-de-Luz**) 274
Biscarrosse 103
Bitche 103
Black Angers 72
Le Blanc 103
Le Blanc-Mesnil 236
Blois 104
Blotzheim 104
Bolbec 105
Bonaparte, Napoléon 13, 51, 52

Bonneval 105
Bonnieux (**Cadenet**) 114
Bordeaux 105
Bordeaux 36
Bouesse (**Argenton-sur-Creuse**) 78
Bougival (**St-Germain-en-Laye**) 273
Bouguenais (**Nantes**) 209
bouillabaisse 46
La Bouille 107
Boullogne-Billancourt 234
Boulogne-sur-Mer 13, 108
Le Boulou 108
Bourg-en-Bresse 108
Bourg-St-Maurice 109
Bourges 109
Le Bourget 237
Le Bourget-du-Lac 109
Bourgneuf-en-Retz 33
Bourgoin-Jallieu 110
Bourgueil 110
Bout-du-Lac (**Annecy**) 74
Brantôme 110
breakdown 54
Bréhal 110
Breil-sur-Roya 110
Brelidy 111
La Bresse 111
Brest 28, 111
Breteuil 111
Briançon 112
Briare 219
Bricquebec 112
Brionne 112
Brive-la-Gaillarde 112
Brousse-le-Chateau 113
Le Bugue 113
Buisson-du-Cadouin (**Le Bugue**) 113
bullfighting 44
Bussang 113
Bussy-St-Georges 114
Buxy (**Chalon-sur-Saône**) 125
Buzançais 114

Cabourg 19
Cabrerets 114
Cadenet 114
La Cadière-d'Azur 115
Cadillac 115
Caen 20, 116
Cahors 117
Calacuccia 143
Calais 13, 117
Calés (**Rocamadour**) 259

Callian (**Fayence**) 157
Calvi 52
The Camargue 43, 86
Cambrai 118
Camembert 19
Camiers 118
Camors 118
Camps (**Argentat**) 78
Canal du Midi 42
Cancale 24, 118
Candé-sur-Beuvron (**Blois**) 104
Cannes 50, 118
Cap d'Ail (**Monte-Carlo**) 199
Cap d'Antibes (**Antibes**) 76
Cap Gris-Nez 120
Carcassonne 120
Carennac 121
Carentan 121
Carnac 29, 121
Carpentras 122
Carsac-Aillac (**Sarlat-la-Canéda**) 290
Carteret-Barneville 22
Cassis 122
Casteljaloux 123
Le Castellet 123
Castera-Verduzan 123
Castres 123
Catalan, language of 40
Caudebec-en-Caux 124
Cauterets 124
Cavaillon 124
Cavalaire-sur-Mer (**La Croix-Valmer**) 146
Cavalière 48
Cergy-Pontoise 124
Cernay-la-Ville (**Rambouillet**) 253
Ceyrat 125
Chablis 125
Chagny 125
Challans 125
Challes-les-Eaux (**Chambery**) 126
Chalon-sur-Saône 125
Châlons-sur-Marne 126
Chambery 126
Chambord 126
Chambray-les-Tours (**Tours**) 304
Chamonix 126
Chamouille (**Laon**) 181
Champagnac 128
champagne 308
Champagnole 128

Champagny-en-Vanoise 128
Champeaux (**St-Jean-le-Thomas**) 276
Champigné (**Angers**) 72
Champtoceaux 129
Chamrousse 129
Le Change (**Périgueux**) 239
Le Chant du Monde 73
Chantilly 129
Chaource 130
La Chapelle-d'Andaine (**Bagnoles-de-l'Orne**) 88
La Chapelle-en-Ferval (**Chantilly**) 129
La Chapelle-en-Valgaudemar 130
La Chapelle-en-Vecors 130
La Chapelle-St-Mesmin (**Orléans**) 218
Charenton 237
Charolles 130
La Chartre-sur-le-Loir 131
Chartres 131
chartreuse 169
Chasseneuil-du-Poitou (**Poitiers**) 244
Château d'If 46
Château-Thierry 131
Château-du-Loir 131
Châteaubourg 132
Châteaubriant 132
Châteaudun 132
Châteauneuf-sur-Loire 132
Châteauneuf-sur-Sarthe 133
Châteauroux 133
Châtelaillon-Plage 133
Châtillon-sur-Seine 133
La Châtre 134
Chaumes-en-Brie (**Guignes**) 172
Chaumont 134
Chaumont-sur-Tharonne 135
Chelles 135
Chenonceaux 135
Cherbourg 22, 135
Le Chesnay (**Versailles**) 316
Chinon 136
Chitenay (**Blois**) 104
La Ciotat 46, 136
Cipières (**Grasse**) 167
Civray-de-Touraine (**Chenonceaux**) 135
Claix (**Grenoble**) 169

Claye-Souilly (**Marne-la-Vallée**) 192
Clécy 136
Clermont-Ferrand 136
closing days 59
La Clusaz 137
Coast of Megaliths, the 29
Coast of Roses 41
Cognac 137
Collioure 41, 137
Colmar 138
Colombey-les-Deux-Eglises 139
Coly 140
Combeaufontaine 140
Combloux 140
Combourg 140
Compiègne 140
Comps-sur-Artuby 141
Concarneau 29, 141
Condé-sur-Noireau 141
Condrieu 142
La Conquet 142
Contres 142
La Coquille 142
La Corse (Corsica) 51, 143
Cosne-Cours-sur-Loire 144
Cosquer cave, the 46
Côte Basque 39
Côte Bleue 44
Côte d'Albâtre 16
Côte d'Amethyste 42
Côte d'Amour 31
Côte d'Argent 37
Côte d'Azure 49
Côte d'Emeraude 23
Côte d'Opale 13
Côte de Beauté 36
Côte de Granit Rose 25
Côte de Jade 32
Côte de l'Estérel 49
Côte de la Lumière 33
Côte de la Plaisance 28
Côte des Baies du Soleil 46
Côte des Calanques 45
Côte des Charentes 35
Côte des Légendes 26
Côte des Maures 47
Côte des Mégalithes 29
Côte du Bessin 20
Côte du Cotentin 21
Côte du Nacre 19
Côte Fleurie 17
Côte Sauvage 30
Côte Vermeille 40
Cotenières (**Versailles**) 316
Côtes des Roses 41

Coucouron 144
Courbevoie 235
Courchevel 145
Courçon (**La Rochelle**) 261
Courseulles-sur-Mer 145
Coutances 22, 146
Couture-sur-Loir (**Montoire-sur-le-Loir**) 203
Creac'h, lighthouse 27
Crépon (**Bayeux**) 92
Crest 146
Creully (**Bayeux**) 92
Criel-sur-Mer 146
croissants 245
La Croix-Blanche (**Agen**) 65
La Croix-Valmer 146
Crosmières (**La Flèche**) 159
Croutelle (**Poitiers**) 244
Crozon 146
Cuiseaux 146
customs 60

D-Day 20
Dardilly (**Lyon**) 187
Deauville 18, 147
Derain 41
Dieppe 16, 147
Digne-les-Bains 148
Dijon 148
Dinan 25, 150
Dinard 25, 151
Dissay-sous-Courcillon (**Chateau-du-Loir**) 131
distance conversion 56
Dolancourt (**Bar-sur-Aube**) 90
Donzenac 151
Donzy (**Cosne-Cours-sur-Loire**) 144
Dordogne 239
Douai 152
Douarnenez 152
Doullens 152
Draguignan 152
driving licence 56
druids 28
Ducey 152
Duingt (**Annecy**) 74
Dune du Pilat 38
Dunkerque 152
Duras 153
duty 61

Les Echelles 153
Echemiré (**Baugé**) 91
Ecrainville-par-Goderville (**Goderville**) 166

Eiffel, Gustave 271
Elne 41
Emerald Coast, the 23
emergency 60
Entraigues 153
Entraygues-sur-Truyere 153
Epernay 154
Epinal 154
L'Epine (**Châlons-sur-Marne**) 126
Erdeven 154
Ernee 154
Erquy 154
Esplanade des Quinconces 106
Espondeilhan (**Béziers**) 102
Estaing 154
Etoges (**Epernay**) 154
Etréaupont (**Vervins**) 317
Etretat 17
Eu (**Le Tréport**) 307
European parliament 298
Eurotunnel 54
Euskara, language of 39
Evian-les-Bains 155
Evisa 143
Evreux 156
Excideuil 156
Eybens (**Grenoble**) 169
Les Eyzies-de-Tayac 156
Eze 157

Fagnières (**Châlons-sur-Marne**) 126
Fayence 157
La Feclaz 158
Fermanville (**Cherbourg**) 135
Ferney-Voltaire 158
Ferrette 158
La Feuillée (**Roscoff**) 264
Feurs 158
Feytiat (**Limoges**) 183
Finistère 27
Flagy (**Fontainebleau**) 160
La Flèche 159
Florac 159
foie gras 297
Font-Romeu 160
Fontaine-Châlais (**Senlis**) 293
Fontainebleau 160
Fontevraud-l'Abbaye 161
Forcalquier 161
forêt d'Orient 309
forêt de Paimport 256
La Forêt-Fousesnant 162
Forges-les-Eaux 162

Fort-Mahon-Plage 162
Fouesnant 162
Fouras-les-Bains (**Rochefort**) 261
Franqueville-St-Pierre (**Rouen**) 264
Fréhel (**Sables-d'Or-les-Pins**) 267
Fréjus 49
Fresnay-sur-Sarthe 163
Frouard (**Nancy**) 208
Futuroscope 245
La Gacilly 163
Ganges 163
Gap 163
Garrevaques (**Revel**) 257
Gatteville Phare, lighthouse 22
Gaugiun, Paul 29
Gavarnie 164
Gavrelle (**Arras**) 81
Genlis 164
Genouillac 164
Gérardmer 164
Gevrey-Chambertin 165
Gien 165, 219
Gironde 36
Giroussens (**Lavaur**) 182
Givet 165
Gobelin tapestries 98
Goderville 166
Le Golfe-Juan 166
Gordes 166
Gorges des Guiers Mort 169
Gouesnou (**Brest**) 111
Gourdon 166
Goya 124
Gramat 166
La Grand-Motte 43, 167
Les Grangettes (**Pontarlier**) 249
Granville 23, 167
Grasse 167
Gratentour (**Toulouse**) 302
Le Grau-du-Roi 168
Graufthal (**La Petite-Pierre**) 241
Graveson (**Avignon**) 85
Grenoble 169
Gréoux-les-Bains 171
Gressy 171
Grignan 171
Groix 172
Grotte de Lascaux 239
Grotte de Rouffignac 157
Gruissan 41
Guebwiller 172

Guérande 32, 172
Guignes 172
Guilliers (**Ploërmel**) 246
Guise 172
Gutenberg 297

Haguenau 172
Hallines (**St-Omer**) 281
Hardelot 173
Le Havre 17, 173
Hazebrouck 174
Hendaye (**St-Jean-de-Luz**) 274
Henry V 308
Hitler's Atlantic wall 13
Honfleur 17, 174
Hossegor 174
Husseren-les-Châteaux (**Colmar**) 138
Hyères 47, 175

Ilay (**St-Laurent-en-Grandvaux**) 277
Ile d'Oléron 36
Ile d'Ouessant 27
Ile de Groix (**Groix**) 172
Ile de Noirmoutier 33
Ile de Ré 35, 254
Ile Rousse 143
Ile-aux-Moines (**Vannes**) 313
Ile-de-Bréhat (**Paimpol**) 221
Ingrandes-sur-Loire 175
insurance, medical 53
insurance, motoring 53
insurance, personal 53
Isigny-sur-Mer 176
Island of Perfume 36
L'Isle-d'Abeau (**Bourgoin-Jallieu**) 110
Isle-Jourdain 176
Les Issambres (**Ste-Maxime**) 287
Issoire 176
Issoudun 176
Ivry-en-Montagne (**Beaune**) 96

La Jaille-Yvon (**Le Lion-d'Angers**) 184
Jaurès, Jean 124
Joan of Arc 218
Joinville 176
Joué-les-Tours (**Tours**) 304
Joyeuse 177
Juan-les-Pins 177
Julienas 177

Kaysersberg 178

Labastide-Murat 178
Labouheyre 178
Lac d'Allier 318
Lacanau-Océan 178
Lalinde 178
Lamastre 179
Lamballe 179
Lancieux (**Dinan**) 150
Landes, forests of 37
Landivisiau 179
Langeais 179
Langres 180
Langue d'oc 42
Lannion 25, 180
Lanslebourg 180
Lantosque 181
Lanvollon (**St-Quay-Portrieux**) 282
Laon 181
Laval 181
Lavaur 182
Lesconil 182
Lesneven 183
Lesquin (**Lille**) 183
Lessay 22
Levens 183
Liesse (**Laon**) 181
lights 56
Lille 183
Limay (**Mantes**) 192
Limeuil (**Le Bugue**) 192
Limoges 183
Limoux 184
Lindberg-Plage 22
Le Lion-d'Angers 184
Lion-sur-Mer 19
Lisieux 184
Loches 184
Lodève 184
Lons-le-Saunier 185
Loon-Plage (**Dunkerque**) 152
Lorient 29
Loudeac 185
Lourdes 185
Lourmarin (**Cadenet**) 114
Louviers 185
Louvres (**Roissy**) 262
Luc-sur-Mer 186
Luché-Pringé (**La Flèche**) 159
Luchon (**Bagneres-de-Luchon**) 87
Luçon 186
Le Lude 186
Lumbres 187

Lumière, Antoine 188
Lusignan 187
Lux (Chalon-sur-Saône) 125
Luxeuil-les-Bains 187
Luynes prés Tours (**Tours**) 304
Lyon 187

Mâçon 190
Madières (**Ganges**) 163
Magnant 191
Les Maisons sur l'Agoût 123
Manciet 191
Mandelieu la Napoule 191
Le Mans 191
Mantes 192
maps 57
Marais de Grande Briere 31
Margeride mountain/forêt 271
Marguerittes (**Nîmes**) 214
Marmande 192
Marne-la-Vallée 192
Marquay (**Les Eyzies-de-Tayac**) 156
Marseille 192
Marseille 45
Martigues 193
Massiac 193
Matisse 41
Maures, the 47
Maurs 193
Maussane-les-Alpilles 193
Mayenne 193
megaliths 26, 29, 30
Megève 194
Menat 194
Mende 194
Menton 51, 194
Les Menuires 195
Les Mères 188
Méribel 195
Meslay-du-Maine (**Laval**) 181
Mesnil-Val (**Le Tréport**) 307
Metz 196
Meudon 235
Meursault 197
Meyrueis 197
Migennes 198
Millau 198
Mirambeau 198
Mirebeau 198
Miromensil 16
Modane 199
Molène 27
Mollans-sur-Ouvèze (**Vaison-la-Romaine**) 310

Mollkirch 199
Monaco, Principality of 49, 199
Monpazier (**Sarlat-la-Caneda**) 290
Mont Crussol 312
Le Mont-Dore 200
Mont-Louis 200
Le Mont-St-Michel 23, 200
Montaigu 201
Montargis 201
Montauban 201
Montauban-de-Bretagne 201
Montauroux (**Fayence**) 157
Montbard 202
Montbazon 202
Montbéliard 202
Monte-Carlo 51, 199
Montélimar 202
Montigny-la-Resle (**Auxerre**) 84
Montigny-le-Roi 202
Montlouis-sur-Loire (**Tours**) 304
Montluçon 203
Montmélian 203
Montoire-sur-le-Loir 203
Montpellier 43, 203
Montreuil 204
Montrichard 205
Moreilles (**Luçon**) 186
Morlaix 26
Mornac-sur-Seudre 205
Mornas 205
Mortagne-au-Perche 206
Morzine-Avoriaz 206
motoring organisations 55
motorways 54/55
Moulins 206
Mount Ventoux 86
Mulhouse 206
Munster 207
Mur-de-Barrez 207
Murat 207
Murbach (**Guebwiller**) 172
La Mure 208
Mus 208
mustard 149

Nancy 208
Nans-les-Pins (**Aix-en-Provence**) 67
Nantes 209
Nantua 210
Napoléon 13, 51, 52, 105, 163
Narbonne 41, 211

Naucelle 211
Nay 212
Nazelles (**Amboise**) 71
Néant-sur-Yvel (**Ploërmel**) 243
Neauphie-le-Château 212
Nelson, Horatio 52
Nemours 212
Neris-les-Bains (**Montluçon**) 203
Neufchâteau 212
Neuville-aux-Bois 212
Nevers 213
Nice 50, 213
Nîmes 214
Niort 215
Noé 216
Noirmoutier-en-L'Ile 216
Noisy-le-Grand 237
Normandy 19
Normandy, Battle of 20
nougat 312
Noyon 216
Nuits-St-Georges (**Dijon**) 148

Obernai 216
Oizon (**Gien**) 165
Olargues 216
Oléron,Ile de 217
Olivet (**Orléans**) 218
Omonville-la-Petite 217
onions 219
Opal Coast, the 13
opening hours 59
Orange 217
Orbey 218
Orcines (**Clermont-Ferrand**) 136
Orgeval 218
Orincles (**Lourdes**) 185
Orléans 218
Ornaisons (**Narbonne**) 211
Orthez 220
Oucques 220
Ouistreham 220
overloading 56
Oyonnax 221
oysters 24, 36, 106

Padirac (**Gramat**) 166
Paimpol 26, 221
Palais des Papes 85
La Palmyre 37
Parc du Haut Languedoc 124
Paris 223
Paris North-East 236
Paris South-East 237

Paris West 234
Pas de Calais 13
Pau 238
Pauillac 238
Payrac 239
péage 54
Pearl Coast, the 19
pelota, game of 40
Penmarc'h (St-Guénole/Penmarc'h) 273
Périgueux 239
Peronne 240
Perpignan 41, 240
Perros-Guirec 26, 241
La petite France 298
La Petite-Pierre 241
Petreto-Bicchisano, Corse (Porto-Pollo) 144
petrol 56
Peyrat-le-Château 242
Philippsbourg (Bitche) 103
phones 59
Picasso, Pablo 50
Pierrefontaine-les-Varans 242
Pierrelatte 242
Pink Granite Coast, the 25
Plan-d'Orgon 243
Plan-du-Var (Levens) 183
Plancoët 243
Pléneuf-Val-André 243
Pleugueneuc (Dinan) 150
Pleumeur-Bodou (Perros-Guirec) 241
Ploërmel 243
Plogoff (Audierne) 244
Ploneour-Lanvern 244
Plouer-sur-Rance (Dinan) 150
Plouescat 244
Plougasnou 244
Ploumana'ch 26
Poitiers 244
Poix-de-Picardie 246
police 57, 60
Polliat (Mâcon) 190
Pompadour 246
Pons 246
Pont d'Aquitaine 105
Pont du Tancarville, suspension bridge 17
Pont St-Bénézet 85
Pont-Audemer 247
Pont-Aven 29, 247
Pont-de-Menat (Menat) 194
Pont-de-Vaux 247
Pont-du-Gard 248

Pont-l'Abbé 248
Pont-l'Evêque 248
Pont-sur-Yonne 249
Pontarlier 249
Pontault-Combault (Marne-la-Vallée)
Pontivy 249
Pontorson 249
Pornic 32, 249
Port Camargue (Le Grau-de-Roi) 168
Port-en-Bessin (Bayeux) 92
Port-la-Nouvelle 250
Porte Noire 100
Porte Rivotte 101
Porto-Pollo, Corse (Corsica) 144
Pouilly-en-Auxois 250
Pouilly-sur-Loire 250
Le Pouldu 251
Pouzauges 251
Prahecq (Niort) 215
Prats-de-Mollo-la-Preste 251
Préfailles (Pornic) 249
priority 56
Privas 251
prohibited goods 61
Propriano, Corse (Corsica) 144
Proust, Marcel 19
public holidays 59
Puteaux 236
Puy-de-Dôme 137
Le Puy-en-Velay 251
Puy-l'Eveque 252
Pyrénées-Atlantiques 39

Quenza 144
Quimper 28, 252
Quincie-en-Beaujolais (Beaujeu) 95

radio 60
railways 58
Ramatuelle (St-Tropez) 285
Rambouillet 253
Rancourt 253
Randan (Vichy) 318
Raphèle-lès-Arles (Arles) 79
Raray (Senlis) 293
Ré, Ile de 35, 254
Recques-sur-Hem 254
Reims 254
Remiremont 255
Rennes 255
Replonges (Mâcon) 190

Requista (Naucelle) 211
Revel 257
Réville 257
Ribeauvillé 257
Ribérac 258
Richelieu 258
Riom 258
Riquewihr 258
the Riviera 49
road signs 55
roads 55
Roanne 258
Rocamadour 259
La Roche-Canillac (Argentat) 78
La Roche-Posay 260
La Roche-sur-Yon 260
Rochefort 36, 261
La Rochelle 35, 261
Rocroi 262
Rodez 262
Roissy 262
Rolleboise (Vernon) 316
Romaneche-Thorins 263
Ronchamp 263
Roquebrune-Cap-Martin 263
Rosay-sur-Lieure (Rouen) 264
Roscoff 27, 264
Rothau (Schirmeck) 292
Rouen 264
roundabouts 57
Roussillon-en-Provence (Gordes) 40, 166
Royan 37, 265
Royat (Clermont-Ferrand) 136
Roye 266
Rue 266
Rueil-Malmaison 236

Sable-sur-Sarthe 267
Les Sables-d'Olonne 34, 267
Sables-d'Or-les-Pins 267
Sadroc (Donzenac) 151
Saignes 267
Saille 32
St-Guénole/Penmarc'h 273
St-Affrique 268
St-Agnan-en-Vercors (La Chapelle-en-Vercors) 130
St-Alban-sur-Limagnol 268
St-Amand-Montrond 268
St-André-des-Eaux (La Baule) 91
St-Andre-les-Alpes 268

St-Anthème 269
St-Benoît-sur-Loire 219
St-Brévin-les-Pins (St-Nazaire) 281
St-Brieuc 269
St-Capraise-de-Lalinde (Lalinde) 178
St-Céré 269
St-Chartier (La Châtre) 134
St-Circq-Lapopie 269
St-Claude 269
St-Cloud 236
St-Cyprien 269
St-Cyr-sur-Mer 270
St-Didier (Carpentras) 122
St-Didier (Châteaubourg) 132
St-Dizier 270
St-Emilion 270
St-Etienne 270
St-Etienne-de-Maurs (Maurs) 193
St-Firmin (La Chapelle-en-Valgaudemar) 130
St-Florentin 270
St-Flour 270
St-Gaudens 272
St-Geniez-d'Olt 272
St-Germain-en-Laye 273
St-Grégoire (Rennes) 255
St-Hilaire-du-Harcouet 273
St-Hilaire-St-Mesmin 273
St-Hippolyte 274
St-James 274
St-Jean-de-Monts 275
St-Jean-de-Monts 34
St-Jean-de-Luz 40, 274
St-Jean-du-Doigt (Plougasnou) 244
St-Jean-le-Thomas 276
St-Jean-Pied-de-Port 277
St-Lary-Soulan 277
St-Laurent-en-Grandvaux 277
St-Léger (Pons) 246
St-Léonard-des-Bois (Alençon) 69
St-Maclou (Pont-Audemer) 247
St-Malo 24, 278
St-Marcel-Vernon (Vernon) 316
St-Martial-Viveyrois 280
St-Martin-de-Crau (Arles) 79
St-Martin-de-la-Place (Saumur) 291
St-Martin-en-Bresse 281

St-Martin-la-Meanne 281
St-Maurice 237
St-Michel-de-Montaigne (Ste-Foy-la-Grande) 287
St-Michel-en-Grève 25
St-Nazaire 32, 281
St-Nicolas-des-Eaux (Pontivy) 249
St-Omer 281
St-Paul-de-Vence 281
St-Paul-Trois-Châteaux 282
St-Pee-sur-Nivelle 282
St-Pierre-de-Oléron 217
St-Pierre-des-Nids (Alençon) 69
St-Pol-sur-Ternoise 282
St-Prest (Chartres) 131
St-Quay-Portrieux 282
St-Quentin 283
St-Raphaël 49, 283
St-Rémy-de-Provence 283
St-Restitut (St-Paul-Trois-Châteaux) 282
St-Romain-de-Lerps 312
St-Salvy-de-la-Balme 124
St-Symphorien (Le Mans) 191
St-Symphorien-le-Château 284
St-Tropez 48, 285
St-Vaast-de-Hougue 285
St-Vallier-de-Thiey (Grasse) 167
St-Véran 286
St-Vincent-sur-Jard (Les Sables-d'Olonne) 267
St-Yrieux-la-Perche 286
standing stones 29
Stanislas Leszcynski 208
Ste-Cécile (Villedieu-les-Poêles) 320
Ste-Foy-la-Grand 287
Ste-Marie-de-Campan (Bagneres-de-Bigorre) 87
Ste-Maure-de-Toutaine 287
Ste-Maxime 288
Ste-Menehould 288
Stella-Plage 297
Les Stes-Maries-de-la-Mer 43, 288
Saintes 288
Salaunes 288
Salbris 289
Salers 289
Saliers-par-Arles (Arles) 79
Salies-de-Béarn 290
Salon-de-Provence 290
Sanary-sur-Mer 46

Sangatte 13
Sarlat-la-Canéda 290
Satie, Erik 18
Saujon 37
Saulges 291
Saumur 291
Sausset-les-Pins 292
Saut du Doubs waterfall 101
Sauveterre-de-Rouergue (Naucelle) 211
Saverne 292
Schirmeck 292
Sébazac (Rodez) 262
Seclin 293
Sées 293
Selonnet (Seyne) 294
Senlis 293
Sens 294
Sept-Saulx (Reims) 254
Serezin-du-Rhône (Lyon) 187
Serre-Chevalier 294
Serrières (Annonay) 76
Sète 42, 44, 294
Sevignacq-Meyracq (Pau) 238
Sewen (Mulhouse) 206
Seyne 294
Seyssel 295
Silver Coast, the 37
Sisteron 295
Sommières 295
Sorges 295
Soubise (Rochefort) 261
Souillac 296
Sourzac-Mussidan 296
La Souterraine 296
speed limits 57
Stevenson, Robert Louis 47
Strasbourg 297
Sully-sur-Loire 219

Tain-l'Hermitage 312
Talloires 299
Talmont 37
télécarte 59
Le Temple-sur-Lot (Villeneuve-sur-Lot) 322
Tende (Nice) 213
Théoule-sur-Mer 300
Thiers 300
Thionville 300
Thonon-les-Bains 301
Thorenc 301
Thueyts 301
Thury-Harcourt 301
Toulon 47, 302
Toulouse 302
Le Touquet 16, 303

Le Touquet-Paris-Plage (**Le Touquet**) 303
Tournon-sur-Rhône 304
Tournus 304
Tours 302
Touzac (**Puy-l'Eveque**) 252
Tracy-sur-Mer (**Bayeux**) 92
traffic lights 57
Trébeurden 26
Trégastel 26
La Tremblay-sur-Mauldre (**Versailles**) 316
Trémolat 306
Le Tréport 307
Trinité-sur-Mer 307
Trôo (**Montoire-sur-le-Loir**) 203
Trouville-sur-Mer 18, 307
Troyes 307
truffles 239
Les Ulis 309

Uzerche 310

Vaas (**Le Lude**) 186
Vaison-la-Romaine 310
Val-Cenis (**Lanslebourg**) 180
Val-Thorens 310
Valbonne 311
Valence 311
Valenciennes 312
La Valette (**Toulon**) 302
Valgorge 312
Vallon-Pont-d'Arc 313
Valognes 313
Valras-Plage 313

Vals-près-le-Puy (**Le-Puy-en-Velay**) 251
Van Gogh, Vincent 45
Vannes 30, 313
Venasque (**Carpentras**) 122
Vence 314
Vendée 32
Vendeuil 314
Vendôme 314
Verdun 315
Vergèze 315
Vernet-les-Bains 315
Verneuil-sur-Avre 316
Vernon 316
Versailles 316
Vervins 317
Le Veurdre 317
Vézelay 318
Vialas 318
Vichy 318
Vieillevie 319
Vienne 319
Vierzon 319
Vieux-Mareuil 320
Le Vigeant (**Isle-Jourdain**) 176
Villandry (**Tours**) 304
Villedieu-les-Poêles 320
Villefort 320
Villefranche-de-Lauragais 321
Villefranche-de-Rouergue 321
Villefranche-sur-Mer 321
Villefranche-sur-Saône 321

Villeneuve-lès-Avignon (**Avignon**) 85
Villeneuve-sur-Lot 322
Villers-Cotterêts 322
Villers-sur-Mer 18
Villevallier (**Sens**) 294
Vimoutiers 322
Vimy ridge 81
Vineuil (**Chambord**) 126
Violes (**Orange**) 217
Vitrac (**Aurillac**) 83
Vittel 322
voltages 60
Vouvray-sur-Loir (**Château-du-Loir**) 131
Voves 322

warning triangle 56
William the Conqueror 116
Wimereux 322
Wissant 323
Wissembourg 323

Yachting Coast, the 28
Ydes (**Saignes**) 267
Ys, drowned city of 28
Yzeures-sur-Creuse (**Roche-Posay**) 260

INDEX

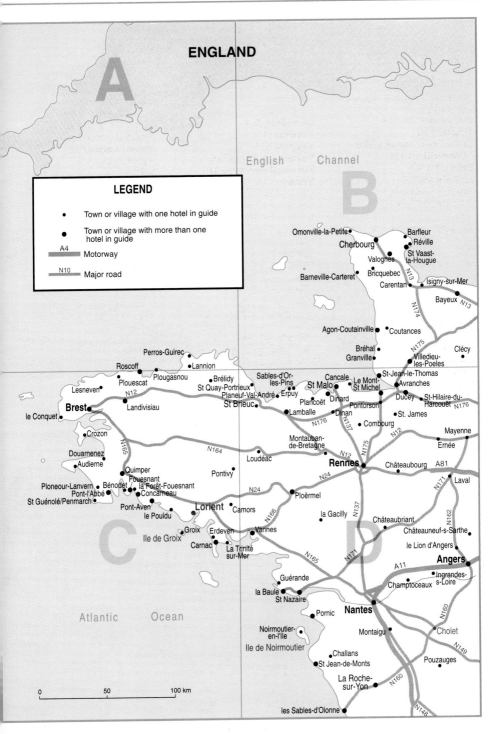

ENGLAND

English Channel

LEGEND

- Town or village with one hotel in guide
- Town or village with more than one hotel in guide
- A4   Motorway
- N10   Major road

Omonville-la-Petite
Cherbourg
Valognes
Barneville-Carteret
Bricquebec
Carentan
Barfleur
Réville
St Vaast-la-Hougue
N13
Isigny-sur-Mer
Bayeux   N13
N174

Agon-Coutainville   Coutances
Bréhal
Granville
N175
Villedieu-les-Poeles
Clécy

Perros-Guirec
Roscoff
Plouescat   Plougasnou
Lesneven
N12
Brest
Landivisiau
le Conquet
Crozon
N165
Douarnenez
Audierne
Quimper
Fouesnant
Ploneour-Lanvern   Bénodet   la Forêt-Fouesnant
Pont-l'Abbé   Concarneau
St Guénolé/Penmarch
Pont-Aven
le Pouldu
Lorient   Camors
Groix
Ile de Groix
Erdeven
Carnac
La Trinité-sur-Mer
Vannes

Lannion
Brélidy
St Quay-Portrieux
Planeuf-Val-André   Erpuy
St Brieuc
Lamballe
N164
Loudéac
Pontivy
N24
Ploërmel
la Gacilly
N165

Sables-d'Or-les-Pins
St Malo
Plancoët   Dinard
Dinan
N176
Montauban-de-Bretagne
Rennes
N24
N12

Cancale   Le Mont-St Michel
St-Jean-le-Thomas
Avranches
Ducey   St-Hilaire-du-Harcouët   N176
Pontorson
St. James
Combourg
N175
N12
Châteaubourg   A81
Mayenne
Ernée
Laval
N171

Guérande
la Baule
St Nazaire
Pornic
Nantes
Noirmoutier-en-l'Ile
Ile de Noirmoutier
Challans
St Jean-de-Monts
La Roche-sur-Yon
N160
les Sables-d'Olonne
N148

Châteaubriant
Châteauneuf-s-Sarthe
le Lion d'Angers
A11
Angers
Ingrandes-s-Loire
Champtoceaux
Montaigu
Cholet
N149
Pouzauges
N162
N171

Atlantic   Ocean

0   50   100 km

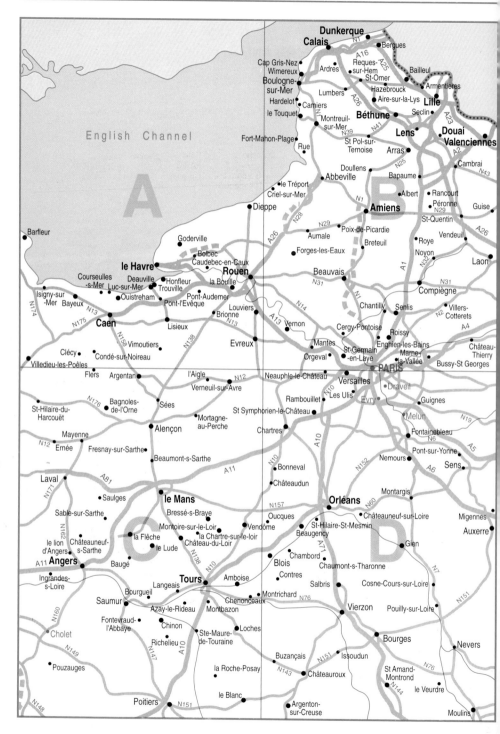

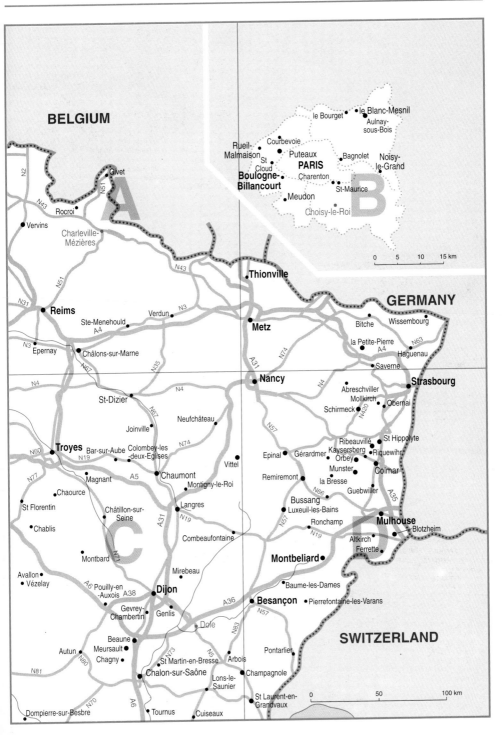

BELGIUM

le Bourget • • le Blanc-Mesnil
Aulnay-
sous-Bois

Courbevoie
Rueil-
Malmaison • Puteaux • Bagnolet Noisy-
St • PARIS le-Grand
Cloud
Boulogne- Charenton
Billancourt St-Maurice •
Meudon •
Choisy-le-Roi

0 5 10 15 km

N2

Givet

N51

A

N43

Rocroi •

Vervins •

Charleville-
Mézières

N43

Thionville •

N51

GERMANY

N31

Reims • Verdun • N3
Ste-Menehould Metz • Bitche • Wissembourg
A4
la Petite-Pierre
N3 A4 N63
Epernay • Châlons-sur-Marne Haguenau
N67 N35 Saverne •
N31 A31 N74

N4 Nancy • N4
St-Dizier Abreschviller • Strasbourg •
Mollkirch • Obernai •
N4 Schirmeck • N420

N67 Neufchâteau •
Joinville • N57

Ribeauvillé • St Hippolyte
N60 Troyes • Bar-sur-Aube Colombey-les N74 Epinal • Gérardmer Kaysersberg • Riquewihr
N19 -deux-Eglises Orbey •
Vittel • Munster • Colmar
N77 Magnant • A5 Chaumont Remiremont • la Bresse • A35
Chaource • Montigny-le-Roi N66 Guebwiller •
St Florentin • Châtillon-sur- Langres Bussang •
Seine A31 N19 Luxeuil-les-Bains •
Chablis • Ronchamp • Mulhouse •
N57 N19 Blotzheim
Combeaufontaine • Altkirch •
D
Montard • Ferrette •
N71 Mirebeau • Montbeliard •

Avallon •
Vézelay • A6 Pouilly-en Baume-les-Dames •
-Auxois A38 Dijon •
Gevrey- A36 Besançon • Pierrefontaine-les-Varans
Chambertin Genlis N57
Dole •
Beaune • N73 N5
Autun • Meursault • Pontarlier •
N80 Chagny • St Martin-en-Bresse Arbois •
N81 Chalon-sur-Saône • Champagnole • SWITZERLAND
Lons-le-
Saunier
N70 St Laurent-en- 0 50 100 km
Dompierre-sur-Besbre • A6 Tournus • Cuiseaux Grandvaux

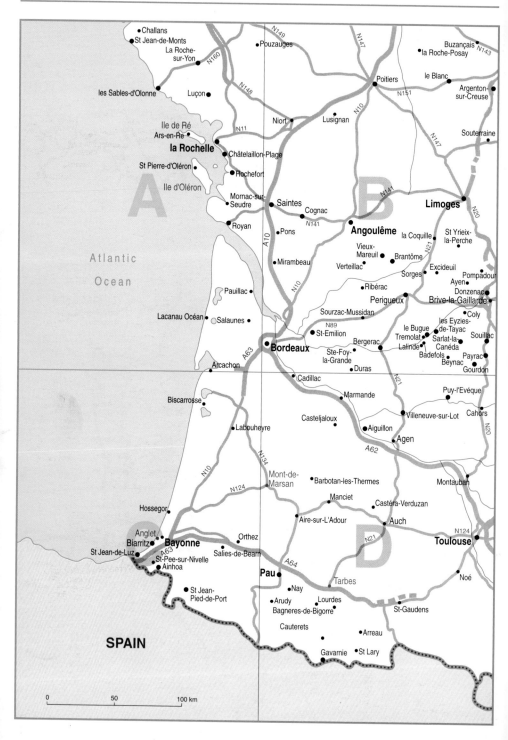

Challans
St Jean-de-Monts
La Roche-sur-Yon
N160
Pouzauges
N149
N147
Buzançais
la Roche-Posay
N143

les Sables-d'Olonne
Luçon
N149
Poitiers
le Blanc
N151
Argenton-sur-Creuse

Ile de Ré
Ars-en-Re
la Rochelle
N11
Niort
Lusignan
N10
N147
Souterraine

St Pierre-d'Oléron
Châtelaillon-Plage
Rochefort

Ile d'Oléron

A

Mornac-sur-Seudre
Saintes
Cognac
N141
Limoges
N20

Royan
Pons
N141
Angoulême
la Coquille
St Yrieix-la-Perche

Vieux-Mareuil
Brantôme
N21

Mirambeau
Verteillac
Sorges
Excideuil
Pompadour
Ayen
Donzenac
Brive-la-Gaillarde

Atlantic

Ocean

A10

N10

Pauillac
Ribérac
Perigueux

Lacanau Océan
Salaunes
Sourzac-Mussidan
N89
St-Emilion
le Bugue
Tremolat
Lalinde
les Eyzies-de-Tayac
Sarlat-la-Canéda
Souillac
Coly

Bordeaux
Bergerac
Ste-Foy-la-Grande
Badefols
Beynac
Payrac
Gourdon

A63
Arcachon
Duras

Cadillac

Biscarrosse
Marmande
N21
Puy-l'Evéque
Cahors

Casteljaloux
Villeneuve-sur-Lot
N20

Labouheyre
Aiguillon
Agen
A62

N10
N134

Mont-de-Marsan
N124
Barbotan-les-Thermes
Montauban

Manciet
Castéra-Verduzan

Hossegor
Aire-sur-L'Adour
Auch
N124

Anglet
Biarritz
Bayonne
St Jean-de-Luz
St-Pee-sur-Nivelle
Ainhoa
A63
Orthez
Salies-de-Bearn
A64
D
N21
Toulouse

Pau
Noé

St Jean-Pied-de-Port
Nay
Tarbes

Arudy
Lourdes
Bagneres-de-Bigorre
St-Gaudens

Cauterets

SPAIN
Arreau

Gavarnie
St Lary

0   50   100 km

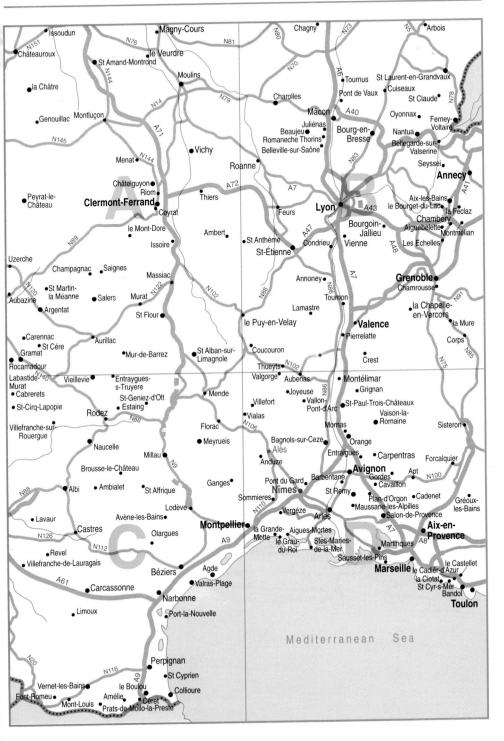

Issoudun
Châteauroux
N151
N76
le Veurdre
St Amand-Montrond
Magny-Cours
N81
N80
Chagny
N73
N5
Arbois
la Châtre
N144
Moulins
N70
N79
Charolles
A6
Tournus
Pont de Vaux
St Laurent-en-Grandvaux
Cuiseaux
St Claude
N78
Genouillac Montluçon
A71
N14
N145
Menat
N144
Vichy
Mâcon
A40
Juliénas
Beaujeu
Romaneche Thorins
Belleville-sur-Saône
Bourg-en-
Bresse
N83
Oyonnax
Nantua
Bellegarde-sur-
Valserine
Ferney-
Voltaire
Seyssel
Annecy
Peyrat-le-
Château
N89
Châtelguyon
Riom
Clermont-Ferrand
Ceyrat
le Mont-Dore
Issoire
A72
Thiers
A7
Feurs
Lyon
A43
Bourgoin-
Jallieu
Condrieu
Vienne
Aix-les-Bains
le Bourget-du-Lac
A41
la Féclaz
Chambéry
Aiguebelette
Les Echelles
A48
Montmélian
Ambert
St Anthème
St-Étienne
Uzerche
Champagnac
Saignes
N120
St Martin-
la Méanne
Aubazine
Argentat
Salers
Murat
N122
Massiac
St Flour
N102
le Puy-en-Velay
N88
Annoney
A7
N86
Tournon
Lamastre
Grenoble
Chamrousse
la Chapelle-
en-Vercors
N91
la Mure
Valence
Pierrelatte
Crest
Corps
N85
N75
Carennac
St Céré
Gramat
Rocamadour
Aurillac
Mur-de-Barrez
St Alban-sur-
Limagnole
Coucouron
Thueyts
N102
Labastide-
Murat
Cabrerets
St-Cirq-Lapopie
Vieillevie
Entraygues-
s-Truyere
St-Geniez-d'Olt
Estaing
Rodez
N88
Valgorge
Mende
Villefort
Aubenas
N86
Joyeuse
Vallon-
Pont-d'Arc
Montélimar
Grignan
St-Paul-Trois-Châteaux
Vaison-la-
Romaine
Sisteron
Villefranche-sur-
Rouergue
Naucelle
Millau
N9
Brousse-le-Château
Florac
N106
Meyrueis
Vialas
Bagnols-sur-Ceze
Alès
Anduze
Mornas
Orange
Entraigues
Carpentras
Forcalquier
Avignon
Apt
N100
Albi
Ambialet
St Affrique
Ganges
Pont du Gard
Nîmes
Barbentane
St Remy
Gordes
Cavaillon
Plan-d'Orgon
Maussane-les-Alpilles
Cadenet
Gréoux-
les-Bains
N88
Lavaur
Castres
N126
Revel
Villefranche-de-Lauragais
A61
N112
Olargues
Avène-les-Bains
Lodève
Montpellier
A9
Sommieres
N110
Vergéze
Aigues-Mortes
Arles
Salon-de-Provence
Aix-en-
Provence
A7
A8
Martigues
Sausset-les-Pins
Marseille
le Cadière-d'Azur
la Ciotat
St Cyr-s-Mer
Bandol
Toulon
Carcassonne
Béziers
Agde
Valras-Plage
Narbonne
Port-la-Nouvelle
Limoux
la Grande-
Motte
le Grau-
du-Roi
Stes-Maries-
de-la-Mer
le Castellet
N20
Perpignan
N116
St Cyprien
Vernet-les-Bains
le Boulou
Amélie-
Colliqure
Font-Romeu
Mont-Louis
Ceret
Prats-de-Mollo-la-Preste
A9
Mediterranean Sea

Arbois Malbuisson

Bonlieu St Laurent-en-Grandvaux **SWITZERLAND**
St Claude N78 Evian-les-Bains
Thonon-les-Bains
Oyonnax Ferney-Voltaire Abondance
Nantua Annemasse Morzine
Bellegarde-sur-Valserine
A40
Hauteville-Lompnes
la Clusaz Chamonix
Annecy Megeve Combloux
N504 A41
Aix-les-Bains Talloires
le Bourget-du-Lac la Feclaz Bourg-St Maurice
N90
Aiguebelette **Chambéry** Champagny-en-Vanoise
Méribel Courchevel
les Menuires Lanslebourg
Grenoble N6 Val-Thorens Modane
N532
Chamrousse 'Alpe-d'Huez N91
Serre-Chevalier
la Mure Briançon
N85 la Chapelle-en-Valgaudémar N94 St Veran
N75

Gap

ITALY

Seyne

Sisteron
Digne-les-Bains
Lantosque
Forcalquier St André-les-Alpes N202 Breil-sur-Roya
N100 Levens Roquebrune-Cap-Martin
N85 Thorenc Vence **Menton**
Comps-sur-Artuby St Paul Eze Monte-Carlo
Gréoux-les-Bains Alguines **Cagnes-sur-Mer** Villefranche-sur-Mer
Fayence Valbonne **Nice** Beaulieu-sur-Mer
Aix-en-Provence Mandelieu-la- **Grasse** Antibes
Draguignan Napoule Juan-les-Pins
A8 Agay **Cannes** le Golfe-Juan
Théoule-sur-Mer
Ste Maxime
le Castellet St Tropez
la Ciotat la Cadière-d'Azur N98 la Croix-Valmer
St Cyr-s-Mer
Bandol **Toulon** Hyères le Lavandou

Mediterranean Sea

Île-Rousse

D Calacuccia
Evisa
Porto N198
N193

CORSICA
Ajaccio
Quenza
Porto-Pollo
Propriano

0   50   100 km

DÉPARTEMENTS

01 Ain	32 Gers	64 Pyrénées-Atlantiques
02 Aisne	33 Gironde	65 Hautes-Pyrénées
03 Allier	34 Hérault	66 Pyrénées-Orientales
04 Alpes-de-Haute-Provence	35 Ille-et-Vilaine	67 Bas-Rhin
05 Hautes-Alpes	36 Indre	68 Haut-Rhin
06 Alpes-Maritimes	37 Indre-et-Loire	69 Rhône
07 Ardèche	38 Isère	70 Haute-Saône
08 Ardennes	39 Jura	71 Saône-et-Loire
09 Ariège	40 Landes	72 Sarthe
10 Aube	41 Loir-et-Cher	73 Savoie
11 Aude	42 Loire	74 Haute-Savoie
12 Aveyron	43 Haute-Loire	75 Paris
13 Bouches-du-Rhône	44 Loire-Atlantique	76 Seine-Maritime
14 Calvados	45 Loiret	77 Seine-et-Marne
15 Cantal	46 Lot	78 Yvelines
16 Charente	47 Lot-et-Garonne	79 Deux-Sèvres
17 Charente-Maritime	48 Lozère	80 Somme
18 Cher	49 Maine-et-Loire	81 Tarn
19 Corrèze	50 Manche	82 Tarn-et-Garonne
2A Corse-du-Sud	51 Marne	83 Var
2B Haute-Corse	52 Haute-Marne	84 Vaucluse
21 Côte-d'Or	'53 Mayenne	85 Vendée
22 Côtes-du-Nord	54 Meurthe-et-Moselle	86 Vienne
23 Creuse	55 Meuse	87 Haute-Vienne
24 Dordogne	56 Morbihan	88 Vosges
25 Doubs	57 Moselle	89 Yonne
26 Drôme	58 Nièvre	90 Territoire-de-Belfort
27 Eure	59 Nord	91 Essonne
28 Eure-et-Loir	60 Oise	92 Hauts-de-Seine
29 Finistère	61 Orne	93 Val-de-St-Denis
30 Gard	62 Pas-de-Calais	94 Val-de-Marne
31 Haute-Garonne	63 Puy-de-Dôme	95 Val-d'Oise

RAC
HOTELS
IN FRANCE

HOTEL REPORT 1994

The publisher of this guide welcomes your comments about any hotels visited that appear in this guide. Whatever your experience, good, indifferent or poor, do write to RAC Publishing, PO Box 8, Harleston, Norfolk IP20 0EZ expressing your views.

Hotel name

Town

Dates of stay

Please tick the appropriate box		Yes	No
Did any of the hotel staff speak English?		☐	☐
Were the staff helpful?		☐	☐
Did the hotel have a restaurant?		☐	☐
Was the hotel quiet?		☐	☐
Were the parking facilities adequate?		☐	☐
Was the service	*good?*	☐	
	adequate	☐	
	poor	☐	
Was the food	*good*	☐	
	average	☐	
	poor	☐	

Hotel report

continued

Hotel report *continued*

Name

Address

HOTELS IN FRANCE

HOTEL REPORT 1994

The publisher of this guide welcomes your comments about any hotels visited that appear in this guide. Whatever your experience, good, indifferent or poor, do write to RAC Publishing, PO Box 8, Harleston, Norfolk IP20 0EZ expressing your views.

Hotel name

Town

Dates of stay

Please tick the appropriate box		Yes	No
Did any of the hotel staff speak English?		☐	☐
Were the staff helpful?		☐	☐
Did the hotel have a restaurant?		☐	☐
Was the hotel quiet?		☐	☐
Were the parking facilities adequate?		☐	☐
Was the service	*good?*	☐	
	adequate	☐	
	poor	☐	
Was the food	*good*	☐	
	average	☐	
	poor	☐	

Hotel report

continued

Hotel report *continued*

_____

_____

_____

_____

_____

_____

_____

_____

_____

_____

_____

_____

_____

_____

_____

_____

_____

_____

_____

_____

Name

Address

HOTELS
IN FRANCE

HOTEL RECOMMENDATION 1995

The publisher of this guide welcomes your suggestions for hotels which might be included in future editions of this guide. Please write to RAC Publishing, PO Box 8, Harleston, Norfolk IP20 0EZ expressing your views.

Hotel name

Address

Telephone   *Fax*

Dates of your stay

Reason for suggestion

HOTELS IN FRANCE

HOTEL RECOMMENDATION 1995

The publisher of this guide welcomes your suggestions for hotels which might be included in future editions of this guide. Please write to RAC Publishing, PO Box 8, Harleston, Norfolk IP20 0EZ expressing your views.

Hotel name

Address

Telephone   *Fax*

Dates of your stay

Reason for suggestion